D1163387

Readings in Urban Dynamics:
Volume 2

Readings in Urban Dynamics:

Volume 2

Edited by
Walter W. Schroeder III, Robert E. Sweeney,
and Louis Edward Alfeld

Wright-Allen Press, Inc.
238 Main Street
Cambridge, Massachusetts 02142

Library of Congress catalog card number: 73-89545
ISBN 0-914700-02-2

Foreword

Twenty years ago at M.I.T. we began to examine dynamic characteristics of social systems. At first, research focused on "industrial" dynamics and corporate management. A methodology—system dynamics—was developed to identify the essential structure of complex systems and to show how structure produced the typical behavior of a system. With a structure that would produce the behavior of a system, models could be used to design policies for improving that behavior.

Urban Dynamics in 1969 presented a theory of urban growth and decline as well as a general policy program. The debate surrounding the book led to a program of research into urban behavior during the past six years. *Readings in Urban Dynamics: Volume 1*, published in 1974, drew together the major conclusions from the first three years of urban dynamics research, detailed several revisions to the *Urban Dynamics* model, and described early efforts to apply the model to the real city of Lowell, Massachusetts. Now with this appearance of *Readings in Urban Dynamics: Volume 2*, the record of urban dynamics research through 1974 is available. This second volume offers a treatment of issues in urban modeling, responds to many initial criticisms of *Urban Dynamics*, presents further results of applying the methodology in Lowell, and describes model extensions to account for land rezoning, housing abandonment, and city-suburb interactions.

The *Urban Dynamics* model has now been sufficiently revised and extended that it should provide a consensus-building basis for conceptualizing and identifying the sources of urban decay. The urban dynamics models, and extensions of them, should be a basis for three avenues of future influence on urban political decisions. First, when modified to reflect a city's specific features, the model can be employed as a policy guide for urban planning. Second, extensions of the models can focus on specific urban issues such as education, transportation, and crime. Third, the models can provide a basis for a clearer public descriptive understanding of urban processes and a better-informed perception of how different aspects of a city affect one another.

We express our deepest appreciation for generous support of our urban dynamics program to the Independence Foundation of Philadelphia, Mr. Kenneth Germeshausen, and the United States Department of Housing and Urban Development.

Jay W. Forrester

November, 1975
Massachusetts Institute of Technology

Contents

1

Urban Dynamics and the City Boundary

Walter W. Schroeder III

The 1960s marked a period of increasing federal and state involvement in urban affairs. This involvement stemmed from widespread fears that the problems of cities were far greater than the capabilities of cities to manage alone. Urban Dynamics *has attracted attention largely because it suggests that the problems of an urban area arise from internal decision making rather than from external influences. The book argues further that, if the causes of urban decline lie within cities, so do the fundamental solutions.*

This reading focuses on the continuing debate over the boundary of the Urban Dynamics *model. Much of the controversy seems to arise from a misunderstanding of the model's purpose. Rather than attempting to incorporate all the forces that affect urban behavior, the* Urban Dynamics *model portrays the city in relation to its environment.* Urban Dynamics *asks: what policies within the realm of local control can improve the city's condition? The boundary of the* Urban Dynamics *model should therefore be evaluated against the objective of local policy analysis.*

1
Urban Dynamics and the City Boundary

1.1 Overview

Urban Dynamics presents the theory that the significant behavior of cities is generated by forces within the urban boundary. Since the boundary of the *Urban Dynamics* model coincides roughly with a city's jurisdictional boundary, it ascribes greater importance to internal dynamics than to state or federal forces in explaining the causes of urban decline. Forrester's boundary choice attracted considerable attention among urban modelers from other modeling disciplines, who suggest that the real causes of urban behavior originate outside cities and therefore outside the boundary of the *Urban Dynamics* model. For example, economist Jerome Rothenberg questions whether the model boundary in *Urban Dynamics* corresponds to a sufficiently large physical area to contain the important forces that produce urban behavior.

> Just because internal interactions *could* account for some observed phenomena does not mean they do. The issue is whether in fact it is the external rather than the internal forces which are most influential. What portion of the real observed variations in urban circumstances [behavior] is in fact explainable by the kind of processes treated as endogenous and what part is explainable by exogenous processes?[1]

Rothenberg asks an important question. What is the proper framework for studying the problems of urban areas? Do internal system interactions or external forces primarily cause the growth and decline of cities?

1.2 The Source of Change in a City

To understand and improve a city, its officials must be able to identify and control the forces that can change city conditions. In the real world, both external (federal, state, or regional) and internal (local) officials have responsibility for managing our cities. The many levels of urban decision making are evidence of the numerous sources of change in urban conditions. But how can change in cities best be understood? Changes within a city can be visualized as flows. Housing construction, industrial development, and migration are all flows that change city conditions. When no flows exist in a system, then no changes are taking place; system conditions are neither worsening nor improving. City conditions represent the accumulation of flows over time. For example, the level (amount) of housing in a city equals the total accumulation of past construction minus demolition.

Changes in city conditions result from (1) internally created flows and (2) flows that cross the city boundary. Figure 1-1 illustrates both types of flows: the amount of population (a system state, or conditions) is influenced by both the net birth rate and the net migration rate. The net birth rate equals the total number of births per year minus the total number of deaths. However, the number of births and deaths can be defined as a yearly percentage of the population *within* the city. For the most part, therefore, internal population conditions influence the flow of net births. Internal conditions also primarily determine many other flows in the urban system: housing construction and demolition (modulated by local demand conditions), the rate of upward economic mobility of the unskilled (controlled by local employment conditions), and the rate of change in local tax needs (a function of locally financed public expenditures).

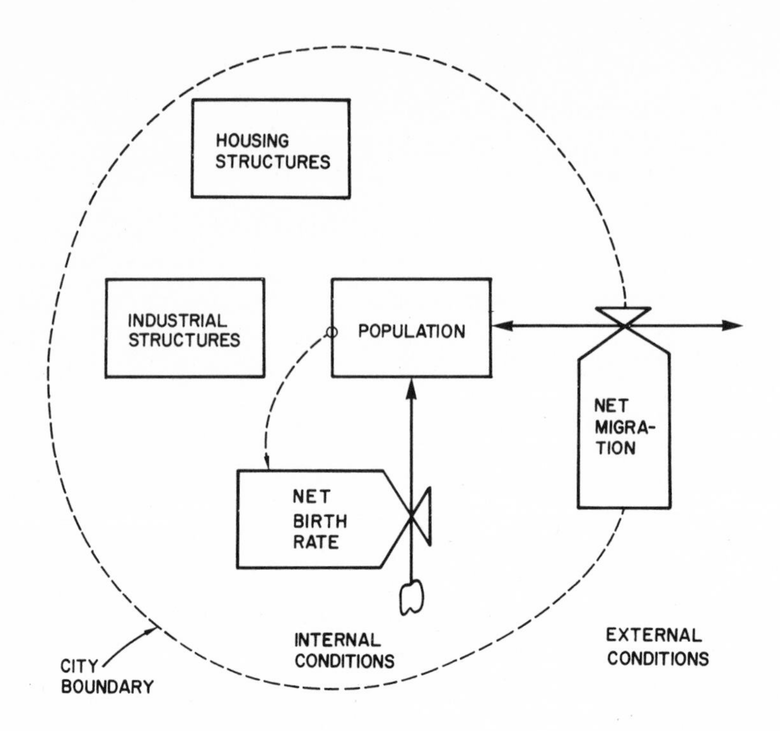

Figure 1-1 Population conditions change with the flow of net births and the flow of migration

Many other flows that change city conditions move across the city boundary. Migration, the relocation of industry (and jobs), and the transfer of revenues are flows that connect a city to its environment. Conditions in both the internal and the external environment influence the flows that cross a city boundary. Cross-boundary flows occur when conditions inside a city differ from those outside. When employment conditions inside a city differ from those in the external environment, pressures arise for migration from the higher to the lower unemployment area. If the city and the external environment are similar in all but employment conditions and if no barriers to migration exist, then migration takes place and continues until employment conditions are equal once more. Industry tends to locate according to a pattern in which more attractive areas are carefully chosen over less attractive areas.[2]

Figure 1-2 extends Figure 1-1 to show how both internal and external conditions influence flows across a city boundary. The differences between the attractiveness of the urban area (determined by internal conditions) and the attractiveness of the environment modulate the flows across the city boundary. If there are no differences in attractiveness, then normal flows take place. Attractiveness differentials modify normal flow rates according to the magnitude of the differences in attractiveness.

Any change in a city or its environment creates a difference between internal and external conditions. Changes in the external environment influence flow rates across a city boundary. Wars and depressions, for example, can profoundly influence migration

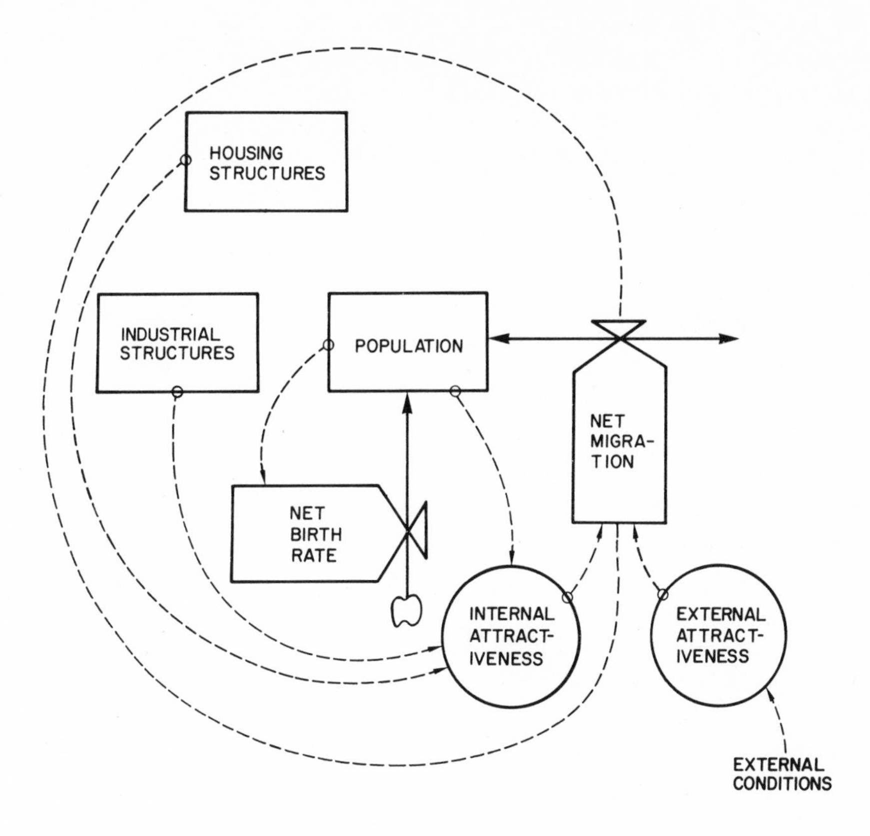

Figure 1-2 Flows across the urban boundary are created by differences between internal and external conditions

and industrial development. As unemployment rises in the external environment, a city can expect additional labor in-migration that slackens only when city employment conditions fall to equal employment conditions in the external environment. Conversely, improvements in the external environment normally lead to improvements within a city.

Changes in the external environment are not the only source of urban change. Any actions taken within a city to alter its attractiveness relative to the external environment also trigger flows across the city boundary. Actions undertaken entirely within the city boundary create flows across the boundary, not by affecting the external environment but by internally changing the city relative to its external environment. Even when its external environment remains unchanged, a city can alter its relative attractiveness and thereby induce flows across its boundary.

Obviously, conditions in cities are always changing. Flows within a city and across its boundary accumulate over time to become the city's observed condition. Perhaps the key question affecting the choice of a proper boundary for urban analysis is: Where do the important causes of a city's behavior lie, within the city boundary or in the external environment? The question is significant not only for understanding how city problems come into being but also for solving the problems.

The *Urban Dynamics* model shows how dynamic forces within a city boundary independently bring about urban growth and decline. Flows within the city boundary change city conditions; in turn, the changes affect flows across the city boundary. Current conditions give rise to a behavior that creates different future conditions. The city is a system communicating with its external environment; however, fundamental urban behavior arises within the city boundary. Forrester likens the behavior of cities to the behavior of any living system:

> The aging of a city is here conceived as an internal process, like the aging of a person. Aging is not a series of changes generated and imposed primarily by the outside environment, although changes from the outside might hasten or retard the process. . . . The flows from or to the outside are controlled only by conditions within the system.[3]

Urban Dynamics portrays the city as a self-controlling system that regulates its own flows of people and business activity to and from the outside environment. In the *Urban Dynamics* model, city problems for the most part are caused by internal interactions. Flows are the mechanism by which a city changes relative to its outside environment. Local conditions influence all the flows in the model. Local management actions that control internal flows are causally connected through internal conditions to flows that cross the city boundary. In the *Urban Dynamics* model, local actions have the greatest influence on both the evolution and the treatment of urban problems. Several reviewers have criticized the emphasis on forces originating within the geographical boundary of cities.[4] Rothenberg complains that the model boundary is too narrow to describe the important determinants of urban behavior:

> . . . by drawing the system boundaries as narrowly as they have been drawn, the forces for change which can be considered to be endogenous comprise a very narrow family. Those which have been excluded as exogenous form a most imposing set. Indeed they constitute by far the most important determinants of the fate and development of particular urban areas.[5]

Indeed, forces in the environment external to a city may affect flows within or across the city boundary. An outside force that alters the rates of flow across a city boundary clearly affects city conditions. But Rothenberg never explicitly proposes any external forces as the "dominant determinants of the origin, growth, and development of cities."[6] Nor does he even hint at how external forces alter flow rates within or across the urban boundary. His criticism touches a fundamental issue, but his arguments provide no constructive basis for evaluating the alleged need for the broader system boundary that he apparently favors. Rothenberg's criticism stems from a difference of opinion, but he offers no means for resolving the difference. Observations of actual patterns of urban development shed light on the issue of whether internal interactions or external forces predominate in creating urban behavior. Because different cities grow and decline at different times and with different rates, all cities are not equally attractive. If all areas were equally attractive, no one city would grow faster than others. But cities *are* different from one another and from their external environment (which for each city contains all other cities). The observable differences between any one city and its external environment conflict with the alternative theory that the major forces acting on cities originate in the environment. Although forces in the external environment can influence city behavior, they may be insufficient to account for the relative difference between the internal conditions in a city and the conditions in the external environment. Since urban problems are universally defined by differences in internal versus external conditions, outside forces that influence both the city and its external environment apparently do not create the problems. Forces that originate outside a city may affect the city without necessarily affecting the difference between the city and its external environment. Perhaps external forces affect different areas in different ways. But the external forces are not sufficient to explain why the differences between a city and its external environment persist so obdurately through time. During their growth periods, cities founded in the 1700s showed the same basic internal characteristics exhibited by today's growing cities. Many American cities began to decline as early as 1900, while other cities are only now showing initial signs of distress. The urban life cycle is a highly regular phenomenon, yet the beginning, magnitude, and duration of each city's cycle can vary. If forces in the external environment account for the urban life cycle, the external forces must have a discernible differential impact on cities and a timing of impact that corresponds to actual urban behavior. Forces in the external environment could hardly create growth in one city, decline in a city nearby, and no observable change in a third city. The differences in observed behavior cannot possibly result from random events outside the city boundary. More plausibly, forces that generate the behavior cycle common to cities have intimate ties to each city. *Urban Dynamics* provides an alternative to the theory that the dominant forces lie outside the city boundary, describing the urban life cycle as a function of the internal dynamics of each city. The *Urban Dynamics* model requires no regular pattern of recurring external events to explain the observed behavior of cities.

Questions regarding the proper choice of a model boundary for explaining urban growth and decline have no simple answers. The preceding discussion in no sense constitutes a "proof" that the *Urban Dynamics* model boundary is correct. A technical method for proving that a model has the appropriate boundary may not exist. On the other hand, real-world urban behavior does not contradict the theory that important dynamic causes lie within a city boundary. Whether the boundary of the *Urban Dynamics* model is conceptually correct deserves careful debate. The issue has significant implications not only from a technical standpoint but also from the practical perspective of local urban officials.

1.3 The Perspective of Local Administrators

Local urban administrators always hope to improve their city. But local officials have limited options, for they can do little to affect the external environment of their city. Any improvements resulting from local action take the form of creating and sustaining a desired difference between the city and its environment. The image of a city floating in a changing environment resembles a ship in a turbulent sea. Both the local policy maker and the ship's captain are far more concerned with their respective local system's performance relative to the changing environment than with any absolute conditions. The captain does not care whether his ship lies 200 or 2,000 feet above the ocean floor. His primary concern is whether the ship floats or sinks relative to the sea level. Similarly, the local policy maker defines a local unemployment problem and his unemployment goal not in terms of absolute levels but in relation to the national or state average. Local policies actually attempt to increase the desired (or reduce any undesired) difference between local conditions and those of the environment.

If conditions within the city boundary control relative changes between the city and its external environment, the outside environment can furnish an implicit reference. The perspective of both local officials and the *Urban Dynamics* model are congruent here. Forrester describes how the model perspective, while focusing on the city relative to its external environment, does not freeze the environment as an unchanging reference.

> This approach does not assume that either the area or the outside world is static. It assumes that the technology, the living standards, and the nature of economic activity in the area change to keep pace with the outside. The changing outside environment is not pertinent to this book. We are here concerned only with how the urban area performs relative to that outside.[7]

"We," as used in the last sentence, refers to local urban officials and all others who seek a better understanding of the dynamics of the urban system.

Local actions control many internal flows in a city, and these flows directly change city conditions and affect the attractiveness of a city relative to that of its external environment. The relative differences in attractiveness stimulate flows across a city boundary. By controlling some flows, local actions have a dynamic influence on many other flows. When viewed from the perspective of the *Urban Dynamics* model, local decision making takes on added importance as the source of urban improvement. Cities are affected by forces in their external environment, but the responsibility for making city conditions worse or better than conditions in the outside environment rests squarely on the shoulders of local city officials.

1.4 Conclusions

The boundary of the *Urban Dynamics* model is drawn to include dynamic forces relevant to the creation and cure of general urban problems. By definition, urban problems include undesired differences between a city and its external environment. Flows within and across a city boundary seem to be the only means of affecting internal city conditions relative to conditions outside. Therefore, the essential question involves whether forces within or external to cities govern the flows.

The answer to this question is far from obvious. The theory that internal interactions dominate most urban behavior remains unproven. Critics of the *Urban Dynamics* model assert that the model boundary is too narrow, but they have presented no evidence to invalidate the model boundary. To date, no formal proofs for the correctness of a given model boundary exist. Observations of the behavioral cycle of cities tend to support the theory that the most important dynamic forces lie within the city boundary. Further research into the viability of the *Urban Dynamics* model boundary should be extremely useful. If the model boundary proves to be dynamically sound, by implication, far more attention should be focused on local levels of urban decision making.

Notes

1. Jerome Rothenberg, "Problems in the Modeling of Urban Development: A Review Article on *Urban Dynamics*, by Jay W. Forrester," *Journal of Urban Economics*, vol. 1 (1974), no. 1, p. 14.

2. For a general discussion of the issues involved in industrial location, see U.S., Congress, House, Committee on Banking and Currency, Ad Hoc Subcommittee on Urban Growth, *Hearings on Industrial Location Policy*, pt. 3, 91st sess., 1971.

3. *Urban Dynamics*, p. 17.

4. Reviewers who have raised doubts about the appropriateness of the original model boundary include (a) Rothenberg; (b) Gregory K. Ingram, book review of *Urban Dynamics*, in *Journal of the American Institute of Planners*, May 1970, pp. 206–208; and (c) H. A. Garn and Robert H. Wilson, "A Look at *Urban Dynamics*: The Forrester Model and Public Policy," *Proceedings of the Second Annual Pittsburgh Conference on Modeling and Simulation* (Pittsburgh; University of Pittsburgh, 1971).

5. Rothenberg, p. 14.

6. Ibid., p. 15.

7. *Urban Dynamics*, p. 18.

2

Urban Dynamics: A Rejoinder to Averch and Levine

Jay W. Forrester and Nathaniel J. Mass

This reading responds to a review of Urban Dynamics *by Harvey Averch and Robert A. Levine, whose arguments are representative of many criticisms of the* Urban Dynamics *model. They allege that* Urban Dynamics *offers no constructive programs for urban revival, that the recommended policies improve the local urban area only by forcing the lower-income population out of the city, and that the available data do not support the assumptions incorporated in the* Urban Dynamics *model. However Averch and Levine misinterpret the* Urban Dynamics *revival program, which actually improves the lot of the urban poor, and ignore the great variety of evidence supporting the* Urban Dynamics *theory. The reading also provides a general discussion of parameter sensitivity and the role of alternative data sources in social systems modeling.*

2
Urban Dynamics: A Rejoinder to Averch and Levine

2.1 Introduction

In June 1971, *Policy Sciences* published a review by Harvey A. Averch and Robert A. Levine[1] of *Urban Dynamics*. This paper draws upon the results of urban dynamics research to respond to the specific criticisms of *Urban Dynamics* raised by Averch and Levine in their review. The reviewers read a defeatist tone into *Urban Dynamics*, claiming that the book concludes that urban problems are insoluble. On the contrary, the book offers a number of programs that should contribute to a revival of our urban areas. Averch and Levine also succumb to several basic misunderstandings of the nature of dynamic systems. As a result, they misinterpret the workings of the *Urban Dynamics* model.

2.2 Positive Programs and Revival Policies

In their review, Averch and Levine repeatedly assert that *Urban Dynamics* offers no hope for the future of our cities:

> Although Banfield's model is sociological and Forrester's is economic and physical, both imply that not much can be done to alleviate urban problems. . . . [p. 143]
> The attempts to change or control the logic of growth only mean that the city ends up in worse shape because of the attempt. . . . The temptation to seize upon analysis that indicates not much can be done, and that what can be done is more wrong than right, is likely to be powerful at a time when public officials feel strongly that fiscal and organizational resources are in short supply. [p. 145]

However, their remarks do not adequately reflect the tenor and message of *Urban Dynamics*. Chapters 4 and 5 of *Urban Dynamics* provide a detailed examination of the costs and benefits accompanying alternative national and local programs. On the basis of this analysis, the book suggests a combination of policies for reviving our nation's cities. Averch and Levine appear to have misinterpreted *Urban Dynamics*, for the book in no way suggests that current urban problems are irresolvable. It does indicate why many of the past programs directed at the cities by state and federal agencies have had little positive effect. Averch and Levine apparently interpret this result to imply that nothing can be done to help the cities. But their arguments fail to survive even a casual reading of *Urban Dynamics*, as the following extracts show:

> Chapter 5 examines a series of policies for reversing urban decline. These policies are directed, not at a frontal and expensive assault on the symptoms of trouble, but instead at the causes. . . .
> Probably no active, externally imposed program is superior to a system modification that changes internal incentives and leaves the burden of system improvement to internal processes. . . .
> This chapter, after exploring several policies, concludes that urban revival requires demolition of slum housing and replacement with new business enterprise. Only by this shift. . . will the internal mix become healthy. . . .
> Figure 5-16 shows the effect of policies that combine slum-housing demolition with active encouragement for new-enterprise construction. . . . the number of underemployed has declined 11%. . . . During the first 10 years there is almost no change in either the underemployed-arrival rate UA or the underemployed-departure

> rate UD (arrivals have actually increased a little more than departures). The change in underemployed population is accounted for almost entirely by the increased net upward mobility. . . into the labor group. [*Urban Dynamics*, pp. 7, 111, 71, 101–103]

Averch and Levine repeat the misconceptions of a number of reviewers by charging that the *Urban Dynamics* revival policies improve the city at the expense of the underemployed, whom they incorrectly assert are forced out of the metropolitan area to seek new homes elsewhere. They sum up the *Urban Dynamics* policy proposals as a program for "attracting the 'productive' component of the labor force from the undefined hinterland . . . and sending the unproductive ones back to this hinterland" (p. 155). But this statement by the reviewers is contrary to the behavior shown in *Urban Dynamics*. As noted in the previous quotation from *Urban Dynamics*, the effect of the book's proposals is to *increase* the underemployed arrival rate and *decrease* the underemployed departure rate once the policies are implemented. In the *Urban Dynamics* model, "At all times after the inauguration of the new policies, the underemployed-arrival rate into the city is higher and the departure rate is lower than before the policy changes"[2] (*Urban Dynamics*, p. 8). An analysis of the critics' argument shows how they arrived at their misunderstanding. Averch and Levine contend that "Urban renewal, for example (in Forrester's terminology 'slum-housing demolition'), is a highly successful program for the city because it clears out unattractive people, particularly if it is unaccompanied by rehousing programs (Forrester, pp. 83–89)" (p. 155). The preceding quotation refers to Section 5.5 in *Urban Dynamics*. But Section 5.5 presents one of the policy-development steps leading up to the policies recommended in Section 5.7. The text in Section 5.5 clearly points out that slum-housing demolition is not by itself a recommended program but must be combined with other actions identified later in Section 5.7: "Other policies, discussed in Section 5.7, appear to revitalize a city without forcing a net outward migration of underemployed" (*Urban Dynamics*, p. 89). Section 5.5 of *Urban Dynamics* is the fifth in a series of seven steps in the testing and evaluation of a comprehensive revival program. Averch and Levine have lifted this fifth section from the book's context and thereby misinterpreted its message. The text of Chapter 5 clearly builds toward Section 5.7, which describes the policies suggested for urban revival. However, the reviewers completely ignore Section 5.7. The same faulty reasoning that led Averch and Levine to misinterpret the local economic benefits deriving from the *Urban Dynamics* revival policies also causes them to misunderstand the national impacts of the policies.[3]

In particular, Averch and Levine argue that the simultaneous application of the revival policies to a large number of cities would be untenable:

> If Forrester's recommendations were adopted by urban decisionmakers throughout the country or if they were adopted as national policy (and if they were correct), similar "attractiveness" in all places would result in their cancelling each other out. This is particularly the case for cities today, because rural areas no longer provide an unlimited reserve of "unproductive" people nor do unproductive people tend to move from cities to rural areas. Instead of attracting the "productive" component of the labor force from the undefined hinterland as Forrester would have it and sending

the unproductive ones back to this hinterland, the play is back and forth among the cities. [p. 155]

Since the revival policies, as shown earlier, do not depend on driving the underemployed out of the city, the application of the policies to a particular city would not impose a burden on other cities. Similarly, applying the revival policies to a collection of cities would not induce any "cancelation" caused by forced movements of underemployed among urban areas. Therefore, the revival policies should succeed whether applied on a national or a local basis. In fact, the widespread application of the policies should enhance their effectiveness within any one city. During revival, the modeled city in *Urban Dynamics* experiences a net increase in underemployed arrivals of about 4,400 men per year (*Urban Dynamics*, pp. 104–105); many poor are attracted to the improved local economic climate of the city. If the revival policies were initiated in all cities, the inward flow of underemployed to any single area would decrease, thus raising the capacity of each urban area to generate upward mobility and attain a favorable local balance of population and jobs. Increased economic activity in all urban areas could also have a mutually supportive effect by raising local incomes and the aggregate demand for producer and consumer goods.

Despite the benefits accruing from the application of the revival policies on a national basis, the independence of one city from another makes the recommendations in *Urban Dynamics* particularly important. An individual city can provide for its own revival without transferring its problems to other cities and without becoming a trap for the poor and unskilled from other cities. The soundest national urban policies will probably originate at the local level, thereby eliminating the need for massive coordination by federal or state government. Local determination also gives individual cities more discretion in the exact mix of policies to be applied.

2.3 Misunderstanding of Dynamic Behavior

Averch and Levine make several errors in their article because they apparently misinterpret the dynamic behavior of the *Urban Dynamics* model. For example, they recognize fragments of the dynamic behavior of the *Urban Dynamics* model, but their review nowhere reflects a coherent understanding of the underlying causal processes. In summarizing the dynamics of growth and decay they conclude that, "Insofar as there is a central causal phenomenon, it appears to be the deterioration of housing" (p. 153). This description is partially correct, but it misses the accompanying effect of aging on industry and the dynamic interaction between the subsystems of housing and industry. *Urban Dynamics* portrays growth and stagnation occurring within a fixed urban land area. During the growth phase of an area, population, housing, and industry all grow exponentially. Moreover, "industry has a high intensity and employment per unit area of industrial land is high. At the same time housing is constructed for those engaged in the expanding industry, the residential population is economically successful, and the population density is low per unit of residential land area" (*Urban Dynamics*, p. 3). Gradually, however, new construction of housing and industry is suppressed as the particular land area fills. During this transition stage, rising land prices, difficulties in locating large, single-story plants within the area, and problems in expanding local industry in proximity to existing facilities all deter new industrial construction and divert business activity to outlying areas.[4] The construction of housing encounters similar constraints. Once building activity declines, the composition of local housing and industry shifts toward reduced employment and increased living densities. As *Urban Dynamics* describes:

> Then, as the structures age, the industrial vitality declines, new industries start elsewhere, and employment per unit of industrial land declines. But the opposite happens to population as housing ages. Rental costs decline and the kind of occupancy shifts to those people whose economic circumstances force more crowded population density per unit of residential land. In short, starting from a balance between industry and people at the end of the growth phase, employment declines while population rises until an equilibrium is reached in which the economic condition of the area falls far enough to limit further growth in population. . . .
>
> In the stagnant city there is crowding and empty housing at the same time. The ratio of people to housing may be low, but for economic reasons many of the dwelling units are unoccupied. Scarce jobs and low income force people to share space and rental costs. [*Urban Dynamics,* pp. 3, 8]

Chapter 3 of *Urban Dynamics* provides additional insight into the dynamics of urban growth and decay. During the transition interval between growth and equilibrium, there is

> a reversal of the roles of housing and jobs for the underemployed. Jobs, as shown by the rising underemployed/job ratio, are becoming less available. At the same time, housing, as shown by the underemployed/housing ratio, is becoming more available. The increase in housing is generated by the deterioration of the older parts of the city into a housing category no longer acceptable to the managerial and labor classes. At the same time construction of new industry has slowed or declined, and there has been a rise in the labor/job ratio LR. As jobs for skilled labor become less available, jobs requiring less skill are taken by more skilled labor, leaving even fewer jobs for the underemployed. . . . The urban area has shifted from a shortage to an excess of housing for the underemployed. Because the capacity of the area is limited in absorbing the underemployed, some of the multipliers must fall to low enough values to generate the low attractiveness required to stabilize the population. The underemployed/job multiplier UJM carries the main burden of reducing attractiveness. . . . In other words, the underemployed flood into the area until their falling economic circumstances act as a brake on further inward migration. [*Urban Dynamics,* p. 48]

In stagnation, the city has essentially become a social trap. The available low-quality housing exceeds the job opportunities for potential residents. People move in until the population sufficiently exceeds the job opportunities so that the average standard of living falls far enough to stop migration. In the equilibrium condition of a depressed city, available housing continually serves as an attractant. Such other urban features as job opportunities, crime, drug addiction, and schools must worsen to counterbalance the increased attractiveness resulting from extra housing. The supply of housing is greater than the area can economically support.[5] More housing can only accentuate this difficulty. On the other hand, more jobs do no good in the presence of surplus housing. Extra jobs simply attract extra people, leaving the standard of living as low as before. Since the standard of living primarily regulates population under these particular conditions, any action aimed directly at raising the standard of living instead only increases the population. This perverse behavior will continue to occur until internal forces appear that are powerful enough to limit the population inflow to a rate that the city can absorb. Because most components of urban attractiveness have relatively little leverage, housing seems to be the most effective policy instrument for population control. At the present time, however, taxes, zoning, and building code regulations interact to encourage an excess of aging housing. *Urban Dynamics* discusses those processes in detail, but Averch and Levine fail to recognize that the aging of housing and industry is closely linked to the balance between urban population and jobs.

The reviewers also fail to understand the elementary principles of dynamic behavior related to the overshoot of population that precedes equilibrium:

> The description above conveys Forrester's picture of urban change. It does not explain why the rate of change in the three urban systems differs so that rather than reaching a satisfactory equilibrium there is an overshoot into deterioration. . . . [p. 153]
>
> The reason the system overshoots is that there is a lag in the receipt and assimilation of information and responsiveness to such information. Information is summarized in a key concept of the model, the "attractiveness-for-migration multipliers." The attractiveness of the city for the three classes of labor force members differs over time. Moreover, it is perceived by members of these classes only with lags so that response occurs at times different from those in which the more or less attractive conditions actually existed. What happens then and *what causes all the trouble* is that the attractiveness of the city at different times brings in the "right" people (that is, professional-managerial people and workers in the correct proportion) and the "wrong" people (underemployed people as well as more workers than the economy can sustain) at different rates with different lags. . . . [p. 154; emphasis added]
>
> Even if Forrester's structure provides a reasonable description of city development—including the highly simplified analysis of the factors entering attractiveness—it can be argued that timing of information flows in the real world are such that attractiveness tapers off well before equilibrium is passed and the system has overshot. [p. 157]

The preceding quotations from the reviewers actually embody two criticisms of the *Urban Dynamics* model. Both are fallacious. First, Averch and Levine seem to attribute to perception delays in the model not only transient behavior but the very nature of the deteriorated conditions to which the model settles in equilibrium. This attribution, of course, cannot possibly be correct. In equilibrium, a perception delay has exactly the same input and output values, so the presence of a delay has absolutely no effect upon equilibrium values.[6] Final system conditions are totally independent of perception delays. Thus Averch and Levine incorrectly assert that the specification of perception delays "causes all the trouble." As discussed earlier, the aging of housing

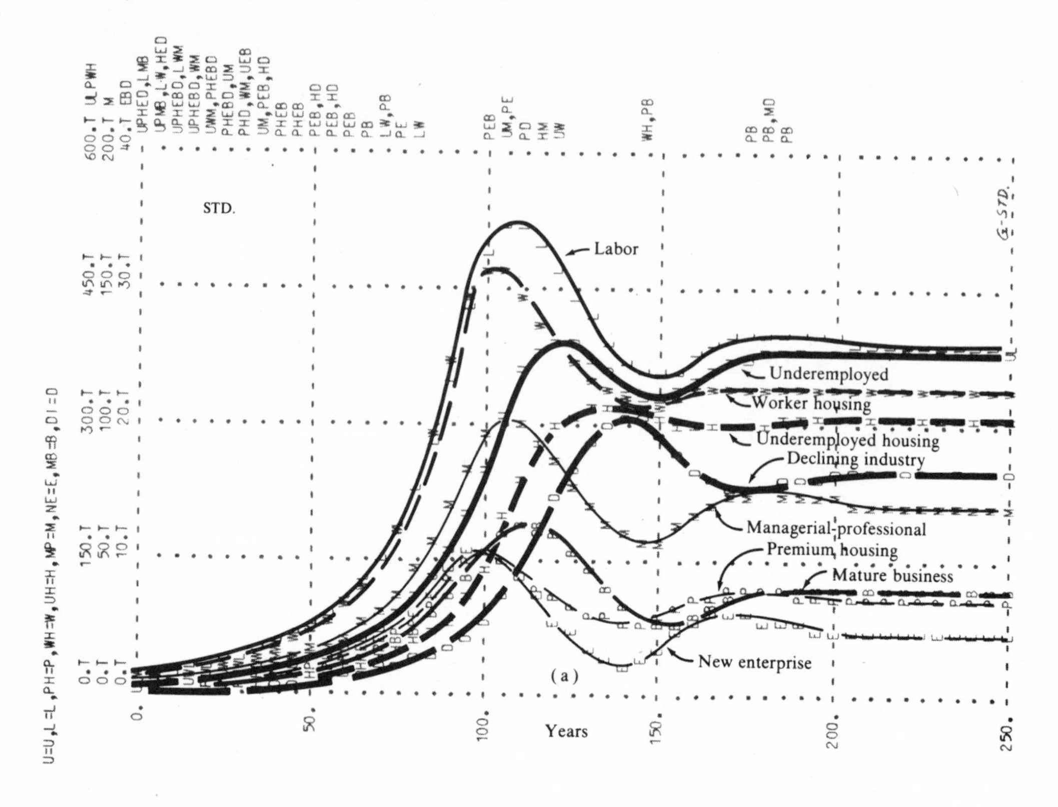

Figure 2-1 Standard growth run of the *Urban Dynamics* model
Source: Reprinted from *Urban Dynamics* by Jay W. Forrester by permission of The MIT Press, Cambridge, Massachusetts, Figure 3-1, p. 41.

and industry determines a city's equilibrium mix of employment availability and housing adequacy. Second, Averch and Levine have raised the rather unimportant question of whether the path followed by the *Urban Dynamics* model to reach equilibrium depends upon the perception delays. They seem to believe that the overshoot shown in Figure 3-1*a* of *Urban Dynamics* comes about through the perception delays to which they refer. By their implication, the overshoot would not occur if the *Urban Dynamics* model did not contain these perception delays. This assertion can be tested entirely within the model. Removing the perception delays from the *Urban Dynamics* model is a simple matter.[7] We can eliminate these delays and then simulate the model to demonstrate the degree to which the reviewers' intuition serves as a reliable guide to model behavior, or to the behavior of any real-world urban system that the model represents.[8] Figure 2-1 duplicates Figure 3-1 from *Urban Dynamics* and provides a comparative basis for evaluating the effect of removing the perception delays in the *Urban Dynamics* model. Figure 2-2 shows the system behavior when the perception delays have been eliminated. The system overshoot still occurs; in fact, the oscillatory behavior becomes even more pronounced than before. The intuition of the reviewers has failed to indicate even the direction of the effect, and, contrary to their assertions, the equilibrium conditions of the system do not change.

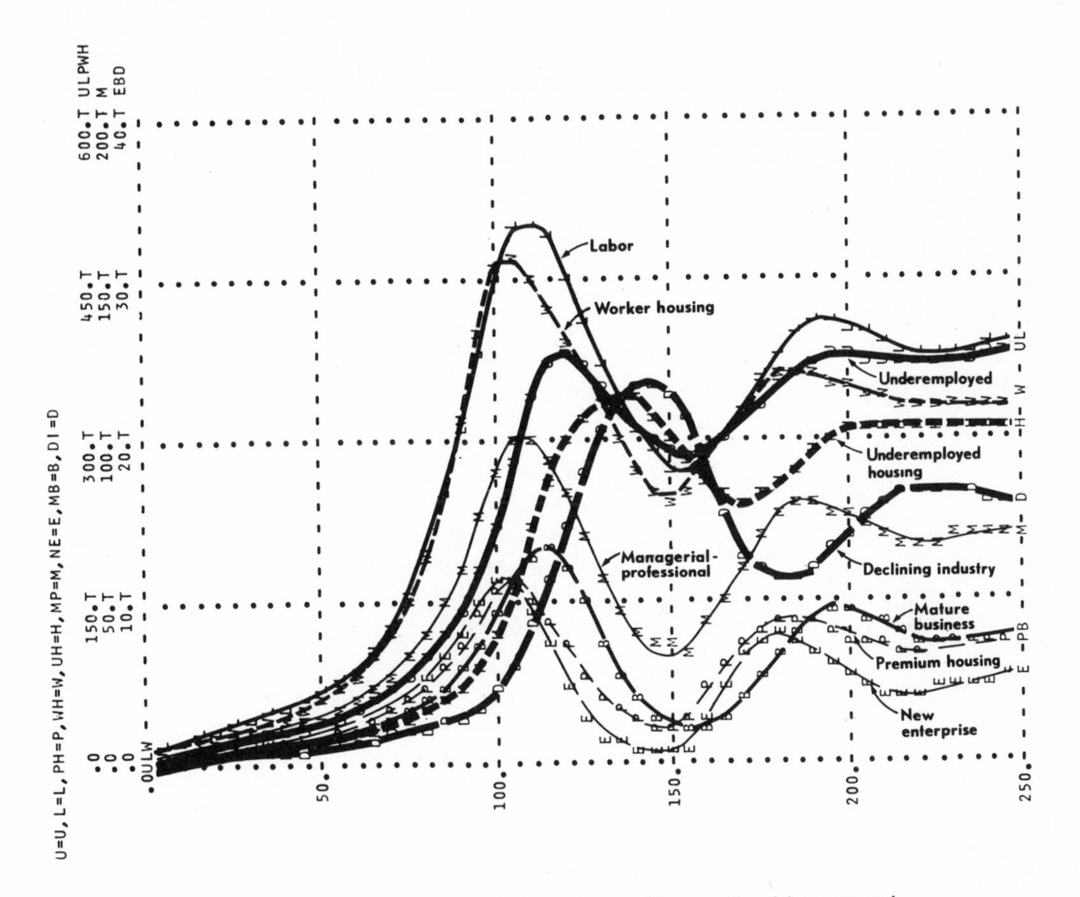

Figure 2-2 *Urban Dynamics* standard growth run with perception delays removed

2.4 The Use of Data in Urban Model Building

In their review, Averch and Levine also express concern about the absence of data citations in *Urban Dynamics*:

> Forrester's method is entirely quantitative, but he makes no attempt whatever to use data from the real world. . . . [p. 152]
>
> But do Forrester's model and his conclusions from that model portray reality at all? The answer unfortunately is that we cannot tell, nor can he. We cannot tell because Forrester arrives at his conclusions using no real world data whatever. Every function and every number in this highly numerical model is an assumption rather than any sort of empirical estimate. No empirical grounds are ever offered for any assumption. Conventional wisdom suggests that Forrester's model cannot possibly be a portrayal of the real world. . . . [pp. 155–156]
>
> Thus, we need data to estimate the structural (the functional) relationships within the model to see whether they operate in the way Forrester postulates. It may be that some of the crucial ones are very weak or operate in a reverse way, implying that the whole model will fail to operate in the assumed way. [p. 157]

These criticisms are primarily of a general nature and do not contain any tangible data or information contradicting the assumptions in *Urban Dynamics*. The reviewers cite only one example of an *Urban Dynamics* model relationship that allegedly may contradict observed facts, and they present no evidence to support their own hypothesized relationship.[9] Nonetheless, the arguments raised by Averch and Levine concerning empirical data are representative of a large number of criticisms of *Urban Dynamics*, and they reflect current thought and practice in the social sciences. For these reasons, the criticisms merit discussion.

General Theories of Urban Behavior. The *Urban Dynamics* model incorporates a general theory of long-term urban growth and decay. As *Urban Dynamics* states:

> This book examines the life cycle of an urban area. . . . The growth model starts with a nearly empty land area and generates the life cycle of development leading to full land occupancy and equilibrium. . . .
>
> [A] purpose of this study is to focus attention on the entire life cycle of an urban area. A few of those interested in urban areas have shown a tendency to turn away from the old, decaying inner city and to concentrate on new cities as a solution to the urban problem. But a new city becomes old. If the normal processes of stagnation and decay are allowed to continue in young cities that are still in good health, they too will falter. Furthermore, the processes of stagnation and decay that one sees in today's urban areas will, unless preventive measures are taken, overwhelm the present healthy suburban areas. Urban difficulties are not a matter of location so much as a phase in the normal life cycle of occupied land. . . .
>
> The urban problem is not limited to any single country, society, or historical era. The behavior of a city is much more directly dependent on its own economic merit and its changing internal mix of industry, housing, and population. Most urban areas seem to evolve through a similar pattern. [*Urban Dynamics*, pp. 1–2, 10–11, 15]

Figure 2-3 shows that many urban areas have indeed followed a similar pattern of growth, transition, and decay. The figure graphs population over time for several older American cities. Each city, although differing from the other cities in total size, location, resident primary ethnic groups, and other dimensions, shows a similar overall development path. As suggested in the preceding quotations from *Urban Dynamics*, suburban areas have also begun to encounter problems of declining population and rising proportions of poor and unskilled residents. Nassau County, for example, which gained population as upper-income groups left New York City, has recently experienced a population decrease;[10] more-distant Suffolk County continues to expand. These observations lend credence to the usefulness of a general theory of long-term urban development, such as the theory offered in *Urban Dynamics*. In their review article, however, Averch and Levine adopt a more limited perspective. They seem to doubt the utility of a general theory by arguing that:

> What is clearly needed is statistical testing using real world data to find out to which parameters "urban" systems have historically been sensitive. And if we go to the real world, we find that cities have developed differently on many dimensions—their population structure differs, their economies differ, their politics

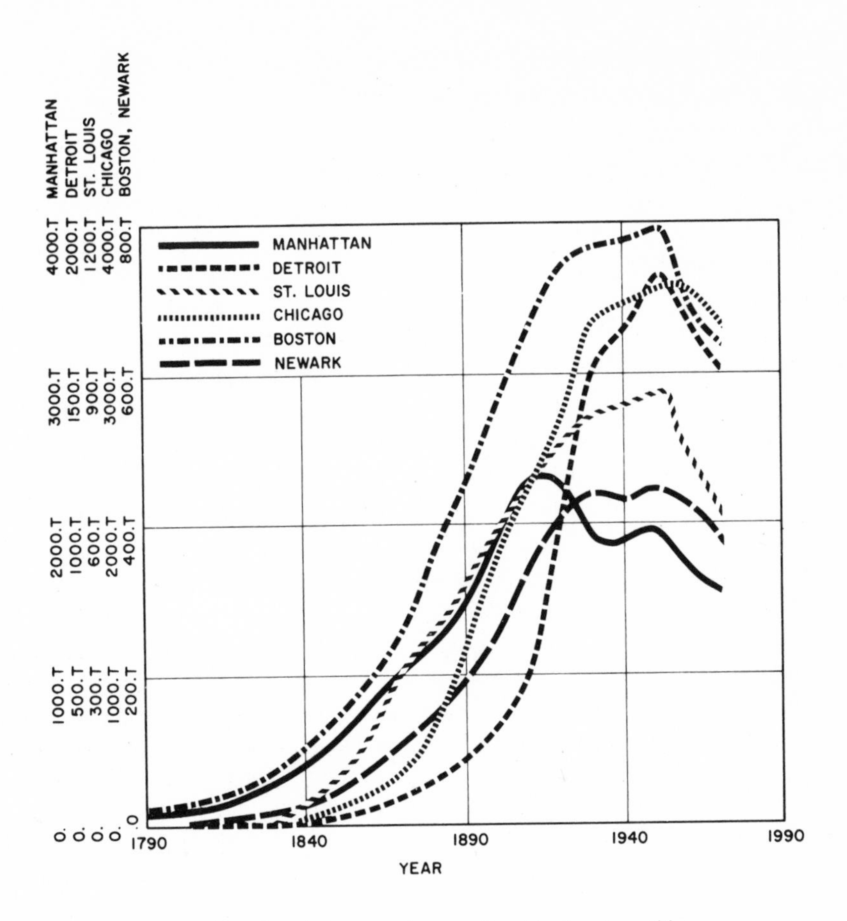

Figure 2-3 Population growth curves for older American cities

> differ. One wonders whether an untested model at this level of generality really can be useful to urban policy makers or analysts. [p. 157]

The preceding quotation contains several unjustified assertions. First, the existence of a general urban structure does not preclude differences among cities. With parameter values altered to represent specific economic, sociological, geographical, and cultural features, a general urban model should be able to show important differences between specific cities.[11] Averch and Levine recognize differences among cities, but they do not trace these differences to varying stages of the urban life cycle, different parameter values characterizing various cities, or the absence of similarities in the long-term development of urban areas.

Similarly, they do not present empirical evidence to suggest that the behavior of the *Urban Dynamics* model is inconsistent with the behavior of real-world cities. Averch and Levine apparently do not disagree that the conditions of urban stagnation described in *Urban Dynamics* reflect actual conditions in our older cities. Nor do they question the reasonableness of the policy simulation results in *Urban Dynamics*.

Nonetheless, they assert that the generic *Urban Dynamics* model "cannot possibly be a portrayal of the real world." Their criticism appears to emerge from a methodological orientation that fundamentally emphasizes the need for statistical data in theory construction, thereby precluding the possibility of building a model of a general class of real-world systems. The statistical model builder is confined to studying those systems and system conditions for which he has detailed numerical data. The dominant reliance on statistical data in theory construction can easily lead to a narrow perspective that prevents the analyst from adequately generalizing his observations or from examining long-term issues and policy questions.[12] Such a short-term perspective is apparent in the review article by Averch and Levine. They acknowledge differences among cities without attempting to relate them to the broad sweep of urban growth, maturity, and stagnation.[13] The opposite viewpoint, reflected in *Urban Dynamics*, is to consider a general, long-term urban structure that transcends particular demographic, geographical, or economic features of cities. That general structure can, if necessary, be adapted to reflect the parameters and functional relationships characterizing a specific city. The philosophy underlying the general-to-specific modeling and design process is stated in *Urban Dynamics*:

> When first modeling a social system it is usually best to model the general class of system rather than a specific system. Here, this means a model to represent the central processes common to all urban areas rather than to represent those of a specific area. The general model will be simpler and more basic because it omits the peripheral considerations that may be special to a particular place. It focuses on those system components that are always to be found interacting in urban growth and stagnation. The model should include only those processes necessary to the creation and correction of urban decay. [*Urban Dynamics*, p. 14]

The Use of Data in Theory Construction. From the preceding discussion, Averch and Levine appear to differ fundamentally with *Urban Dynamics* on the use of statistical data in model building. The reviewers state:

> A major reason for Forrester's substantive irrelevance is his failure to use data. He makes his reasons for this explicit, and they deserve to be taken seriously (p. 157). . . .
>
> None of this, however, excuses Forrester from the analyst's duty to use the vast quantities of data that *are* available. Data are needed to test not only the sensitivity of outcomes to particular parameters but also whether the assumed structural relations have any real counterpart at all. [*Urban Dynamics*, pp. 157, 158]

In the preceding quotation, Averch and Levine seem to admit only statistical summaries to the category of data. However, statistics are only one category of data relevant to modeling. The definition of datum in *Webster's Third New International Dictionary* shows the breadth of the concept: "something that is given either from being experientially encountered . . . something upon which an inference or an argument is based or from which an intellectual system of any sort is constructed . . . material serving as a basis for discussion, inference, or determination of policy . . . detailed information of any kind."[14] The statistical information on which the reviewers would rely represents a small part of the total available information about cities. Certainly we do not wish to restrict our modeling efforts to such a small fragment of information. The need for a broader information base holds particularly true because available statistics were gathered and processed on the basis of underlying, but not explicitly stated, assumptions that collected data are more important than the unmeasured elements in the real-world system.[15] Until the validity of statistical information itself becomes more clearly established in the context of the dynamic nature of our social systems, we must exercise great caution in using that information for model validation. Averch and Levine do not address themselves to the nonstatistical body of knowledge containing most of our total information. The *Urban Dynamics* model draws upon that wider body of information:

> The history of this effort explains why there are no references to the urban literature in this book. Several reviewers of the manuscript criticized the absence of ties to the literature on the assumption that such ties must exist but had not been revealed. Actually the book comes from a different body of knowledge, from the insights of those who know the urban scene firsthand, from my own reading in the public and business press, and from the literature on the dynamics of social systems for which references are given. There are indeed relevant studies on urban behavior and urban dynamics, but to identify these is a large and separate task. [*Urban Dynamics,* Preface, p. x]

The preceding quotation from *Urban Dynamics* establishes the ground rules for evaluating the *Urban Dynamics* model. Nonstatistical data were employed in constructing the model to provide the basic observations and behavioral insight needed for a general theory of urban development; statistical data were intended to play a role in subsequent tests of the theory and model extensions to particular urban areas.[16] This approach is consistent with the emphasis placed by E. H. Phelps Brown, in his presidential address to the Royal Economic Society, on observation rather than numerical statistics as a source of theory:

> But the running of regressions between time series is generally a very different matter. Where, as so often, the fluctuations of different series respond in common to the pulse of the economy, it is fatally easy to get a good fit, and get it for quite a number of different equations. Nor in any case do I see how any statistical procedure can enable us to distinguish causal from merely contingent relations, so as to "explain" or "account for" the variable taken as dependent. . . . I conclude that though fortunately some possibilities do exist of testing assumptions about behavior against statistical aggregates, running regressions between time series is only likely to deceive. . . . For our knowledge of the behavior of economic agents we must rely mainly on the patient accumulation of direct observations. . . . my argument implies the removal of the traditional boundary between the subject-matters of economics and other social sciences. . . . For the economist whose search for causes brings him up against convention, mood, passion or culture to say "At this point I stop: you must send for another trade" is quite usual but quite stultifying. When the actual way in which decisions are reached in the board room or across the bargaining table has been discussed, it has been said that economics as such has nothing to contribute. . . . Where an economic problem arises, let us observe

> whatever seems significant, and follow clues to causes wherever they may lead. . . . economists can gain insight into historical experiences by studying them. . . . My argument further calls for some change of esteem. In every science the ascending scale of intellectual status tends to be one of rarification: the more abstract, the more rigorous, the more general, so much the more distinguished. . . . In economics at least those who devote themselves to the direct observation of attitudes and behavior have . . . been . . . called hewers of wood and drawers of water. The findings of those who have been at pains to ask businessmen what they actually do, have been smiled at as impressionistic, as somehow unprofessional. In the present stage of our science, at least, I believe that this relative valuation should be inverted: we ought to value powers of observation more highly than powers of abstraction, and the insight of the historian more than the rigour of the mathematician.[17]

A quotation from the Averch and Levine review illustrates the relative importance of statistical and nonstatistical data in theory construction. In the *Urban Dynamics* model, housing availability is hypothesized as one of the determinants of migration to an urban area. The general relationship appears in Figure 2-4. A low aggregate population-to-housing ratio (at the left of the figure) implies a slack housing market, low rents, and relatively high opportunities for satisfying individual preferences with regard to housing style and proximity to schools and shopping. Under these conditions, the migration rate to the area is assumed to be relatively high, all other influences remaining constant. To the right of Figure 2-4, a high aggregate population-to-housing ratio indicates high rents and low vacancy rates, which are assumed to deter in-migration. Averch and Levine doubt that housing exerts any influence on migration:

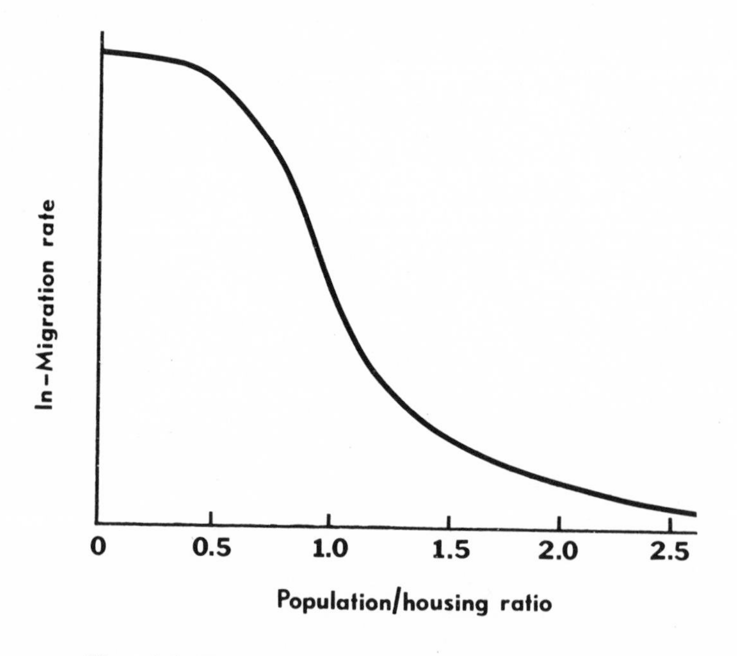

Figure 2-4 The influence of housing availability on in-migration

> For example, Forrester gives a central role to the attraction of housing, particularly to underemployed people. Our own hypothesis, stemming from some analysis of migration data, is that housing has very little to do with it. Job availability and the general economic situation seem to be the chief factors in directing migrational streams to different cities. [p. 157]

Averch and Levine reference migration studies by Ira Lowry and Peter Morrison to support their claim that housing availability exerts no influence on migration. However, these studies do not include housing availability as an explanatory variable.[18] An argument can be made (and such a position presumably underlies the assertion by Averch and Levine) that since other variables adequately explain (in the statistical sense) migration behavior, housing availability can have no additional effect. But this argument is vulnerable to precisely the criticism raised by E. H. Phelps Brown that, "Where, as so often, the fluctuations of different series respond in common to the pulse of the economy, it is fatally easy to get a good fit, and get it for quite a number of different equations." The case of housing and job availability affords an excellent example of the pitfalls of regression analysis. Throughout the growth run of the *Urban Dynamics* model, housing and job conditions tend to be linearly related with a negative slope (ignoring the first twenty years, when behavior includes transients from improper initial conditions). Figure 2-5, which plots the underemployed/job ratio UR and the underemployed/housing ratio UHR over the 250-year period of growth in the model, clearly displays the relationship.

During the city's growth stage (approximately years 0–90 in Figure 2-5), the local housing stock and industrial base are expanding, so new housing and new business structures tend to predominate over old structures. As a result, jobs for the underemployed become relatively abundant while low-quality housing remains relatively scarce. In other words, during the growth period, the underemployed-to-job ratio (a measure of unemployment) is relatively low, and the underemployed-to-housing ratio (a measure of housing crowding) is high. As urban growth begins to falter, employment opportunities become scarcer, and low-quality housing increases in supply. Throughout the cycle, housing and job availability are negatively correlated. Because of this strong negative correlation between job and housing conditions, it is not surprising that job availability statistically explains the influence of both housing and job availability upon population migration.[19] However, contrary to the interpretation of Averch and Levine, the statistical correlation of job availability and migration does not preclude the possible role of housing availability as a causal determinant of migration. A simple argument can show that housing availability must influence urban migration. Let us conduct a simple *gedanken* (thought) experiment on the relationship in Figure 2-4. Suppose that an urban area has absolutely no housing relative to other areas. This condition corresponds to an infinitely high population-to-housing ratio.[20] Would many migrants be attracted to the area? Presumably not.[21] A similar argument can show that the relationship in Figure 2-4 must be steadily downward sloping. In a city with an aggregate housing stock containing units that differ in price, quality, and location, in-migration should fall steadily in the face of a rising population-to-housing ratio. The preceding analysis has shown that housing availability must exert an inde-

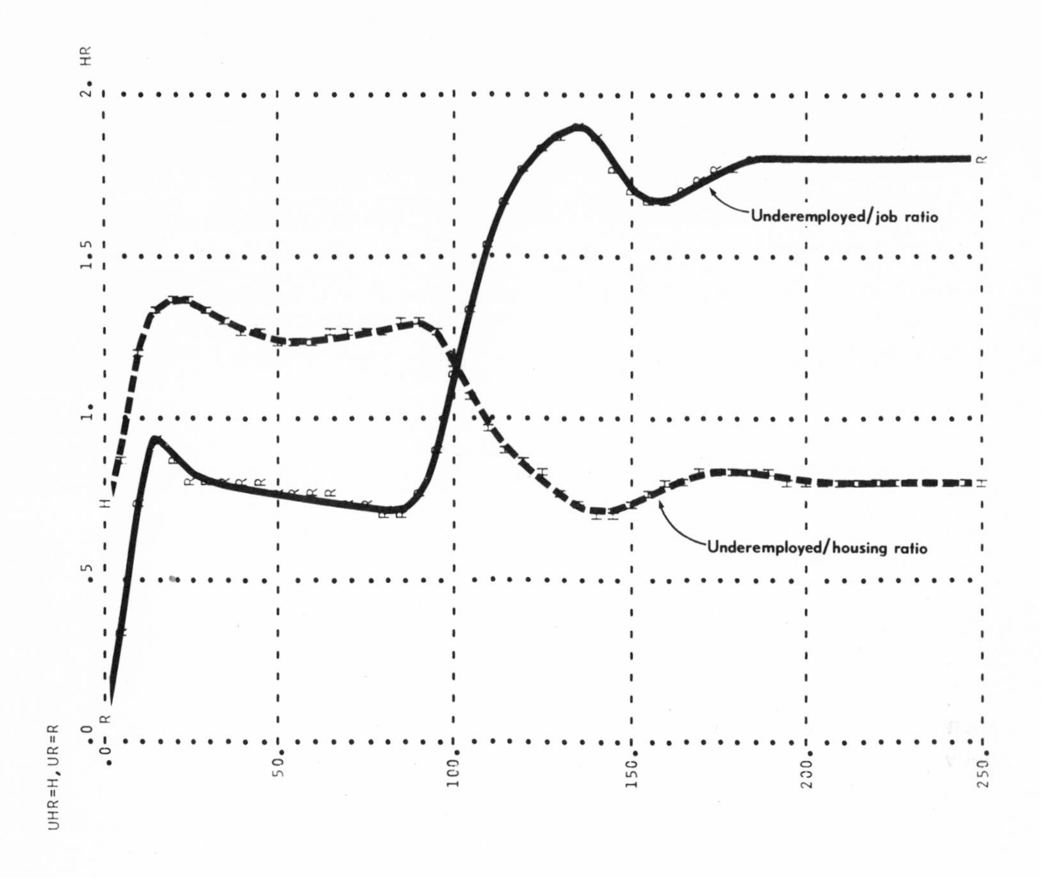

Figure 2-5 Changes in job and housing availability during urban growth and transition

pendent influence on urban migration. The existence of such a function is important from a policy standpoint, since the revival policies in *Urban Dynamics* rely on a tight housing market to limit population size to what the city can absorb. However, the function may be difficult to verify or estimate statistically because job and housing conditions may be correlated in time or because migration data for cities may relate to short time spans over which market processes keep housing conditions within narrow bounds.[22] In their review article, therefore, Averch and Levine apparently asserted the importance of data, without recognizing the narrowness of their use of that concept or the statistical problems involved in applying data to dynamic models. They rely upon short-term statistical correlations in their research, but their arguments reveal an inadequate understanding of how interactions in the urban system produce these correlations. Progress in developing techniques for applying empirical data to social systems will require more careful attention to the behavior and properties of dynamic feedback systems than Averch and Levine have demonstrated.

Parameter Sensitivity. Averch and Levine also express reservations about model sensitivity to parameter values:

> Forrester uses no statistical data whatever, arguing that the logic of his model is so strong that it is insensitive to variations in real world magnitudes. . . . [p. 145]
>
> He assumes values for the hundreds of variables used in his model and then contends the results are insensitive to his arbitrary choice of numbers. . . . [p. 152]
>
> Forrester's failure to use real world data avoids any attempts to distinguish between sensitivity and insensitivity. His specification makes the system highly sensitive to certain parameters (particularly the attractiveness multipliers) and insensitive to others. . . . [p. 156]
>
> Even within Forrester's particular mode[l], for instance, the system seems highly sensitive to whether the attractiveness multipliers overattract undesirable people. Overattraction versus underattraction is a matter that must be sensitive to the data. [p. 157]

Averch and Levine seem to confuse the sensitivity of model parameters with the question of whether the *Urban Dynamics* model structure and parameters adequately represent the real world. When the authors raise questions about the sensitivity of the model to parameter changes, these questions can be answered by observing how model behavior responds to these changes. Averch and Levine completely ignore the entire forty-two pages of Appendix B of *Urban Dynamics*, which focus on exactly this question. In particular, Section B.3 deals explicitly with the nature of parameter sensitivity and the kinds of sensitivity that would affect policy recommendations. That appendix demonstrates that the question of parameter sensitivity is important from a policy viewpoint only when parameter changes would render a proposed policy ineffective. Pages 236–237 of *Urban Dynamics* show that a change in the parameter values must be extreme in order to invalidate the recommended policies for urban improvement. The recommended policies provide economic opportunity and a rising standard of living by enforcing a tight housing situation to protect the city from inundation by excessive population. In nations whose poor are far more destitute than the poor in the United States and where a tropical climate makes shacks and lean-tos an acceptable form of housing, the control of housing may not be a feasible means for limiting migration. Such conditions do not exist, however, in the United States.

Urban Dynamics discusses parameter sensitivity at length and with considerable precision. In contrast, Averch and Levine have made assertions contrary to, and without recognition of, the major section of the book that deals with the issue of parameter sensitivity. They have also failed to consider a major policy question related to the data and parameter sensitivity issues. Since, as the reviewers acknowledge, available statistical information on cities is extremely limited, how can we devise effective urban-management policies that do not depend on complete knowledge of all system parameters? Research results suggest that the use of *feedback* or *adaptive* revival policies can reduce the sensitivity of policy changes to system parameters.[23] Such control policies can facilitate urban policy analysis even with less than complete information about cities.

2.5 Conclusions

This paper has examined the principal criticisms of *Urban Dynamics* raised by Averch and Levine. The reviewers' concerns about data, parameter sensitivity, and the impact of policies, have been shown to rest on misunderstandings of both *Urban Dynamics* and the principles of dynamic systems modeling. Averch and Levine assert that, "As it stands, Forrester has certainly created an elegant educational device. It can be used to teach the concepts of system, complexity, interaction. But its usefulness as a substantive aid for policymaking is in grave doubt" (p. 157). How can a tool for policy making be an elegant educational device if it is not useful for policy making? Perhaps the social sciences teach too many methods and techniques that fit this contradiction: they are thought to be elegant but are not, at the same time, useful. Urban dynamics theory should meet the highest and most comprehensive evaluation standards. The theory has real value only if simultaneously "an elegant educational device," and a policy-making tool, and addressed to major urban issues. The reviewers state that "the past year has seen two new and influential books on the 'urban crisis' [p. 143]. . . . [and] they are both likely to be influential in Washington and elsewhere [p. 145]." Why do the reviewers suggest that *Urban Dynamics* (one of the two books), which runs so counter to present "conventional liberal wisdom," and which will require great effort and persistence to implement, should have much influence? The answer would seem to lie in the confidence inspired by the *Urban Dynamics* model's explanation of current urban conditions and past failures of urban policy. The extensive support for the model from available data and observations strengthens the hope that *Urban Dynamics* may be a first step toward a new understanding of urban behavior.

Notes

1. Harvey Averch and Robert A. Levine, "Two Models of The Urban Crisis: An Analytical Essay on Banfield and Forrester," *Policy Sciences*, vol. 2, no. 2 (June 1971), pp. 143–158. The same paper has also appeared as a Rand Corporation working paper, RM-6366-RC (September 1970). This reading responds only to those portions of the Averch and Levine article dealing with *Urban Dynamics*. Page references for quotations from the review in *Policy Sciences* are given in the text.

2. A more extensive summary of the impacts of the *Urban Dynamics* revival policies on migration and upward mobility appears in Alan K. Graham, "Understanding Urban Dynamics: An Analysis of Garn's Interpretation," in *Readings in Urban Dynamics*, vol. 1, ed. Nathaniel J. Mass (Cambridge, Mass.: Wright-Allen Press, 1974).

3. In addition to misinterpretations of *Urban Dynamics*, Averch and Levine have altered the quotation (p. 155 of their article), taken from p. 129 of *Urban Dynamics*, dealing with national policies. In the following quotation Averch and Levine left out the first two sentences in italics. The omission weakens the original statement. The last sentence in italics and enclosed in parentheses does not even appear in *Urban Dynamics*, and is added by the reviewers:

> The city has been presented here as a living, self-regulating system which generates its own evolution through time. It is not a victim of outside circumstances but of its own internal practices. *As long as present practices continue, infusion of outside money can produce only fleeting benefit, if any.* If the city needs outside help, it may be legislative action to force on the city those practices that will lead to long-term revival. *Such outside pressure may be necessary if internal short-term considerations make the reversal of present trends politically impossible.* The revival of the city depends not on massive programs of external aid but on changed internal administration. (*Thus national programs are reduced to education and improved public understanding while each particular city pursues a laissez-faire policy designed to benefit "productive" economic forces.*)

4. See "Urban Dynamics and Land Rezoning," Reading 9 of this volume. A detailed examination of the impact of land prices and land zoning policies on urban development appears in Nathaniel J. Mass, "A Dynamic Model of Land Pricing and Urban Land Allocation," in Mass, *Readings*.

5. One major symptom of the housing excess characteristic of decaying urban areas is the rising incidence of abandoned housing. An extension of the *Urban Dynamics* model to encompass abandonment is described in Reading 10 of this volume.

6. Appendixes E and H of Jay W. Forrester, *Industrial Dynamics* (Cambridge, Mass: The MIT Press, 1961), discuss the formulation and properties of information delays.

7. Technically, the process involves reducing all the perception delays, which vary from ten to twenty years, to one year, a short enough period to be negligible. The corresponding model changes are:

C AMMPT = 1	C LAMPT = 1
C UMMPT = 1	C MAMPT = 1
C UTLPT = 1	C TRNPT = 1
C LMMPT = 1	C LRPT = 1

8. Inexplicably, Averch and Levine did not perform this experiment themselves. Otherwise, they would have recognized that the overshoot mode arises principally because of the assumptions embodied in the model regarding aging of housing and industry. Delays in perceptions are not important in this respect.

9. This example concerning the relation between housing availability and migration is discussed further on in this reading.

10. "U.S. Reports First Drop in Population of Nassau," *New York Times*, October 29, 1973, p. 37; also, "Growth Has Its Limits," ibid., November 4, 1973, sec. 4, p. 8.

11. Several parameter changes incorporated in the *Urban Dynamics* model to portray Lowell, Massachusetts, are described in Walter W. Schroeder, III and John E. Strongman, "Adapting Urban Dynamics to Lowell," in Mass, *Readings*. Although Schroeder and Strongman altered only such basic parameters as land area, housing densities, and family size, the resulting model behavior closely matched population statistics for Lowell and observed trends in housing and job availability.

12. The role of statistical data in model building is discussed further in Section 2.4 of this reading.

13. In their discussion of overshoot behavior, for example, Averch and Levine seem to be unaware that such overshoot clearly stands out in population data for older cities.

14. *Webster's Third New International Dictionary* (Springfield, Mass.: G. C. Merriam Company, 1971), p. 577.

15. Professor Tjalling Koopmans of Yale has argued that a priori theories of social behavior "filter" the methods for gathering and interpreting information. See T. C. Koopmans, "Measurement without Theory," *Review of Economic Statistics*, vol. 29, no. 1 (August 1947), pp. 161–172.

16. The model-validation process is discussed in chap. 13 of Forrester, *Industrial Dynamics;* also, see Jay W. Forrester, "Industrial Dynamics—A Response to Ansoff and Slevin," *Management Science*, vol. 14, no. 9 (May 1968), pp. 613–616. Also published in *Collected Papers of Jay W. Forrester* (Cambridge, Mass.: Wright-Allen Press, 1975). As mentioned in no. 11, empirical tests already performed on the *Urban Dynamics* model have lent support to the theory underlying the model.

17. E. H. Phelps Brown, "The Underdevelopment of Economics," *Economic Journal*, vol. 82, no. 325 (March 1972), pp. 6–9.

18. A thorough review of the migration literature related to housing availability and further elaboration of the arguments presented in this response appear in Reading 4 of this volume.

19. The approximately linear negative relationship between the underemployed/job ratio UR and the underemployed/housing ratio UHR can be seen by plotting the two variables against each other over time. Assume, then, that there exists a relationship of the form:

$$UHR = a + b \times UR, \qquad (1)$$

where a and b are constants. Also assume, for purposes of exposition, that a linear regression equation for the migration rate M is formulated as below:

$$M = c + d \times UR + e \times UHR \qquad (2)$$

Substituting from equation (1) for UHR into equation (2) yields:

$$\begin{aligned} M &= c + d \times UR + e(a + b \times UR) \\ &= (c + e \times a) + (d + e \times b)UR \end{aligned}$$

Thus the omission of UHR from equation (2) would not alter the statistical fit of the regression, although the equation would be incorrectly specified from a causal standpoint.

20. The relationship in Figure 2-4 represents the impact of housing on migration for given conditions of market supply and demand. The relationship should not be confused with market processes that regulate construction activity in response to the prevailing supply and demand for housing. The latter influences appear in other functional relationships of the *Urban Dynamics* model.

21. A less extreme situation than zero housing availability appears in many suburban areas where the small stock of low-cost housing limits the in-migration of the poor.

22. See Michael R. Goodman and Peter M. Senge, "Issues of Empirical Support for the Migration Formulations in *Urban Dynamics*," in Mass, *Readings*.

23. Nathaniel J. Mass, "Self-Learning Revival Policies in *Urban Dynamics*," in ibid. This paper illustrates that slum-housing demolition can serve as an acceptable negative counterbalance to migration so long as tight housing poses some deterrent to population inflow. From a cost-benefit standpoint, however, other migration counterbalances besides tight housing may clearly be relatively desirable in urban areas where housing conditions exert very little influence on migration.

3

Urban Management Actions

Walter W. Schroeder III

Actions taken by urban managers almost always produce unexpected side effects. This reading offers an explanation for the frequent failure of management actions to meet their intended purpose. From the system dynamics perspective, actions take effect through complex feedback loops. These feedback loops are usually responsible for the success or failure of the actions. The compensating, neutralizing, or reinforcing effects of the feedback loops can control or even reverse the overall influence of a management action. Urban management decisions suffer because of the inability of policy makers to foresee these side effects and adjust their actions accordingly. Urban dynamics models can be very helpful in conceptualizing and understanding the feedback loops that create counterproductive side effects. The reading examines the tax-abatement program as an illustration of such a use of urban dynamics models.

3
Urban Management Actions

3.1 Management Actions Alter System Conditions

A management action, taken either by urban officials or by the public, attempts to change the condition of a city toward some goal. Streams of management actions can be viewed as flows. The flow of actions (or decisions) is governed by policies. Figure 3-1 presents action streams and management policies in terms of system dynamics concepts. The policy controlling an action stream is influenced by the information about the condition of the system and translates it into action. As the condition of the city changes, the action stream adjusts accordingly. For example, suppose a policy calls for new schools to be built until the average number of pupils per classroom is twenty. The policy, using the number of students and the number of classrooms as information inputs, generates a stream of school construction to control classroom crowding. A management action stream is actually part of a feedback loop, as shown in Figure 3-2. A guiding policy controls the action stream that changes a level in the system. For example, the school-construction stream directly changes the level of classrooms. A feedback loop exists when one or more information inputs to a policy depend on a level directly affected by the policy. In Figure 3-2, information about the level constitutes the observed condition of the system. Any discrepancy between desired and observed conditions stimulates corrective management action. A policy may be defined as the set of decisions that governs the action stream and attempts to reduce the discrepancy. In short, the feedback loop implicitly compares information about the system level with a desired condition and then generates a stream of actions to alter the system level. The cycle is continuous.

In system dynamics, a *level* is an accumulation resulting from the flows of one or more action streams in a system. The distinction between population and migration illustrates the difference between a level and an action stream. The number of people in an urban system is a level, while the net migration of people into or out of the system is an action stream. The number of people (or the level) in the system at any point in time is the accumulation of past net migration (the action stream). An *action stream* is controlled by a system *policy* whose information inputs include both the discrepancy between desired and observed conditions and any other influences from other parts of

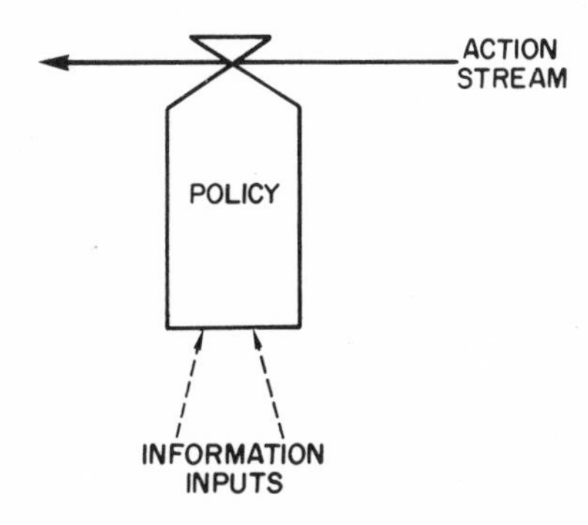

Figure 3-1 Policy interprets information to generate a stream of decisions and actions

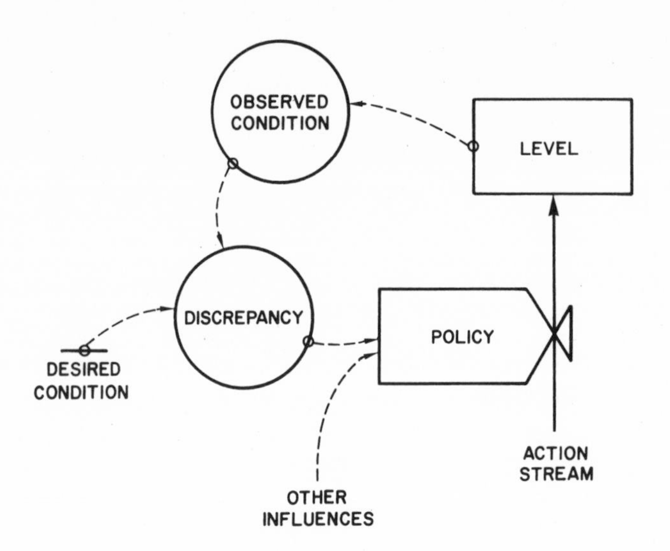

Figure 3-2 The management action stream is part of a feedback loop

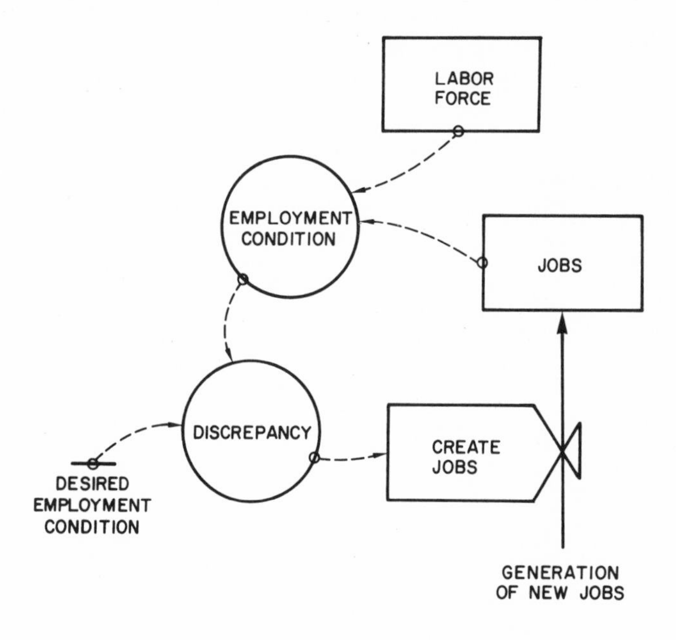

Figure 3-3 An example: a job-creation action stream

the system. Any *discrepancy* between the desired and the observed condition in a system provides an information input to the policy. The desired condition is a system goal. An observed condition is based on available information about the system level. Figure 3-3 provides an example of the system described in Figure 3-2. The management policy in Figure 3-3 aims to create jobs and thereby adjust observed employment conditions toward desired employment conditions. Information about the level of jobs in the system is combined with information about the level of the local labor force to compute the labor fraction currently unemployed (measured as labor force – jobs/labor force). This fraction is an indicator of local employment conditions. A discrepancy between desired and actual employment conditions operates through the job-creating policy to stimulate management actions that will create more jobs. The stream of actions changes the observed employment condition toward the desired condition. When the desired condition is achieved, management action may cease, but the decision rules that will govern future actions remain intact within the system. An actual employment system is of course more complex than the one shown in Figure 3-3, which only serves to show how management action streams are embedded in feedback loops. Management action streams operate continuously. Actions depend upon information about the system level. The action stream changes the system level, and information about the changed status of the system in turn modifies future management actions. The feedback structure produces a continuous stream of actions that influence and are influenced by the system level.

3.2 Management Action Streams Generate Compensating Reactions

Real urban systems contain many interconnected action streams and levels. One level can function as an information input to policies guiding several action streams. Moreover, the action stream that controls a change in one level can have a cascaded influence on several other action streams.

In complex systems the desired condition often reflects the condition of a composite of levels rather than a single level. A policy designed to govern the action stream controlling one level in the composite may indirectly influence other levels as well. Whether the resulting change reduces or increases the system discrepancy depends upon the type of feedback loop connecting the action stream to all the levels. In Figure 3-3 the desired employment condition is a function of two levels: labor force and jobs. The policy adjusts the action stream to generate more jobs and thereby improve the employment condition. Figure 3-3 explicitly treats only the feedback loop governing the level of jobs. But what happens if the level of the labor force also changes according to the employment condition? Figure 3-4, an expansion of the structure illustrated in Figure 3-3, helps to answer the question. The structure in Figure 3-4 also contains two levels (jobs and labor force) and has two corresponding action streams (the generation of jobs and labor migration). The lower portion of the diagram is identical to Figure 3-3. In Figure 3-4, however, the level of the labor force in the system changes according to the migration rate into or out of the city. The local employment condition is assumed to modulate labor force migration. If employment conditions in the city are favorable relative to the average condition of other cities, an in-migration of labor takes place. When jobs are scarcer than elsewhere, some labor tends to leave the local urban system.

Figure 3-4 contains a second feedback loop that has a compensating effect on the management action stream in the first feedback loop. By generating new jobs, the action stream in the first loop improves the employment condition and narrows the

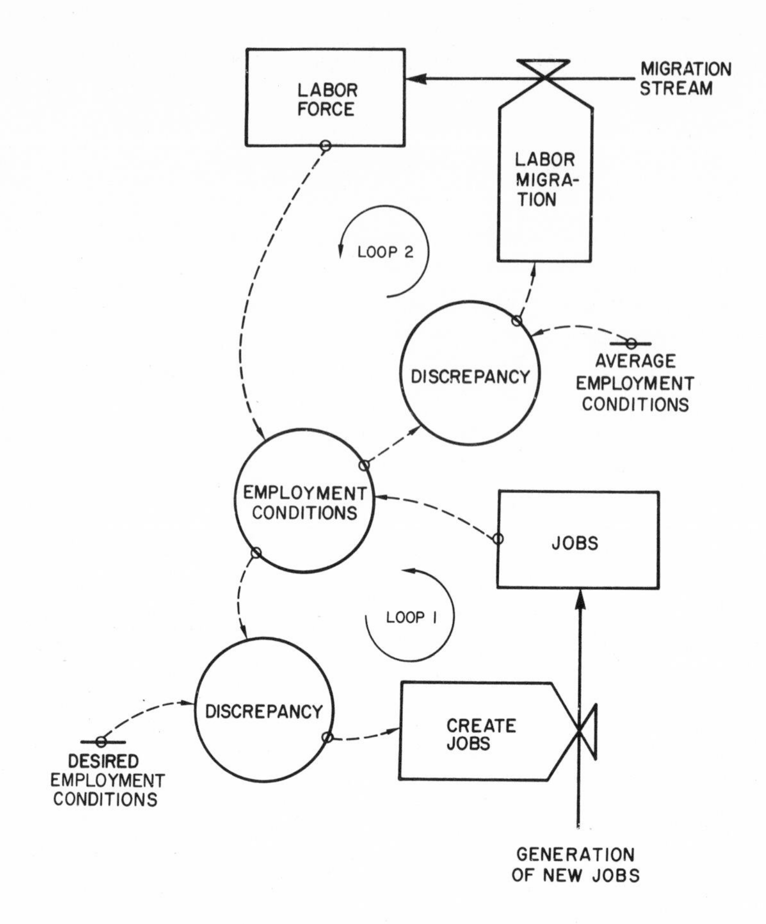

Figure 3-4 An employment system in which the level of jobs and the level of labor can change

discrepancy between the observed and the desired condition. But as the employment condition improves, more labor migrates into the area. An increase in the labor force in loop 2 tends to counteract any improvement in the employment condition generated by loop 1. The generation of jobs alters the employment condition and thereby stimulates the in-migration of labor. The larger labor force in turn diminishes the improvement in employment conditions. The feedback structure of the system in Figure 3-4 may inherently defeat policies and action streams aimed at controlling the employment condition through job creation. The variables in this simplified employment system interconnect so that the feedback loop generating the compensating effect (loop 2) is not the loop containing the management action stream. If the employment condition already matches average conditions in the environment and if neither local officials nor the local general public have any direct control over labor force migration, then urban management cannot possibly further improve the local employment condition. The feedback structure in the urban system creates many similar compensations that diminish the effectiveness of management actions. Some other compensating feedback loops prevent the flow of corrective management actions. For example, Figure 3-5 shows the rezoning action stream as part of a simple feedback loop. The level is the amount of industrially zoned land. The desired condition is assumed to be a desired amount of industrially zoned land. In light of the discrepancy and other influences, zoning officials in control of the rezoning action stream decide how much land to rezone. The action stream functions to remove any discrepancy between the existing and the desired amount of industrial land.

However, local residents may look upon an increasing amount (level) of industrial land in the local urban system as a threat to the safety of their children and to the value of their property. As the level of industrially zoned land increases, local opposition to any further rezoning for industry also increases. In Figure 3-6 the level of residential opposition to rezoning forms part of a second feedback loop that couples to the feedback loop in Figure 3-5.

In Figure 3-6, local residents compare the current amount of industrially zoned land with the amount of industrially zoned land that they believe is appropriate for their city. A discrepancy between the desired and the actual amount of industrially zoned land produces an action stream that increases the level of opposition by residents to rezoning. The level of the opposition to rezoning influences the stream of rezoning through political or social pressure. Local residents may voice their concern at city council or zoning board meetings. An increase in opposition to rezoning does not directly alter the discrepancy that the corrective management action stream is attempting to eliminate. Instead, the opposition prevents some percentage of management rezoning actions from taking place.

Figure 3-6 depicts a different kind of system compensation from that in Figure 3-4. The difference centers upon the point where the compensating feedback loop impinges upon the first feedback loop. In Figure 3-4 the compensating loop affects the system condition that the action stream is trying to correct. No amount of management

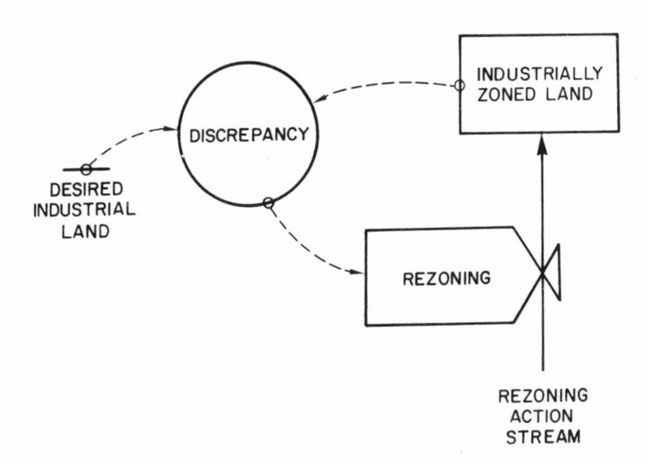

Figure 3-5 A rezoning action stream in a feedback loop

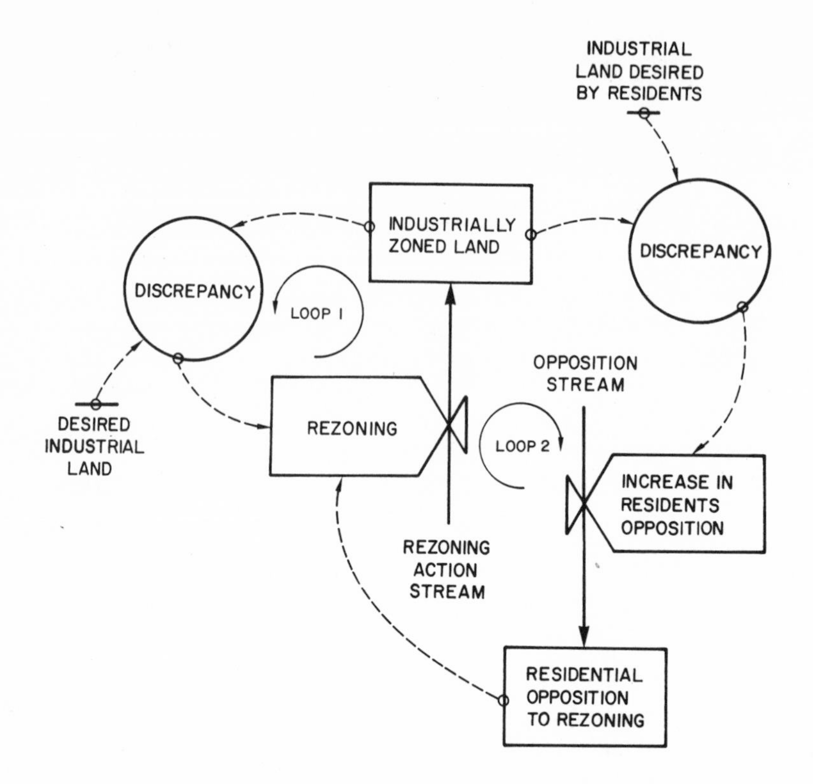

Figure 3-6 The rezoning stream increases residential opposition to further rezoning

action can produce the desired system condition. In contrast, the management action stream in Figure 3-6 is structurally capable of producing the desired condition, but compensating feedback loops prevent the potential flow of corrective actions within the action stream. The compensating feedback loops that oppose and prevent management action streams are often subject to some degree of managerial control. The zoning official has at least a small degree of choice over how much he responds to (or ignores) residential opposition to rezoning. He can sometimes soften local opposition to industrial zoning. If urban managers can successfully control compensating pressures that prevent action and if the action stream is structured to avoid self-defeating compensations, management action has a much greater chance of being effective. Feedback interactions within a complex system do not always produce compensating effects. Management actions frequently trigger secondary feedback loops that tend to reinforce, rather than compensate for, the desired effect of an action stream. Reinforcing loops either:

1. further reduce the discrepancy between desired and actual conditions or
2. permit actions to take place at an accelerated pace.

The feedback loop in Figure 3-7 gives rise to a reinforcing mechanism. The policy in loop 1 attempts to restrict the rate of new housing construction in the community. Reducing the rate of housing construction causes the city's housing supply to grow less rapidly. The reduced housing availability in turn slows the growth of the local workforce. When the labor force exceeds available jobs, the housing policy reduces housing construction, thereby tending to restrict the size of the labor force. A smaller labor force improves the balance between workers and jobs. Loop 1 in Figure 3-7 does not directly influence the job supply, but it does directly influence the size of the workforce. Therefore, the loop can modify the discrepancy between desired and actual employment conditions. Loop 2 in Figure 3-8 illustrates a positive secondary effect that reduced housing construction can have on the supply of jobs. Because the supply of jobs helps to determine city employment conditions, loop 2 can reinforce the effects of loop 1 in improving the balance between workers and jobs. Loop 2 assumes that constrained housing construction makes relatively more land available for industrial development. Increased industrial construction raises the total amount of industry in the area and thus adds to the supply of jobs. Employment conditions, as affected by loop 2, improve over and above the positive effects produced by loop 1. The feedback structure in Figure 3-8 creates an interesting phenomenon: management actions to reduce or control one activity (housing construction) create positive system pressures with respect to other city activities (industrial construction). The two action streams

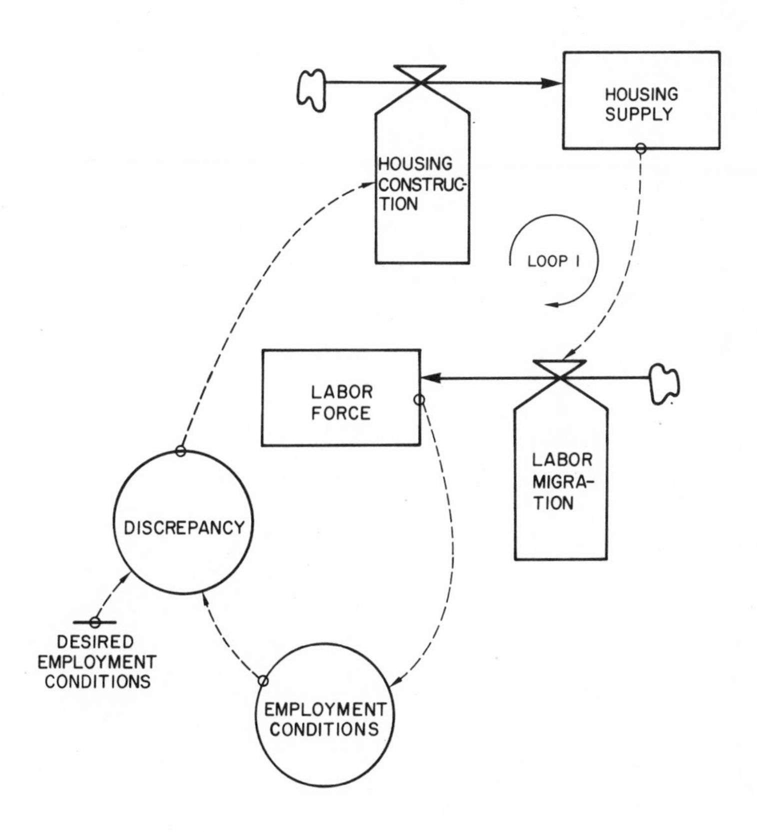

Figure 3-7 Reduced housing can further improve employment conditions by making more land available for industry

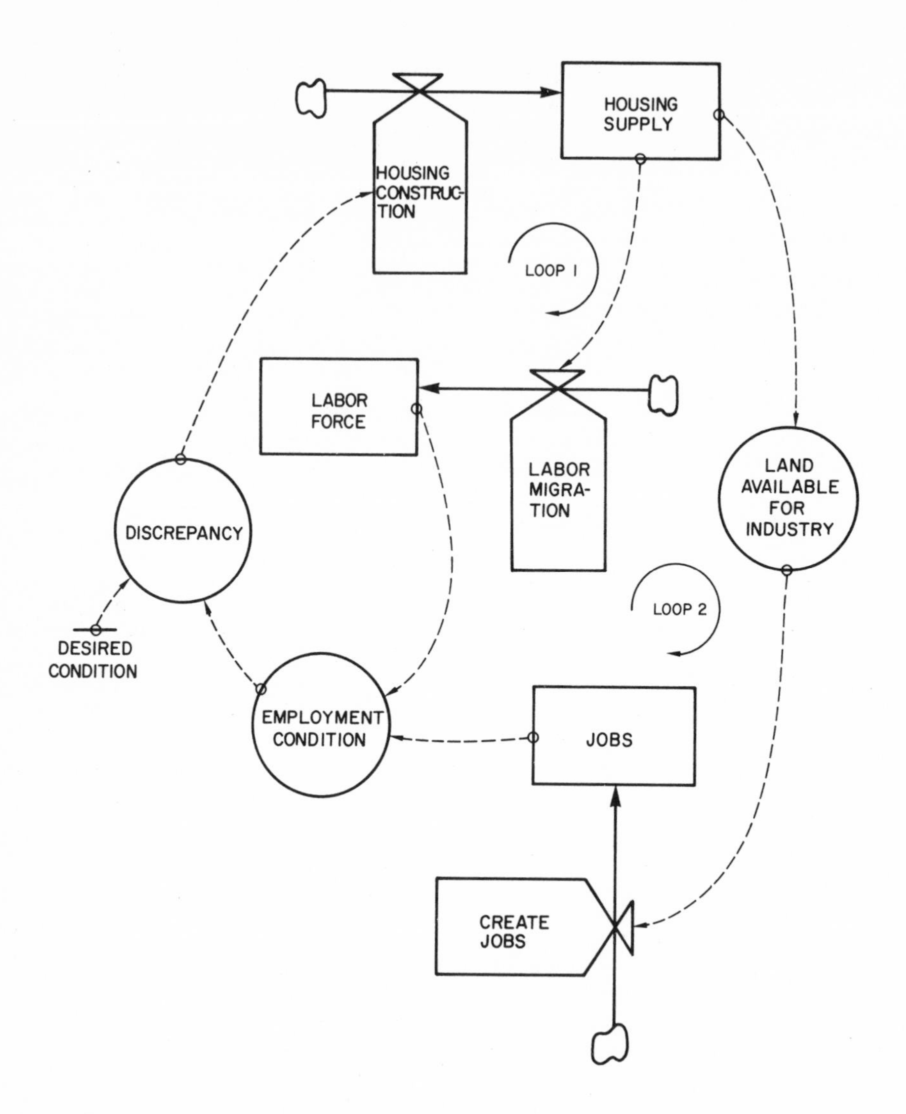

Figure 3-8 The effect of the property-tax ratio on the rate of new-enterprise construction with lowered assessed valuations.

reinforce one another with respect to improving the city employment condition. A management policy to limit housing construction may be dynamically more sound than direct job creation, because reduced housing construction limits the size of the workforce. In Figure 3-4, direct job creation tended to stimulate the in-migration of workers, thereby impairing the management action stream intended to create more job opportunities for the available labor force. A system dynamics model can help to identify the potentially most effective action streams for achieving city goals. City officials and the public should examine in a dynamic model both the short-term (zero to five years) and the long-term (ten to forty years) consequences of different policies for guiding any specific urban action stream. When altered through a change in governing policy, some action streams can substantially improve city conditions in terms of desired goals. Other action streams only accelerate compensating counteractions or indirectly prevent the flow of corrective action. To be effective in moving a city toward its goals, a policy (which guides one or more action streams) must pass both the following tests:

1. If counteracting feedback loops would otherwise compensate for the proposed policy with respect to a particular action stream, other feasible policies must be available to neutralize the counteractions. A combination of actions, as in Figure 3-8, is often necessary to prevent self-defeating internal compensation.
2. To the extent that counteracting forces prevail, the policy must be amenable to public education and explanation designed to attenuate political resistance to the new policy, as in Figure 3-6.

A dynamic model can both identify potential compensating feedback loops triggered by management actions and guide the selection of policies to produce a predominantly reinforcing effect. Before attempting to adopt a new policy to guide a particular action stream, the manager must know whether it will produce reinforcing or compensating effects with respect to other local policies. A dynamic model ultimately produces a management strategy (or a combination of policies to guide several different action streams) to ensure that reinforcing loops in the urban system operate freely, while compensating loops are kept under control. Such strategies permit system conditions to move in desired directions and to induce overall improvement in city conditions.

3.3 Survey of Urban Management Action Streams

Most people tend to confuse causes, symptoms, actions, and goals. All four are apt to be referred to as problems, with no distinction among their sharply different characteristics. A city manager who talks about the problem of reducing unemployment can only mean that one of his city's most undesirable qualities is high unemployment. But mentioning unemployment is not a statement of cause. "To reduce unemployment" is not a direct avenue for action. The manager can start a skill-training program, add the unemployed to the public payroll, or provide transportation to jobs, but such actions will not necessarily reduce unemployment. A goal of 3 percent unemployment is not the same thing as a stream of actions for achieving that goal. Few social goals unambiguously imply an appropriate remedial action stream; few, if any, action streams are immune to counteracting feedback loops that lie within the system structure. A social system can change only in response to the flow of actions within the system. Goals are not actions. Intent is not an action. The recognition of symptoms does not necessarily imply action. To make a change for the better requires an identification of the possible alternative action streams and a subsequent anticipation of how each specific action stream can influence the system. A listing of the possible action streams in an urban setting should help to unravel the often confused concepts of causes, symptoms, goals, and actions. If the goal, the system level directly influenced, and the potential system compensations could be clearly identified for every urban-management action, managers would be in a better position to choose among available alternatives. The following discussion of common actions provides a sample of the complex relationships present within the urban system:

1. Grant tax-abatement requests on older industrial and commercial property
2. Zone more land for industrial use
3. Demolish abandoned housing
4. Condemn low-quality housing
5. Adopt rent control
6. Build lower-income housing
7. Extend mass transit lines
8. Expand the police force
9. Demolish older industrial and commercial buildings
10. Lower maximum floor area zoning restrictions
11. Petition for more state and federal aid
12. Extend sewer lines to undeveloped city land
13. Widen certain classes of city roads
14. Initiate job training
15. Grant more building permits
16. Increase the school budget
17. Reduce taxes

Grant Tax-Abatement Requests on Older Industrial and Commercial Property. Tax assessments determine how the various categories of property in a city bear the tax burden. A tax *abatement* is a temporary reduction in the assessed property valuation that city assessors can grant to owners of overvalued property. The value of older industrial and commercial property falls when buildings are not well maintained or when tenants are hard to find. Owners of obsolete property often request tax abatements based on eroded property value. As with other tax changes, the consequences of a stream of abatement actions can shift the tax burden and thereby affect incentives for both maintenance and new construction. The ultimate results often differ greatly from those anticipated or intended.

Zone More Land for Industrial Use. The zoning action stream controls land use. A zoning board, operating under various legal restrictions, controls the allocation of land from one use category to another. Pressures for increasing the flow of industrial rezoning in a city generally come from industrial developers. Residents living near land proposed for rezoning for industrial use may object, anticipating traffic hazards, attendant pollution, noise, and other side effects of increased industrial activity.

Demolish Abandoned Housing. The action stream of demolishing abandoned housing constrains the blight and physical hazards associated with deteriorating and inadequately maintained buildings. Pressure on the mayor and the building department to demolish abandoned housing comes from local residents whose own property values are threatened by the blight or from developers who might put the cleared land to better use. Because of the high cost of demolition, the city usually turns to housing demolition only when the state or federal government will pay the cost (as in urban renewal programs).

Condemn Low-Quality Housing. The city building department condemns housing structures that fail to meet minimum fire or health standards. Building condemnation does not always necessitate demolition; owners may rehabilitate or abandon their buildings. Inspectors resist condemning low-quality housing whenever possible because tenants would have to relocate and because the city would lose a portion of its tax base. The condemnation action stream often serves only as a last resort when property owners are unwilling or unable to upgrade their housing to meet minimum standards.

Adopt Rent Control. A city sometimes adopts rent control to protect its residents from rising rents. Rent control impinges on many other action streams, including housing and industrial construction, the deterioration and demolition of buildings, and migration. Pressures to adopt rent control usually come from resident tenants, while landlords are generally opposed to it.

Build Lower-Income Housing. A policy to raise the availability of good housing for lower-income families normally controls the action stream that generates lower-income housing in a city. The rate of construction of lower-income housing is determined by at least three factors: the preparation of applications for outside funds by local agencies, endorsements by the city council, and approval by the outside funding source—generally the U.S. Department of Housing and Urban Development (HUD) or the state. Other influences on the rate of lower-income housing construction include the local press, interest groups, and housing developers.

Extend Mass Transit Lines. Actions to extend mass transit facilities are usually undertaken to improve access to a city's central business district and to move people between their homes and jobs. Particularly as a city's parking facilities and roads become inadequate, demands for better mass transit begin to receive increasing attention. The pressure for mass transit extensions comes from ecologists, business, and the general public. Mass transit extensions require local approval and financing, then state or federal capital funding.

Expand the Police Force. Every mayor, city councillor, and resident wants to reduce the local crime level. City officials commonly attempt to reduce crime by hiring more police, but the number of people that can be added to the police force is limited by a city's financial capacities.

Demolish Older Industrial and Commercial Buildings. Older business structures, when underused or empty, contribute few jobs and meager tax revenues to a city. An aging structure consumes valuable inner-city land that might otherwise be put to more productive land use. Cities that are eager to stimulate the action stream of demolishing older industrial buildings to induce new industrial development often find the cost prohibitive. A city with an excessive number of older industrial structures may not have the financial strength to undertake expensive demolition. Public pressure on the city council and mayor to restrain spending often prohibits this option.

Lower Maximum Floor Area Zoning Restrictions. Buildings usually must conform to many local regulations, including a maximum allowable floor/area ratio. The action stream that controls zoning density constrains high-density construction while keeping land open for less intensive development. Local residents, concerned by rising densities, crowding, and the resulting higher cost of living, can appeal for controls on density. The zoning board sets and enforces zoning ordinances in response to the observed needs of the community.

Petition for More State and Federal Aid. City revenues seldom equal or exceed city expenditures. The discrepancies between a city's income and outlay continually impel mayors to seek new sources of revenue to finance expanding city services without having to increase the local property tax rate. Mayors often resort to the action stream of petitioning the state to take over such local burdens as welfare and education. A similar action stream is aimed at eliciting revenue from the federal government.

Extend Sewer Lines to Undeveloped City Land. Land has relatively little value to a developer in the absence of accessible roads, sewers, and power. To attract new construction and add to a city's tax base, the city can extend sewer services into undeveloped areas. The pressure for extensions comes primarily from developers who stress the potential value of properly serviced land. Local bond issues must receive local and then state or federal approval to raise the necessary funds for sewer extensions. Because the city, like any fiscal entity, has a debt ceiling, chances for approval diminish if the city is not in a strong financial condition.

Widen Certain Classes of City Roads. Nearly everyone in a city uses its roads. The condition and congestion of city roads therefore usually draws considerable local attention. The mayor controls the action stream of improving and widening roads to ease commuting, improve commerce, and prevent general public dissatisfaction. But widening roads to reduce congestion and travel time will be ineffective if an increasing number of drivers use the roads.

Initiate Job Training. Job-training programs are intended to give the poor and unskilled in a city access to upward economic mobility. Local antipoverty agencies usually apply for and administer federal or state funds for the programs. The action stream of initiating manpower-training programs generally meets with little, if any, local resistance. These programs exist in nearly every major city. If they draw still more unskilled workers to the city, job-training actions may not improve the local balance between workers and jobs.

Grant More Building Permits. Requests for and grantings of building permits follow routine action streams. A builder must have city permission to construct or modify a building. The building department normally grants permits as long as the proposed building design and use conform to zoning and health regulations. A city that wants to discourage some types of building construction should consider a more restrictive policy in granting building permits.

Increase the School Budget. To decrease the discrepancy between the desired and the actual capacity or quality of city schools, a school committee will often increase its proposed operating budget. The school budget is a major issue because it normally represents the largest single city expenditure. Although budget increases presumably lead to improved education, the extra cost often forces the mayor to resist the action stream of budget increases. The quality of education may be viewed as a trade-off against the quality of other city services that also depend on local funding. Where local funds are limited, the decision to budget more money to one activity is also, by default, a decision not to increase the funding for some other activity.

Reduce Taxes. The mayor and the city council can reduce taxes only by constricting the action streams that channel spending. Most city budgets are likely to draw a mixture of support and opposition. A mayor should expect to be criticized by the department heads and residents directly affected by any spending cut. Depending upon his sensitivity or fortitude, the official may relax or intensify constraints on spending. Urban budgeting in reality may be based as much upon the short-term pressure to keep department heads happy as upon a conscious effort to move the city toward any long-term goals.

3.4 The Tax-Abatement Action Stream—An Example

The *Urban Dynamics* model can take the urban manager several steps further than the brief analysis of the specific action streams presented above. A closer look at a specific action stream in the context of the urban feedback structure can lead to better decision making. The action stream chosen for closer study here is the city tax assessor's response to requests for property-tax abatements. Rather than fully modeling and evaluating different tax-abatement policies, the examination concentrates on the conceptual steps that should precede actual modeling.

An urban dynamics analysis of tax abatement begins with two related questions:

1. To what extent can the *Urban Dynamics* model be used to examine abatement policies?
2. How can the *Urban Dynamics* model be altered to represent abatement policy influences not explicitly represented in the model?

As noted, tax abatements are temporary (usually one- to three-year) reductions in the assessed valuation of property, which lower tax bills on property and tend to reduce a city's tax base. Continuously renewed abatements permanently reduce a city's tax base just as effectively as a reassessment of the property at a lower value. In fact, any property that wins repeated abatements is commonly reassessed downward.

A property's assessed value is supposed to depend on a determination of its fair-market value. An abatement request is an appeal process through which taxpayers can obtain a hearing and a redetermination of the assessed value of their property. An alleged overvaluation of property commonly leads to an abatement request. If denied an abatement or if not satisfied with the decision, a taxpayer may then appeal through the courts—normally a long and expensive process.

Local property assessment and tax-abatement practices vary widely. Assessing is at best an inexact science. The assessment-abatement-appeal system is designed to eliminate discrepancies and ensure equitable treatment for all taxpayers. However, the concept of equity depends on the law, intent, and traditions. Within a certain range, local custom determines assessment and abatement policies. A substantial departure from current assessment policy might necessitate a complicated and time-consuming legal revision. For the example presented here, assume for the moment that the current abatement policy favors newer buildings and penalizes older buildings. In other words, within the range of discretion or possible legal changes, abatement and assessment procedures are altered to increase the taxes on deteriorating structures and to reduce the taxes on new structures. Such a policy, not necessarily achievable in any given community, is intended to encourage internal self-renewal of a city. The assumed tax-abatement policy discourages abatements (increases effective assessments) for deteriorating property but favors new property, which will contribute relatively more to a city's economic base. The effect of biasing tax-abatement policies against older buildings can be represented in the *Urban Dynamics* model by increasing the parameters that define the assessed valuations of deteriorating buildings (declining-industry assessed value DIAV and underemployed-housing assessed value UHAV) and simultaneously decreasing the parameters that define the assessed valuations of the newest buildings (new-enterprise assessed value NEAV and premium-housing assessed value PHAV). For simplicity, assume that the assessments on mature industry and worker housing do not change. However, the *Urban Dynamics* model is not designed to test changes in assessed valuations. To represent the direct effects of reassessments requires a second set of model changes. Three nonlinear table functions (enterprise-tax-multiplier table ETMT, premium-housing-tax-multiplier table PHTMT, and manager-arrival-tax-multiplier table MATMT) must be altered to introduce the immediate and direct behavioral response to the new assessment policy. The effects of higher taxes on both declining-industry demolition and slum-housing demolition must also be detailed in the model.

Lowering the assessed valuations (and therefore the property tax bill) of new-business property in a city raises the financial incentive to construct new buildings. Lower property taxes reduce the cost of doing business. A reduction in assessment should encourage the construction of new job-creating buildings.

Because tax assessments are assumed to be constant for each type of building in the *Urban Dynamics* model, the effect of taxes on construction in a city is not modeled from the tax bill on property but, rather, from the tax ratio (a normalized tax rate assumed to apply equally to every building type). The effect of a reduced assessment is to reduce the tax bill that the property owner must pay. Therefore, a reduced assessment is equivalent to reducing the tax ratio TR. The dotted curve in Figure 3-8 is the original curve (Figure A-53 in *Urban Dynamics*) relating the tax ratio TR to incentives for enterprise construction (enterprise-tax multiplier ETM). The solid curve in Figure 3-8 reflects a policy change that reduces property assessments (and tax bills) on new-enterprise structures.

The altered enterprise-tax-multiplier table ETMT does more than just stimulate new industrial construction in the *Urban Dynamics* model. It also shows that the rate of obsolescence of new-enterprise structures and mature-business structures slows. The curves defining the premium-housing-tax-multiplier table PHTMT and the manager-arrival-tax-multiplier table MATMT should be changed in a fashion similar to ETMT. When the assessed valuations of new premium housing decline, for example, tax bills drop and the city becomes slightly more attractive to the managerial-professional group.

In the *Urban Dynamics* model, no equations explicitly represent the influence of building assessments and property-tax bills on the rate of demolition of older structures (except, as explained, through the effect of the enterprise-tax-multiplier table ETMT on declining-industry demolition (DID). To include the influence on demolition, the model would require modifications to represent the effects of property taxes on both the rate of demolition of older business structures (declining industry DI) and the rate of demolition of older residential structures (slum-housing demolition SHD). The changes suggested here represent a first approximation of how to incorporate an altered tax-abatement policy in the *Urban Dynamics* model. However, in real life, the proposed policy changes may lie embedded within feedback loops not accounted for by the model. Therefore, a valid test of the specific urban action stream governing tax abatement requires adding to the model any other feedback loops that might significantly affect that action stream. Since the *Urban Dynamics* model was designed specifically to show the dynamic behavior of the urban life cycle, it contains only the major feedback loops that affect primary urban behavior. Several feedback loops that might change the dynamic outcome of tests of alternative tax-abatement policies are missing from the model. One such loop appears in Figure 3-9, which shows the kind of counteracting influence described in Section 3.2 of this reading.

The feedback loop in Figure 3-9 shows how assessment policy can affect market values to counteract at least part of a change in assessment policy. Assume that a city's assessment policy is structured to increase the assessed value of a property. The resulting higher property-tax bill makes the property less desirable and reduces its market value. The reduced market value creates grounds for a tax abatement and a reduced assessment. The feedback loop partially compensates for an attempt to alter the assessed valuation. An increased assessment can lead to a lowering of property values so that owners become eligible for reduced assessments sometime in the future.

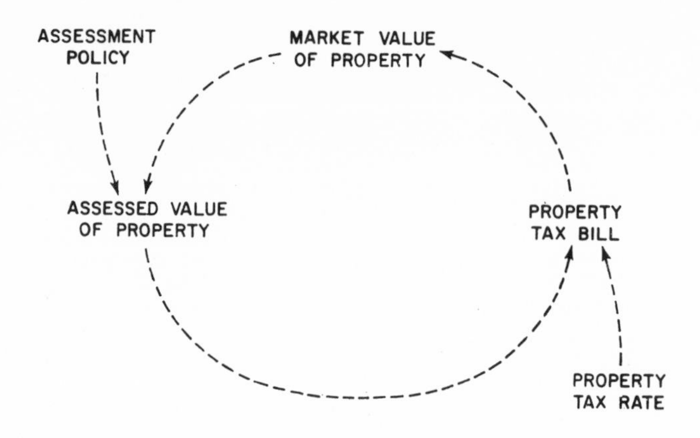

Figure 3-9 Feedback loop needed to test policy of tax bias against older buildings

The compensating pressure tends to undermine the effectiveness of any altered tax distribution. Because changes in taxes, zoning, and other action streams in a city may cause compensating changes in prices, rents, and wages, a more complete treatment of urban modeling than *Urban Dynamics* would have to include the relevant financial loops.

3.5 Summary

A system dynamics model can be used to design policies for improved urban decision making. By focusing on policies and action streams rather than on individual actions, the urban official can acquire further insights about how flows of actions operate through time to change conditions in the urban system. In any complex system a new policy encounters a variety of compensating and reinforcing pressures. Any policy may be ineffective if it (1) triggers compensating feedback loops involving system levels other than the level that the action stream directly controls, or (2) induces opposing pressures that prevent or impede implementation of the new policy.

Policies can be tested in a system dynamics model to discover whether they fall into either of those two categories. Policies that trigger compensating feedback effects should be coupled to other policies for controlling such compensations. Potentially promising policies that meet with political or financial opposition require a different kind of management response in the form of public debate and deeper substantive analysis. A better understanding of urban feedback interactions should lead to decisions that generate fewer negative side effects and more consistent advancement of city goals.

4

Housing and Migration in *Urban Dynamics*

Alex Makowski

The effectiveness of the urban revival program proposed in Urban Dynamics *depends in part on the assumption that a housing shortage inhibits the in-migration of lower-income families to the city. This reading argues that the sensitivity of migration to the availability of housing is theoretically plausible, and that the available statistical evidence does not controvert such a sensitivity. The original housing-migration assumptions in* Urban Dynamics *are actually quite reasonable as a basis for designing better urban policies.*

4
Housing and Migration in *Urban Dynamics*

4.1 Introduction

Migration is a recurrent theme in the controversy surrounding *Urban Dynamics*. Population movements into and out of a city have an important behavioral impact in the *Urban Dynamics* model. Migration effects can be key determinants of the long-term efficacy of alternative city revival policies. Although most reviewers of *Urban Dynamics* agree that population response is an essential, but often overlooked, dimension for policy analysis, there is less consensus that the causes of migration, as specified in the *Urban Dynamics* model, are correctly represented. In particular, several criticisms have been directed at the assumption that housing availability is a significant factor influencing migration decisions.[1] The focal points for the controversy over housing are the three table functions that operate to make the city's housing market appear relatively attractive to potential residents when housing is relatively abundant. Conversely, the tables contribute to a less attractive city when housing is scarce. Figure 4-1 displays one table function: the dependence of the underemployed/housing multiplier UHM on the underemployed/housing ratio UHR. The underemployed/housing multiplier is one of five factors that, in combination, determine the model city's overall attractiveness as perceived by underemployed migrants. Two similar table functions define the housing multipliers for labor and managerial-professional families. Figure 4-1 reflects the assumption in *Urban Dynamics* that migration is sensitive to changes around a normal housing availability of one housing unit per family (UHR = 1).

Assuming that all other city qualities stay constant, if UHR increases by 10 percent, migration will drop by 20 percent. *Urban Dynamics* further assumes that large shifts away from the normal UHR value of 1 drastically influence migration. At extreme regions of Figure 4-1, migration may increase by 250 percent or drop by 80 percent from the normal value. Many critics dispute the sensitivity of migration to

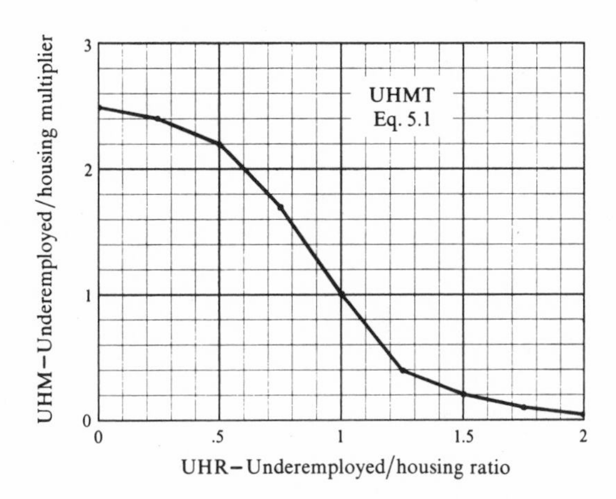

Figure 4-1 The curve defining the *Urban Dynamics* housing-migration relationship
Source: Reprinted from *Urban Dynamics* by Jay W. Forrester by permission of The MIT Press, Cambridge, Massachusetts, Figure A-3, p. 140.

housing; they argue that empirical research fails to confirm any sensitivity to housing. A few studies, which even seem to show an insensitivity of migration to housing availability, have led many critics to imply that the table function for UHM should resemble either the solid or the dotted curve in Figure 4-2. The solid curve in Figure 4-2 reflects the assumption that large changes in housing availability create relatively small changes in in-migration. The dotted curve in Figure 4-2 reflects the view of one reviewer, M.I.T. Professor Jerome Rothenberg, that variations in crowding have little effect around the normal occupancy. On the other hand, Professor Rothenberg postulates a high degree of sensitivity of migration to extreme conditions of housing surplus or shortage.[2] Which curve is correct? Figure 4-1? The curves in Figure 4-2? Some other unspecified curve? The following presentation attempts to combine the existing knowledge about housing markets and migration into a plausible set of housing-migration functions.

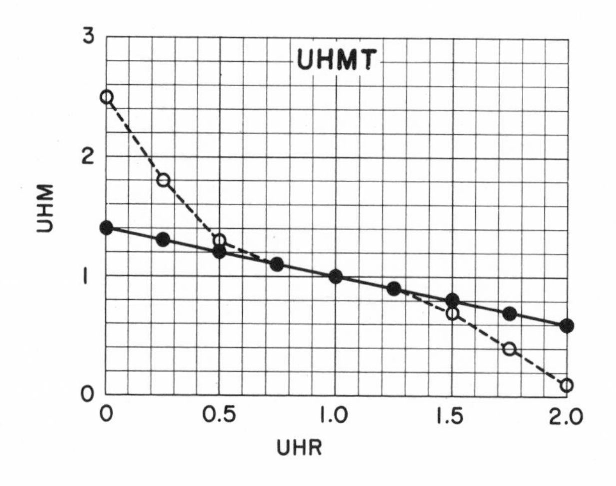

Figure 4-2 Alternative assumptions for the influence of housing on migration

4.2 Housing Availability and Crowding

In discussing any causal relationship, including the relationship between housing availability and migration, an analysis of extreme conditions provides a good starting point. With all extraneous factors removed, the fundamental and incontrovertible principles often become apparent. Therefore, the analysis of the influence of housing availability on migration begins with the case where a given land area contains no housing structures at all. Both the meaning of housing availability and the effect of zero housing availability on migration should be clarified by such an examination. The concept of housing availability requires a careful definition before we can analyze its influence on migration. Housing availability is the potential of a particular location to house an in-migrant. If a given area contains no housing structures, then that area has a housing availability of zero. Housing structures include any form of shelter: house, apartment, hotel room, tent, mobile home, or, for short periods of time, even a car. If the area has some housing structures but all are filled to absolute capacity, the area still has a housing availability of zero. If the existing housing structures are empty but potential residents cannot live in any of them (due to price, condemnation, or discrimination), then the area still effectively has a housing availability of zero. Does an area with no housing structures, no forms of shelter at all, have any potential for in-migration? For example, how many oilmen would migrate to Alaska's North Slope in the absence of any housing? Or, suppose a mine opens in the wilderness and the company provides no shacks or tents for housing. How many men will come and stay to work the mine? For the truly extreme (and unlikely) case where no housing exists and construction is impossible, housing availability certainly and obviously deters in-migration. Few people would migrate to an area with absolutely no available housing. Zero housing availability clearly deters migration. Does such a state of zero (or near zero) housing availability actually ever prevail in a settled area? The answer would seem to be yes. For many Americans, suburbs are a place of near-zero housing availability. Suburbs offer a desirable environment, good schooling, and numerous other amenities, but few lower-income people ever migrate into the suburbs. Although housing structures are for sale in the suburbs, the potential for habitation by lower-income residents is quite low. Given meager incomes and the high price of suburban housing, lower-income families are confronted with a condition of near-zero housing availability in the suburbs. Zero housing availability is perhaps the main reason why poor families for the most part do not live in the suburbs. In certain extreme conditions, therefore, housing availability has a visible effect on migration. When housing availability approaches zero, the potential for in-migration substantially declines. Lower-income families cannot migrate to *suburbs* that contain no housing at prices they can afford. However, *cities* contain housing at a great range of price levels. Can cities ever approach zero housing availability for some income group? Suppose for a moment that a city has no vacant living quarters. All houses and apartments are occupied. All hotels display no-vacancy signs. Rigid city ordinances prevent sleeping in tents or cars. In such extreme conditions, housing availability must be very low. Ignoring market forces for now, city housing would be available only to in-migrants with accommodating relatives and friends already in the city. In-migration must diminish because only the potential in-migrants with relatives and friends in the city can move in. Again ignoring market forces, imagine the consequences of depleting the supply of friends and relatives with room to spare. City housing is now absolutely filled. Any resident willing to board extra people already has a friend or relative sleeping on the sofa. Housing availability has effectively reached zero because no housing at all remains for would-be in-migrants. With zero housing availability, as other examples have shown, net in-migration is severely suppressed. Zero housing availability is not limited to the wilderness or the suburbs. It is plausible even in a central city. If a city approaches zero housing availability, in-migration must be drastically reduced. The preceding analysis has established the proper shape for the right-hand portion of the housing-migration table function. As a city's housing supply fills far beyond normal capacity, housing availability and the potential for in-migration drop even closer to zero. The right-hand side of Figure 4-1 is an example of a curve that asymptotically approaches the horizontal axis for high population-to-housing ratios.

By definition, the underemployed/housing multiplier UHM curve must also pass through the point (1,1) in Figure 4-1. When local housing availability is neither greater nor less than housing availability in other cities, the local population-to-housing ratio exerts a neutral effect on the in-migration rate; UHM must therefore equal 1. The number 1 is a normal value. When multiplied with other numbers, the normal value of 1 exerts neither a positive nor a negative effect. What is the correct shape for the UHM curve between (1,1) and the right-hand extreme? Does the curve fall asymptotically, or does it drop off more suddenly, as suggested by the dotted relationship in Figure 4-2? Perhaps the best way to answer this question is to look first at the relationship between the local family-to-housing ratio and housing availability as perceived by the potential in-migrant. If availability falls smoothly with increasing family-to-housing ratios (more acute crowding), then the city's attractiveness to the potential migrant should follow the same general pattern. *Urban Dynamics* lumps housing into three categories distinguished by their quality and their rough price. But, in real life, the urban housing market contains an entire spectrum of housing from the viewpoint of any individual. Even units identical in quality and price have other features that influence potential migrants: location relative to the rest of the city, ethnic neighborhoods, and school quality. Many potential migrants, motivated by other considerations, decide to move to a city before all housing units fill up. However, as housing fills up, fewer potential migrants can satisfy all their other preferences for location, neighborhood, and school quality. What can be said to summarize the effect of crowding on housing availability? Far below maximum occupancy, where the underemployed-to-housing ratio is small, the city's capacity to accommodate an in-migrant is high. As the underemployed-to-housing ratio increases, housing availability decreases. Further potential in-migrants cannot satisfy their living preferences. Housing availability decreases smoothly as the occupancy of existing housing increases and continues to fall smoothly through the point where no vacant housing units remain. Therefore, further crowding in a city must inhibit in-migration, all other things being equal. In-migration does not come to a sudden halt because, even with all housing occupied, the possibility for overcrowding individual units still remains.

4.3 The Housing-Migration Relationships in *Urban Dynamics*

The general characteristics of a plausible UHM/UHR curve are clear, but thus far without any quantitative precision. The presentation has so far made no choice between the *Urban Dynamics* curve in Figure 4-1 and Rothenberg's dotted curve in Figure 4-2; nor has it determined whether the asymptotic approach of the UHM curve to the horizontal axis begins at a UHR of, say, 1.5 or 2.5; nor has it pinpointed the slope of the UHM curve near the normal (1,1) point at minus 2.0 or minus 0.2. A precise and final definition of the curve must await more extensive research into migration. However, even without a perfect specification of the shape of the UHM/UHR curve, the *Urban Dynamics* model can be a valuable policy aid. If decision makers are willing to acknowledge that increased housing shortages must decrease in-migration, they can begin to design policies, along the lines recommended in *Urban Dynamics,* that are effective regardless of the exact housing-migration relationship. "Self-Learning Revival Policies in *Urban Dynamics*," by Nathaniel J. Mass[3], describes how policies similar to the *Urban Dynamics* revival policies of new industry encouragement and housing demolition can further the city's socioeconomic vitality, no matter how slight the negative slope of the housing-migration curve. By continuously cutting back its housing supply, a city can increase the local population-to-housing ratio and move housing conditions to a point on the curve where UHM is considerably less than 1 (normal). Sufficiently scarce housing tends to limit in-migration enough to ensure adequate employment opportunities for city residents. At some population-to-housing ratio, the housing availability decreases enough to deter further in-migration.

4.4 Measuring the Housing-Migration Relationship

No empirical studies have established a strong relationship between housing supply and migration. But *an investigator should not expect to be able to measure any clear influence of housing occupancy on migration in our cities*. Current conditions in urban housing markets nearly always permit potential in-migrants, particularly members of middle- and upper-income groups, to find housing. Some in-migrants can afford hotel rooms. If no hotel rooms are vacant, they can bid up the rates for presently occupied rooms. Landlords may respond to increased housing demand by marking up rents. Over the longer term, living units can be subdivided to create additional housing. Many mechanisms in the housing market act to adjust the supply of housing to the demands of those who can afford to pay. Ultimately, of course, the market tends to respond to demand for housing by adding new structures. The construction time for new living quarters ranges from one to four years, a delay comparable to the delay involved in the average migration decision. The potential migrant first experiences a perception delay because his impression of the actual state of a city is based on information that is from several months to several years out of date. He also faces a disentanglement delay while removing himself from employment, neighborhood, and family ties. Given these delays, potential migrants normally respond to changing city conditions even more slowly than the internal housing construction process. Because of its somewhat quicker response time, the city housing system can easily adapt to increased in-migration and housing needs to maintain a satisfactory (from the viewpoint of those in need of housing) population-to-housing ratio.

As illustrated in Figure 4-3, if a city's population-to-housing ratio stays within a narrow range, then housing occupancy has little effect on migration. Because American cities enjoy housing markets capable of sustaining adequate population-to-housing ratios, they all fall within some narrow region on the underemployed/housing ratio UHR axis. The clustering of cities prohibits much variation in the underemployed/housing multiplier UHM on the vertical axis. Under such conditions of generally similar housing availability, potential migrants respond to other economic variables (jobs and taxes, for example) while appearing to be unresponsive to housing conditions. Modern city housing markets are flexible enough to adapt quickly and smoothly to increased demand. Therefore, most cities might be expected to have similar

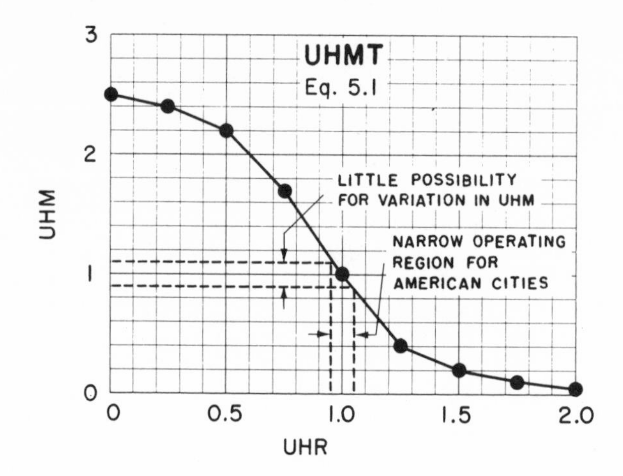

Figure 4-3 Because all cities have similar population-to-housing ratios, there is little possibility for variation in the underemployed/housing multiplier UHM

population-to-housing ratios. In fact, census data on urban housing densities confirm the uniformity of urban housing markets and support the contention that recent empirical research should indicate that migration among cities is less responsive to housing than to employment conditions, wage levels, or welfare payments.

All American cities have had housing available for potential in-migrants. Therefore, research on migration to cities during the 1950s and 1960s (a period of normal housing market operations after alleviation of the critical postwar shortages) should not be expected to isolate housing as a major influence. Since all cities had a similar housing availability during this period, potential migrants were free to choose among cities on other economic and social grounds.

Although the *Urban Dynamics* housing-migration curves of Figure 4-1 have been disputed, the migration literature cited by critics focuses only on migration to our cities since the late 1940s. The critics have not investigated the sources of earlier migration flows. Interestingly, wartime migration data do provide empirical evidence that housing influenced migration flows during World War II. Furthermore, current migration to the American suburbs should provide another empirical basis for an analysis of housing availability as it affects household location decisions. The lack of empirical evidence supporting the *Urban Dynamics* migration assumptions cannot be fairly interpreted as evidence that no such relationship exists. Empirical analyses since 1945 would uncover only a narrow section of the plausible range of population-to-housing ratios portrayed in Figure 4-1.

A proper validation of the hypothesis that cities tend toward similar population-to-housing ratios cannot be conducted without a measure of housing occupancy. The federal census furnishes one such measure: the persons per room (PPR) ratio, which some migration researchers believe provides the best available index of housing conditions in a particular city.[4] Figure 4-4 lists 1960 PPR statistics for ten American cities selected to provide a sample of urban areas of different size, age, and geographical

	Persons Per Room		
	0.50 or less	0.51 to 0.75	0.76 to 1
Boston	46	25	22
Los Angeles	45	23	22
New York	36	28	24
Dallas	40	26	22
Chicago	41	24	25
Seattle	45	24	23
Philadelphia	50	25	17
Detroit	42	23	26
Baltimore	46	24	20
Buffalo	47	24	21

Figure 4-4 The occupancy distribution of housing stock for ten American Standard Census Areas (SCA)
Source: U.S., Bureau of the Census, *Statistical Abstract*, 1960.

location.[5] The statistics, which are the percentage of each area's total housing stock that falls within a certain occupancy range, testify to a uniformity among urban housing markets. All ten cities show roughly the same distribution of housing stock among various occupancy ranges. None of the cities has significantly crowded or empty housing. The census results support the initial premise that a potential migrant choosing among various American cities encounters similar housing conditions. Because of the mathematical and procedural impediments to measuring the responsiveness of migration to large changes in housing availability, most contemporary migration literature shows no strong housing influence. But, surprisingly, the migration studies cited by critics as evidence against the *Urban Dynamics* migration hypothesis do not explicitly consider housing at all. Ira Lowry, for example, hypothesizes that migration from one area to another depends upon the difference between economic conditions in the two areas, the distance between the two areas, and the population of the two areas.[6] Michael Greenwood argues that the influence of education, income, employment, temperature, degree of urbanization, and prior history of migration all have a role.[7] Other researchers have studied the impact of race.[8] But the preceding studies do not directly address the issue of housing. A few researchers have explicitly considered housing. John Shyrock concludes:

> A majority of adult males move to take a job or to look for work. . . . Even among adult males, reasons not directly concerned with employment, such as a change in marital status, a housing problem, or a health problem, account for many moves. These reasons are more prominent in the shorter than in the longer type of moves.[9]

J. R. Pack and John Pearson have performed regression analyses to measure the influence of housing; their conclusions show no more than a minor response of migration to city housing conditions.[10] However, under the urban conditions prevalent during their study, such findings come as no surprise. The presently published migration literature barely touches on the influence of extreme housing conditions on migration. Unfortunately, the instances in which extreme housing shortages have prevailed have not been well researched. The World War II years, for example, spawned a tight housing market in many parts of the United States. As the country's industry geared up for heavy war production during the early 1940s, the demand for labor in key manufacturing cities soared. These cities seldom had enough housing available for workers migrating to jobs; housing markets tightened rapidly. The tight housing began to divert migration streams, attracted by the economic and social incentives of defense jobs. Mobile, Alabama, had plentiful jobs but little housing; workers eager to migrate to Mobile had to settle as far as fifty miles away.[11] As vacancy rates in Mobile and cities with similar conditions fell, whole families could no longer move. Leaving the family behind, fathers would migrate alone.[12] Finally, tight housing forced many men to quit their jobs: "In twelve months, Gulf Shipbuilding lost 4,500 men; most frequent single reason given by the quitting men: they couldn't find housing."[13] Migration to the suburbs also illustrates the effects of limited housing. Suburbs assumed a prominent place in the national economy during the middle of the twentieth century. As first residential and then industrial development increased, the growing suburbs with their employment opportunities and residential amenities began to present a favorable alternative to city life. Millions of Americans left their homes in the cities for the suburbs. Migration to the suburbs has not, for the most part, included lower-income people. As the public media have noted, housing conditions have severely limited their migration:

> Negroes complain that, at a time when many jobs are moving out from cities into suburbs, black workers are unable to follow the jobs because of difficulties in obtaining housing.[14]
>
> This corporate migration [to the suburbs] has created a vast, new blue-collar job market in the suburbs—but one that is, for the moment, physically inaccessible to the urban blue-collar workers the corporations have left behind them. . . . restrictive zoning laws ban the sort of federally subsidized housing that would permit the urban poor to settle near their own jobs.[15]

Housing conditions have certainly restricted lower-income and black migration to the suburbs. Although most suburban communities offer employment opportunities and other attractions to the urban lower-income population, in-migration has taken place only in those few suburban communities with housing available at low prices.

4.5 Moral Aspects of Crowded Housing

A fundamental urban goal since World War II has been quality housing for every family. Few people would disagree with the proposition that either private forces or the government should provide housing for the needy. Against the background of such a housing goal, crowded housing seems to take on immoral overtones. However, housing is only one element in the urban system; quality housing for all, only one urban goal. Judgments about housing conditions, no matter how noble, have no meaning in isolation from other elements of the urban system and the full range of urban goals.

Americans today have exceptional mobility. Because few barriers prevent movement from one city to another, housing can become crowded only in a city that offers compensating advantages to hold city residents or attract migrants. Unless a city has good schools, clean air, plentiful jobs, or other desirable qualities, people may refuse to accept the crowded housing and move out of the city. Therefore, crowded housing is not morally evil by itself. Housing becomes crowded only if people find other aspects of the city sufficiently desirable to offset the discomfort of housing inadequacies. A city may also choose to protect its amenities by consciously adopting a policy of crowded housing. A city with clean air, good jobs, excellent schooling, and available housing would soon be inundated by in-migrants. Before long, such a city would have crowded schools, dirtier air, and scarcer jobs. By restricting its housing supply and accepting the discomforts of overfilled housing, a city can preserve its desirable features. Of course, such a policy must not impose hardships on poor local residents. The policy would necessitate strict zoning and building codes to prevent evasion of the restrictions and regulations. But all current residents who want to remain must be protected against uncompensated removal or displacement. In fact, a city that successfully inhibits excess in-migration is in a better position to help its own underemployed through greater employment opportunities and greater access to upward socioeconomic movement.

4.6 Conclusions

The *Urban Dynamics* revival policies assume that migration into a city is sensitive to the local population-to-housing ratio. The assumption appears to be well founded. Migration must conform to the capacity of the living space in an area. As the density of housing occupation in a city increases, the availability of housing decreases. And when housing becomes less available, the pressure against in-migration intensifies.

The proposition that migration may be sensitive to the availability of housing is not contradicted by empirical studies of the normal city housing system. The uniformity of urban housing markets all but guarantees that housing cannot normally exert a significant pressure on migration. But if a city consciously adopts a policy of cutting back on its housing supply, a deterrent effect on in-migration should ensue. By accepting the discomfort of crowded housing, as *Urban Dynamics* advocates, cities can restrict in-migration and thereby preserve quality jobs, schools, environment, and other urban features for its current residents.

Notes

1. Reviews critical of the housing-migration assumption include J. R. Pack, "Models of Population Movement and Urban Policy," *IEEE Transactions on Systems, Man, and Cybernetics*, April 1972; Jerome Rothenberg, "Problems in the Modeling of Urban Development: A Review Article on *Urban Dynamics*, by Jay W. Forrester," *Journal of Urban Economics*, vol. 1, (1974), no. 1, pp. 1–20; Harvey Averch and Robert A. Levine, "Two Models of the Urban Crisis: An Analytical Essay on Banfield and Forrester," *Policy Sciences*, vol. 2, no. 2 (June 1971), pp. 143–158; and James Hester, "Systems Analysis for Social Policies," *Science*, vol. 168, no. 3932 (May 8, 1970), pp. 693–694.

2. See ibid., Rothenberg.

3. Nathaniel J. Mass, "Self-Learning Revival Policies in *Urban Dynamics*," in *Readings in Urban Dynamics*, vol. 1, ed. Nathaniel J. Mass (Cambridge, Mass.: Wright-Allen Press, 1974), pp. 227–243.

4. See John Pearson, "The Significance of Urban Housing in Rural-Urban Migration," *Land Economics*, vol. 39, no. 3 (August 1963), pp. 231–239, fn. 28.

5. U.S., Bureau of the Census, *Statistical Abstract*, 1960.

6. Ira S. Lowry, *Migration and Metropolitan Growth: Two Analytical Models* (San Francisco: Chandler Publishing Co., 1966).

7. Michael Greenwood, "An Analysis of the Determinants of Geographic Labor Mobility in the United States," *Review of Economics and Statistics*, vol. 51, no. 2 (May 1969).

8. Allan Askin, "An Economic Analysis of Black Migration," Ph.D. dissertation, M.I.T., June 1970; Library-Microreproduction 14-0551. See also Andrei Rogers, "A Regression Analysis of Inter-Regional Migration in California," *Review of Economics and Statistics*, vol. 49, no. 2 (May 1967); P. Nelson, "Migration, Real Income, and Information," *Journal of Regional Science*, vol. 1, no. 2 (Spring 1959), pp. 43–74; and Vernon Renshaw, "The Role of Migration in Labor Market Adjustment," Ph.D. dissertation, M.I.T., June 1970; Library-Microreproduction 14-0551.

9. John Shyrock, *Population Mobility within the United States* (Chicago: University of Chicago Press, 1964), p. 424. Much the same observation emerges from the research of Peter Morrison, "Urban Growth, New Cities, and 'the Population Problem'" (Santa Monica: The Rand Corporation, 1970), p. 14.

10. See Pack, p. 191, and Pearson.

11. "Housing for War," *Fortune*, October 1942.

12. U.S., Congress, House, Select Committee Investigating National Defense Migration, *Hearings*, pt. 27 (Washington, D.C.: Government Printing Office, 1942).

13. "Housing for War," *Fortune*, October 1942.

14. "Government Reviews Pressure for Integrated Suburbs," *U.S. News and World Report*, June 28, 1971.

15. "The Battle of the Suburbs," *Newsweek*, November 15, 1971. See also "Battle to Open the Suburbs: New Attack on Zoning Laws," *U.S. News and World Report*, June 22, 1970; J. L. Hecht, "Quest for Community, Mixed Housing in the Suburbs," *Nation*, March 6, 1972; and L. Davidoff et al., "Suburbs Move to Open Their Gates," *New York Times Magazine*, November 7, 1971.

5

The Sensitivity of Migration to Housing Availability

Walter W. Schroeder III

The extent to which the availability of housing influences migration is a subtle and complicated issue. Urban Dynamics *suggests that cities can favorably alter their internal conditions by controlling the housing availability. But what is the range of plausible relationships between housing and migration? And, if the table functions relating housing to migration in the* Urban Dynamics *model are altered, do the* Urban Dynamics *policy recommendations still hold? This reading proposes several simple tests to determine whether the validity of the book's policy recommendations depends upon an exact measurement of the housing-migration relationship.*

5
The Sensitivity of Migration to Housing Availability

5.1 The Shape of the Housing and Migration Relationship

There is only one relationship in the *Urban Dynamics* model that is known to affect the validity of the recommended policies. That relationship is the assumed dependence of migration on the availability of housing.

Urban Dynamics (pages 236–240) describes an experiment in which

> underemployed movement to and from the urban area has been made much less dependent on availability of housing than in the original model. Figure B-12 [reproduced here as Figure 5-1] shows the new curve for UHMT. It has no effect on the original equilibrium condition of the system because the two curves cross at the equilibrium value of UHR at Point A. . . . With a [modified] housing influence as shown in Figure B-12, the revival policies are in several ways less effective [than with the original curve]. [*Urban Dynamics*, pp. 236–237]

Revival policies calling for housing demolition and enterprise encouragement are less effective with the modified curve because a housing shortage no longer acts as a deterrent to in-migration. Extra jobs created by new enterprise tend to raise the city's attractiveness to the underemployed. Although the policy still reduces the stock of underemployed housing (after 50 years, the underemployed/housing ratio UHR reaches 1.8) as indicated by point C, the shortage does not deter in-migration because the value of the underemployed/housing multiplier UHM at point C is still greater than 1.0. The modified curve in Figure 5-1 permits the reviving city to attract far greater numbers of underemployed than the original curve allows. Low economic opportunity prevails. The revival policies produce no significant improvement because in-migration is not constrained. The success of the same policies with the original housing-migration curve is possible because housing demolition impels the system to move to point B in Figure 5-1. At that point the value of UHM drops well below 1.0,

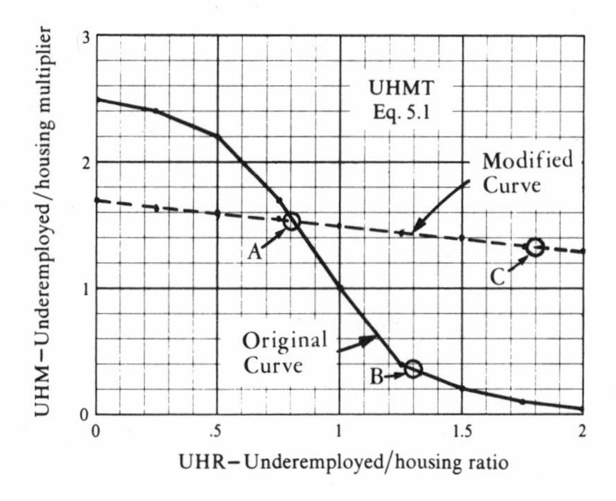

Figure 5-1 The original and modified curves in *Urban Dynamics* relating housing availability and migration

Source: Reprinted from *Urban Dynamics* by Jay W. Forrester by permission of The MIT Press, Cambridge, Massachusetts, Figure B-12.

thereby counterbalancing improved economic conditions in the urban area. The city's net attractiveness remains about the same, but its internal housing and job opportunities change significantly.

Since the efficacy of the revival policies depends upon whether the real-world underemployed/housing-multiplier table UHMT curve looks more like the original or the modified curve in Figure 5-1, reviewers of *Urban Dynamics* have given the question considerable attention. But a number of critics have misinterpreted Figure 5-1. For example, several urban economists dispute the validity of the curve because a housing shortage allegedly stimulates additional construction or rehabilitation to prevent an adverse impact on in-migration. As discussed in Reading 4, several critics argue that a real housing market adjusts housing availability to prevent serious shortages. These critics then conclude that the original curve in Figure 5-1 is invalid because housing shortages have never been shown to have a measurable impact on in-migration.

However, a close examination of the original curve in Figure 5-1 reveals that the criticisms and the *Urban Dynamics* model assumptions do not necessarily conflict. Figure 5-1 covers a far broader range from housing excess to housing shortage than is experienced (or measured) in the normal urban setting. Critics point out that the normal urban housing market (through construction) tends to adjust itself so that at the ratio of families to occupiable units stays within a very narrow segment of the range plotted in Figure 5-1. If the ratio of underemployed-to-underemployed housing overall were to increase (indicating an increasingly tight housing market), housing construction will also increase, so that the ratio moves back toward its earlier value. The UHMT curve in *Urban Dynamics* allegedly ignores this self-regulating feature of the urban housing market.

However, the market-adjustment process just described is represented in the *Urban Dynamics* model's housing sector, but it has relatively little to do with the housing-migration curve in Figure 5-1. To help illustrate the point, suppose Figure 5-1 is redrawn to include only the observed behavior of a normal housing market. The shaded area in Figure 5-2 leaves out the extreme regions of the curve in Figure 5-1. If a city's housing vacancy rate normally lies between 3 percent and 8 percent of the total stock, then nearly a one-to-one ratio of families to the housing units prevails. Therefore, the shaded portion of Figure 5-2 covers the normal range of housing-market behavior. Expanding the shaded portion produces the curve shown in Figure 5-3, which covers the region between an underemployed-to-housing ratio of 0.95 and 1.05.

The curve in Figure 5-3 is nearly horizontal in comparison with the curve in Figure 5-1. The impact of housing availability on overall urban attractiveness for in-migration is virtually neutral across the entire range of Figure 5-3. But remember that the curve in Figure 5-3 encompasses only a portion of the curve in Figure 5-1. The latter subsumes Figure 5-3 within a small range of its coverage. Therefore, the *Urban Dynamics* model fully accords with the argument that a city's housing does not tend to be a measurably strong influence on in-migration under normal conditions. The lack of influence is attributable to the fact that the normal (observed) operation of the urban

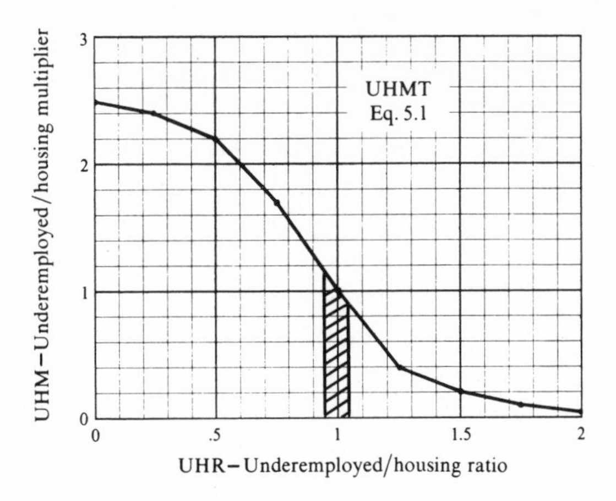

Figure 5-2 The normal (shaded) operating region of the underemployed-housing-multiplier table UHMT curve for a typical city is only a very small portion of the overall relationship

Source: The original curve is reprinted from *Urban Dynamics* by Jay W. Forrester by permission of The MIT Press, Cambridge, Massachusetts, Figure A-66.

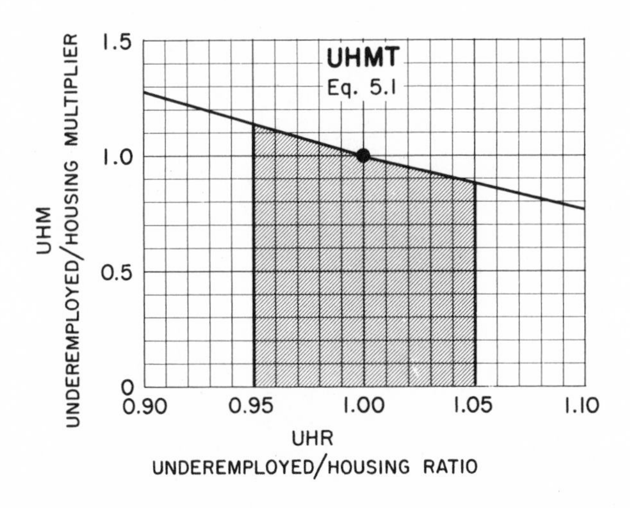

Figure 5-3 Over the normal (shaded) operating region of the underemployed-housing-multiplier table UHMT curve, changes in housing availability produce only minor changes in the city's overall attractiveness and therefore in the city's rate of in-migration.

housing market tends to prevent housing scarcities, so that factors other than housing availability exert a stronger influence on migration.

Figure 5-1 differs from Figure 5-3 only in that it covers a much wider range of housing conditions. The extreme ranges in Figure 5-1 do not imply that cities normally achieve underemployed-to-housing ratios of 0.4 or 2.5, just that such ratios are physically possible. Extremes do not impinge upon the normal life cycle of a city, and could occur in reality only if a city's policies radically interfered with the normal housing market.

The *Urban Dynamics* model includes the extreme ranges to show what happens under any conceivable conditions of housing excess or shortage. Several advisers to the urban dynamics research program at M.I.T. originally challenged the curve in Figure 5-1. Once shown that the curve in Figure 5-1 intentionally subsumes not only the observed operating range of urban housing markets but also all extreme regions, the advisers unanimously agreed upon the plausibility of the entire curve.

What is the actual shape of the curve representing housing's influence on migration? Figure 5-1 represents one estimate. Slightly different curves have also been proposed. However, there is general agreement that, as a city moves into the region of extreme housing shortages, in-migration must drop. High rents, overcrowding, and other residential instabilities tend to accompany an extreme housing shortage. Such factors usually make a city less attractive and thereby inhibit in-migration.

Given agreement on the *direction* of the curve's slope, the remaining major issue involves the *magnitude* of the slope. Different advisers have proposed the three alternative curves shown in Figures 5-4, 5-5, and 5-6.

The original curve from *Urban Dynamics* (Figure A-66) is reproduced in each figure for purposes of comparison. Figure 5-4 argues for a high degree of response of in-migration to housing availability at extreme points but relatively little responsiveness through the middle range. Figure 5-5 suggests that unusually high housing availability (the left-hand side of the curve) does not act as a strong positive influence on in-migration. The right-hand side of Figure 5-5 indicates that a housing shortage

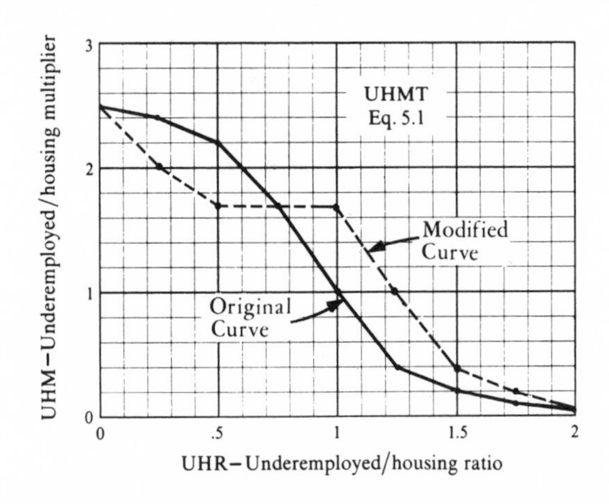

Figure 5-4 An underemployed-housing-multiplier table UHMT curve slightly less sensitive than in the *Urban Dynamics* model

Sources: The original curve is reprinted from *Urban Dynamics* by Jay W. Forrester by permission of The MIT Press, Cambridge, Massachusetts, Figure A-66.

Note: UHMT (modified) = 2.5/2.0/1.7/1.7/1.7/1.0/0.4/0.2/0.1

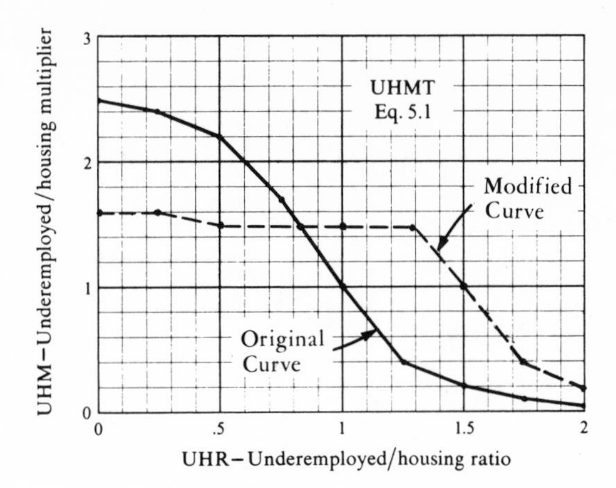

Figure 5-5 An underemployed-housing-multiplier UHMT curve considerably less sensitive than in the *Urban Dynamics* model

Source: The original curve is reprinted from *Urban Dynamics* by Jay W. Forrester by permission of The MIT Press, Cambridge, Massachusetts, Figure A-66.
Note: UHMT (modified) = 1.8/1.8/1.7/1.7/1.7/1.7/1/.4/.2

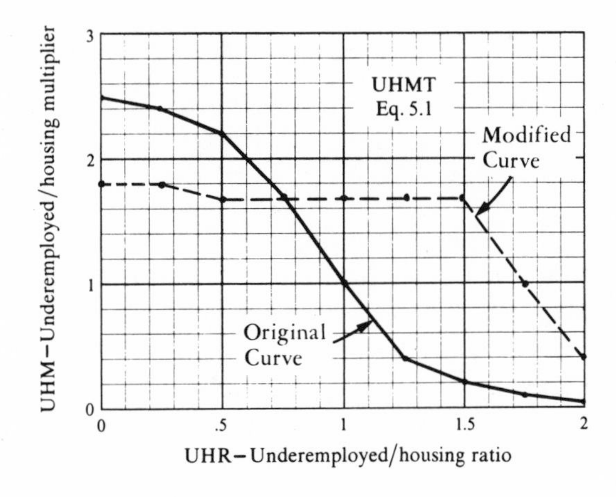

Figure 5-6 An underemployed-housing-multiplier table UHMT curve of extreme insensitivity

Source: The original curve is reprinted from *Urban Dynamics* by Jay W. Forrester by permission of The MIT Press, Cambridge, Massachusetts, Figure A-66.
Note: UHMT (modified) = 1.8/1.8/1.7/1.7/1.7/1.7/1.7/1/.4

reduces urban attractiveness, but only during more extreme shortages than those represented by the curves in Figures 5-1 and 5-4. Figure 5-6 resembles Figure 5-5 except that Figure 5-6 assumes that the underemployed are even less sensitive to low housing availability. In other words, as housing becomes increasingly scarce, in-migration does not drop by as much in Figure 5-6 as in Figure 5-5.

The three curves, along with the curve from the *Urban Dynamics* model, fall within a plausible range (as shown in Figure 5-7). The question is whether any of the proposed alternative curves alters the behavior of the *Urban Dynamics* model sufficiently to change the policy recommendations in *Urban Dynamics*.

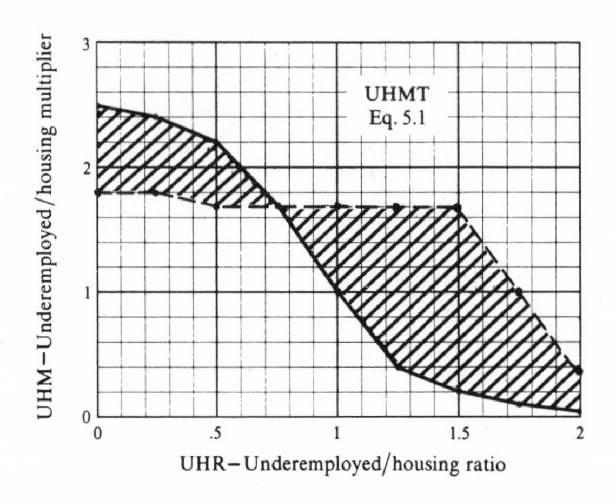

Figure 5-7 The underemployed-housing-multiplier table UHMT curves in Figures 5-1, 5-4, 5-5, and 5-6 all fall within a plausible (shaded) range

Source: The original curve is reprinted from *Urban Dynamics* by Jay W. Forrester by permission of The MIT Press, Cambridge, Massachusetts, Figure A-66

5.2 Policy Test with Alternative Housing and Migration Curves

The revival strategy in *Urban Dynamics* calls for the annual demolition of 5 percent of slum housing and a 40 percent increase in the rate of new-enterprise development. The policy is effective because slum demolition tightens the housing market to constrain in-migration. The additional jobs created by industrial expansion therefore go to current city residents rather than to in-migrants. *Urban Dynamics* notes that the effectiveness of the revival program depends on the extent to which a reduction in per capita housing availability leads to reduced in-migration. Consequently, the shape (and especially the downward slope) of the curve in Figure 5-1 is very important from the standpoint of policy analysis and design.

Each of the modified curves in Figures 5-4, 5-5, and 5-6 represents a different hypothetical response (or preference) pattern of underemployed in-migration to changes in housing availability. The effectiveness of the *Urban Dynamics* revival policies is expected to change if any of the three alternative curves replaces the original curve shown in Figure 5-1. For example, the curve in Figure 5-6 indicates that in-migration is less sensitive to housing shortages than the curve in Figure 5-1. With an underemployed/housing ratio UHR of 1.5, or conditions of extensive overcrowding, the curve in Figure 5-6 does not inhibit in-migration. The underemployed/housing multiplier UHM has a value of 1.0. By contrast, in Figure 5-1 an underemployed-to-housing ratio of 1.5 reduces the value of UHM to 0.2, an 80 percent reduction in in-migration. Figure 5-6 permits more underemployed in-migration during implementation of the revival program. As more people enter a city in response to improved employment conditions, the balance between people and jobs improves by less than if in-migration is more constrained, as in Figure 5-1.

The following tests were undertaken to help measure the extent to which the revival policies become less effective as the housing-migration curve in the *Urban Dynamics* model changes to reflect a lower sensitivity of underemployed migration to a housing shortage. The model runs were made to test the revival policies on an urban dynamics model identical to the original version except for the underemployed-housing-multiplier table UHMT. The policy runs were evaluated by means of a standard procedure of running a model 250 years to equilibrium, inserting policy changes, running the model for 50 more years, and finally comparing the end results with the original equilibrium conditions. The runs also test whether adjustments in the revival program can restore its original effectiveness even if the housing-migration curve lies in the region of extreme insensitivity in Figure 5-7.

Test Number One. The curve in Figure 5-4, the subject of the first test, represents a hypothesized relationship visually quite different from the curve used in the *Urban Dynamics* model; Figure 5-4 shows a high degree of sensitivity to housing conditions only at extreme values. For example, the underemployed/housing multiplier UHM rises above 2 only when the underemployed/housing ratio UHR falls below 0.2 (or 5 housing units per family), a severe housing excess. Conversely, the value of UHM drops to 0.4 only when UHR reaches 1.5. In comparison with the original curve shown in Figure 5-1, the curve in Figure 5-4 requires relatively higher crowding (a higher underemployed-to-housing ratio) to suppress in-migration. Therefore, the revival policy should be somewhat less effective in suppressing underemployed in-migration. Figures 5-8a through 5-8c and 5-9 describe the effects of testing the revival policies from *Urban Dynamics* (new-enterprise construction normal NECN = 0.07, slum-housing-demolition rate SHDR = 0.05) on a model identical to the *Urban Dynamics* model except that the original UHMT curve was altered to the shape of Figure 5-4. Figures 5-8a through 5-8c plot the same variables that were tested in Chapters 4 and 5 of *Urban Dynamics*. Figure 5-9 summarizes the plots and tabulates (in column 4) the effects of the *Urban Dynamics* revival program. The differences between columns 3 and 4 (computed in column 5) of Figure 5-9 are due solely to the altered shape of the UHMT curve.

The revival policies are slightly less effective when the original UHMT curve is replaced by the curve in Figure 5-4. But city conditions still improve significantly. For example, in Figure 5-8a, new enterprise NE increases by 57 percent and labor L and managerial-professionals MP increase by 49 percent, while the number of underemployed U increases by only 2 percent. Therefore, the socioeconomic population mix has shifted toward a condition of higher average incomes. Figure 5-8b shows a 32 percent decrease in the underemployed-to-job ratio, an index of unemployment. Col-

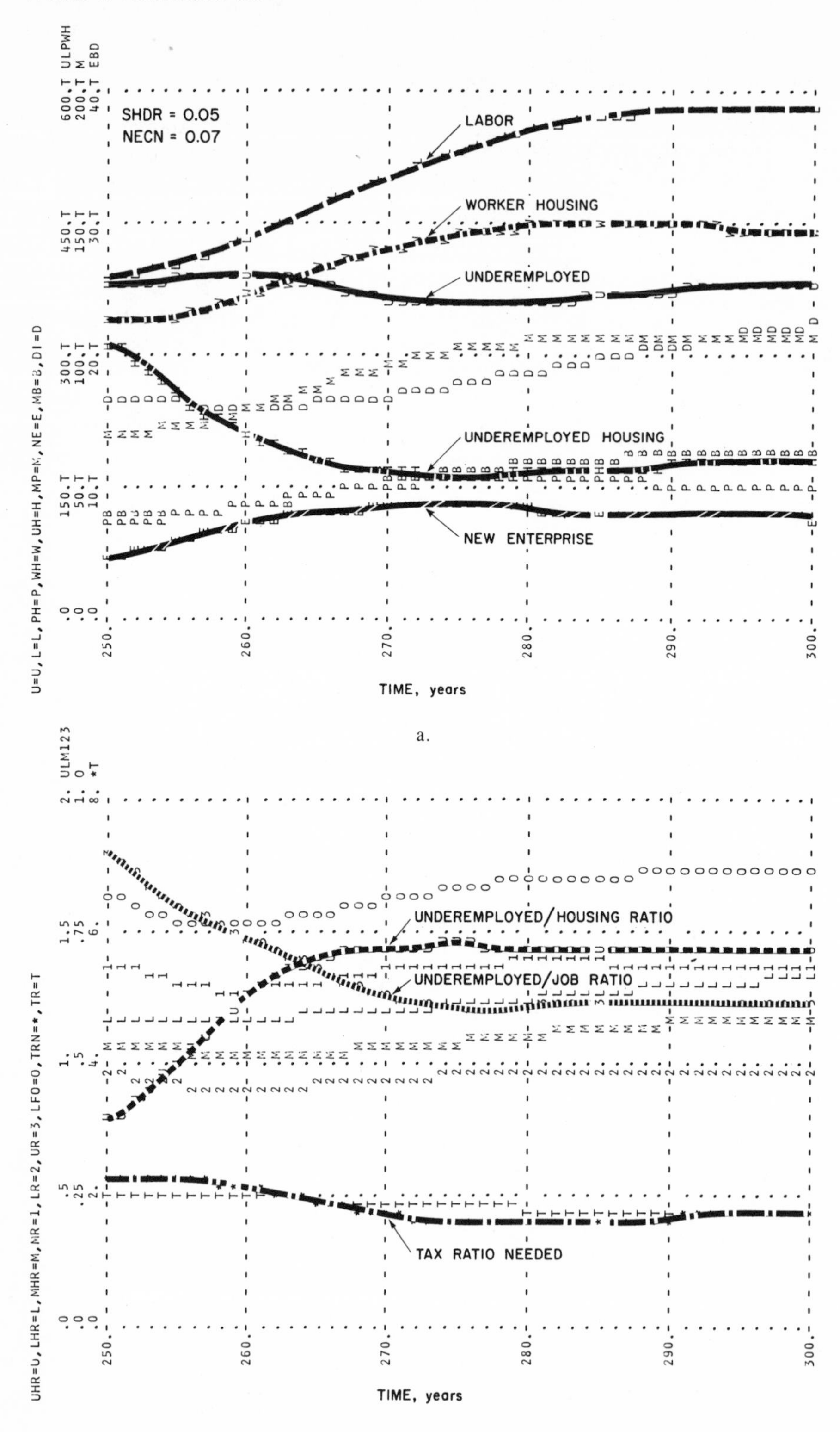
SHDR = 0.05
NECN = 0.07
LABOR
WORKER HOUSING
UNDEREMPLOYED
UNDEREMPLOYED HOUSING
NEW ENTERPRISE
TIME, years
UNDEREMPLOYED/HOUSING RATIO
UNDEREMPLOYED/JOB RATIO
TAX RATIO NEEDED
TIME, years

a.

b.

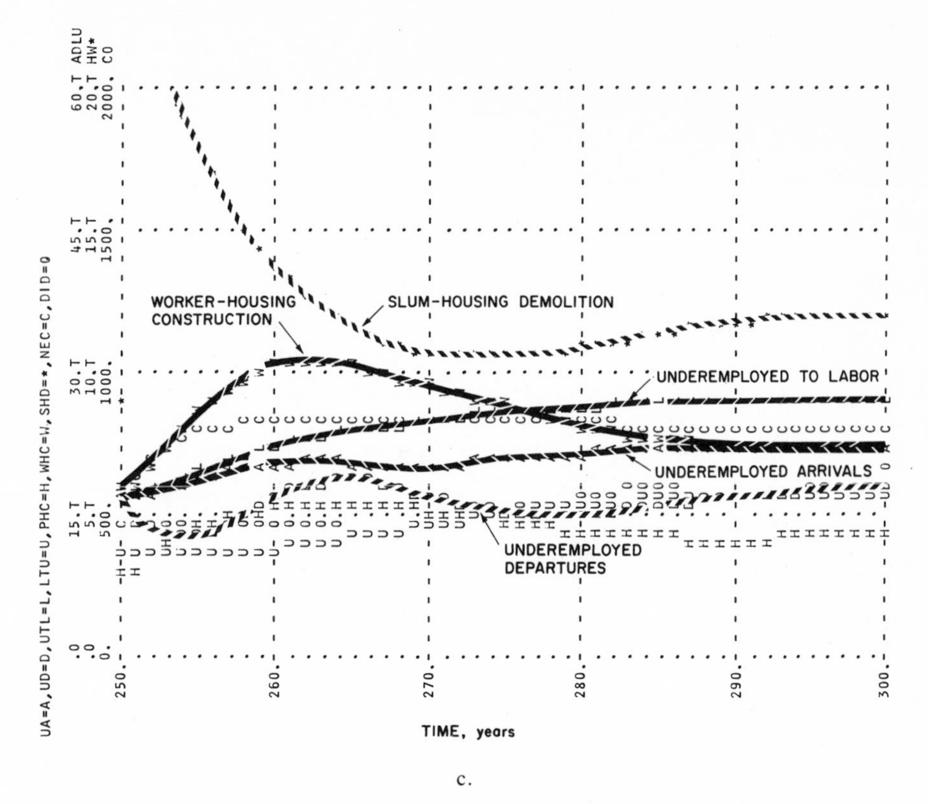

c.

Figure 5-8 The *Urban Dynamics* revival program tested on a model with the underemployed-housing-multiplier table UHMT curve modified as in Figure 5-4

(1) Variable Name	(2) Symbol	(3) Change (%)	(4) Change in Urban Dynamics (%)	(5) Difference (Column 3 − Column 4)
a. Slum-housing demolition	SHD	+33	+36	−3
b. New-enterprise construction	NEC	+72	+80	−8
1. New enterprise	NE	+57	+63	−6
2. Mature business	MB	+60	+64	−4
3. Declining industry	DI	+36	+35	+1
4. Premium housing	PH	+36	+38	−2
5. Worker housing	WH	+31	+34	−3
6. Underemployed housing	UH	−41	−43	+2
7. Managerial-professional	MP	+49	+53	−4
8. Labor	L	+49	+53	−4
9. Underemployed	U	+2	−11	+13
10. Manager/housing ratio	MHR	+9	+11	−2
11. Labor/housing ratio	LHR	+13	+14	−1
12. Underemployed/housing ratio	UHR	+75	+58	+17
13. Manager/job ratio	MR	−1	−1	0
14. Labor/job ratio	LR	0	+1	−1
15. Underemployed/job ratio	UR	−32	−41	+9
16. Tax ratio needed	TRN	−24	−33	+9
17. Underemployed to labor net	UTLN	+76	+67	+9

Figure 5-9 Changes caused by the revival program (SHDR = 0.05, NECN = 0.07) when the underemployed-housing-multiplier table UHMT is modified to the shape in Figure 5-4

umn 5 in Figure 5-9 details the slight reduction in policy effectiveness in comparison with the original policy run; the differences are not large in light of the overall gains in both columns 3 and 4. The revival policy of 5 percent slum demolition and 40 percent more new-enterprise construction is still highly effective for the hypothesized housing-migration curve in Figure 5-4.

Test Number Two. Figure 5-5, which implies the need for an even more extreme housing shortage to discourage in-migration, looks quite different from the original curve in Figure 5-1. Figure 5-5 has lower values than the original curve at its left-hand side; a housing excess does not strongly attract the underemployed. The new curve drops off to the right even more gradually than the curve in Figure 5-4. Figures 5-10a, 5-10b, 5-10c, and 5-11 display the results of testing the revival policies with the curve in Figure 5-5. In general, revival still leads to a significant improvement in city conditions. However, the underemployed/housing ratio UHR, which fell to 1.42 in Figure 5-8b, only reaches 1.57 in Figure 5-10b. The higher value of UHR means that more underemployed are willing to accept a housing shortage to obtain other policy benefits. Underemployed U, which increased by 2 percent in test number one, increases by 15 percent in test number two. The larger underemployed population in Figure 5-10b diminishes any improvement in the city underemployed/job ratio UR. Figure 5-11 shows that UR, which fell by over 30 percent in test number one, falls by only 22 percent in test number two. Figures 5-8 and 5-10 confirm that the *Urban Dynamics* revival program loses some of its effectiveness if the underemployed are less sensitive to a housing shortage. However, as long as the curve has some downward sloping portion and as long as the policy pushes the system to operate in that portion, then a housing shortage tends to deter in-migration. A downward sloping housing curve means that housing can influence the size of the local population and thereby allocate economic gains to current residents. No one seriously questions whether a downward sloping region exists in the real-world housing-migration curve. Rather, the debate focuses on where the downward slope begins and how steeply the slope proceeds beyond that point.

Test Number Three. This test serves as the final test to determine whether the most extreme curve within the plausible range (defined by Figure 5-7) produces significant improvement in city conditions. Suppose that housing availability has almost no influence on migration. Figure 5-6 represents such an assumption. Housing constrains in-migration only after the underemployed/housing ratio UHR reaches 1.5 (one-third of a city's underemployed families have doubled up). Although such a curve may not be realistic, the assumption nevertheless does represent an extreme test of the *Urban Dynamics* revival program. Figure 5-12a, 5-12b, 5-12c, and 5-13 show that the city improves even with the extreme curve in Figure 5-6. New enterprise and jobs still increase substantially, while the underemployed/job ratio UR falls by 13 percent. As depicted in column 3 in Figure 5-13, the housing-migration curve in Figure 5-6 seriously erodes the program's benefits, but the net outcome still represents an overall improvement.

Figure 5-12b indicates a high degree of willingness on the part of the underemployed to endure a housing shortage. The underemployed/housing ratio UHR eventually exceeds 1.7 (approaching an average of two underemployed families for every underemployed housing unit). The values seems to lie well outside any crowding ratio acceptable to even the poorest city dwellers. Given the unreasonableness of the behavior illustrated in Figure 5-6, such a curve can hardly be representative of the actual relationship between housing availability and underemployed in-migration. A curve lying somewhere between the original curve in Figure 5-1 and the curve in Figure 5-5 seems most plausible. But even outside the plausible range, as in Figure 5-6, the *Urban Dynamics* revival policies still generate some significant improvement.

5.3 Adjusting Local Policy to Enhance Program Effectiveness

The 5 percent slum-demolition program in *Urban Dynamics* forces the system into a region where a lack of housing discourages further in-migration. But if the underemployed are actually less sensitive to housing shortages (as assumed with the curves in Figures 5-4, 5-5, and 5-6), then the 5 percent demolition rate may not suffice to create a housing constraint. Higher demolition rates, of perhaps even 10 percent per year, may be appropriate. The rate of demolition required to make the revival program most effective is a direct function of the sensitivity of the underemployed to a housing shortage. In Figure 5-6, the most extreme alternative curve, the underemployed are not discouraged from in-migrating until one-third of the local underemployed families are forced to double up. If the underemployed are actually willing to endure moderate crowding ratios, then they will not strongly oppose public efforts to demolish some more housing. Although the extra demolition may induce more crowding, it is necessary to protect the gains in local employment. Public administrators who apply the revival program *must* adjust the rate of demolition to the point where a housing shortage begins to discourage in-migration. The housing policy is not designed to achieve some arbitrary underemployed-to-housing ratio but, instead, to control in-migration by limiting the amount of available housing. In the final run, the underemployed are assumed to be extremely insensitive to a housing scarcity, as in Figure 5-6. Can city officials effectively adjust the revival program to restore its positive impacts? Figures 5-14a, 5-14b, 5-14c, and 5-15 suggest how public policy might be adjusted to meet the objective of limiting in-migration. The run in Figure 5-14 differs from the run in Figure 5-12 only in that the slum demolition policy has been raised from 5 percent per year to 10 percent per year. Figure 5-6, the extreme case of underemployed insensitivity to a housing shortage, is retained from the model in Figure 5-12. The higher demolition rate is intended to create a sufficient housing shortage to permit more significant and lasting job opportunities and to enhance upward socioeconomic mobility for the underemployed. Whether the adjusted strategy improves employment conditions as much as the original revival program in *Urban Dynamics* provides one measure of the effectiveness of the revision.

Figure 5-14a shows that the revised program leads to a strong improvement in city conditions. For example, the amount of new enterprise NE increases by 75 percent. The resulting increase in jobs improves (reduces) the underemployed/job ratio UR

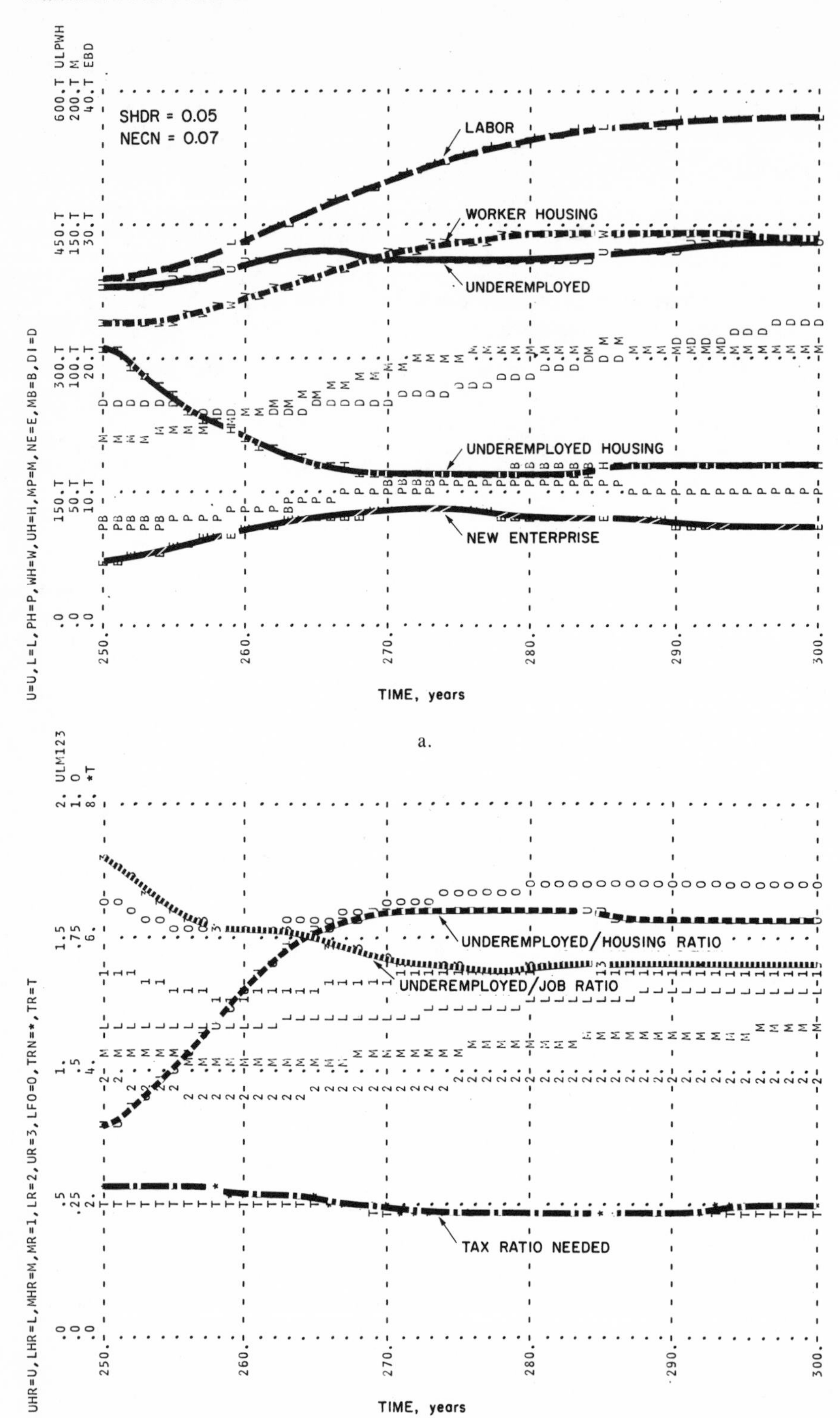

SHDR = 0.05
NECN = 0.07
LABOR
WORKER HOUSING
UNDEREMPLOYED
UNDEREMPLOYED HOUSING
NEW ENTERPRISE
TIME, years
UNDEREMPLOYED/HOUSING RATIO
UNDEREMPLOYED/JOB RATIO
TAX RATIO NEEDED
TIME, years

a.

b.

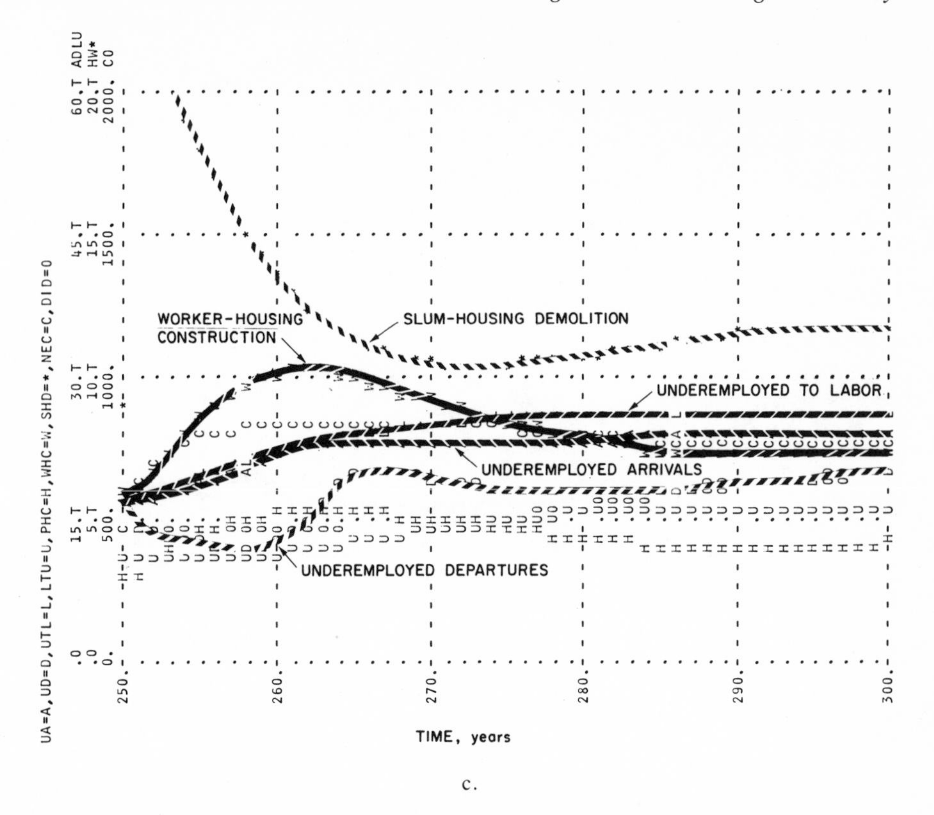

c.

Figure 5-10 The *Urban Dynamics* revival program tested on a model with the underemployed-housing-multiplier table UHMT curve modified as in Figure 5-5

(1) Variable Name	(2) Symbol	(3) Change (%)	(4) Change in Urban Dynamics (%)	(5) Difference (Column 3 – Column 4)
a. Slum-housing demolition	SHD	+39	+36	+3
b. New-enterprise construction	NEC	+66	+80	−14
1. New enterprise	NE	+49	+63	−14
2. Mature business	MB	+55	+64	−11
3. Declining industry	DI	+39	+35	+4
4. Premium housing	PH	+35	+38	−3
5. Worker housing	WH	+29	+34	−5
6. Underemployed housing	UH	−40	−43	+2
7. Managerial-professional	MP	+46	+53	−7
8. Labor	L	+45	+53	−8
9. Underemployed	U	+15	−11	+26
10. Manager/housing ratio	MHR	+8	+11	−3
11. Labor/housing ratio	LHR	+12	+14	−2
12. Underemployed/housing ratio	UHR	+93	+58	+35
13. Manager/job ratio	MR	−1	−1	0
14. Labor/job ratio	LR	−1	+1	−2
15. Underemployed/job ratio	UR	−22	−41	+19
16. Tax ratio needed	TRN	−12	−33	+21
17. Underemployed to labor net	UTLN	+80	+67	+13

Figure 5-11 Changes caused by the revival program (SHDR = 0.05, NECN = 0.07) when the underemployed-housing-multiplier table UHMT is modified to the shape in Figure 5-5

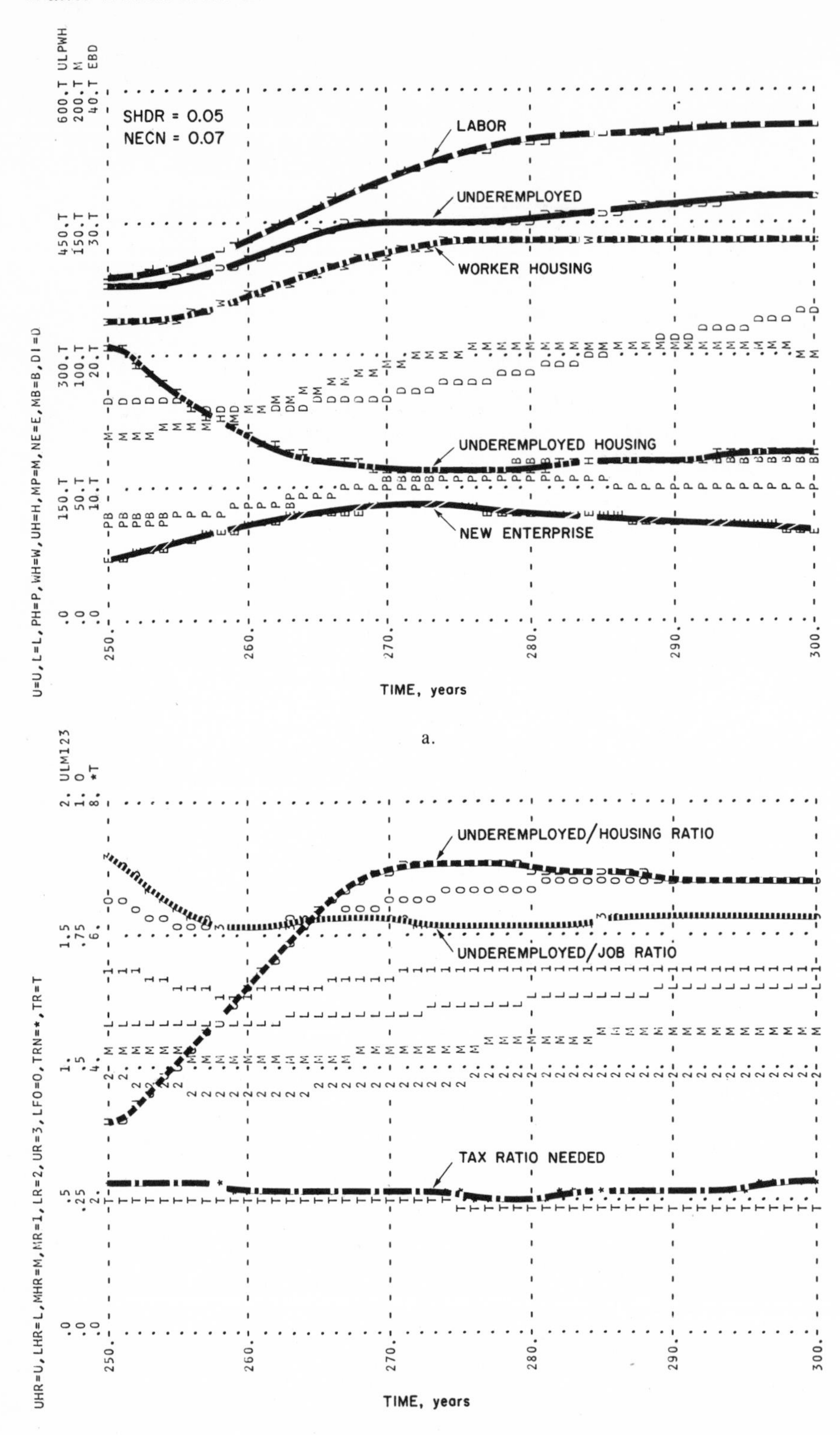
SHDR = 0.05
NECN = 0.07
LABOR
UNDEREMPLOYED
WORKER HOUSING
UNDEREMPLOYED HOUSING
NEW ENTERPRISE
U=U, L=L, PH=P, WH=W, UH=H, MP=M, NE=E, MB=B, DI=D
TIME, years
UNDEREMPLOYED/HOUSING RATIO
UNDEREMPLOYED/JOB RATIO
TAX RATIO NEEDED
UHR=U, LHR=L, MHR=M, MR=1, LR=2, UR=3, LFO=O, TRN=*, TR=T
TIME, years

a.

b.

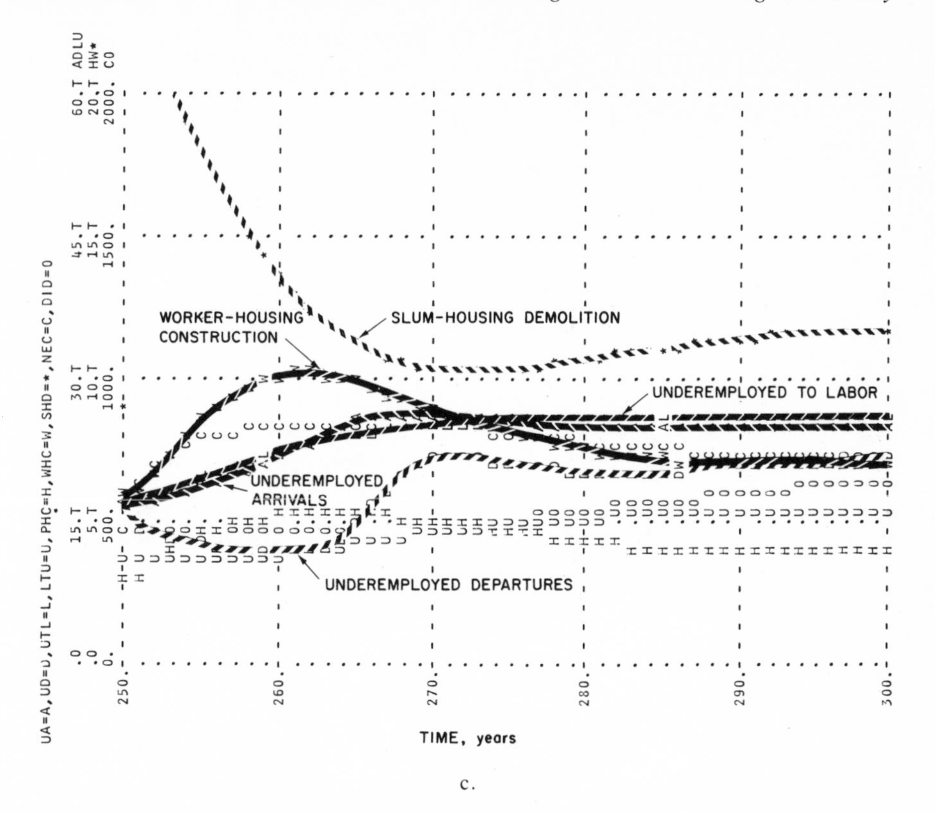

c.

Figure 5-12 The *Urban Dynamics* revival program tested on a model with the underemployed-housing-multiplier table UHMT curve modified as in Figure 5-6

(1) Variable Name	(2) Symbol	(3) Change (%)	(4) Change in Urban Dynamics (%)	(5) Difference (Column 3 – Column 4)
a. Slum-housing demolition	SHD	+47	+36	+11
b. New-enterprise construction	NEC	+91	+80	+11
1. New enterprise	NE	+42	+63	−21
2. Mature business	MB	+50	+64	−14
3. Declining industry	DI	+41	+35	+6
4. Premium housing	PH	+47	+38	+9
5. Worker housing	WH	+27	+34	−7
6. Underemployed housing	UH	−39	−43	+4
7. Managerial-professional	MP	+42	+53	−11
8. Labor	L	+41	+53	−12
9. Underemployed	U	+27	−11	+38
10. Manager/housing ratio	MHR	+7	+11	−4
11. Labor/housing ratio	LHR	+12	+14	−2
12. Underemployed/housing ratio	UHR	+110	+58	+52
13. Manager/job ratio	MR	−1	−1	0
14. Labor/job ratio	LR	−2	+1	−3
15. Underemployed/job ratio	UR	−13	−41	+28
16. Tax ratio needed	TRN	−1	−33	+32
17. Underemployed to labor net	UTLN	+80	+67	+13

Figure 5-13 Changes caused by the revival program (SHDR = 0.05, NECN = 0.07) when the underemployed-to-housing-multiplier table UHMT is modified to the extreme shape in Figure 5-6

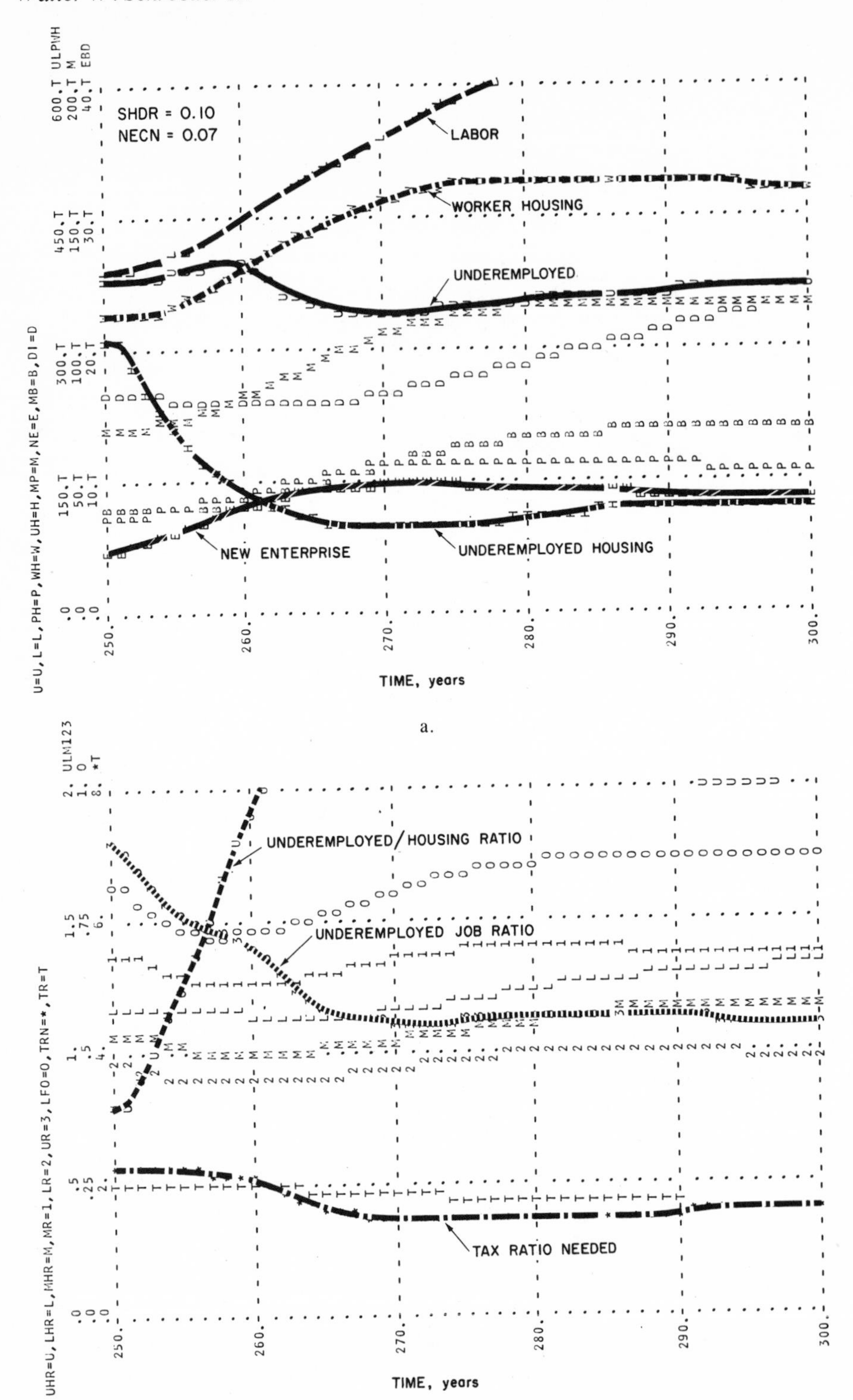

SHDR = 0.10
NECN = 0.07
LABOR
WORKER HOUSING
UNDEREMPLOYED
NEW ENTERPRISE
UNDEREMPLOYED HOUSING
TIME, years
UNDEREMPLOYED/HOUSING RATIO
UNDEREMPLOYED JOB RATIO
TAX RATIO NEEDED
TIME, years

a.

b.

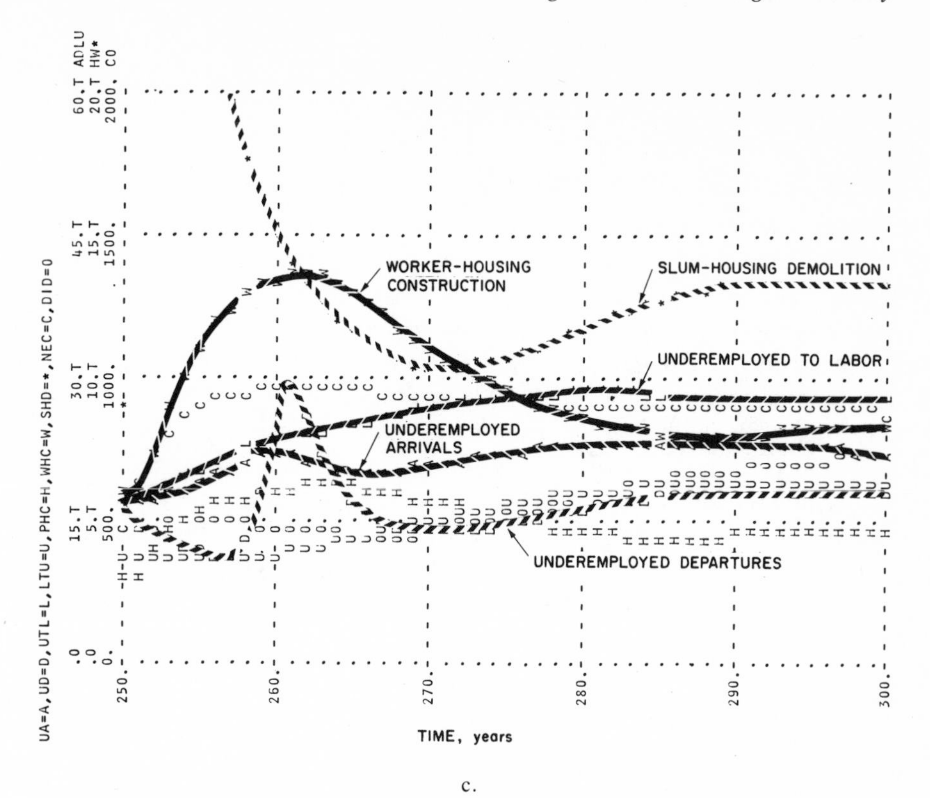

c.

Figure 5-14 An adjusted *Urban Dynamics* revival program (SHDR increased from 5% to 10%) on a model with the underemployed-housing-multiplier table UHMT curve modified as in Figure 5-6

(1) Variable Name	(2) Symbol	(3) Change (%)	(4) Change from Urban Dynamics (%)	(5) Difference (Column 3 – Column 4)
a. Slum-housing demolition	SHD	+28	+36	−8
b. New-enterprise construction	NEC	+57	+80	−23
1. New enterprise	NE	+75	+63	+12
2. Mature business	MB	+78	+64	+14
3. Declining industry	DI	+43	+35	+8
4. Premium housing	PH	+48	+38	+10
5. Worker housing	WH	+44	+34	+10
6. Underemployed housing	UH	−61	−43	−18
7. Managerial-professional	MP	+63	+53	+10
8. Labor	L	+63	+53	+10
9. Underemployed	U	−2	−11	+9
10. Manager/housing ratio	MHR	+10	+11	−1
11. Labor/housing ratio	LHR	+13	+14	−1
12. Underemployed/housing ratio	UHR	+151	+58	+93
13. Manager/job ratio	MR	−2	−1	−1
14. Labor/job ratio	LR	0	+1	−1
15. Underemployed/job ratio	UR	−40	−41	+1
16. Tax ratio needed	TRN	−31	−33	+2
17. Underemployed to labor net	UTLN	+77	+67	+10

Figure 5-15 Changes caused by a modified revival program (SHDR = 0.1, NECN = 0.07) with the underemployed-housing-multiplier table UHMT as in Figure 5-6

in Figure 5-14b by 40 percent. The 31 percent drop in the tax ratio needed TRN testifies that the city's tax base expands faster than its needs for revenue. The rate of upward economic advancement for the city's underemployed (underemployed-to-labor net) in Figure 5-14c increases by 77 percent. Column 4 of Figure 5-15 suggests that the improvements in column 3 are approximately equal in magnitude to the improvements generated by the original *Urban Dynamics* revival policies. For example, the original program leads to a 63 percent increase in new enterprise NE; the modified program creates a 75 percent increase. Therefore, the revised program actually proves to be 12 percent more effective than the original program with respect to attracting industry and jobs. The revised program produces a 40 percent improvement in the underemployed/job ratio UR, whereas the original revival program leads to a 41 percent improvement. Therefore, the revised program is slightly less effective (by about 1 percent) than the original program for reducing unemployment. The underemployed/housing ratio UHR with the modified program exceeds the original by 151 percent. The high underemployed-to-housing ratio, which exceeds 2.0 in Figure 5-14b, comes about because the extreme assumption of Figure 5-6 provides that underemployed migration drops off only after the ratio reaches 1.75 or more. Thus the revised program successfully creates a sufficient housing shortage to permit a sustained improvement in the socioeconomic environment for the city's underemployed.

5.4 Conclusions

Several of the issues raised in the controversy surrounding the presumed influence of housing upon migration are best investigated through model experiments. Looking closely at the original UHMT curve in Figure 5-1, the alleged inconsistencies between observed housing-market behavior and the *Urban Dynamics* model become less visible. In fact, many of the criticisms of the particular housing-migration assumption arise from a misunderstanding of the assumption's relation to the normal response of the urban housing market, represented elsewhere in the *Urban Dynamics* model. Testing the revival policies against alternative plausible UHMT curves confirms that, as long as there is a downward sloping portion, the policies can help to restore socioeconomic vitality. If the underemployed are assumed to be insensitive to conditions of extreme crowding, the original revival policies provide relatively less improvement. But even under extreme assumptions, an adjusted revival program based on accelerated housing demolition proves to be just as effective as the revival policies originally presented in *Urban Dynamics*.

6

The Use of Data in Modeling: A Discussion

Jay W. Forrester and others

What is the proper role of data in building, calibrating, and verifying a model? The question is important for urban modelers because reliable empirical data about major relationships in the urban system often do not exist. Conventional statistical modeling approaches, which employ recorded data to construct important model relationships, have diminished usefulness when such data are fragmentary or nonexistent. From the perspective of system dynamics, alternative sources of evidence–for example, expert opinion, published descriptions, and survey results–may lead to more accurate structural representations. This reading presents excerpts from the transcript of a seminar conducted by several urban modeling experts at M.I.T. The seminar participants discuss a variety of modeling topics that bring out the differences between the system dynamics methodology employed in Urban Dynamics *and in other modeling disciplines. The participants were:*

Louis E. Alfeld
Director of Planning
Marlborough, Massachusetts

Wyndham Clarke
Office of Science & Technology
U.S. Department of Housing and Urban Development

John F. Collins
Consulting Professor of Urban Affairs M.I.T.
Former Mayor of Boston

Dr. Alexander Ganz
Director of Research
Boston Redevelopment Authority

Dr. Britton Harris, Chairman
Department of City and Regional Planning
University of Pennsylvania

Dr. Gregory Ingram
Professor of Economics
Harvard University

Walter W. Schroeder III
Director of
Urban Dynamics Research
System Dynamics Group M.I.T.

Dr. George Sternlieb, Director
Center for
Urban Social Science Research
Rutgers University

Editors' note: The transcript begins with a brief introduction by Professor Forrester describing the background and progress of the modeling seminars. The discussion moves quickly into the specific assumption relating housing availability and in-migration. The larger question of the appropriate role of data modeling is then considered.

FORRESTER: During the past eight months we have enjoyed an extremely valuable communication between our group at M.I.T. and other urban modelers—I hope in both directions. Perhaps in future phases of our effort we can continue to move deeper into some of these issues. Progress has been satisfying, although many more issues remain unexplored.

CLARKE: I am specifically interested in whether the inputs of other people have affected any of the basic assumptions about the dynamic processes in the *Urban Dynamics* model. Would you comment on any areas where you felt that changes in your basic formulation or modifications came about as a result of these interchanges?

FORRESTER: I think each question that's raised calls for some sort of reaction and response. But sometimes the best response begins with clearer explanations. In some cases, the response should be new modeling and model changes. For example, the questions that were raised about suburbs have not by any means been fully disposed of because they are really many different questions. But new modeling has begun around a few specific issues, such as what happens if jobs in the city are held by people that don't live in the city? This question is more easily answered by modeling than by discussion, partly because the issue is so complex. And the two papers on land rezoning and housing abandonment are of that same class where one extends or alters the first simple model in order to resolve some other question or issue that has been raised.[1] Responding to critiques is a progressive task; each question may call upon any one of several kinds of response.

To illustrate a case where clarification has been at least as useful as new modeling, consider the following example. The *Urban Dynamics* model contains a relationship in which the ratio of underemployed to available housing is one of the five factors that influence underemployed migration. A substantial number of reviewers and commentators have taken exception to this assumption. In working with Professor Rothenberg, one of the most specific of the critics on this issue, we seem to have discovered that the degree of aggregation and the nomenclature in the model are more at fault than any structural defect of the model. Professor Rothenberg does not accept the assumption at face value because price, vacancy rates, and market supply are not considered explicitly. He does agree, however, that each of those three factors depends on the underemployed-to-housing ratio in the *Urban Dynamics* model. In other words, each of those factors in turn depends on what is in the model in the first place; and he agrees that each has the same overall effect on migration as the original aggregated effect. Therefore, his three separate assumptions, if modeled explicitly, could never have reversed the correctness of the single assumption in the model. But in subdividing and identifying the effect of intermediate variables, we translated the assumption into a nomenclature closer to the way some people tend to think. Hence a big part of the issue was neutralized in the process of improving communication. Greg, you were in on those discussions. Am I giving a fair interpretation?

INGRAM: I would say so. I think you could argue that the model contains a particular kind of "reduced form" that subsumes a lot of other relationships. The issue is fundamentally a question of what shape the curve is; in that sense, I think we all agree on that basic shape, which is where we left the issue.

SCHROEDER: You've described a phenomenon that I think applies to most of these issues. It's as much of a job to *define* the issue as to *resolve* it. We must clarify an issue to the point where different people from different disciplines are communicating before there can be any chance of resolution. It took us a long time to understand exactly what bothered Professor Rothenberg about the curve. Many of our most significant accomplishments during the program fall into the category of achieving a much better understanding of where the issues really lie and in identifying the next step toward resolution.

INGRAM: I think that's right. Speaking for myself at least, I think we're not speaking past each other so much. At our first meeting or two it seemed like we were two ships passing in the night. An example is the suburb issue. But once you made the first crude model of the suburbs within the scope of the original model, then we could begin talking about how to formally extend that model. I wanted to see transportation issues treated in the *Urban Dynamics* model, as I have said before.[2] Suburban growth tends to be very dependent on accessibility between suburb and city. So a model extension should focus on accessibility. In a sense, my comments were premature and went well beyond the range of what you could have done in the last twelve months.

FORRESTER: But not beyond the range of what we agree should be done. You used the term "ships that passed in the night," and it is quite appropriate. I was fascinated by the three hours or more that we spent trying to determine the communication problem on the housing and migration issue. At the end of a half-day session, we finally identified the real issue; then there was another session or two on it afterward. But as I recall, for quite a long time, the model was being perceived entirely differently by different people. In system dynamics, we look upon those relationships in the model as essentially static, long-term equilibrium curves that say "if there is a housing shortage, what effect does it have? If there were no housing at all, what effect would that have?" And a lot of people responded by saying that there never is a housing shortage; developers will come in and build housing, so the condition never exists. Therefore, you see, the two groups weren't addressing themselves to the same issue; one was essentially saying "it will never happen"; the other was saying "*if* it happens, what is the effect?" Whether or not housing is getting built has nothing to do with that particular assumption. In a sense the two groups were looking at a different degree of dynamic disaggregation, a different sort than I spoke of before. In such a case, the most important step is to consolidate the different views.

INGRAM: I would urge that, as a next step in many of these issues, we estimate the relationships with greater accuracy. Estimation is tricky because the data aren't usually what you'd like, the relationships are nonlinear, and there is always a chance that you are misspecifying the relationship. But I think you have to go ahead. Some work that Peter Senge[3] is doing here should help us better understand how serious a misspecification can be. But there's no question that, if the specification is correct, then empirical estimation can work.

FORRESTER: Peter has been working on this, and his results are interesting. In order to correctly use estimation techniques, it's my understanding that you need perfect information on every variable in the model. As soon as you depart from perfection, you begin to get into difficulty.

INGRAM: Yes, and his paper gives you an idea of how fast that happens.

FORRESTER: It's very fast in terms of the problems inherent in the collection of real-world data.

INGRAM: My impression is the opposite; that in fact the experiments show the estimation process to be more robust than I had thought.

FORRESTER: This is an important basis for future discussion. Most of the people using the techniques have never even asked the questions that are of critical importance. I hope we can continue to work on this complex set of issues.

CLARKE: I'm much too far away from your work, Jay, in any substantial way, to be able to offer this comment with much confidence, but wasn't one of the major thrusts in the original design of the HUD program to try to use data and do some of that "reality testing" on the model?

FORRESTER: Well, you have a big step to do before "reality testing" can begin. You have to decide what "reality testing" means. We're still at that stage. We've arrived at a point in our research where I would be fascinated to dig deeper into the major issue Greg and I were just discussing. It would be a big task, but could greatly enhance our understanding of the appropriateness of what have come to be common beliefs among social science modelers.

From the "operator's" viewpoint, I am really quite skeptical about the validity of many of the statistical methods. The "operator" is the politician, the manager, the engineer, or the voting member of the public who has to act today. He cannot wait for perfect answers. The important question is, "Are these techniques valid from *his* standpoint?" My observation is that the estimation techniques don't reach out far enough to ascertain whether the process in fact touches real life, or whether the results are useful in actual decision making. So I would say that one area in which I have doubts, and which should be the basis of future discussion, is whether the current methods really do what outside observers have been led to think they do. Technical approaches to establishing model validity often have little visible relevance to whether a model is going to be useful for decision makers.

CLARKE: But you'd have to give me an example, Jay, before I can really understand what you're driving at.

FORRESTER: Well, take the best example of criticism that has been leveled at *Urban Dynamics*. It goes back again to the presumed effect of housing on migration. A lot of people have said that there are studies and data from the social science research literature that prove the assumption in the book is incorrect. Those who venture a source for this quite often cite a book by Ira Lowry.[4] Now I've searched the book by Lowry quite carefully; it doesn't even use the word housing once, and it uses the word dwelling just once. The book is silent on the effect of housing except in an indirect way. It deals with the effect of jobs on migration, finds a good correlation, and therefore says jobs are the cause of migration. Readers of Lowry believe that his book implicitly says housing has no effect on migration, but the book never actually looks at housing. The mistaken general impression was that Lowry had proven housing to have no effect; so it's a misinterpretation that directly affects public reaction to the assumption in *Urban Dynamics*. We've never been able to find any literature, really, that deals explicitly with the effect of housing on migration in any substantial, quantitative way. The impressions of those who believe housing is not a significant influence are quite consistent with the original model because the model, under conditions found in the present-day American city, runs with a housing excess. The model itself is doing exactly what people perceive: housing is not very important in the normal mode of urban behavior. The whole issue revolves around what would happen if you shifted the mode of the city to create a shortage of housing. So we must ask more than the question of what the data shows. There is also the question of whether you can reliably extract these relationships in highly nonlinear, multiple feedback loop configurations from even perfect data.

Mr. Clarke made the comment a while ago that measuring the values of parameters used in the *Urban Dynamics* model may have been part of our original scope of effort. Now, some people, I think, really thought that we could go into Lowell or any city and get data from which we could justify or alter most of the parameter values in the model. I consistently said that I didn't think one could find enough data to touch scarcely any of them. We've made a good search, and I believe that is the state of affairs. In a place like Lowell, you don't have the data necessary to even go through the process—never mind any doubts about the process that I've expressed—to get the parameters that are in the model. So you have first of all the nonavailability of data. But more important, you have the question of whether you in fact need data, or even if you had data, whether you could get what you want out of it. I think the biggest task in this whole matter at the moment is not to go out and try to verify parameters from data but to hold a very deep and enduring set of discussions about what we should do. We should run some laboratory experiments, along the lines of Peter Senge's interests, which might settle some of the questions about whether these experiments are promising. Depending on just what assumptions about reality the statistical methods must make in order to be useful, other considerations may turn out to be more central to model validity or usefulness. For example, to what extent do the policy recommendations depend on precise estimates of the parameter values anyway? There's a very big difference in opinion between us and most readers of our work as to the degree of sensitivity to parameters. This area of investigation hasn't been thoroughly explored by this advisory group or others.

Suppose we are looking at a specific parameter assumption. One relevant question is whether all values of the parameter within the range of plausibility produce the same overall model behavior. Do policy recommendations change if we alter the parameter within its plausible range? If we can answer this question *before* going out and gathering data, we can focus our estimation efforts far more efficiently. But, as I say, this first step in "reality testing" should precede the more detailed tasks associated with statistical verification.

STERNLIEB: Too many people put too much faith in data. I once wrote a short piece on the sociology of statistics. Statistics are to us what the sticks and stones of previous societies are to archaeologists. Unfortunately, they also represent nearly as much of a chance acquisition process. If you look at the history of most of the data series that we use, they began in the distant past; some variable excited some attention at the time, and so was recorded into the present. But these records may measure reality only as much as the unlikely assertion that Egyptians built exclusively with stone, because that's the only thing preserved to measure their behavior. So I agree that there are limitations here.

HARRIS: I agree with you, Jay, that there are severe difficulties with the traditional use of statistics. One difficulty is the adventitious nature of data, as Professor Sternlieb suggests. Another problem is the "addiction," you might say, of statistical methods to a linear framework, which makes the methods inapplicable here. At best, very weak methods exist for fitting complex, nonlinear, and discontinuous models; there are equally weak statistical measures of performance. So the use of statistical verification techniques is an extremely expensive process with only limited value. But I believe that some future work should be done in this area.

One possibly valuable area for investigation arises from the fact that time-series data are not just adventitious; they are practically nonexistent over the one hundred year, or more, time period that would relate the model to individual cities. Hence one element that ought to be on your research agenda is to learn how much you can extract from cross-sectional data. You will have to be careful, because different cities at different points in the urban life cycle cannot be directly compared. But I think you could make some progress with the approach.

Another part of the scheme has got to be an extremely careful, self-critical review of all the kinds of assumptions in the theory, and whether in fact they are reproduced in the *Urban Dynamics* model. This task is not just a matter of gathering time series and matching them, and so on, but also whether certain critical events occur. For instance, I suspect that there are a number of towns, of medium to large size, over the United States which have ceased to grow without filling up their land base. There are a large number of towns, mostly in the Middle West, that have plenty of land, but which have stopped growing. I doubt very much if the model as it now stands would predict their failure to grow. So I think there are other factors relating to metropolitan development that belong in the model. The System Dynamics Group has not, to my knowledge, made a systematic examination of any particular issue of this kind, except for the way the population growth curve matches certain selected cities. Now we don't know what a larger group of representative cities might show. So I'm proposing that you consider a very extensive program of verification of the model, which I think would lead to some suggested changes.

FORRESTER: Let me raise a question that comes directly out of your comments. The issue is the nature of professional responsibility for model verification. You have suggested that the proponents of the model should do all these things. I would agree that it's desirable insofar as they can and have resources. But I would differ with any implication that they have an obligation to and *must* do it, as some people say, before the model is even published. I would say that the proponent has an obligation for his own effectiveness to present enough evidence of validity so that other people will take the theory seriously and proceed themselves to deal with the question of validity. Now, in that sense, *Urban Dynamics* has followed that pattern, because there were book reviews. Very few people concerned with urban affairs have been able to totally ignore the book. To begin with, the book had enough face validity to demand some attention. I don't think the kind of procedure you're speaking of can be done by the proponents of a model because, no matter what they do, their efforts will be suspect. I could line up all kinds of case histories and say that they demonstrate the validity of the model, and the proper rejoinder would be, "Well, you have just sorted out the ones that support your case." I also believe we must face squarely the nonavailability of data. I consistently said I didn't think we could find enough data to estimate any parameters. We've made a good data search, but I believe the result is what I had anticipated. Regardless of any theoretical doubts I may have about the estimation process, the data are simply not available in a place like Lowell to even go through the process. Isn't that right?

INGRAM: There's no doubt about it.

STERNLIEB: I would be a little more sympathetic to your problems if you hadn't adopted the role of "doctor" instead of "researcher." But if you really want to get into the job of prescribing changes for cities, you've got to go further than the *Urban Dynamics* model takes us. You've got to know the price, risks, and failsafes attendant on each proposed action. What are the startup costs, not merely in money, but in terms of possibly losing a few other patients below that point where they can be revived. Your policies are going to make it more difficult for people to get into the central city to patronize that struggling downtown department store that still has some suburban customers. You're going to lose some of your retail. You're going to lose some of your service facilities and the like. It seems to me that you have stopped at an untenable stage of the game. You either have to go further down the pipeline of prescription, or you have to withdraw somewhat from prescription.

FORRESTER: George, this is an interesting point you've raised about staying away from prescription, because it differs a great deal from my impression of the strength and place of a system dynamics model. Somebody is always going to prescribe. Action is going to be taken. You can't stop the clock and wait fifty or one hundred years for perfect answers. A system dynamics model is primarily a wrapping-up of the mental knowledge on which we are otherwise going to act. The model helps anticipate the consequences of what we are now assuming and the alternatives now available to decision makers. The model should therefore be taken not as an object of science but as an operational tool, and criticised on that basis. The criticism may be just as severe, but it should be on the basis of whether the model has captured what we think we know, what we are assuming, and what we're now doing, and whether the model sheds some light on what is otherwise going to happen. The key question is not whether the model is perfect. We know absolutely that it's not. Instead, the important question is whether the model throws light on what we'd otherwise be doing today. If you think it doesn't, then we should sit down and identify the assumptions that people *are* making and incorporate those. One benefit of operational models is that, as soon as you make the assumptions explicit, they may get better.

COLLINS: Mayors are not interested in the detailed output of any model; they're interested in the ability of the model to help them better understand the city which they govern, to help them understand better how it functions. You can believe me: mayors in general don't have any idea of how the city functions. And I doubt very seriously whether there are many people in Washington who understand the dynamic forces at work. This may not be a perfect model. It may not ever give the mayor a perfect understanding of his city, but the test of the usefulness of this approach is whether or not he can use the model to do something better than hope that, for any ten decisions he makes, five may be right and five may be wrong.

FORRESTER: John, you wrapped up two phrases that I would like to separate. You expressed "this model" as you mentioned "this approach." I hope that the distinction is clear in everyone's mind. There is not one model that has to be fully defended, but a progression of models that moves forward with each constructive criticism and model refinement. *Urban Dynamics* obscures the distinction between a model and the process because, in order to write the book, I had to freeze the process and describe the model at one point in its evolution. System dynamics models are examined, upgraded, and used in just the same manner as our mental models. I see the playing field for systems dynamics models as lying in the center of those mental models otherwise used. In system dynamics, we try to draw from those mental images, to generate a formal model, and to use feedback to improve the mental models. If the formal model looks much more persuasive than his present mental model, the decision maker may start to act on something like an urban dynamics model. He does so with all the risks normally attached to adopting someone else's mental model. The formal model has some hazards and limitations, to be sure, but so have all the models we otherwise might choose. It is not a matter of guaranteeing the model's correctness; it is a matter of making a choice based on which of two alternatives seems more plausible in the particular circumstances. Now, all that's been said about validity is relevant because we must keep investigating where the models should be used and where they shouldn't. We must try to improve the formal models.

GANZ: May I comment here on some of the issues? It might be helpful if I describe the way we are using the *Urban Dynamics* model in Boston, and why we find it useful. Basically, the value of the model to us is the concept of interrelating jobs, population, and housing in a network of variables that affect the city. The model construct leads us to ask broader, more important questions than are typically asked in a city. At our stage of analysis, I would say the model serves as an intermediate station that encompasses some prescription, but primarily description.

Notes

1. See Readings 9 and 10 of this volume.

2. See Gregory K. Ingram, book review of *Urban Dynamics*, in *Journal of the American Institute of Planners*, May 1970, pp. 206–208.

3. Peter M. Senge, "An Experimental Evaluation of Generalized Least Squares Estimation," System Dynamics Group Memorandum D-1944-7 (Cambridge, Mass.: M.I.T., 1974).

4. Ira S. Lowry, *Migration and Metropolitan Growth: Two Analytical Models* (San Francisco: Chandler Publishing Co., 1966).

7

The Parameter Sensitivity Issue in *Urban Dynamics*

Kenneth R. Britting and John G. Trump

Do the values chosen for a particular set of parameters in the Urban Dynamics *model significantly affect the results of the policies recommended in the book? Published critiques of* Urban Dynamics *have focused on four specific objections with respect to the issue of parameter choice:*

1. *The* Urban Dynamics *model does not employ sophisticated empirical methods to verify parameter values.*
2. *A complete parameter sensitivity analysis has not been performed.*
3. *The population density and land area in the* Urban Dynamics *model are not typical of real cities.*
4. *Parameter values in* Urban Dynamics *are not consistent with urban theory and reflect the biased results of an effort to satisfy a priori conclusions.*

This reading experimentally examines how the choice of a particular set of parameters in the Urban Dynamics *model affects the* Urban Dynamics *revival program. The results of ten other parameter tests are also reported here.*

7
The Parameter Sensitivity Issue in *Urban Dynamics*

7.1 Introduction

Critics of *Urban Dynamics* have frequently raised an important issue: How dependent are the book's policy conclusions on the numerical values of the parameter assumptions? This reading attempts to resolve the question of parameter sensitivity by focusing on whether changes in the parameter values in the *Urban Dynamics* model in fact disturb the original policy conclusions.

The *Urban Dynamics* model contains 87 constant parameters and 53 table functions, all of which must be numerically specified. The constants represent such quantities as housing densities, normal flow rates, numerical distributions of personnel within business units, land area, and initial conditions. Generally speaking, table functions account for nonlinear relationships in the model. Modelers typically use table functions to represent multiplicative factors that modify the normal rates of flow as conditions within the modeled system change.

The issue of parameter sensitivity is intimately linked to the purpose of the *Urban Dynamics* model: to test alternative policies for their effects on the overall condition of an urban area. In an absolute sense, the dynamic behavior of all models depends upon the given parameter values. Parameter changes can lead to altered transient behavior, different equilibrium conditions, and new modes of response. A set of parameter values must be representative of a given dynamic system to obtain reasonable behavior from a model of the system. The key question involves whether the model parameters are specified with sufficient precision to support policy conclusions based on model behavior.

7.2 Presentation of Criticisms

Urban Dynamics has encountered the widely raised criticism that many model parameters are unsupported by empirical data and generally inaccurate. Jerome Rothenberg, Gregory Ingram, and D. L. Babcock, among others, have each expressed concern about possible errors in the parameter estimates. In his review of *Urban Dynamics*, Professor Jerome Rothenberg of M.I.T.'s Department of Economics questions the lack of empirical verification of parameter values:[1]

> Very simply stated, no parameters in the quantified version of the model were derived by sophisticated empirical procedures. . . . Not only are all the parameters arbitrary in this sense, some of them seem unreasonable on the basis of empirical studies that do exist but of which Forrester did not avail himself. [p. 23]

Rothenberg goes on to suggest the insufficiency of testing for parameter sensitivity by varying parameter values one at a time:

> Since all parameters are arbitrary, all are suspect. It is not at all inappropriate to make substitutions in whole clusters of parameters at a time. The model is very likely to display extreme sensitivity to such a relevant examination. [p. 24]

He concludes:

> The upshot of these strictures about parameter estimation is that the model as presently quantified cannot safely be used to make policy recommendations. [p. 25]

Professor Gregory K. Ingram of the Department of Economics at Harvard is also concerned with parameter sensitivity:[2]

> The reader of *Urban Dynamics* must be warned that neither has a complete sensitivity analysis been carried out on the model nor has an empirical estimation been done of parameters already found to be important. [p. 207]

Ingram acknowledges an important feature of all complex feedback systems:

> . . . the policy conclusions are robust with respect to variations in the value of many of the parameters when these parameters are altered one at a time. [p. 207]

But he has far less confidence in the applicability of the *Urban Dynamics* conclusions to a real city for which many parameters may have to be simultaneously readjusted:

> Since the model contains many non-linearities, varying several "insensitive" parameters at once still could have a significant effect on the policy conclusions. [p. 207]

He later identifies one such set of parameters that combine to produce unreasonable model behavior:

> . . . the actual simulation deals with an area of one hundred and fifty six square miles with a population of 5.7 million during stagnating equilibrium. This corresponds to an area somewhat larger than the city of Philadelphia (one hundred and thirty square miles) with a population nearly three times as great as Philadelphia's in 1960. [p. 207]

Ingram here makes an observation substantiated by general urban data: the population densities and land area found in the *Urban Dynamics* model are not characteristic of many cities.

Some critics have also asserted that the unfavorable equilibrium conditions exhibited by the model result from an incorrect choice of parameter values. Professor D. L. Babcock of the University of Missouri so argues:[3]

> These equilibrium conditions are the product of bias in the model created by specific parameter values and relationships arbitrarily chosen by Forrester; when alternative values and relationships derived from urban theory and data are submitted, a much closer balance between jobs, workers, and housing is predicted. [p. 21]

Babcock reports on parameter modifications that he claims to have made in the *Urban Dynamics* model in an effort to improve conditions at equilibrium in the model city:

> I do claim to have shown, however, that modifications of the Urban Dynamics model in an effort to have it more consistent with urban theory and data dramatically change the "inevitable conditions" of the mature city predicted by Forrester. These "inevitable conditions" are in no way proven by the Forrester model, but are instead created by a set of a priori assumptions built into the *Urban Dynamics* model as a bias with no effort at their justification. Further, the "solution" to the "urban problem" recommended by Forrester depends entirely on the validity of these a priori assumptions. [p. 19]

7.3 Analysis of Criticisms

Empirical Methods Not Used. Critics have expressed a strong sense of uneasiness about the lack of sophisticated empirical verification of the parameter values in the *Urban Dynamics* model. Unfortunately, empirical verification of parameter values is seldom possible for models of complex social systems because of a general lack of data and the theoretical weakness of statistical estimation techniques. Naturally, some more easily measured parameters, such as average family size and housing densities, are available. On the other hand, a modeler can rarely determine empirically, and must on occasion completely hypothesize, the shapes and values for functions describing attitudes, values, other influences not readily conducive to empirical measurement, and ranges of operation not previously encountered in historical experience.

The *Urban Dynamics* model describes a representative urban area rather than a specific city. The generic feature of the model compounds the difficulties of incorporating specific data because the data must be collected and suitably averaged for many cities. One major effort to fit the model to a specific city has already been undertaken in Lowell, Massachusetts. The adaptation required the alteration of several constants to reflect the physical characteristics of Lowell.[4] The *Urban Dynamics* model can in fact be adjusted to specify a great variety of urban areas. Critics suggest that the use of sophisticated empirical procedures for estimating parameter values in the *Urban Dynamics* model should be a relatively straightforward and routine matter. That assumption is in all likelihood unjustified. The statistical estimation methods presently available are generally inappropriate for evaluating highly nonlinear multiloop dynamic models. The successful application of statistical methods to dynamic models, such as the *Urban Dynamics* model, is an as yet unattained research objective. System identification, a subset of the theory of statistical estimation, uses empirical data to estimate parameter values in a model. Despite much work in this area, the theory remains incomplete, particularly with regard to nonlinear systems.[5] The only unequivocally successful application of statistical estimation techniques to dynamic systems has been associated with the guidance and control of aerospace vehicles. In aerospace applications, the structure of the relevant model is defined in terms of well-established physical laws. Moreover, a careful analysis and an exhaustive testing of the hardware and physical processes determine the statistical character of exogenous system inputs. Finally, the purposes and mathematical formulation of aerospace models lend themselves to linear or quasi-linear analytical techniques.

Social systems models, however, have so far defied a successful application of system identification theory. For social systems, the model structure does not obey well-established physical principles. Instead, the structure depends upon a less formal perception of causally related feedback processes that operate within social systems. The structure of a social systems model should generate behavior patterns that compare favorably with the performance of the real world.[6] Since many structures can reasonably replicate dynamic behavior, a unique structure cannot be obtained for social systems models. Variables in dynamic systems exhibit a complex closed-loop relationship; no one can observe the behavior of one variable in isolation from others. Although the statistical estimation technique can theoretically extract the open-loop parameter values from closed-loop time-series data, the resulting parameter estimates depend enormously on ideal, and therefore unrealistic, structural assumptions about the given model.[7] Given the dynamic multiloop character of social systems, statistical estimation must be carried out within the context of the entire system model. Single-equation estimation techniques are generally inappropriate, since the estimation process does not account for the presence of random measurement noise and cross-correlated exogenous random noise. Moreover, information delays and material delays in social systems frustrate single-equation estimation techniques. While the modeler of physical systems can perform a series of controlled experiments to establish statistical characteristics, the modeler of social systems must deal with time-series data collected under uncontrolled conditions as the social system evolves over time. Meaningful applications of statistical estimation techniques require a precise specification of the statistical character of important variables. Since time-series data represent only one unique subset of possible outcomes, the required statistical characteristics can be established only in a rather crude fashion. The modeler is forced to assume that observed statistical behavior is characteristic of all possible behaviors.[8] Social systems frequently owe their more significant behavioral characteristics to phenomena mathematically described as nonlinear. For example, in the *Urban Dynamics* model, job availability has a nonlinear effect on in-migration. The assumption of nonlinearity seems to be quite reasonable. Given a large excess of jobs in the city, a small change in the job market has little effect on migration. Conversely, if jobs and population are in balance, a small change in the job market has a relatively larger effect on migration. Since the statistical estimation techniques for dynamic systems require linear mathematical representation, the routine use of available estimation methods for nonlinear social systems models is not feasible. With a relatively large expenditure of effort, the *Urban Dynamics* model can be linearized about a series of particular operating points to obtain statistical estimates of parameter values. But what, if any, useful results are likely to be obtained, given the required statistical and structural assumptions and the limited availability of empirical data? The shapes and functional values of nonlinear table functions represent explicit statements and assumptions about the relationship between two system components. Several years of experience with system dynamics models and real-world management strongly suggest that the shapes of table functions, rather than their absolute numerical values, have primary importance in determining a model's dynamic behavior and response to policy intervention.

The modification (dotted line) shown in Figure 7-1 (solid line identical to Figure A-3 from *Urban Dynamics*) illustrates the importance of the shape of a table function. A decrease in the slope of the underemployed/housing-multiplier table UHMT from the original slope in *Urban Dynamics* also diminishes the assumed sensitivity between housing availability and underemployed in-migration (lower underemployed/housing ratio UHR). The modified table function represents the assumption that, as a component of local urban attractiveness, the importance of housing availability has decreased. The revival policies of slum-housing demolition and the encouragement of new enterprise have somewhat less effect with such a modified UHMT. (See Reading 5 of this collection, "The Sensitivity of Migration to Housing Availability.") The decreased slope of the table function means that housing must become scarcer before in-migration slackens. Nevertheless, the revival program is effective for all downward sloping curves. Only a zero slope, representing the assumption that housing has absolutely no effect on migration, would make the revival policies ineffective.

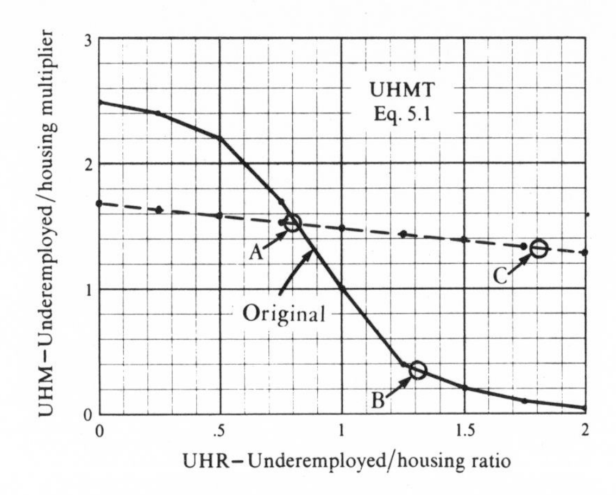

Figure 7-1 The original and modified table function defining the influence of housing availability on underemployed migration

Source: Reprinted from *Urban Dynamics* by Jay W. Forrester by permission of The MIT Press, Cambridge, Massachusetts, Figure A-3.

Empirical research on the influence of housing availability on migration is inconclusive because the underemployed have had access to an abundant supply of housing in our central cities over the past twenty years. Nevertheless, the assumption that housing availability has absolutely no effect on in-migration if housing availability within a city differs considerably from housing availability in the surrounding environment is a very dubious proposition. Unless the model behavior changes substantially when parameter values are varied over a plausible range, the effort and the cost of any attempt to employ sophisticated parameter estimation techniques do not seem justified. No known parameters or clusters of parameters change the relative desirability of the management policies recommended in *Urban Dynamics*. However, such sensitive parameters may exist and could come to light in future investigations. A great deal of unfinished work remains in assessing the potential applicability of statistical parameter estimation techniques to dynamic social system models. The research effort has begun at M.I.T. with a critical examination of the necessary assumptions. Those of most interest pertain to system structure, statistical modeling of uncertainties, and the choice of a ''goodness'' criterion (representing a judgment about what constitutes passing the statistical test—minimum variance, maximum likelihood, least-squares, and so forth). Experiments carried out on a nonlinear, multiloop system dynamics model have yielded promising preliminary results that tend to support the previously expressed doubts about the utility of statistical methods for estimating nonlinear dynamic systems under realistic conditions.[9]

Complete Parameter Sensitivity Studies Not Performed. If no empirical data of sufficient quantity and quality had been available for use in the *Urban Dynamics* model, the demand for a complete parameter sensitivity analysis would be quite understandable. Unfortunately, the behavioral characteristics of dynamic systems preclude such a com-

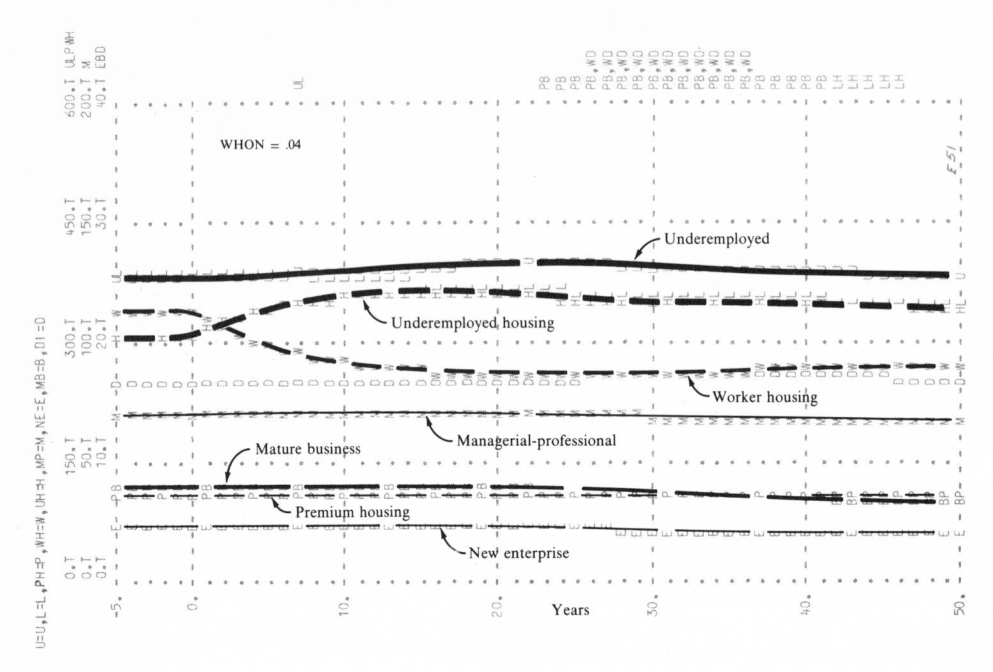
WHON = .04
Underemployed
Underemployed housing
Worker housing
Managerial-professional
Mature business
Premium housing
New enterprise
Years

a.

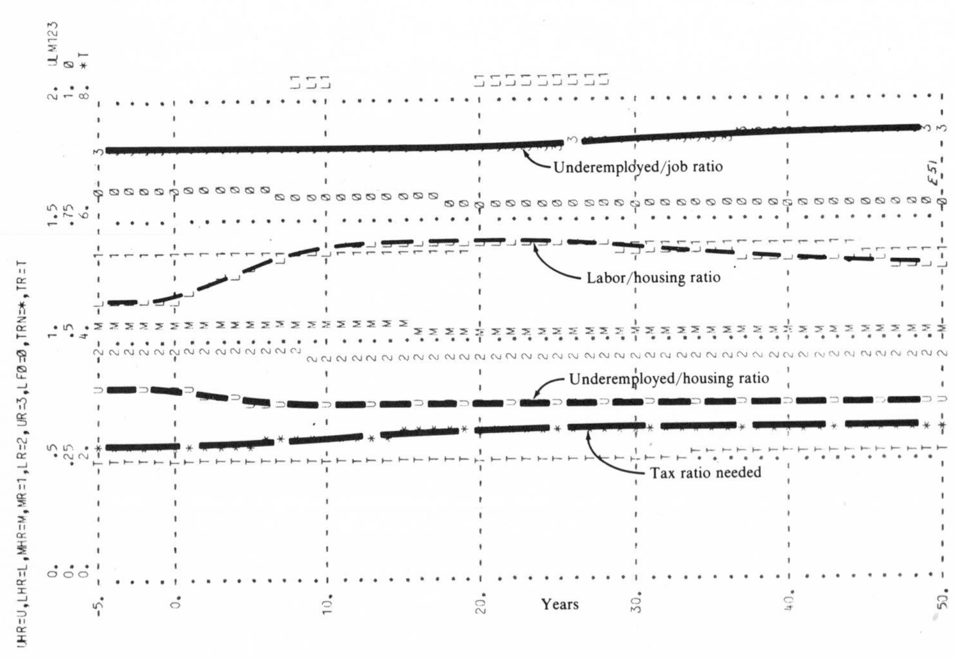
Underemployed/job ratio
Labor/housing ratio
Underemployed/housing ratio
Tax ratio needed
Years

b.

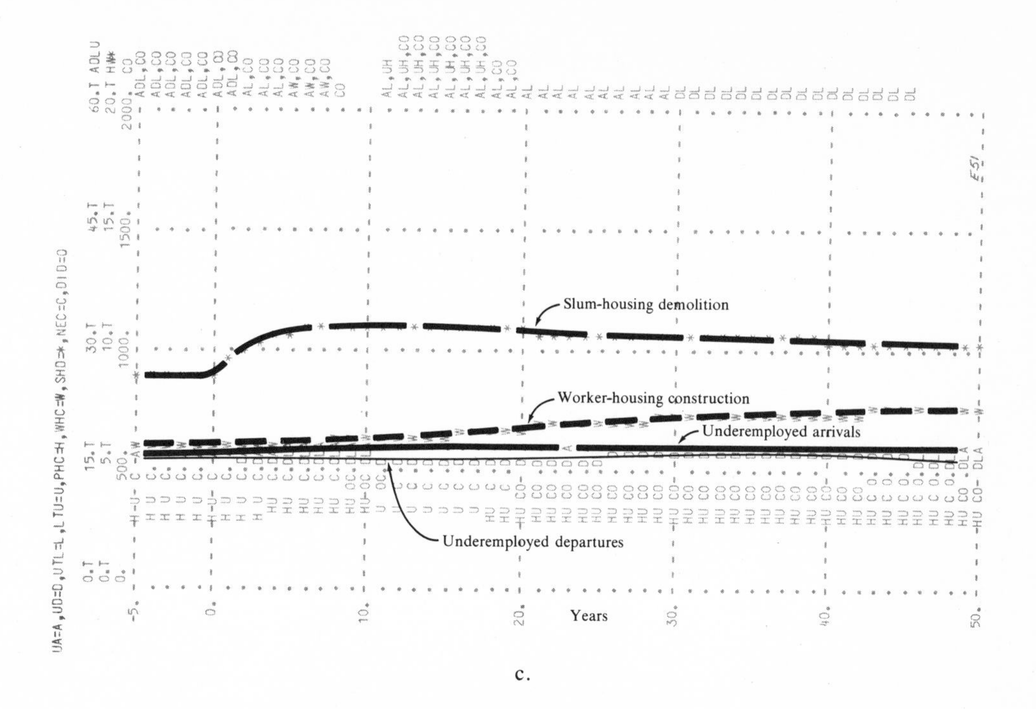

Figure 7-2 Changing the worker-housing normal lifetime from 50 years to 25 years results in only minor changes in the new equilibrium

Source: Reprinted from *Urban Dynamics* by Jay W. Forrester by permission of The MIT Press, Cambridge Massachusetts, Figure B-8.

plete study. A sensitivity study with 87 very small parameter variations requires 87 computer runs. The results obtained with the nominal set of parameter values would be compared with the results obtained by separately varying each parameter. To a first-order approximation, the simple sum of the results from each separate computer run involving the parameters must yield the same results obtained by varying the parameters in a cluster.

In contrast to parameter sensitivity to very small changes, parameter sensitivity results in general change according to the magnitude and direction of the parameter variations. Therefore, each cluster of parameter variations requires an individual test, which makes a complete parameter sensitivity study computationally infeasible. For example, if the constant parameters alone are varied in clusters of five, over 37,000,000 computer runs would be necessary to test all the combinations. The parameter sensitivity testing performed to date indicates a surprising insensitivity of the model to parameter changes. Complex nonlinear feedback systems, like their counterparts in the real world, seem to compensate internally for variations in parameter values. Despite differences in age and location, most real cities display similar patterns in their behavioral characteristics and life cycles. Similar structures within different cities tend to produce similar patterns in the life cycles of the cities, although their physical characteristics (parameter values) may differ widely.

Urban Dynamics offers several examples of significant parameter value changes that produce relatively small behavioral impacts. Figure 7-2 (Figure B-8 in *Urban Dynamics*) shows the results of reducing the normal worker-housing lifetime in the *Urban Dynamics* model from fifty to twenty-five years.

The model compensates for the change, as does the real world, by increasing the rate of worker-housing construction. The system conditions at equilibrium remain virtually unchanged. Figures 7-3 and 7-4 (Figures B-14 and B-15 in *Urban Dynamics*) respectively show the changes needed to keep industrial and housing population densities constant with age and the effects of these changes on the *Urban Dynamics* model. The system readjusts to the new densities by increasing the amount of underemployed housing and decreasing the premium housing so that, overall, most variables return to close to their original equilibrium values. Negative feedback, or goal-seeking behavior, is largely responsible for the *Urban Dynamics* model's insensitivity to parameter changes. For example, Figure 7-5 shows a simple feedback structure. Since the *Urban Dynamics* model contains twenty nonlinearly interlinked system levels, Figure 7-5 does not literally describe the structure of any particular portion of the model; instead, it provides a generic structure that is representative of many feedback loops within the model. The action stream responds to attempts to lessen the difference between the desired level or goal and the observed system level. The amount of corrective action taken depends on the parameter value chosen for the action modulation constant (AMC). Figure 7-6 shows the behavior of the simple structure for two alternative values of AMC and for a constant initial discrepancy. The choice of a specific value for AMC does not affect the equilibrium condition, although transient behavioral characteristics vary considerably with the choice. The structure in Figure 7-5 does not exist in isolation within the *Urban Dynamics* model. Changing conditions within the model give rise to "other influences" on the action stream. The goal-seeking structure generally tends to miti-

Variable Name	**Symbol**	**Equation**	***Urban Dynamics***	**Figure 7-4**
New-enterprise labor	NEL	132.1	20	15
Mature-business labor	MBL	132.2	15	15
Declining-industry labor	DIL	132.3	10	15
New-enterprise management	NEM	37.1	4	2
Mature-business management	MBM	37.2	2	2
Declining-industry management	DIM	37.3	1	2
Premium-housing population density	PHPD	61.1	3	6
Worker-housing population density	WHPD	48.1	6	6
Underemployed-housing population density	UHPD	6.1	12	6

Figure 7-3 Changes in men-per-productive unit and in people-per-housing unit so that densities do not vary with the age of structures.

Source: Reprinted from *Urban Dynamics* by Jay W. Forrester by permission of The MIT Press, Cambridge, Massachusetts, Figure B-14.

gate the effects of other influences on the desired level. The presence of many goal-seeking structures, interlinked in a nonlinear manner, makes a model quite insensitive to parameter variations.

Population Density and Land Area Not Representative. As previously acknowledged, Ingram has correctly noted that the 156-square-mile land area and the equilibrium population density in the *Urban Dynamics* model are not typical of American cities. An adaptation of the model to fit a specific city should permit an evaluation of the possible effects of a significant change in scale. Lowell, Massachusetts, the site of the first major application of urban dynamics in a real city, contains only 5.2 square miles of usable land. Adaptation also requires a simultaneous change of many parameter values in a cluster, and therefore, constitutes a limited test for policy-sensitive parameters. The results of the adaptation of the *Urban Dynamics* model to Lowell are reported in Section 7.4 of this reading.

Model Parameters Biased to Produce Unfavorable Equilibrium. The model parameter values and the definitions of the variables are closely interlinked. Any one can freely redefine terms and choose new parameter values for the *Urban Dynamics* model. Some redefinitions may actually bring numerical relationships in the model more nearly into line with generally accepted values. However, any new parameter values must permit the model's equilibrium conditions to agree with the corresponding conditions of the real city under investigation. Babcock argues that *Urban Dynamics* contains numerical values chosen selectively to create a stagnant equilibrium. This assertion is unsubstantiated and incorrect. The *Urban Dynamics* model was constructed to represent real, observable conditions in our cities. In fact, many American cities display depressed conditions quite similar to the conditions at equilibrium in the *Urban Dynamics* model. Before a policy-oriented model can be used to improve conditions in a deteriorating system, the system conditions must be accurately represented in the model. *Urban Dynamics* attempts to reproduce observable urban conditions, not to bias the policy conclusions. But suppose a modeler believes that a different set of more optimistic parameter values can accurately describe current depressed urban conditions. The modeler must still contend with improving the urban economy and furthering upward economic mobility. The question of revival is crucial for any model whose main purpose is to assist in evaluating alternative urban policies. Redefined parameters and modified parameter values have no relevance unless they improve policy analysis.

7.4 A Test of Policy-Sensitive Parameters

The test reported here responds to the specific criticism that the population density and the land area in *Urban Dynamics* are not typical of most cities. It was designed to determine whether the *Urban Dynamics* revival policies lose their credibility when the population density and land area are adjusted to fit a specific city: Lowell, Massachusetts. The test required a simultaneous change in a cluster of nine parameters. The changes are representative of the alterations necessary to fit the *Urban Dynamics* model to the scale and characteristics of a real city. The test presented here extends

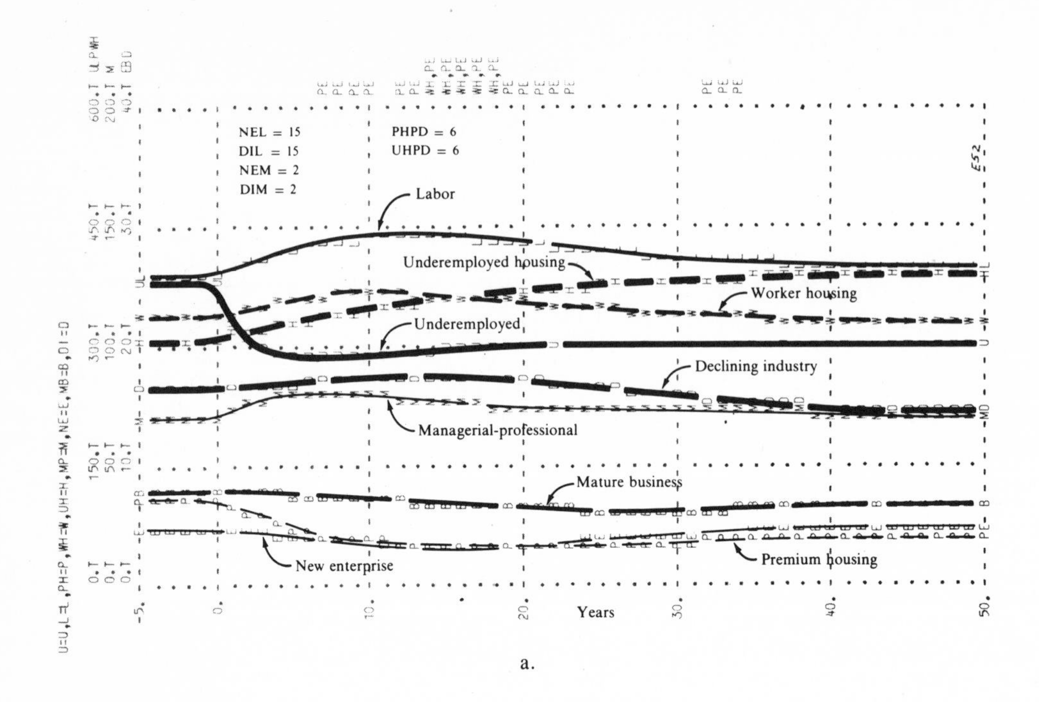
NEL = 15
DIL = 15
NEM = 2
DIM = 2
PHPD = 6
UHPD = 6
Labor
Underemployed housing
Worker housing
Underemployed
Declining industry
Managerial-professional
Mature business
New enterprise
Premium housing
Years

a.

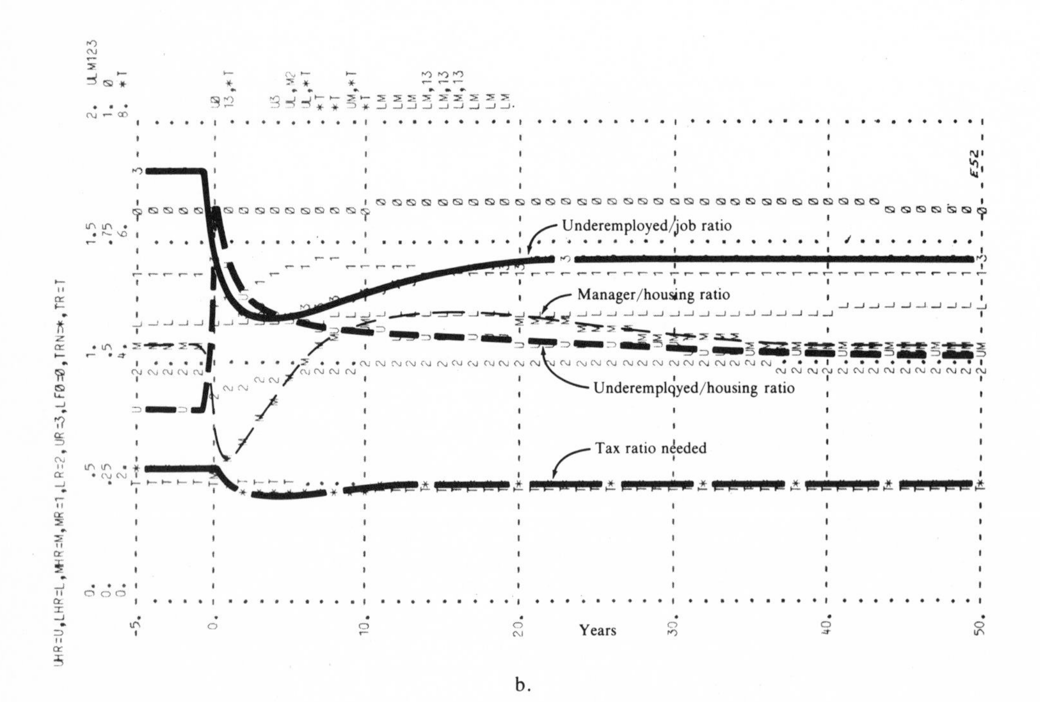
Underemployed/job ratio
Manager/housing ratio
Underemployed/housing ratio
Tax ratio needed
Years

b.

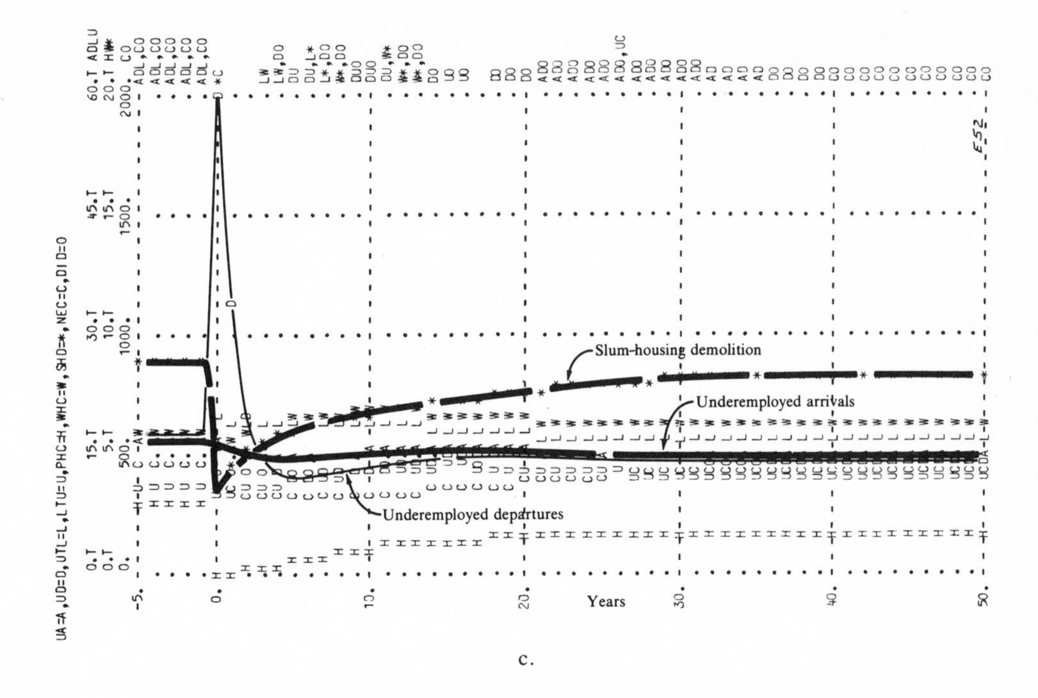

Figure 7-4 The response of the *Urban Dynamics* model to the nine parameter changes in Figure 7-3. Most of the variables tend to seek their original value initial transient.

Source: Reprinted from *Urban Dynamics* by Jay W. Forrester by permission of The MIT Press, Cambridge, Massachusetts, Figure B-15.

those reported in Appendix B of *Urban Dynamics*. It also provides a framework for investigating a suspected set of sensitive parameters to determine their effects on the direction of policy recommendations.

The values for the constants that define land area, housing population densities, family sizes, land per housing unit, and land per production unit in the *Urban Dynamics* model were altered to match observed data for Lowell. The original and new values are listed in Figure 7-7. The life-cycle behavior of the modified model (called the *Lowell* model in this reading) is strikingly similar to Lowell's actual pattern of development. The eleven policies tested in Chapters 4 and 5 of *Urban Dynamics* were resimulated and reevaluated at equilibrium in the *Lowell* model.

In addition to making the parameter changes listed in Figure 7-7, one must also reduce the initial values for all levels in the *Urban Dynamics* model to produce a model that will give characteristic growth behavior. A reduction in initial conditions is necessary because many equilibrium values in the *Lowell* model are smaller than their initial value from the *Urban Dynamics* model. The initial conditions in the *Urban Dynamics* model should therefore be reduced to 1/25 of their value to create a running *Lowell* model suitable for policy testing. To create an equilibrium *Lowell* model equivalent to the equilibrium model used for policy testing in *Urban Dynamics*, one

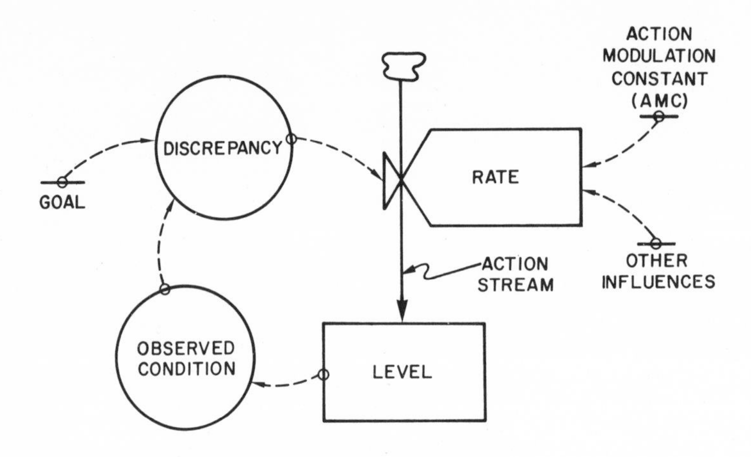

Figure 7-5 Goal-seeking structure

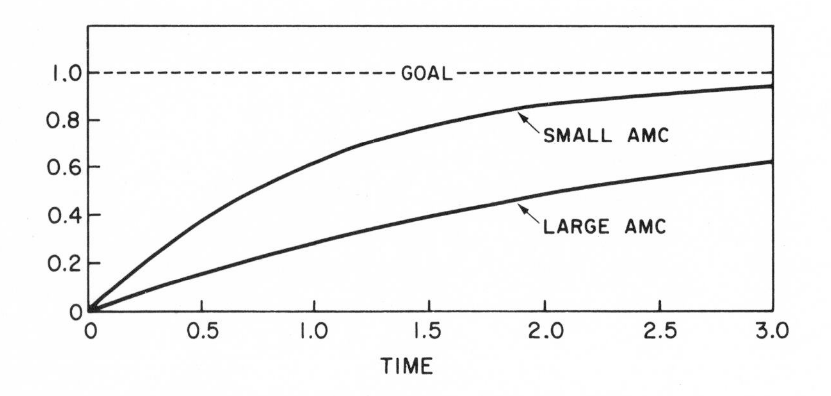

Figure 7-6 Response of goal-seeking structure

should replace the initial conditions described above with the equilibrium conditions obtained at year 300 from the growth run. This procedure is similar to that outlined on p. 216 in *Urban Dynamics*. In Figure 7-9, print-and-plot scales were also adjusted to enhance the resolution of the behavior of levels and rates.

Figure 7-8 compares the equilibrium conditions in the *Urban Dynamics* model and the *Lowell* model. The third column of Figure 7-8 shows the equilibrium conditions reached by the *Lowell* model. They reflect the urban problems in Lowell: high unemployment, underemployed/job ratio UR= 1.71; low upward economic mobility, underemployed to labor net UTLN = 174 men per year (1.7 percent per year of underemployed); and high taxes relative to those in surrounding areas, tax ratio needed TRN = 1.71.

Not surprisingly, equilibrium conditions in the *Lowell* model reflect the problems of an older city even after a significant change in the parameter values. The results provide a specific example of the real-world observation that aging cities experience

(1) Variable Name	(2) Symbol	(3) Units	(4) *Urban Dynamics* Value	(5) *Lowell* Value	(6) Change (%)
Land area	AREA	(acres)	100,000	3,300	−97
Managerial-professional family size	MPFS	(people/ man)	5	3.8	−24
Labor family size	LFS	(people/ man)	6	3.9	−35
Underemployed family size	UFS	(people/ man)	8	4.3	−46
Premium-housing population density	PHPD	(people/ housing unit)	3	5.0	+40
Worker-housing population density	WHPD	(people/ housing unit)	6	7.0	+17
Underemployed-housing population density	UHPD	(people/ housing unit)	12	9.0	−25
Land per house	LPH	(acres/ housing unit)	0.1	0.2	+100
Land per production unit	LPP	(acres/ production unit)	0.2	0.3	+50

Figure 7-7 New parameter values used to modify the *Urban Dynamics* model to reflect the characteristics of Lowell

the same basic problems despite differences in land area, density of industry and housing, and density of population in industry and housing. Even though the simultaneous variation of several changed parameter values brings about a significant shift in the dimensional scale, the equilibrium conditions still describe the problems of an older city suffering from unhealthy economic and social problems. The eleven policies examined in *Urban Dynamics* were reexamined in the *Lowell* model. The analysis that follows focuses specifically on the results of retesting one set of policies: the *Urban Dynamics* revival policies of combined slum-housing demolition and active encouragement of new-enterprise construction. The initiation of the revival policies in the *Lowell* model leads to a transient behavior similar to the corresponding transient behavior shown in *Urban Dynamics*. Figure 7-9 shows the transient behavior of the major levels in the *Lowell* model, and Figure 7-10 (Figure 5-16 in *Urban Dynamics*) shows the corresponding transient behavior of the major levels in the *Urban Dynamics* model. The fourth and fifth columns of Figure 7-8 list, respectively, the new equilib-

(1) Variable Name	(2) Symbol	(3) *Lowell* Model Equilibrium Value	(4) *Lowell* Model Value After 50 Years	(5) Change (%) in *Lowell* Model Values	(6) Change in Figure 5-17 of *Urban Dynamics* (%)
New enterprise	NE	152	259	+70	+63
Mature business	MB	244	412	+69	+64
Declining industry	DI	479	660	+38	+35
Premium housing	PH	1,530	2,140	+40	+38
Worker housing	WH	5,380	7,390	+37	+34
Underemployed housing	UH	5,470	2,920	−47	−43
Managerial-professional	MP	2,180	3,420	+57	+53
Labor	L	11,760	18,450	+57	+53
Underemployed	U	10,530	8,760	−17	−11
Manager/housing ratio	MHR	1.08	1.22	+13	+11
Labor/housing ratio	LHR	1.22	1.39	+14	+14
Underemployed/housing ratio	UHR	0.92	1.43	+55	+58
Manager/job ratio	MR	1.38	1.36	−1	−1
Labor/job ratio	LR	0.98	0.98	0	+1
Underemployed/job ratio	UR	1.71	0.91	−47	−41
Tax ratio needed	TRN	1.71	1.06	−38	−33
Underemployed to labor net	UTLN	174	246	+41	+67

Figure 7-8 Comparison of changes caused by the revival policies of combined slum-housing demolition (SHDR = 0.05) and encouragement of new-enterprise construction (NECN = 0.07) between the *Lowell* model and the *Urban Dynamics* model

rium values in the *Lowell* model after the revival policies have been applied for fifty years and the percentage changes from the initial equilibrium values. In all instances, each variable moves in the same direction and within a few percentage points of the corresponding changes in the *Urban Dynamics* model variables (column 6 of Figure 7-8). Because the revival policies produce such similar changes in each model, the conclusion that the parameter alterations tabulated in Figure 7-7 do not affect the direction of corrective management actions indicated by the revival policies seems to be justified. In other words, the revival policies—the demolition of slum housing and

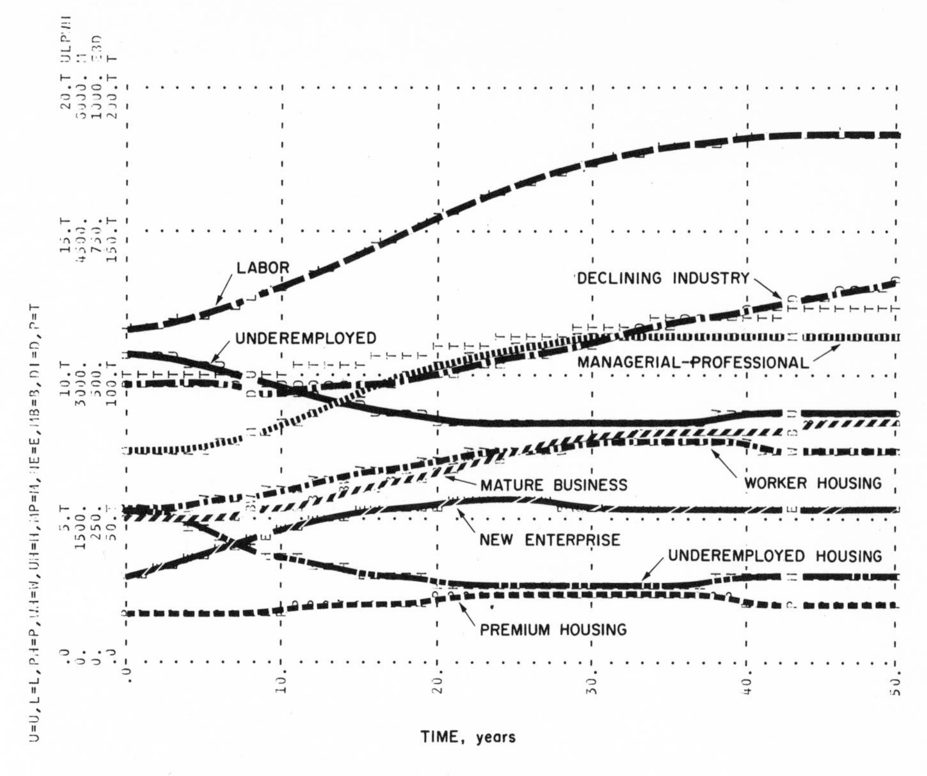

Figure 7-9 Response of major levels in the *Lowell* model to the *Urban Dynamics* revival program

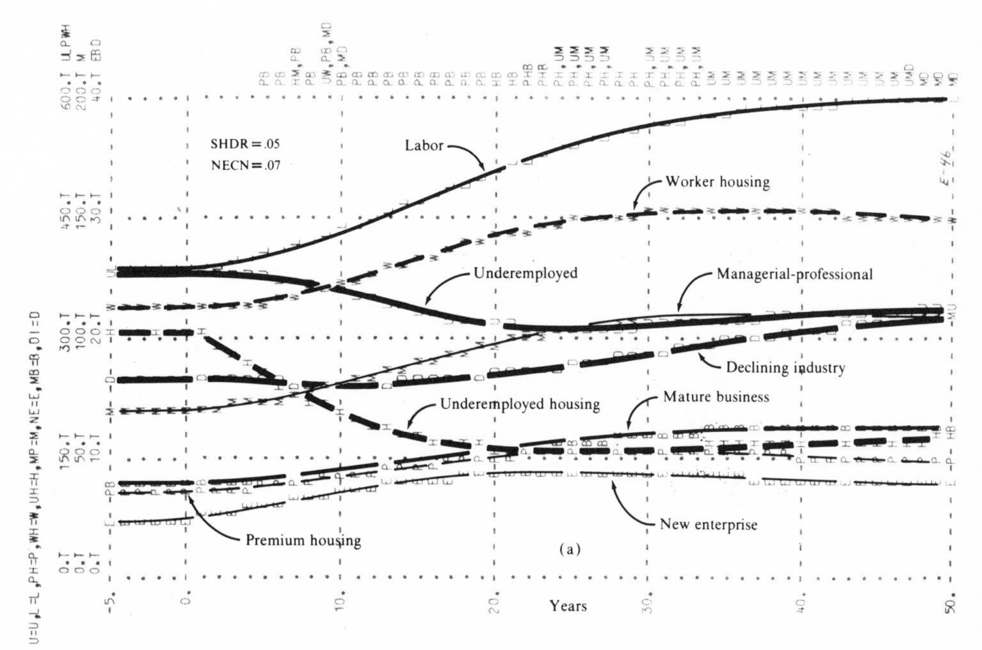

Figure 7-10 Response of major levels in the *Urban Dynamics* model to the revival program

Source: Reprinted from *Urban Dynamics* by Jay W. Forrester by permission of The MIT Press, Cambridge, Massachusetts, Figure 5-16(a).

Variable Name	Symbol	*Lowell* Model Equilibrium Value	Policy 1 Job Program Change (%) *Lowell* Model	*Urban Dynamics* Model
Labor-to-underemployed ratio	LUR	1.12	−9	−12
New enterprise	NE	152	−3	−8
Mature business	MB	244	−2	−3
Declining industry	DI	479	+1	+1
Premium housing	PH	1,530	−3	−4
Worker housing	WH	5,380	−3	−4
Underemployed housing	UH	5,470	+4	+5
Managerial-professional	MP	2,180	−2	−3
Labor	L	11,760	−1	−2
Underemployed	U	10,530	+8	+10
Manager/housing ratio	MHR	1.08	+1	0
Labor/housing ratio	LHR	1.22	+3	+2
Underemployed/housing ratio	UHR	0.92	+7	+5
Manager/job ratio	MR	1.38	0	0
Labor/job ratio	LR	0.98	+1	+1
Underemployed/job ratio	UR	1.71	−7	−6
Tax ratio needed	TRN	1.71	+9	+14
Underemployed-to-labor net	UTLN	174	+22	+24

Figure 7-11 Comparative changes resulting from the policy on the *Lowell* model and on the *Urban Dynamics* model

the encouragement of new enterprise—retain their merit for old industrial cities as a means of improving internal city conditions relative to the outside environment.

7.5 Ten Other Policy Tests

The changes in the system conditions in the *Lowell* model after fifty years for ten other policies, in comparison with the corresponding changes in the *Urban Dynamics* model, are tabulated in Figure 7-11. The ten policies are:

1. job program (UJPC = 0.1)
2. training program (UTR = 0.05)
3. financial subsidy (TPCS = 100)
4. low-cost-housing construction (LCHPC = 0.05)
5. worker-housing construction (WHCR = 0.02)
6. premium-housing construction (PHCR = 0.05)
7. new-enterprise construction (NECR = 0.02)
8. declining-industry demolition (DIDR = 0.05)
9. slum-housing demolition (SHDR = 0.05)
10. discouraging housing construction (SHDR = 0.05, WHCN = 0.015)

Policy 2 Training Program Change (%)		Policy 3 Financial Subsidy Change (%)		Policy 4 Low-Cost-Housing Construction Change (%)		Policy 5 Worker-Housing Construction Change (%)	
Lowell Model	*Urban Dynamics* Model	*Lowell* Model	*Urban Dynamics* Model	*Lowell* Model	*Urban Dynamics* Model	*Lowell* Model	*Urban Dynamics* Model
+21	+21	−7	−6	−34	−30	−1	−1
+19	+18	+1	0	−55	−49	−16	−18
+24	+24	+1	+1	−53	−45	−20	−22
+2	+1	−1	−1	−9	−6	−12	−13
+10	+7	+1	+1	−41	−34	−19	−20
+7	+8	−2	−1	−39	−31	+5	+6
−2	−1	+4	+3	+53	+45	+8	+10
+15	+15	+2	+2	−41	−34	−17	−18
+22	+23	+1	+1	−37	−30	−13	−13
0	+1	+8	+8	−6	−1	−8	−12
+7	+7	+2	+1	+3	0	+3	+3
+14	+14	+3	+3	+2	+1	−16	−18
+2	+2	+4	+5	−38	−32	−15	−20
0	0	+2	+2	0	0	0	0
+7	+9	+1	+1	−5	−4	+2	+3
−5	−2	+9	+9	+35	+30	+11	+8
−10	−8	+8	+8	+43	+36	+2	−4
+188	+205	+39	+40	−37	−31	−49	−45

Figure 7-11 continued

Figure 7-11 lists a number of the important variables that are common to the *Urban Dynamics* model and the *Lowell* model. The variable and its model symbol are given in the first two columns; the next column contains the equilibrium value of those variables from the *Lowell* model. The remaining pairs of columns in Figure 7-11 pertain to each of the ten policy tests conducted on the *Lowell* and *Urban Dynamics* models.

Slight differences between the models in tests of each of the ten policies may be noteworthy from the point of view of understanding a specific city's physical characteristics. However, the differences are too small to affect the relative desirability of the policies. The main conclusion from the comparative policy tests is that revival policies—the encouragement of new enterprise and the demolition of slum housing—are the most effective of the examined policies for improving the economic and social conditions in a city.

An examination of the slum-housing demolition policy may help to explain why three of the tested policies appear to be slightly more effective in the *Lowell* model. Slum-housing demolition, discouraging housing construction, and slum-housing de-

Variable Name	Symbol	*Lowell* Model Equilibrium Value	Policy 6 Premium-Housing Construction Change (%) *Lowell* Model	*Urban Dynamics* Model
Labor-to-underemployed ratio	LUR	1.12	−1	−1
New enterprise	NE	152	−3	−5
Mature business	MB	244	−5	−6
Declining industry	DI	479	−4	−5
Premium housing	PH	1,530	+3	+1
Worker housing	WH	5,380	0	0
Underemployed housing	UH	5,470	+2	+3
Managerial-professional	MP	2,180	−3	−5
Labor	L	11,760	−3	−4
Underemployed	U	10,530	−2	−3
Manager/housing ratio	MHR	1.08	−5	−6
Labor/housing ratio	LHR	1.22	−3	−4
Underemployed/housing ratio	UHR	0.92	−3	−5
Manager/job ratio	MR	1.38	+1	+1
Labor/job ratio	LR	0.98	0	+1
Underemployed/job ratio	UR	1.71	+3	+3
Tax ratio needed	TRN	1.71	+1	+1
Underemployed to labor net	UTLN	174	−12	−13

Figure 7-11 Comparative changes resulting from the policy on the *Lowell* model and on the *Urban Dynamics* model

molition combined with new-enterprise construction have similarities that permit an extension of the reasoning for one to the other two.

The slum-housing demolition policy (9) is slightly more effective in the *Lowell* model than in the *Urban Dynamics* model. Comparing the two models after fifty years of the policy, the *Lowell* model exhibits a roughly 5 percent larger increase in production units (enterprise activity); a larger increase in premium and worker housing; a greater reduction in underemployed housing; a 15 percent greater increase in the labor/underemployed ratio LUR, indicating higher average skills and incomes; a 5 percent greater reduction in the underemployed/job ratio UR, indicating more favorable employment opportunities for the underemployed; and a 3 percent greater reduction in tax ratio needed TRN. Only the upward mobility (underemployed to labor net UTLN) has changed in an unfavorable direction. In the fiftieth year the *Lowell* model projects a UTLN 23 percent lower than before the policy was applied. In contrast, the *Urban Dynamics* model shows a slight increase in UTLN. Except for a similar case involving the policy of discouraging housing construction, the corresponding changes exhibited by both models for each of the ten policies have identical directions (and similar magnitudes). Why is the slum-housing demolition policy more

Policy 7 New-Enterprise Construction Change (%)		Policy 8 Declining-Industry Demolition Change (%)		Policy 9 Slum-Housing Demolition Change (%)		Policy 10 Discouraging Housing Construction Change (%)	
Lowell Model	*Urban Dynamics* Model	*Lowell* Model	*Urban Dynamics* Model	*Lowell* Model	*Urban Dynamics* Model	*Lowell* Model	*Urban Dynamics* Model
+5	+4	−1	−1	+77	+62	+116	+93
+19	+21	+24	+26	+50	+45	+70	+65
+24	+27	+23	+24	+49	+45	+69	+65
+42	+44	−58	−61	+13	+9	+20	+15
+13	+14	−1	−2	+33	+30	+51	+48
−3	−1	−1	−2	+39	+34	+41	+36
+1	+3	−1	−3	−47	−44	−57	−54
+25	+27	0	−1	+39	+35	+56	+52
+21	+24	−8	−10	+40	+35	+53	+48
+15	+20	−6	−8	−21	−16	−29	−23
+11	+11	−3	−4	+5	+4	+4	+3
+25	+26	−7	−8	0	+1	+8	+9
+14	+16	−5	−6	+48	+49	+64	+68
−1	−3	+1	+1	+1	+1	+1	+1
−7	−7	+2	+2	+4	+4	+3	+4
−19	−17	+6	+6	−38	−33	−51	−44
0	+5	−8	−9	−36	−33	−46	−41
+131	+130	−22	−24	−23	+1	−16	+29

Figure 7-11 continued

effective in the *Lowell* model? Figure 7-12 shows that at equilibrium, before the policy application, natural forces demolish a smaller fraction of housing each year in the *Lowell* model than in the *Urban Dynamics* model. However, in the tenth year of the policy implementation, the combination of natural forces and the demolition program eliminates a larger fraction of housing in the *Lowell* model. The demolition program, which removes 5 percent of the underemployed housing each year, is more effective because the *Lowell* model contains a higher proportion of underemployed housing than the *Urban Dynamics* model. Moreover, the *Lowell* model has a higher proportion of underemployed housing because the underemployed (and their landlords) respond to a tighter housing market by more carefully maintaining their structures. Consequently, housing structures have a longer average lifetime than in the *Urban Dynamics* model.

Since the slum-housing demolition policy removes a higher proportion of housing each year in the *Lowell* model, especially during the first years of implementation, more land becomes vacant for job-intensive industry than in the *Urban Dynamics* model. The additional space further stimulates the construction of new enterprise, premium housing, and worker housing. The increased employment opportunities and better housing availability attract more managers and laborers and provide more oppor-

Policy-Related Variables	*Lowell* Model Year			*Urban Dynamics* Model Year		
	0	10	50	0	10	50
Fraction of housing demolished each year: SHD/(PH + WH + UH)	0.026	0.0215	0.0118	0.029	0.0205	0.0115
Fraction of housing demolished by demolition program each year: SHDP/(PH + WH + UH)	0	0.0161	0.0117	0	0.0150	0.0093
Fraction of housing demolished by normal pressures each year: (SHD − SHDP)/(PH + WH + UH)	0.026	0.0054	0.0001	0.029	0.0055	0.0022

Figure 7-12 Comparison between the two models of changes in housing demolition resulting from the slum-housing-demolition policy.

tunities for the upward socioeconomic mobility of the underemployed. Why does the net upward mobility of the underemployed, UTLN, appear to be unfavorable in the fiftieth year of the slum-housing demolition policy in the *Lowell* model: Figure 7-13 shows that the *Lowell* model, compared with the *Urban Dynamics* model, projects a higher fraction of underemployed moving to the labor category (underemployed to labor/underemployed UTL/U) at equilibrium in the tenth year and in the fiftieth year. An underemployed person in the *Lowell* model has a higher probability of moving to a labor job. On the other hand, at equilibrium both models indicate the same fraction of labor moving to underemployed (labor to underemployed/labor LTU/L, or the labor-layoff fraction LLF). After implementation of the policy, the labor-layoff fraction LLF increases in both models as the labor/job ratio LR rises. In the fiftieth year the *Lowell* model exhibits a slightly higher value of LLF than the *Urban Dynamics* model. In both models a laborer has a higher probability of being layed off in the fiftieth year than at equilibrium (but the probability in the fiftieth year is slightly higher in the *Lowell* model). Both an increased in-migration of labor and a greater upward mobility of the underemployed impair labor employment conditions (raise the labor/job ratio LR) and therefore increase LLF. Although the increase in the labor-layoff fraction LLF after implementation of the policy tends to reduce the underemployed to labor net UTLN, or mobility, in both models, the large reduction of UTLN below its equilibrium value in the *Lowell* model results primarily from a shift in the size of the levels (underemployed and labor) that determine the two mobility rates. After fifty years the *Lowell* model projects a 5 percent greater reduction in underemployed than the *Urban Dynamics* model; fewer underemployed remain to benefit from the better chances of moving to labor (higher underemployed to labor/underemployed UTL/U). At the same time the *Lowell* model projects a 5 percent greater increase in labor L; more laborers are likely to be layed off (higher LLF). Therefore, the *Lowell* model displays a net underemployed mobility UTLN (the algebraic sum of the two flows) lower in the fiftieth year than at equilibrium. After the policy application, UTLN decreases in the *Lowell* model instead of

Variable Name	*Lowell* Model			*Urban Dynamics* Model		
	Year			Year		
	0	10	50	0	10	50
Underemployed-to-labor net: UTLN	174	225	134	5,497	7,314	5,578
Underemployed-to-labor net/underemployed: UTLN/U	0.0166	0.0242	0.0161	0.0146	0.0213	0.0178
Fraction of underemployed moving to labor: UTL/U	0.049	0.062	0.081	0.045	0.055	0.071
Fraction of labor moving to underemployed: LLF or LTU/L	0.029	0.028	0.033	0.029	0.028	0.032

Figure 7-13 Comparison between the respective components of net underemployed economic mobilities in the models at equilibrium, in the tenth year and in the fiftieth year after initiation of the slum-housing-demolition policy.

increasing as in the *Urban Dynamics* model. The net upward mobility of the underemployed should improve through implementation of policies that provide additional labor jobs and some simultaneous compensation to prevent increased labor in-migration. The *Urban Dynamics* revival program, combining slum-housing demolition with the encouragement of new-enterprise construction, can achieve such an improvement in stagnant industrial cities. Both models exhibit a substantially higher net upward mobility of the underemployed in the fiftieth year of the revival program than before its initiation.

7.6 Conclusions

The issue of selecting parameter values for dynamic social systems models has subtle and difficult aspects. For a model having the complexity and size of the *Urban Dynamics* model, empirical data are not available in either sufficient quantity or sufficient quality to have a strong impact on the parameter selection process. Moreover, even if empirical data should become available, the capability of current statistical estimation techniques for extracting the model coefficients remains highly questionable.

In light of the state of affairs in empirical data availability and statistical estimation techniques, policy models, such as the *Urban Dynamics* model, must be structured to minimize their dependence on empirical data. Parameter sensitivity tests must ensure that policy conclusions do not change if the parameter values vary over reasonable ranges of values. Although the multiloop nonlinear structure of the *Urban Dynamics* model precludes an exhaustive parameter sensitivity study, the limited testing performed to date indicates that the model parameters are sufficiently precise to support the *Urban Dynamics* policy analysis. Future testing should focus on locating and evaluating possible policy-sensitive parameters. The development of improved parameter-sensitivity evaluation methods and increased confidence in and refinement of the statistical estimation techniques remain far from being accomplished.

Notes

1. Jerome Rothenberg, "Problems in the Modeling of Urban Development: A Review Article on *Urban Dynamics*, by Jay W. Forrester," *Journal of Urban Economics*, vol. 1 (1974), no. 1, pp. 1–20.

2. Gregory K. Ingram, book review of *Urban Dynamics*, in *Journal of the American Institute of Planners*, May 1970, pp. 206–208.

3. D. L. Babcock, "Assumptions in Forrester's *Urban Dynamics* Model and Their Implications," *IEEE Transactions on Systems, Man, and Cybernetics*, vol. SML-2, no. 2 (April 1972), pp. 143–149.

4. See Walter W. Schroeder III and John M. Strongman, "Adapting *Urban Dynamics* to Lowell," in *Readings in Urban Dynamics*, vol. 1, ed. Nathaniel J. Mass (Cambridge, Mass.: Wright-Allen Press, 1974), pp. 199–223. Schroeder and Strongman derive the parameter changes for the *Lowell* model and provide detailed comparisons of Lowell's history with the *Lowell* model's behavior.

5. See F. M. Fisher, *The Identification Problem in Econometrics* (New York: McGraw-Hill, 1966), or A. P. Sage and J. L. Melsa, *System Identification* (New York: Academic Press, 1971).

6. For a general discussion of the criteria to be used in assessing model validity, see Jay W. Forrester, *Industrial Dynamics* (Cambridge, Mass.: The MIT Press, 1961), chap. 13.

7. See C. T. Leondes, *Theory and Applications of Kalman Filtering*, U.S. Department of Commerce, National Technical Information Service, AD704-30D (Washington, D.C., 1970), chap. 4.

8. A random process whose statistical behavior can be inferred from a single data sample is termed ergodic. The assumption is crucial for applying statistical estimation techniques to social systems, but it cannot be justified mathematically.

9. Peter M. Senge, "An Experimental Evaluation of Generalized Least Squares Estimation," System Dynamics Group Memorandum D-1944-7 (Cambridge, Mass.: M.I.T., 1975).

8

Multiplicative Formulations in *Urban Dynamics*

Peter M. Senge

Urban Dynamics *has been criticized for employing multiplicative formulations instead of the additive formulations commonly used in modeling. This reading argues that multiplicative formulations are superior because, unlike additive formulations, they can represent behavior under extreme as well as normal conditions. This wide range is of considerable value in the* Urban Dynamics *model, which was designed to help local officials move their cities toward substantially different conditions. The model, in any case, is demonstrably insensitive to the use of additive instead of multiplicative formulations.*

8
Multiplicative Formulations in *Urban Dynamics*

8.1 Introduction

This reading pursues a two-fold strategy for explaining the use of multiplicative formulations in the *Urban Dynamics* model. First, the multiplicative formulation is contrasted with the more widely used additive formulation as a causal influence on underemployed migration. Second, sensitivity analysis further establishes the adequacy of multiplicative formulations. If the basic behavior and policy responses of the model prove to be insensitive to the distinction between multiplicative and additive forms, then the multiplicative formulations, which cover both normal and extreme conditions, should be retained. Explaining and justifying the use of multiplicative formulations in the *Urban Dynamics* model is part of the ongoing task of model verification. According to Jay W. Forrester, model verification entails, in order of decreasing importance: (1) a justification of the model's scope and boundary, (2) an explicit statement and explanation of the hypothesized interactions between system levels and rates of flow, and (3) a justification of the parameter values chosen.[1] Analyzing the use of multiplicative formulations belongs to the second category—defending the hypothesized relationships. The explanation of multiplicative formulations does not involve a justification of the specific hypothesized input variables themselves; instead, the argument centers on the use of multiplicative formulations as opposed to the use of alternative formulations.

The *Urban Dynamics* model incorporates the hypothesis that a multiplicative combination of forces arising from housing availability (UHR), job availability (UR), available public services based on the tax per capita ratio (TPCR), and perceived economic mobility (UMP) determines the percentage of underemployed in-migration (UA/U + L). The relationship can be expressed as follows:[2]

$$UA/U + L = K \times g_1\,(UHR) \times g_2\,(UR) \times g_3\,(TPCR) \times g_4\,(UM), \qquad (8.1)$$

where the univariate functions, for example, g_1 (UHR), are some general nonlinear functions. The general nonlinear functions are the "multipliers" in *Urban Dynamics*. The following discussion contrasts the effects of equation (1) for computing the underemployed arrivals multiplier to the effects of the corresponding alternative additive formulation:

$$UA/U + L = K + G_1\,(UHR) + G_2\,(UR) + G_3\,(TPCR) + G_4\,(UM), \qquad (8.2)$$

where the univariate functions, G_1 (UHR) and so on, embody the same basic shapes and parameter values as the multipliers in the multiplicative formulation.

8.2 Multiplicative Formulations Plausible in Extreme Conditions

Forrester briefly states the rationale for choosing a multiplicative rather than an additive formulation for the migration rate in *Urban Dynamics* (p. 137). His reasoning is based on the expected performance of the modeled system in extreme conditions. If housing availability drops to zero, Forrester argues, the in-migration rate should also drop to near zero, regardless of the availability of jobs, the tax situation, or the perceived socioeconomic mobility. The representation of such a prevailing influence requires a multiplicative formulation; an additive formulation cannot perform the necessary task. In applying such reasoning for each input to underemployed migrations, Forrester has adopted a standard rarely applied in other modeling methodologies: a good model formulation should be plausible even if the model is pushed into an extreme operating region rarely observed in real life. The condition of zero housing availability is an extreme condition. Similar reasoning underlies all multiplicative formulations in the *Urban Dynamics* model.

8.3 Model Behavior with Underemployed Arrivals Formulated as an Additive Relationship

In general, both additive and multiplicative formulations are approximations of more complex multivariate relationships. Therefore, the question arises: Is an additive or a multiplicative relationship more appropriate for the underemployed in-migration rate in the normal operating regions of the urban system?

A test of the multiplicative and additive formulations against real-world data offers one way of responding to the question. A test might be carried out using statistical estimation methods, but they are fraught with problems that have been discussed elsewhere.[3] Both additive and multiplicative formulations of the underemployed in-migration rate are highly nonlinear and contain significant time delays. Moreover, the task of discriminating between the additive and the multiplicative forms would require an investigation of the entire life cycle of the *Urban Dynamics* model. The span of time implied by such a test far exceeds available data bases. A different approach might rely on testing model sensitivity to the assumption of a multiplicative combination of forces in underemployed migrations. For such a test, an additive formulation would be substituted for the original multiplicative formulation. The investigator could then assess the consequences for the overall system behavior (from year 0 to 250) and policy analysis. That test would require no significant changes in the model structure or parameters other than transforming the multiplicative formulation to an additive formulation. (See the appendix to this reading for the derivation of the additive formulations.) Figure 8-1 (Figures 3-1a and 3-1b from *Urban Dynamics*) displays the basic growth and stagnation behavior of the *Urban Dynamics* model, including the behavior of system levels and significant auxiliary relationships. Figure 8-2 shows consequences for system behavior of transforming the function for computing the percentage of underemployed in-migration UA/(U + L), as shown in equation 8.1, to an additive formulation, as shown in equation 8.2.

Underemployed migration is one of the most sensitive multiplicative formulations in the *Urban Dynamics* model. When the function is transformed to an additive formulation, however, the overall behavioral characteristics of the model do not change. All system levels rise, undergo a minor oscillation (which is less damped with the additive formulation), and equilibrate. The behavior of UR (underemployed/job ratio), UHR (underemployed/housing ratio), and TRN (tax ratio needed) still conveys the same characteristic urban problems of rising unemployment, abandoned housing, and a heavy tax burden imposed by an unfavorable population distribution. The preceding analysis illustrates the relatively minor consequences for the overall system behavior if a single multiplicative formulation is changed to an additive formulation. Are model-based policy tests sensitive to the transformation? The question of

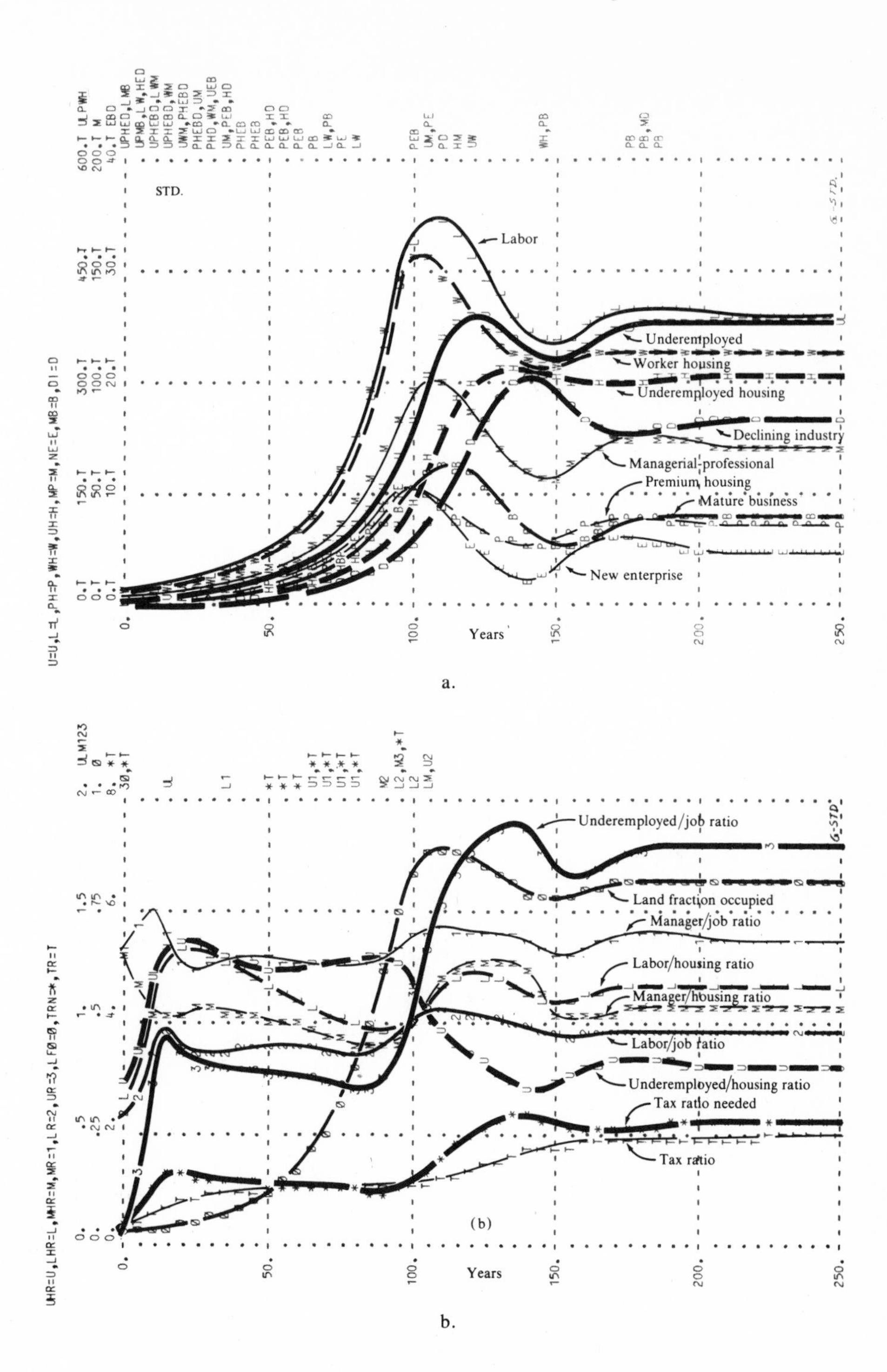

Figure 8-1 Urban development, maturity, and stagnation. Figure 8-la shows the major levels, and Figure 8-1b shows the important ratios.

Source: Reprinted from *Urban Dynamics* by Jay W. Forrester by permission of The MIT Press, Cambridge, Massachusetts, Figure 3-1.

policy sensitivity can be resolved by repeating the sensitivity test for each policy analyzed with the *Urban Dynamics* model. The task has been carried out elsewhere.[4] The results of only two tests—the hypothetical programs of slum-housing demolition and low-cost-housing construction—are reviewed here. They should serve as good examples because the relative beneficence or disutility of each program depends strongly upon underemployed migrations. Figure 8-3 (Figure 5-10 in *Urban Dynamics*) shows the results of the slum-housing demolition program analyzed in *Urban Dynamics*. Figure 8-4 shows the results for the same policy test with an additive formulation used for underemployed migrations.

The test for the slum-housing-demolition program reveals high insensitivity to the additive transformation. None of the qualitative results that led Forrester to favor slum-housing demolition as a revival policy disappear when the policy is reassessed with an additive formulation for underemployed migrations. Furthermore, If reexamined in the presence of an additive migration formulation, the low-cost-housing program has the same negative impact shown in *Urban Dynamics*. Figure 8-5 (Figure 4-8 in *Urban Dynamics*) shows the run from *Urban Dynamics*. Figure 8-6 shows the

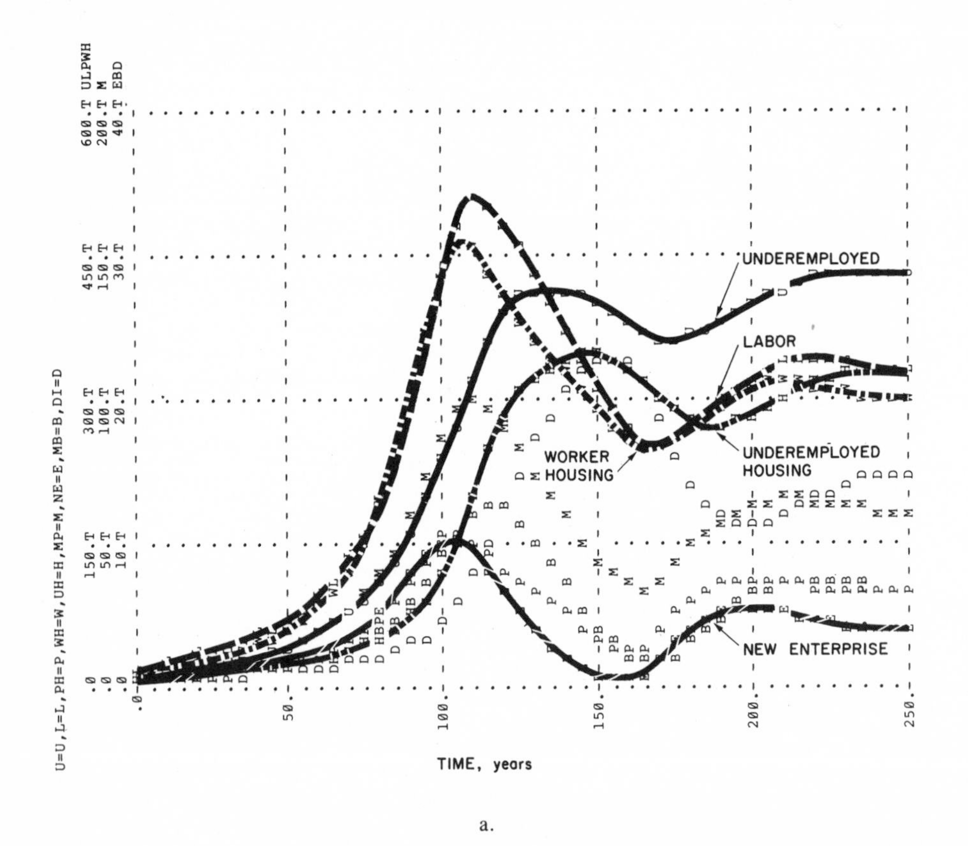

Figure 8-2 Urban behavior with an additive underemployed migration formulation substituted for the original multiplicative version in Figure 8-1

same run with an additive migration formulation. In both Figure 8-2 and Figure 8-6, the additive formulation causes a slower equilibration than the *Urban Dynamics* model. However, this minor shift in behavior has no impact on the pattern of a rising underemployed/job ratio (UR) and tax ratio needed (TRN).

The tests presented here show no significant sensitivity of the tested policies to the choice of an additive or a multiplicative formulation for underemployed migrations. In fact, none of the policies evaluated in *Urban Dynamics* drive that model into an operating region where additive and multiplicative formulations have divergent impacts. However, the same conclusions might not hold for new, untested policies. So far, analysis with the *Urban Dynamics* model has established an operating region that is insensitive to the formulation for underemployed migrations. But no one can say whether new policies will cause the system to move outside the region of established insensitivity.

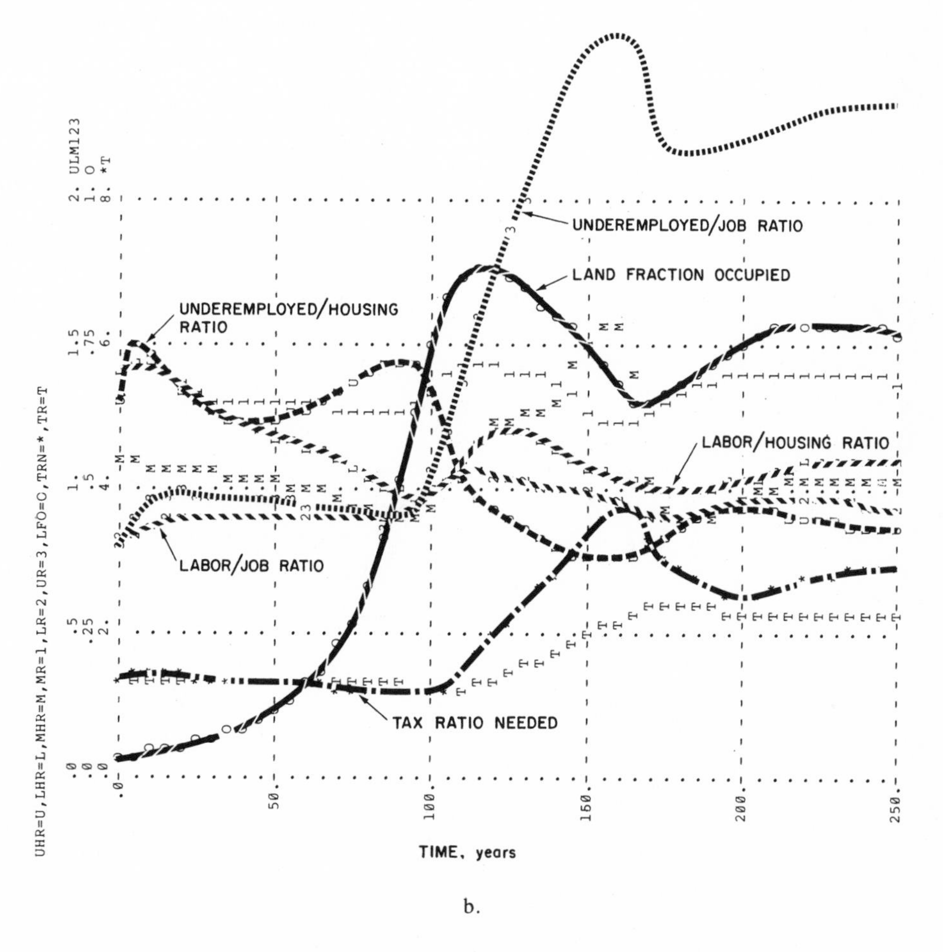

b.

Figure 8-2 cont'd. (The portion of the underemployed/job ratio curve which appears outside the computer grid was plotted from a computer printout of the variable values. This was done to maintain the uniformity of scale.)

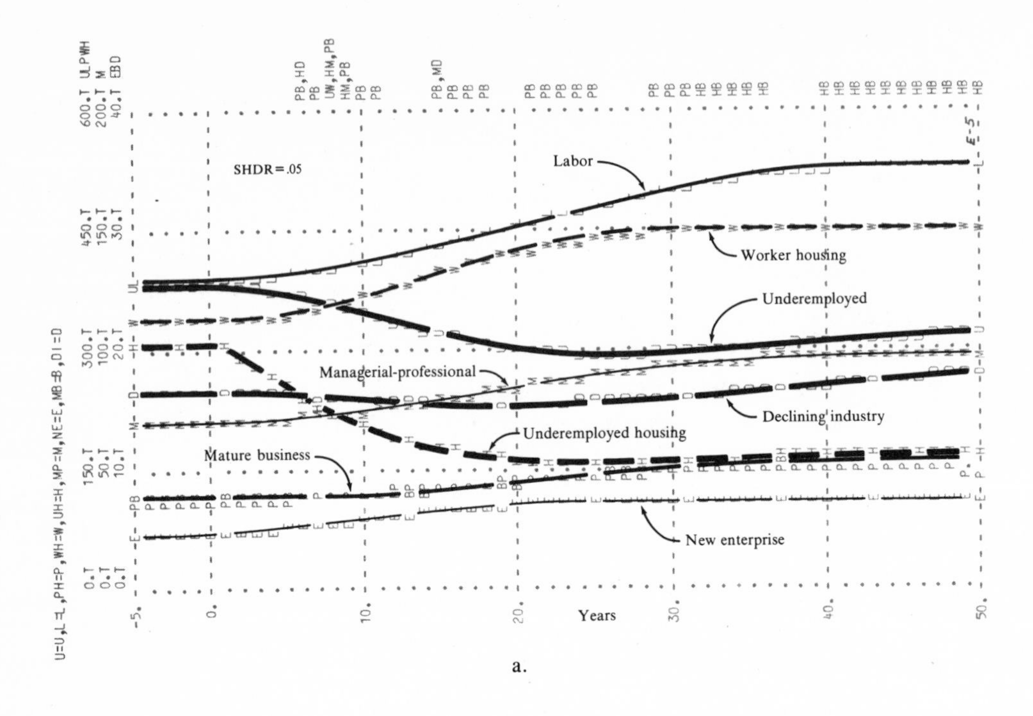

a.

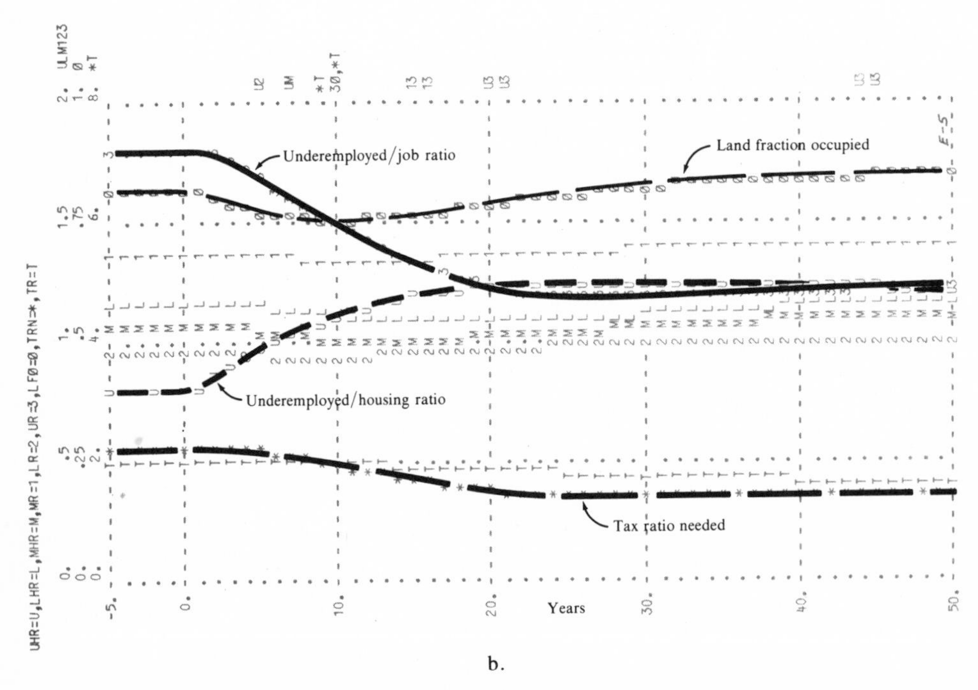

b.

Figure 8-3 Slum-housing demolition that removes 5 percent of underemployed housing each year

Source: Reprinted from *Urban Dynamics* by Jay W. Forrester by permission of The MIT Press, Cambridge, Massachusetts, Figure 5-10.

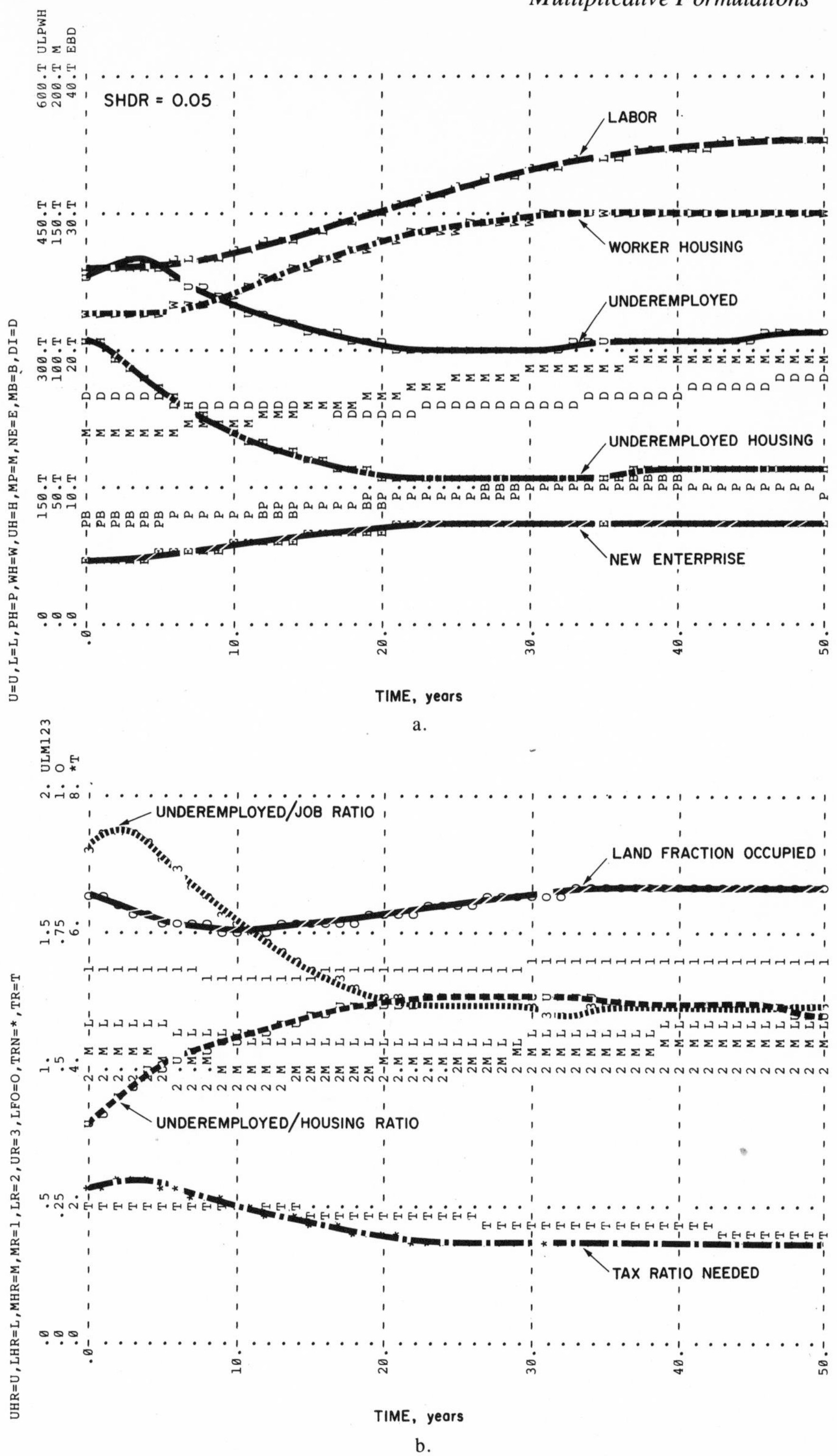

Figure 8-4 The 5 percent demolition program tested on a model containing an additive formulation for underemployed migrations

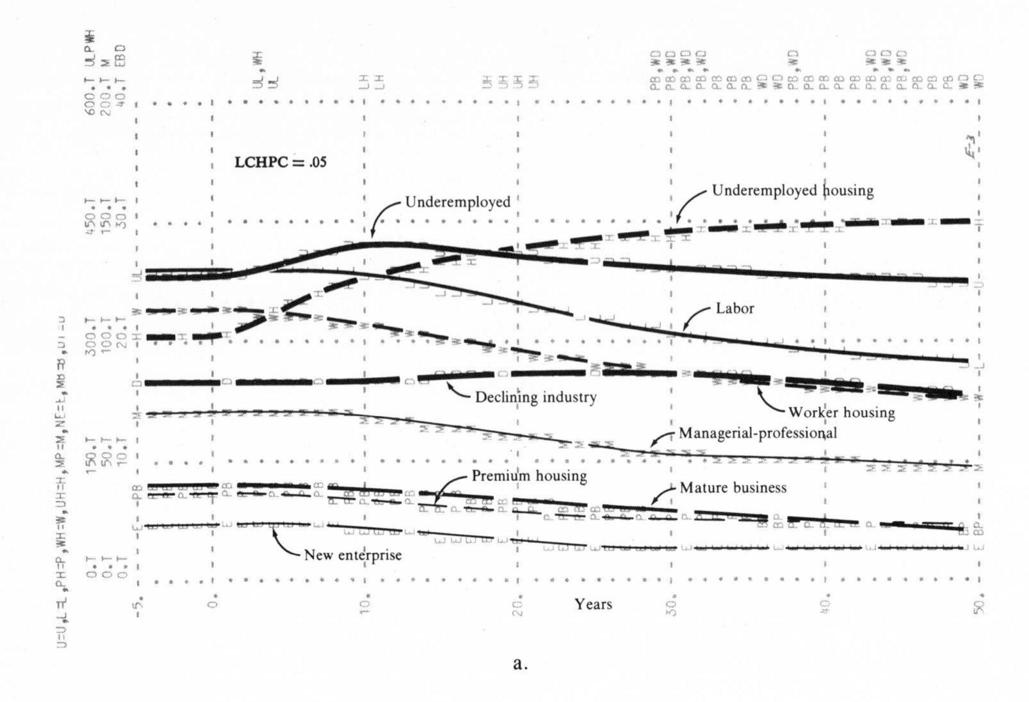

a.

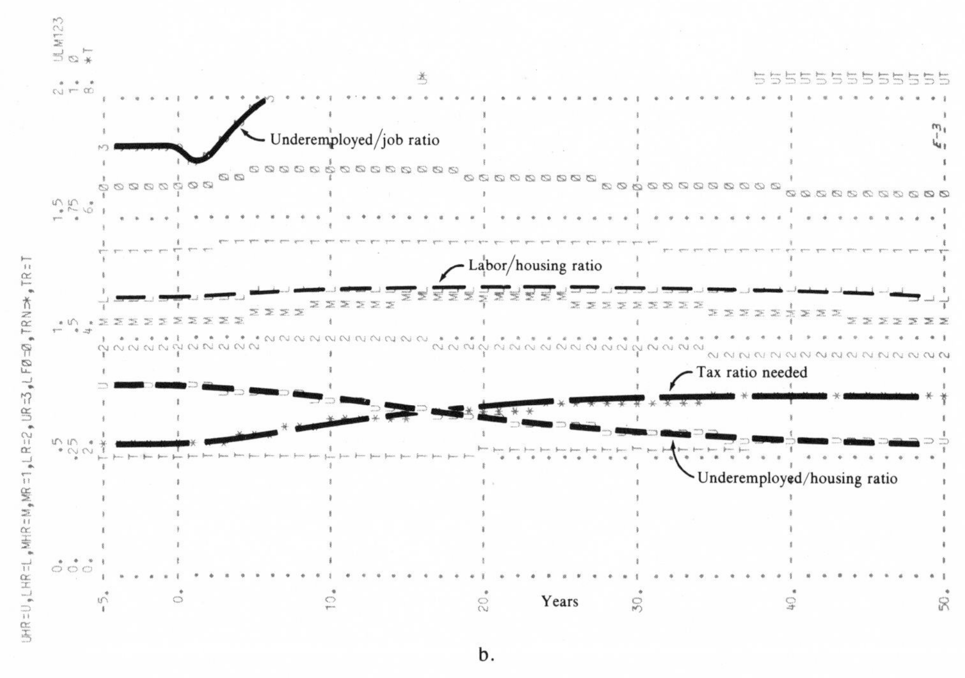

b.

Figure 8-5 Construction of low-cost housing each year for about 2.5 percent of the underemployed

Source: Reprinted from *Urban Dynamics* by Jay W. Forrester by permission of The MIT Press, Cambridge, Massachusetts, Figure 4-8.

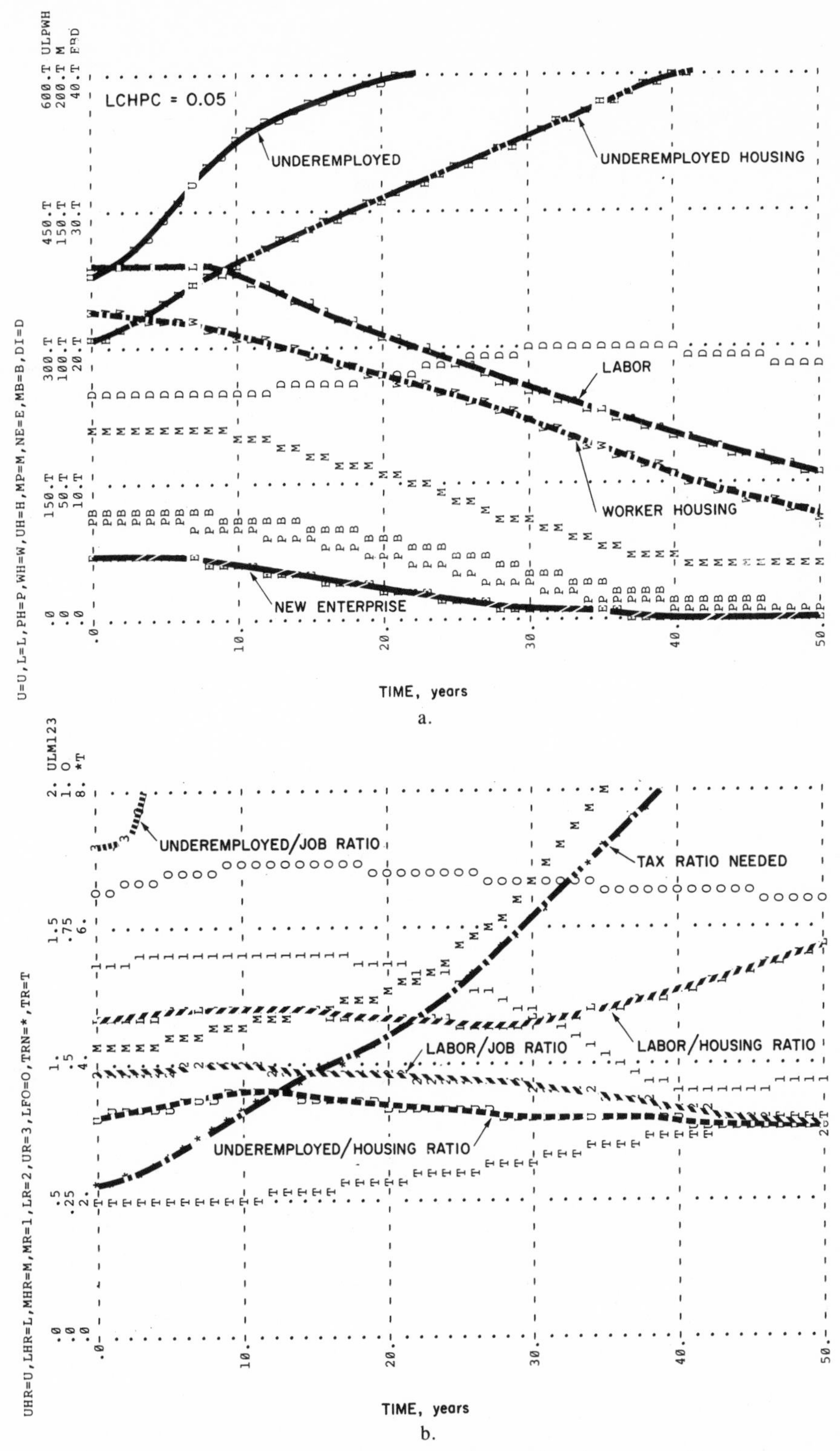

Figure 8-6 The low-cost housing program tested on an urban dynamics model containing an additive formulation for underemployed migration

8.4 Model Behavior with All Multiplicative Formulations Replaced by Additive Formulations

The relative insensitivity of the *Urban Dynamics* model to the use of multiplicative rather than additive formulations for underemployed migration extends to all eight multiplicative formulations that involve three or more variables.[5] Figure 8-7 displays the overall simulated behavior of the model when all eight multiplicative functions are transformed to additive formulations. Figure 8-7 should be compared with Figure 8-1.

Transforming the eight multiplicative formulations has the following results: a virtual elimination of oscillation in the levels between the years 100 and 160, and an extended approach to equilibrium in some levels (for example, the number of underemployed U). However, from the policy analysis point of view, the resulting differences in the overall system behavior are not major. The transformed *Urban Dynamics* model still shows the overall behavioral patterns and the relative mix of equilibrium values characteristic of the original model. If policy analyses are repeated with all eight functions expressed as additive formulations, the general conclusions expressed in *Urban Dynamics* still hold.

8.5 Conclusions

Plausibility under extreme conditions, coupled with insensitivity of behavior and policy results for an alternative additive assumption, makes a sound argument for using multiplicative rather than additive formulations in the *Urban Dynamics* model. The degree of insensitivity demonstrated by the model may surprise many observers unfamiliar with the class of models to which it belongs. Complex nonlinear feedback models can often be expected to demonstrate insensitivity to the use of multiplicative versus additive formulations. The space constraints and limited purpose of this reading permit only a brief explanation of how such insensitivity arises.[6] Both additive and multiplicative formulations are approximations about a point to more general nonseparable multivariate functions. The quality of the separated approximation, as well as the relative sensitivity to additive versus multiplicative formulations, depends to a large extent on how judiciously the operating point is chosen. Forrester's technique of formulating a multivariate function about a set of normal values for all input variables assists the model builder in making an appropriate selection of the operating point. The normal-point technique tends to minimize the likelihood of all input variables simultaneously exerting reinforcing pressures to move the value of the multivariate functions away from its normal value. On the other hand, the technique promotes the influence of countervailing pressures. Countervailing pressures appear when some input variables to the multivariate function exert pressure to produce greater than normal values for the function, while some input variables create pressure for lower than normal values. When countervailing pressures prevail, an operating model will tend to be insensitive to the multiplicative-additive distinction.

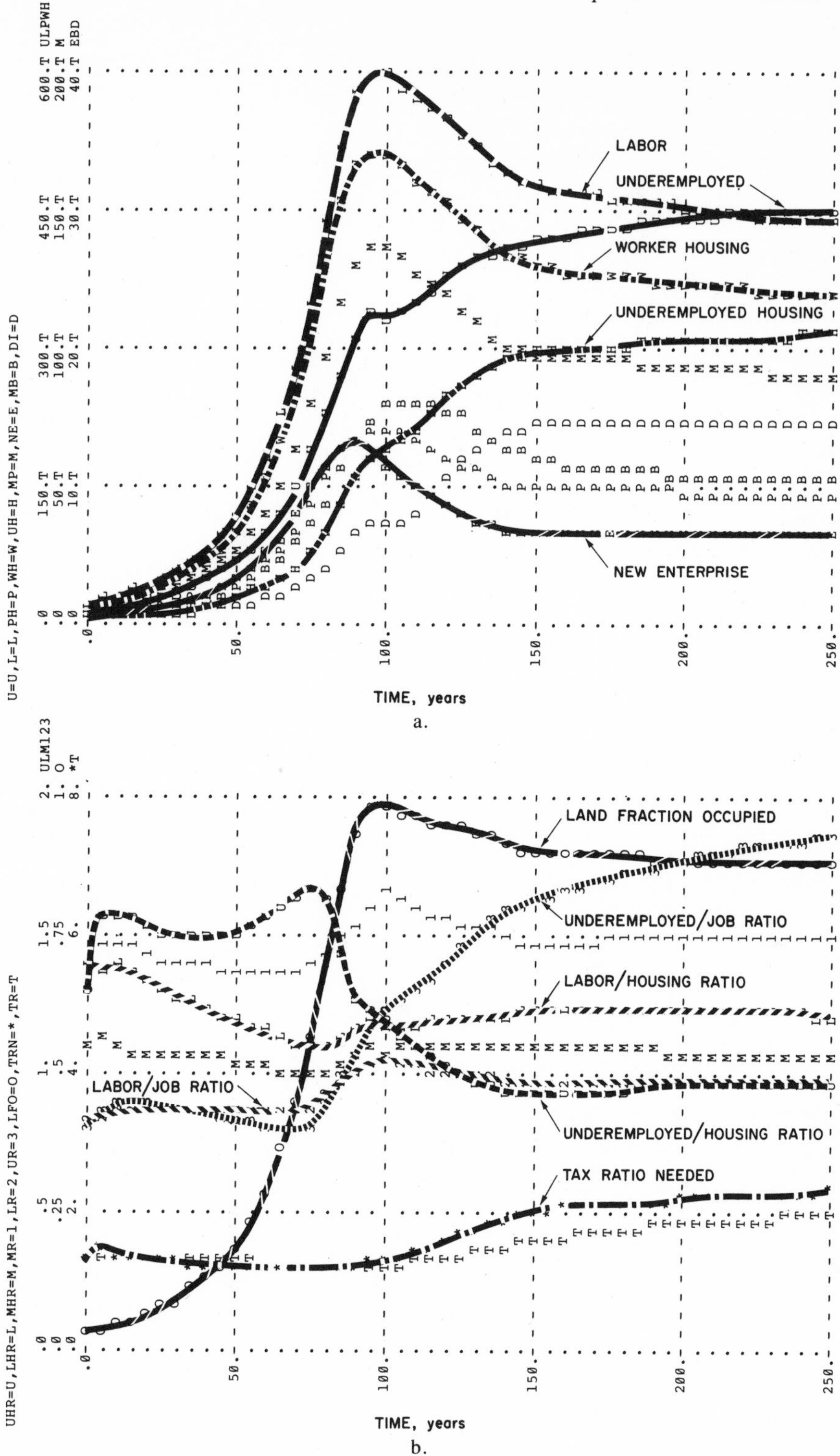

Figure 8-7 Growth behavior of the *Urban Dynamics* model with all multiplicative formulations replaced by additive formulations

Notes

1. Jay W. Forrester, *Industrial Dynamics* (Cambridge, Mass.: The MIT Press, 1961), chap. 3.

2. The information delay relating the attractiveness-for-migration multiplier AMM and attractiveness-for-migration multiplier perceived AMMP is omitted from the discussion in this reading to simplify the presentation. All simulations include the information delay.

3. See, for example, Michael R. Goodman and Peter M. Senge, "Issues of Empirical Support for the Migration Formulations in *Urban Dynamics*," in *Readings in Urban Dynamics*, vol. 1, ed. Nathaniel J. Mass (Cambridge, Mass.: Wright-Allen Press, 1974), pp. 87–101, and Peter M. Senge, "An Experimental Evaluation of Generalized Least Squares Estimation," System Dynamics Group Memorandum D-1944-7 (Cambridge, Mass.: M.I.T., 1974).

4. Peter M. Senge, "Separating Multivariate Causal Functions in Modeling Dynamic Systems," S.M. thesis, M.I.T., 1972; Library-Microreproduction 14-0551.

5. The eight variables are the functions for AMM.K, UMM.K, LAM.K, LMM.K, MAM.K, PHM.K, WHM.K, and EM.K in *Urban Dynamics*.

6. See Peter M. Senge, "Separable Formulations as Approximations to Multivariate Causality in System Models," *Proceedings of the Summer Computer Simulation Conference* (Simulation Councils, Inc., P.O. Box 2228, La Jolla, Ca. 92037, 1973; copies also available from the author), for a more detailed explanation of the insensitivity of complex feedback models to the use of additive versus multiplicative formulations.

Appendix: Transformation from Multiplicative to Additive Formulation

This appendix develops the basic equations required to perform sensitivity tests of the type presented in this reading. The basic equations incorporate the assumptions that both additive and multiplicative formulations approximate a more complex multivariate causality and that both formulations are employed in practice within a similar modeling procedure.

The sensitivity tests conducted with the *Urban Dynamics* model involve transforming a multiplicative formulation of n-variables,

$$f_1(v) = k \times g_1(v_1) \times g_2(v_2) \times \ldots \times g_n(v_n) \qquad \text{(A.1)}$$

to an additive formulation,

$$f_2(v) = k + G_1(v_1) + G_2(v_2) + \ldots + G_n(v_n) \qquad \text{(A.2)}$$

Each multiplicative formulation in *Urban Dynamics* is constructed about a particular operating point chosen as appropriate for the function in question. For example, the formulation in equation A.1 is specified so that there exists some point $(p_1, \ldots, p_n)$ in the domain of $f_1(v)$ so that

$$f_1(p_1, \ldots, p_n) = k$$

and (A.3)

$$g_i(p_i) = 1 \qquad i = 1,2,\ldots,n$$

The constant k is generally labeled as the normal value of the function (for example, underemployed arrivals normal UAN in the formulation for underemployed arrivals in *Urban Dynamics*) associated with some set of normal conditions represented by the point $(p_1, \ldots, p_n)$.

Similarly, the additive formulation (A.2) that replaces the multiplicative formulation (A.1) takes on a neutral influence when all input variables equal their normal values:

$$f_2(p_1, \ldots, p_n) = k$$

$$G_i(p_i) = 0 \qquad i = 1,2,\ldots,n \qquad \text{(A.4)}$$

By assumption, both the additive and multiplicative formulations are approximations to some more complicated causality. The restrictions (equation A.4) on the additive formulation guarantee that both the additive and the multiplicative formulations are approximations about the same point in the domain of the true function.

Given a multiplicative formulation, how can the investigator derive the additive counterpart? The derivation follows from careful consideration of the modeling process underlying the multiplicative formulation, which implies a set of contours in the multivariate causality being modeled. A simple transformation of the contours produces an additive formulation of the form shown in equations A.2 and A.4. Formulating a multivariate causal function as a multiplicative combination of inputs proceeds in two steps: choice of a normal point, and specification of the individual univariate functions (the $g_i(v_i)$). The univariate functions, which Forrester calls multipliers, are specified by considering perturbations away from normal conditions. As an example, in the underemployed migration formulation, the multiplier for housing availability, labeled the underemployed/housing multiplier UHM, is drawn from consideration of expected impacts on underemployed migration resulting from changes in housing availability, *if all other factors remain normal*. The curve that defines the underemployed-housing multiplier, reproduced here as Figure 8-7, was derived by asking such questions as: By what factor would in-migration be reduced if crowding rose to twice its normal value (UHR = 2) but all other factors remained at their normal values (UR = 1, TPCR = 1, UMP = 1)? An assessment of multiplier functions requires a subjective assessment of the shape and values of certain contours of some multivariate causality. More precisely, if $f_t(v)$ denotes the true multivariate function being modeled, then the multiplier $g_i(v_i)$ is:

$$g_i(v_i) = \frac{1}{k} f_T(v) \Big|_{\substack{v_j = p_j \\ j \neq i}} \tag{A.5}$$

where

$$k = f_T(p_1,\ldots,p_n)$$

The multiplier function of the variable v_i corresponds to a contour in the function $f_T(v)$ formed by holding all variables except v_i constant at their normal values and allowing v_i to vary over all its possible values. The contour is then scaled by the factor 1/k to give a multiplicative formulation that meets the restrictions in equations A.3. Therefore, a set of multiplier functions contains an implicit set of subjective assessments of contour. Recovery of the contours from the multipliers utilizes the following transformation:

$$f_T(v) \Big|_{\substack{v_j = p_j \\ j \neq i}} = k \times g_i(v_i) \tag{A.6}$$

where

$$k = f(p_1,\ldots,p_n)$$

Arriving at an additive formulation resembles the process for arriving at a multiplicative formulation. Again, an assessment of the shape of certain contours of the true function is implicit in any assessment of the univariate additive functions (the $G_i(v_i)$). However, the contours must be scaled differently to produce a set of univariate additive functions that meet the restrictions imposed by equations A.4. In particular,

$$G_i(v_i) = f_T(v) \Big|_{\substack{v_j = p_j \\ j \neq i}} - k \tag{A.7}$$

where

$$k = f(p_1,\ldots,p_n)$$

That is, if the normal value, k, is subtracted from each contour, the resulting set of univariate additive functions all equal zero at their normal points. Therefore, in an additive formulation, perturbations from normal conditions result in positive or negative additions to the normal value of the multivariate function. Combining equations A.6 and A.7 shows that an additive formulation can be derived from a multiplicative formulation in the following manner:

$$G_i(v_i) = (k \times g_1(v_i)) - k$$

where

$$k = f(p_i, \ldots, p_n) \qquad (A.8)$$

In summary, to transform any multiplicative formulation of the type represented in equations A.1 and A.3 to an additive formulation of the type represented in equations A.2 and A.4, first multiply each multiplier function by the normal value and then subtract the normal value from that product. The resulting set of univariate additive functions, combined according to equation A.2, produces the desired additive formulation. Consider the underemployed migration rate once again as an example. Given that

$$\begin{aligned} k &= \text{UAN} \\ g_1(\text{UHR}) &= \text{UHM.K} \\ g_2(\text{UJR}) &= \text{UJM.K} \\ g_3(\text{UM}) &= \text{UAMM.K} \\ g_4(\text{TPCR}) &= \text{PEM.K} \end{aligned} \qquad (A.9)$$

the multiplicative migration formulation

$$\frac{\text{UA}}{\text{U} + \text{L}} = \text{UAN(UHM.K)(UJM.K)(UAMM.K)(PEM.K)} \qquad (A.10)$$

is transformed into the additive formulation:

$$\begin{aligned} \frac{\text{UA}}{\text{U} + \text{L}} &= \text{UAN} + (\text{UAN} \times \text{UHM.K} - \text{UAN}) + (\text{UAN} \times \text{UJM.K} - \text{UAN}) \\ &\quad + (\text{UAN} \times \text{UAMM.K} - \text{UAN}) + (\text{UAN} \times \text{PEM.K} - \text{UAN}) \\ &= \text{UAN}[1 + (\text{UHM.K} - 1) + (\text{UJM.K} - 1) + (\text{UAMM.K} - 1) \\ &\quad + (\text{PEM.K} - 1)] \end{aligned} \qquad (A.11)$$

In the sensitivity tests reported in Figures 8-2, 8-4, 8-6, and 8-7, the relationship shown in equation A.11 replaces the multiplicative migration formulation.

9

Urban Dynamics and Land Rezoning

John S. Miller

Urban zoning decisions determine the supply of land available for housing and business construction in a city. The amount and type of urban land influence the present and future housing market, population mix, and employment conditions. Since a city must live with its zoning decisions for a century or longer, local decisions affecting land use should be made in the context of the total urban system. The total system includes interactions over time between land-development patterns and the land market, as well as the impact of land-use allocation on other urban conditions. This reading describes a land-rezoning extension of the Urban Dynamics *model. The refined model, called* Rezone 2, *is amenable to land-rezoning policy tests that cannot readily be performed on the* Urban Dynamics *model.*

9
Urban Dynamics and Land Rezoning

9.1 Background and Overview

Urban Dynamics describes how urban growth gives way to obsolescence and decline as land becomes scarce in the central city. The long-term growth-to-decline process afflicts older central cities and is beginning to diminish the quality of life in many suburbs surrounding central cities. During growth, business structures and houses tend to hold a supportable number of jobs and people. But the aging city eventually spawns an imbalance between jobs and people. Older housing tends to fill up with more lower-income residents, while older business structures tend to provide fewer jobs. New housing and business construction move out of the central city and leave behind an expanding area of low-quality housing, lower-income residents, and poor employment conditions.

To revive an aging city with poor employment conditions, *Urban Dynamics* recommends a coordinated program of industrial expansion and demolition of vacant, substandard housing to clear land for new industrial construction. Land-rezoning policies have a central role in achieving any program for housing demolition and industrial expansion. By influencing the price and availability of land for urban, industrial, and residential development, rezoning policies offer an important leverage point for attaining an improved balance of population, housing, and business.

Several extensions of the *Urban Dynamics* model incorporating the effects of land rezoning have been developed in the past. My doctoral thesis "Refinement of the *Urban Dynamics* Model for Land Rezoning Policy Analysis" [1] presented a fully documented version of the *Rezone* model—a predecessor to the later land rezoning models. Mass in "A Dynamic Model of Land Pricing and Urban Land Allocation" [2] reported on incorporating a land pricing sector into an expanded *Urban Dynamics* model containing a detailed zoning sector.

This article presents a somewhat modified composite version of earlier rezoning models. The *Rezone2* model described here captures the essential dynamics of the rezoning models and illustrates the utility of such models for urban policy analysis.

As with the *Urban Dynamics* model, the information sources for the *Rezone2* model include descriptive literature and the knowledge of people personally experienced with managing cities. [3] Pressures, motivations, and historical patterns of urban land allocation are represented in the *Rezone2* refinement. *Rezone2* combines land-allocation relationships into a feedback structure. When linked to the *Urban Dynamics* model, the added land-rezoning feedback relationships reproduce land-use patterns observed in many American cities.

As described in Makielski's *The Politics of Zoning*, cities first adopted zoning laws to "encourage the city's economy, to protect social values, and hopefully to bring some degree of order and rationality to the present and future development of the city." [4] The rationale for zoning laws is based on the premise of externalities in the land market. Daniel R. Mandelker explains in *The Zoning Dilemma*:

> . . . when we inspect the underlying purpose of the original zoning legislation, we find . . . that its dominant rationale was the separation of incompatibilities in land use in order to limit and prevent the visitation of externalities arising out of land use interdependencies in an urban setting. Note that we stress the concept of use, for use is the underlying legal concept on which the zoning ordinance is based. Regulation

of land uses was to be carried out legislatively. The local governing body was to create zoning districts throughout the municipality which would provide the basis for use allocations, and those uses that were compatible were to be assigned to the same district. In this manner was the development of the community to be ordered.[5]

In theory, the zoning structure is quite simple. "The legislative body of the municipality was to divide the municipality *in advance* into zoning districts. That was it, and that, in simple form, is what the statute authorizes."[6] However, zoning is actually much more dynamic. Zoning has been dominated in practice by *zoning change* in response to private development proposals. "Zoning can do little, therefore, with the problems of fully developed areas, except to hold the line. Its bite comes most as a method of regulating land-use allocations in areas as yet unurbanized, or still developing. It is primarily a mechanism for allocating land uses over time in an urbanizing land market."[7] The *Urban Dynamics* model examines the effects of several different policies over time. When suitably refined, the model would be capable of analyzing the long-term consequences of land-use decisions. For an analysis of land rezoning, the structure of the model must be disaggregated. The *Urban Dynamics* model does not explicitly represent two aspects of the influence of land use on urban conditions: land prices, and land availability as determined by zoning restrictions. With respect to land availability, the *Urban Dynamics* model differentiates only between occupied and unoccupied land, not between land used for business and land used for residence. Unoccupied land is assumed to be equally available for housing construction and new-enterprise construction. The *Rezone2* model divides land into two further categories: residential land and business land. The *Rezone2* model can thereby represent forces that determine the proportions of residential and business land in the city.

9.2 Structure of the Land-Rezoning Sector

In practice, cities can rezone land by (1) direct rezoning as part of a comprehensive plan, (2) the amendment process, (3) the variance process, and (4) the exception process. Both public- and private-interest groups participate in land-rezoning decisions. Public participants include zoning boards, planning boards, city planners, urban executive officers, and legislative bodies. Nongovernmental organizations include builders, architects, real-estate groups, developers, business groups, and homeowner groups.

The various groups do not operate in isolation. Builders usually worry about the effects of rezoning on future building activity. Architects are concerned by bulk regulations that may influence future building. Real-estate groups monitor price changes in the land market as a result of rezoning decisions and lobby to protect past investments rather than to promote future expansion. Developers, wanting maximum future benefit from their investments, favor constantly rising land values. Most business groups are aware of the impact of zoning policy on tax rates, the labor force, congestion, and the availability of building space. They therefore favor industrial development; oppose residential construction in actual or potential industrial sites; and try to anticipate the effects of zoning policy on land prices, the tax base, and commercial expansion. Homeowner and tenant associations often directly oppose business groups. Most homeowners view zoning as a device for maintaining the status quo in their communities. They worry about noise, traffic congestion, pollution, and other nuisances brought to their communities by industrial development. Moreover, single-family homeowners usually resist the construction of multiple-family dwelling units, which tend to bring many of the same nuisances to a community as commercial development. The different groups apply their resources in the political and legal arena to influence land-rezoning policy. The resulting pressures on land-rezoning decisions are situated in a strong feedback loop controlling the land-rezoning process. Conditions in the land market largely determine the degree and type of pressure brought to bear on the rezoning process. The pressures lead to land-rezoning decisions that in turn change conditions in the land market, thereby completing the feedback process. Figure 9-1 shows the DYNAMO flow diagram of the land rezoning portion of the *Rezone2* model. The complete model equations are given in the appendix. Equations 1 to 145 and 269 to 279 are basically from *Urban Dynamics* except for certain changes made to accommodate the interface with the land zoning and land pricing sectors.[8] Equations for the land pricing sector (equations 227 to 268) are described in Mass "A Dynamic Model of Land Pricing and Urban Land Allocation".[9] Only the equations in the land rezoning sector (equations 200 to 226) are described in detail in the following paragraphs. Equations 280 to 288 set up policy switches, etc. for the model behavior analysis described in section 9.3.

Residential and Business Land. Equations 200 and 201 describe the levels of residential and business land that account for all land within the *Rezone2* model. The model AREA is assumed to be initially zoned 5 percent for business uses and 95 percent for residential uses.

```
RL.K=RL.J+(DT)(BLR.JK-RLR.JK)                               200, L
RL=AREA-BL                                                  200.1, N
    BL      - BUSINESS LAND (ACRES)
    RLR     - RESIDENTIAL-LAND REZONING (ACRES/YEAR)
    BLR     - BUSINESS LAND REZONING (ACRES/YEAR)
    RL      - RESIDENTIAL LAND (ACRES)
    AREA    - TOTAL LAND AREA (ACRES)
```

```
BL.K=BL.J+(DT)(RLR.JK-BLR.JK)                               201, L
BL=AREA*BLFI                                                201.1, N
BLFI=0.05                                                   201.2, C
    BL      - BUSINESS LAND (ACRES)
    RLR     - RESIDENTIAL-LAND REZONING (ACRES/YEAR)
    BLR     - BUSINESS LAND REZONING (ACRES/YEAR)
    AREA    - TOTAL LAND AREA (ACRES)
    BLFI    - BUSINESS-LAND FRACTION INITIAL (FRACTION)
```

```
RLR.KL=(RL.K)(RLFR.K)(RLRPF.K)+RLRD.K                       202, R
    RLR     - RESIDENTIAL-LAND REZONING (ACRES/YEAR)
    RL      - RESIDENTIAL LAND (ACRES)
    RLFR    - RESIDENTIAL-LAND FRACTION REZONED
                (FRACTION)
    RLRPF   - RESIDENTIAL-LAND-REZONING POLICY FACTOR
                (DIMENSIONLESS)
    RLRD    - RESIDENTIAL-LAND REZONING DEMAND (ACRES/
                YEAR)
```

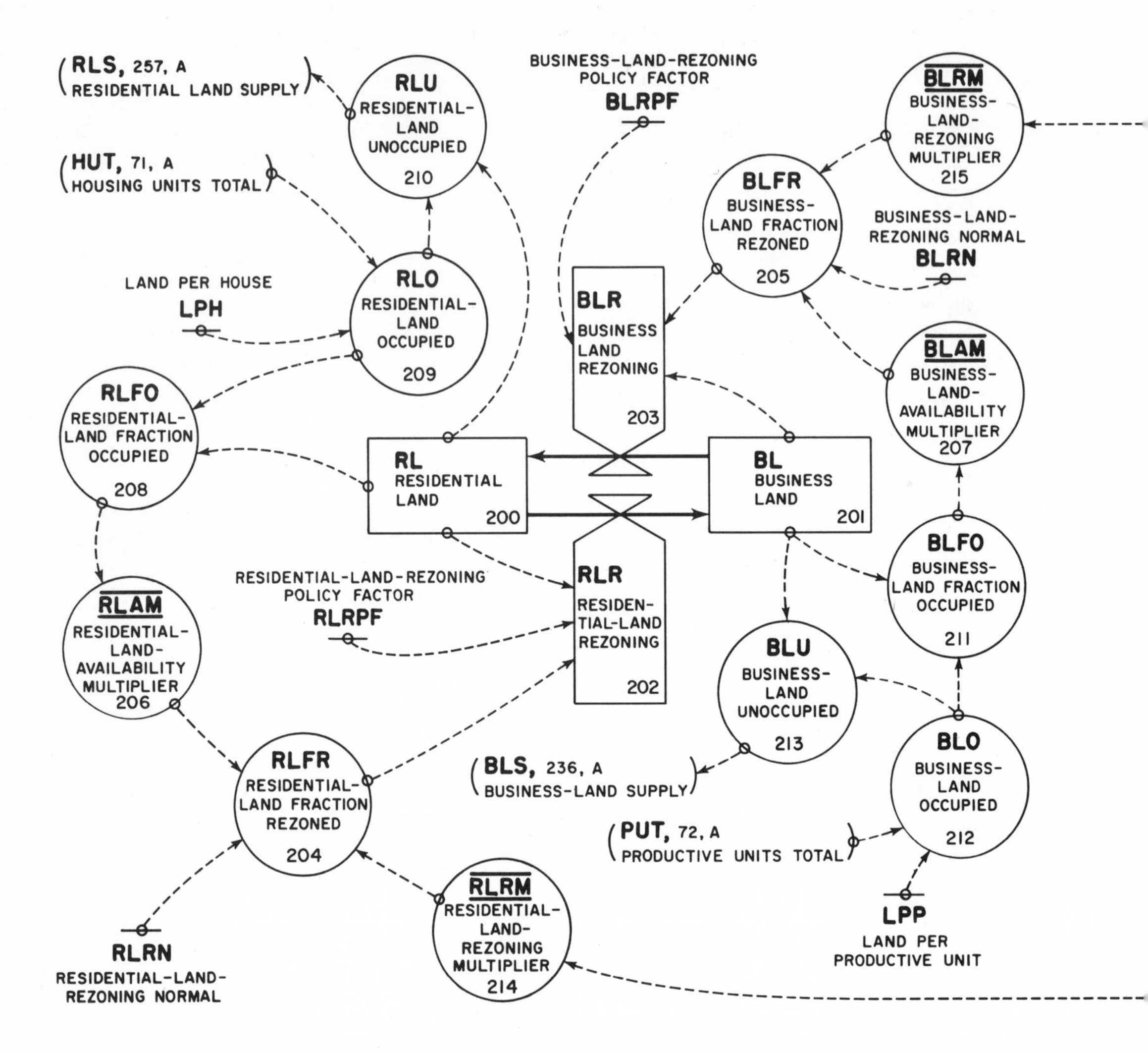

Figure 9-1 DYNAMO flow diagram of the land-rezoning refinement

Rezoning Rates. Two rates allocate land between residential and business use. The rate of residential-land rezoning RLR (equation 202) moves land from residential to business use while the rate of business-land rezoning BLR (equation 203) moves land from business to residential use. Both rates normally equal a fraction of the amount of land available in their respective levels. A policy factor for testing policies that alter the normal rezoning rates also appears in the rate equations.

```
BLR.KL=(BL.K)(BLFR.K)(BLRPF.K)                          203, R
    BLR    - BUSINESS LAND REZONING (ACRES/YEAR)
    BL     - BUSINESS LAND (ACRES)
    BLFR   - BUSINESS-LAND FRACTION REZONED (FRACTION/
               YEAR)
    BLRPF  - BUSINESS-LAND-REZONING POLICY FACTOR
               (DIMENSIONLESS)
```

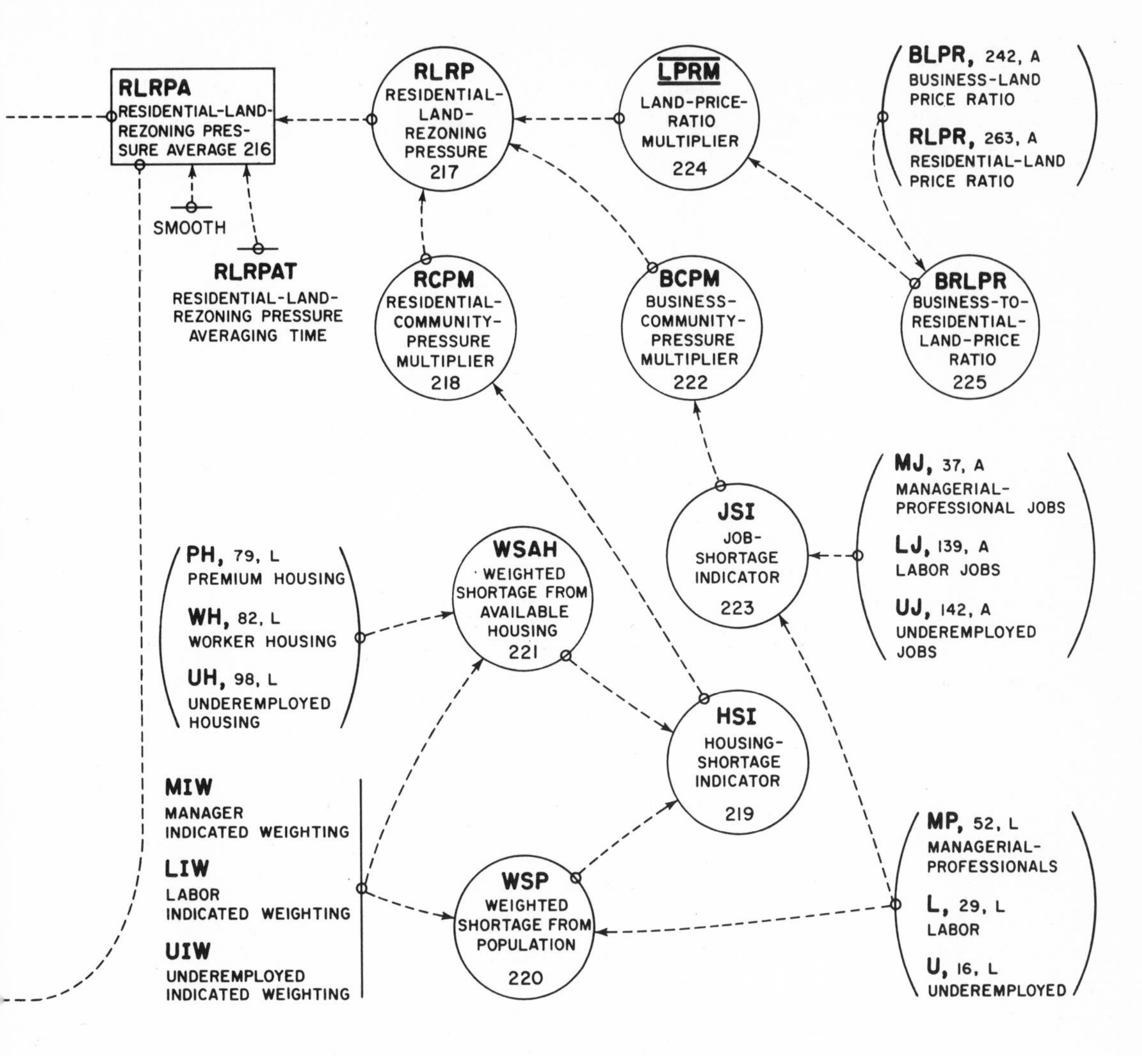

Figure 9-1 continued

```
RLFR.K=(RLRN)(RLAM.K)(RLRM.K)                           204, A
RLRN=.002                                               204.1, C
    RLFR    - RESIDENTIAL-LAND FRACTION REZONED
                (FRACTION)
    RLRN    - RESIDENTIAL-LAND-REZONING NORMAL (FRACTION/
                YEAR)
    RLAM    - RESIDENTIAL-LAND-AVAILABILITY MULTIPLIER
                (DIMENSIONLESS)
    RLRM    - RESIDENTIAL-LAND-REZONING MULTIPLIER
                (DIMENSIONLESS)

BLFR.K=(BLRN)(BLAM.K)(BLRM.K)                           205, A
BLRN=.015                                               205.1, C
    BLFR    - BUSINESS-LAND FRACTION REZONED (FRACTION/
                YEAR)
    BLRN    - BUSINESS-LAND-REZONING NORMAL (ACRES/YEAR)
    BLAM    - BUSINESS-LAND-AVAILABILITY MULTIPLIER
                (DIMENSIONLESS)
    BLRM    - BUSINESS-LAND-REZONING MULTIPLIER
                (DIMENSIONLESS)
```

Land Fraction Rezoned. Equations 204 and 205 identify the fraction of land in each level rezoned each year. The fraction depends upon a normal, given as a very small percentage of total land in each level, and two multipliers representing land availability and rezoning pressures.

Land-Availability Multipliers. Both the residential- and the business-land-availability multipliers (equations 206 and 207) are functions of the respective fractions of land occupied.

```
RLAM.K=TABHL(RLAMT,RLFO.K,0,1,.2)                          206, A
RLAMT=.4/.38/.35/.32/.29/.25                               206.1, T
    RLAM    - RESIDENTIAL-LAND-AVAILABILITY MULTIPLIER
                (DIMENSIONLESS)
    RLFO    - RESIDENTIAL-LAND FRACTION OCCUPIED
                (FRACTION)

BLAM.K=TABHL(BLAMT,BLFO.K,0,1,.2)                          207, A
BLAMT=.4/.38/.35/.3/.2/.1                                  207.1, T
    BLAM    - BUSINESS-LAND-AVAILABILITY MULTIPLIER
                (DIMENSIONLESS)
    BLFO    - BUSINESS-LAND FRACTION OCCUPIED (FRACTION)
```

Figure 9-2 shows that, as the land fraction occupied rises, less and less land can be rezoned. City zoning boards much prefer to rezone unoccupied land instead of occupied land.

As the residential-land fraction occupied RLFO rises, increased resistance by local residents to additional business development forces the residential-land-availability multiplier RLAM downward. As the residential land area fills, land proposed for rezoning from residential to business use will presumably lie more frequently in close proximity to housing. A buffer zone of underdeveloped residential land may no longer separate residential areas from commercial or industrial development. Homeowner resistance is more often focused on land sites bordering residential communities than on land situated farther away. As resistance grows, the number of proposals approved tends to drop. When the residential-land fraction occupied RLFO stays low, indicating few houses and abundant unoccupied residential land, residents

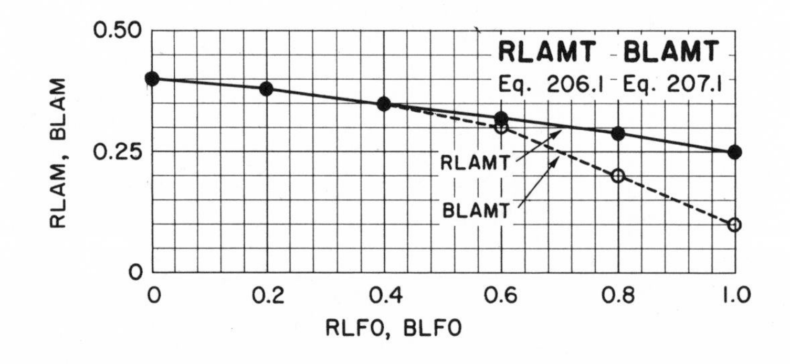

Figure 9-2 As the land fraction occupied LFO increases in either land-use category, pressures to rezone land away from that category fall

exert little or no pressure to stop rezoning. As residential land fills and RLFO approaches a value of 1.0, the residential-land-availability multiplier RLAM suppresses further rezoning of land from residential to business use. The business-land-availability multiplier BLAM subsumes the business community's desire to maintain a land reserve for future business expansion. Businessmen are typically concerned with maintaining some reserve business land to ensure the possibility of future economic growth. Quoting from Makielski:

> MR. HOWARD SWAIN (Brooklyn Chamber of Commerce): Now let me call attention to specific programs. For example, we have a firm employing 1,000 persons, it has increased growth potential, but it can expand only into what you have zoned as an adjacent residential area. If it can't expand here, it will move.[10]

Equation 207 and Figure 9-2 show that, as business land is consumed and unoccupied land becomes increasingly scarce for future business expansion, the business-land-availability multiplier BLAM restricts further land rezoning from business to residential use.

Occupied and Unoccupied Land. Equations 208 through 213 calculate the land fraction occupied and the amount of land occupied and unoccupied in each land-use category. The equations here parallel the original equations for land fraction occupied LFO in *Urban Dynamics*.

```
RLFO.K=RLO.K/RL.K                                          208, A
    RLFO    - RESIDENTIAL-LAND FRACTION OCCUPIED
                (FRACTION)
    RLO     - RESIDENTIAL-LAND OCCUPPIED (ACRES)
    RL      - RESIDENTIAL LAND (ACRES)

RLO.K=HUT.K*LPH                                            209, A
    RLO     - RESIDENTIAL-LAND OCCUPPIED (ACRES)
    HUT     - HOUSING UNITS TOTAL (UNITS)
    LPH     - LAND PER HOUSE (ACRES/UNIT)

RLU.K=RL.K-RLO.K                                           210, A
    RLU     - RESIDENTIAL-LAND UNOCCUPIED (ACRES)
    RL      - RESIDENTIAL LAND (ACRES)
    RLO     - RESIDENTIAL-LAND OCCUPPIED (ACRES)

BLFO.K=BLO.K/BL.K                                          211, A
    BLFO    - BUSINESS-LAND FRACTION OCCUPIED (FRACTION)
    BLO     - BUSINESS-LAND OCCUPPIED (ACRES)
    BL      - BUSINESS LAND (ACRES)


BLO.K=PUT.K*LPP                                            212, A
    BLO     - BUSINESS-LAND OCCUPPIED (ACRES)
    PUT     - PRODUCTIVE UNITS TOTAL (UNITS)
    LPP     - LAND PER PRODUCTIVE UNIT (ACRES/UNIT)

BLU.K=BL.K-BLO.K                                           213, A
    BLU     - BUSINESS-LAND UNOCCUPIED (ACRES)
    BL      - BUSINESS LAND (ACRES)
    BLO     - BUSINESS-LAND OCCUPPIED (ACRES)
```

Land-Rezoning Multipliers. The residential-land-rezoning multiplier RLRM (equation 214) converts an average residential-land-rezoning pressure RLRPA into a multiplier that, together with the residential-land-availability multiplier RLAM, determines the residential-land fraction rezoned RLFR (equation 204). As Figure 9-3 illustrates, when the average residential-land-rezoning pressure RLRPA rises, so does RLRM. In the absence of pressure to rezone, RLRPA would equal zero, and no rezoning would take place. As RLRPA rises, more land is rezoned from residential to business use. The slope of the curve in Figure 9-3 implies that small changes in rezoning pressure induce only small changes in the fraction of residential land rezoned, but greater pressures exert an increasingly heavier influence on the fraction of land rezoned.

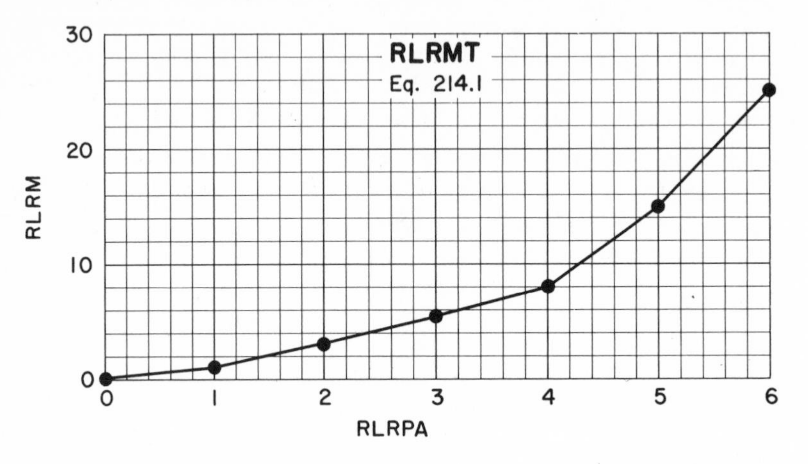

Figure 9-3 Residential-land-rezoning multiplier RLRM as a function of the average zoning pressure

```
RLRM.K=TABHL(RLRMT,RLRPA.K,0,6,1)                          214, A
RLRMT=0/1/3/5.5/8/15/25                                    214.1, T
     RLRM    - RESIDENTIAL-LAND-REZONING MULTIPLIER
                 (DIMENSIONLESS)
     RLRPA   - RESIDENTIAL-LAND-REZONING PRESSURE AVERAGE
                 (DIMENSIONLESS)

BLRM.K=TABHL(BLRMT,1.44*LOGN(RLRPA.K),-3,3,1)              215, A
BLRMT=30/8/3/1/.5/.25/0                                    215.1, T
     BLRM    - BUSINESS-LAND-REZONING MULTIPLIER
                 (DIMENSIONLESS)
     RLRPA   - RESIDENTIAL-LAND-REZONING PRESSURE AVERAGE
                 (DIMENSIONLESS)
```

The shape of the function in Figure 9-3 varies with the political or governmental participants in the rezoning process. The function translates a given pressure into a certain response. For a city whose zoning board or planning commission is very responsive to pressures to rezone land, Figure 9-3 should exhibit a steep slope. But, to represent a zoning board with conservative views on land use, a comprehensive plan, and willingness to resist pressures to rezone land, Figure 9-3 should display a very flat slope. A flat slope means that a large increase in pressure does not produce a large rezoning slope. The business-land-rezoning multiplier BLRM (equation 215) performs exactly the same function as its RLRM counterpart, except that it relates to the opposite land-rezoning flow.

Residential-Land-Rezoning Pressure RLRP. Equation 216 computes the three-year average (a SMOOTH equation) of the shorter-term pressures for residential land rezoning described in equation 217. Equation 215 uses a logarithmic scale to invert the same average rezoning pressures that governed RLRM. The residential-land-rezoning pressure RLRP represents political and legal processes that convert pressures for rezoning into rezoning decisions. Within limits, a given pressure calls forth a specific rezoning response. Pressures to rezone land, indicated by the residential-land-rezoning pressure RLRP, come from peer group attitudes, newspaper articles, or other forms of communication. The pressures may be exerted through voter referendums, petitions, or resolutions at public meetings; or they may be exerted illegally through bribes, payoffs, and other "deals." Although no one has accurately measured the many pressures influencing rezoning, the existence of the pressures is well documented.

> Claims are quite common in the literature . . . of zoning administration that zoning agencies are heavily influenced by public reactions. The claim is advanced, whatever the zoning merits of the proposed change, that the zoning agencies will react negatively whenever sufficient public opposition appears. In this study it was possible to test this hypothesis. . . . These findings . . . confirm the zoning myth to the extent that the commission's reaction to rezonings in which there was public opposition was overwhelmingly negative, in spite of the generally favorable position of the commission on the rezonings as a group.[11]

The *Rezone2* model aggregates rezoning pressures into three multipliers, which then combine to form RLRP.

```
RLRPA.K=SMOOTH(RLRP.K,RLRPAT)                            216, A
RLRPA=1                                                  216.1, N
RLRPAT=2                                                 216.2, C
    RLRPA   - RESIDENTIAL-LAND-REZONING PRESSURE AVERAGE
                (DIMENSIONLESS)
    RLRP    - RESIDENTIAL-LAND-REZONING PRESSURE
                (DIMENSIONLESS)

RLRP.K=(RCPM.K)(BCPM.K)(LPRM.K)                          217, A
    RLRP    - RESIDENTIAL-LAND-REZONING PRESSURE
                (DIMENSIONLESS)
    RCPM    - RESIDENTIAL-COMMUNITY-PRESSURE MULTIPLIER
                (DIMENSIONLESS)
    BCPM    - BUSINESS-COMMUNITY-PRESSURE MULTIPLIER
                (DIMENSIONLESS)
    LPRM    - LAND-PRICE-RATIO MULTIPLIER (DIMENSIONLESS)
```

Residential-Community-Pressure Multiplier RCPM. Equation 218 formulates community pressures that oppose rezoning residential land for business use during conditions of a housing shortage. Figure 9-4 shows how, as conditions of housing shortage arise toward the right-hand side of the table, RCPM drops to discourage the loss of housing land to business use.

Equation 219 defines the housing-shortage indicator HSI as a ratio of the weighted shortages from population and available housing.

Equations 220 and 221 give the weighted shortages. The weightings show that managerial-professionals presumably exert more influence upon rezoning decisions than do either labor or the underemployed.

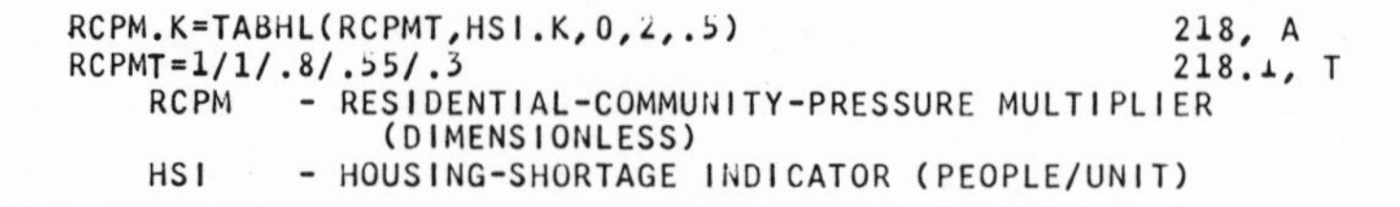

```
RCPM.K=TABHL(RCPMT,HSI.K,0,2,.5)                          218, A
RCPMT=1/1/.8/.55/.3                                       218.1, T
    RCPM    - RESIDENTIAL-COMMUNITY-PRESSURE MULTIPLIER
                (DIMENSIONLESS)
    HSI     - HOUSING-SHORTAGE INDICATOR (PEOPLE/UNIT)
```

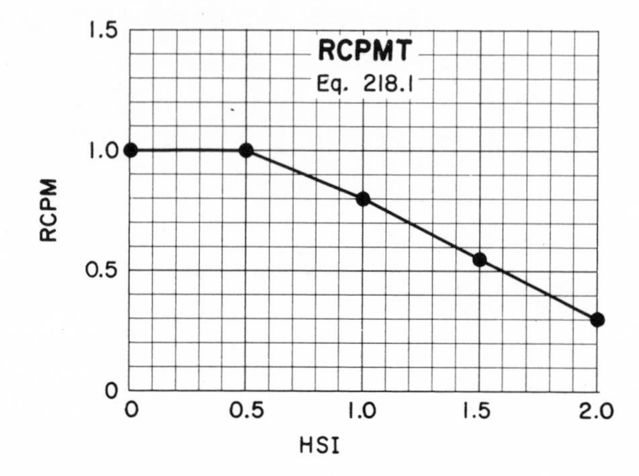

Figure 9-4 As the housing-shortage indicator HSI rises, the residential-community-pressure multiplier RCPM dips to represent opposition to further rezoning from residential to business land

```
HSI.K=(WSP.K)/(WSAH.K)                                    219, A
    HSI     - HOUSING-SHORTAGE INDICATOR (PEOPLE/UNIT)
    WSP     - WEIGHTED SHORTAGE FROM POPULATION (PEOPLE)
    WSAH    - WEIGHTED SHORTAGE FROM AVAILABLE HOUSING
                (UNITS)

WSP.K=(MP.K*MPFS*MIW)+(L.K*LFS*LIW)+(U.K*UFS*UIW)         220, A
    WSP     - WEIGHTED SHORTAGE FROM POPULATION (PEOPLE)
    MP      - MANAGERIAL-PROFESSIONALS (PEOPLE)
    MPFS    - MANAGERIAL-PROFESSIONAL FAMILY SIZE
                (PEOPLE/PEOPLE)
    MIW     - MANAGER INDICATED WEIGHTING (DIMENSIONLESS)
    L       - LABOR (PEOPLE)
    LFS     - LABOR FAMILY SIZE (PEOPLE/PEOPLE)
    LIW     - LABOR INDICATED WEIGHTING (DIMENSIONLESS)
    U       - UNDEREMPLOYED (PEOPLE)
    UFS     - UNDEREMPLOYED FAMILY SIZE (PEOPLE/PEOPLE)
    UIW     - UNDEREMPLOYED INDICATED WEIGHTING
                (DIMENSIONLESS)

WSAH.K=(PH.K*PHPD*MIW)+(WH.K*WHPD*LIW)+(UH.K*UHPD*        221, A
  UIW)
MIW=3                                                     221.1, C
LIW=2                                                     221.2, C
UIW=1                                                     221.3, C
    WSAH    - WEIGHTED SHORTAGE FROM AVAILABLE HOUSING
                (UNITS)
    PH      - PREMIUM HOUSING (UNITS)
    PHPD    - PREMIUM-HOUSING POPULATION DENSITY (PEOPLE/
                UNIT)
    MIW     - MANAGER INDICATED WEIGHTING (DIMENSIONLESS)
    WH      - WORKER HOUSING (UNITS)
    WHPD    - WORKER-HOUSING POPULATION DENSITY (PEOPLE/
                UNIT)
    LIW     - LABOR INDICATED WEIGHTING (DIMENSIONLESS)
    UH      - UNDEREMPLOYED HOUSING (UNITS)
    UHPD    - UNDEREMPLOYED-HOUSING POPULATION DENSITY
                (PEOPLE/UNIT)
    UIW     - UNDEREMPLOYED INDICATED WEIGHTING
                (DIMENSIONLESS)
```

Business-Community-Pressure Multiplier BCPM. Equation 222 and Figure 9-5 depict the assumed relationship between economic conditions in the city (as represented by the job-shortage indicator JSI) and the business-community-pressure multiplier BCPM. As jobs become scarcer (JSI increases), business and the rest of the community tend to agree that more residential land should go to business use.

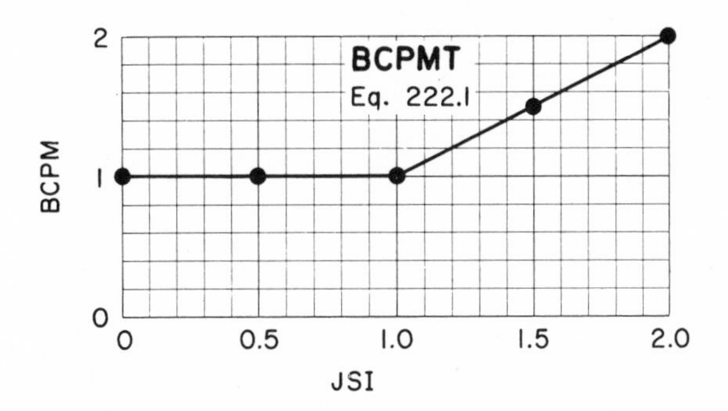

Figure 9-5 As the job-shortage indicator JSI rises in response to worsening employment conditions in the city, the business-community-pressure multiplier BCPM rises to encourage the rezoning of more residential land for business use

```
BCPM.K=TABHL(BCPMT,JSI.K,0,2,.5)                          222, A
BCPMT=1/1/1/1.5/2                                         222.1, T
    BCPM     - BUSINESS-COMMUNITY-PRESSURE MULTIPLIER
                 (DIMENSIONLESS)
    JSI      - JOB-SHORTAGE INDICATOR (PEOPLE/JOB)
```

In his discussion of factors influencing the response of business groups to various rezoning proposals, Makielski refers to the economic viewpoint of business and chamber of commerce groups.[12] The commercial groups respond to a given rezoning proposal in light of current urban economic conditions. The *Rezone2* model represents their responses in a business-community-pressure multiplier BCPM, which in turn is a function of the job-shortage indicator JSI defined in equation 223. JSI measures a city's economic climate through a simple ratio of total labor force divided by total jobs.

```
JSI.K=(MP.K+L.K+U.K)/(MJ.K+LJ.K+UJ.K)                     223, A
    JSI      - JOB-SHORTAGE INDICATOR (PEOPLE/JOB)
    MP       - MANAGERIAL-PROFESSIONALS (PEOPLE)
    L        - LABOR (PEOPLE)
    U        - UNDEREMPLOYED (PEOPLE)
    MJ       - MANAGERIA-PROFESSIONAL JOBS (JOBS)
    LJ       - LABOR JOBS (JOBS)
    UJ       - UNDEREMPLOYED JOBS (JOBS)
```

Land-Price-Ratio Multiplier LPRM. The third multiplier comprising RLRP is the land-price-ratio multiplier LPRM (equation 224).

Equation 225 gives the business-to-residential-land-price ratio BRLPR as the business-land-price ratio BLPR divided by the residential-land-price ratio RLPR.

```
LPRM.K=TABHL(LPRMT,1.44*LOGN(BRLPR.K),-4,2,1)          224, A
LPRMT=.125/.167/.33/.6/1/3/6                            224.1, T
    LPRM    - LAND-PRICE-RATIO MULTIPLIER (DIMENSIONLESS)
    BRLPR   - BUSINESS-TO-RESIDENTIAL-LAND-PRICE RATIO
                (DIMENSIONLESS)

BRLPR.K=BLPR.K/RLPR.K                                   225, A
    BRLPR   - BUSINESS-TO-RESIDENTIAL-LAND-PRICE RATIO
                (DIMENSIONLESS)
    BLPR    - BUSINESS-LAND PRICE RATIO (DIMENSIONLESS)
    RLPR    - RESIDENTIAL-LAND PRICE RATIO
                (DIMENSIONLESS)
```

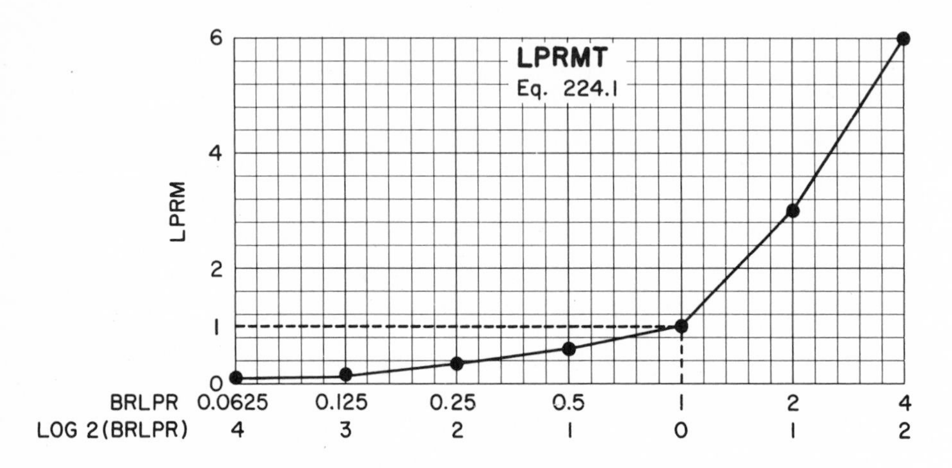

Figure 9-6 Relationship between the business-to-residential-land-price ratio BRLPR and pressure to rezone residential land for business use

Figure 9-6 depicts the relationship between the ratio of the two land prices and LPRM. As the price of business land rises relative to residential land (business-to-residential-land-price ratio BRLPR rises), pressures to rezone residential land to business use increase (land-price-ratio multiplier LPRM increases). On the other hand, if the residential-land-price ratio RLPR rises relative to the business-land-price ratio BLPR, pressures increase to limit the rezoning of residential land to business use. The decrease in rezoning reflects the normal opposition of property owners to zoning actions that might devalue their property. The relative price of residential land compared with business land is probably the most important factor in land-rezoning decisions. Land-rezoning literature comprehensively describes the pressures exerted by landowners and developers:

> If the number of sites allocated for development is limited then the value of each of these sites will be higher than if more were available. As a consequence, land values will fall more steeply on those sites on which development is not to be allowed, and the disparity in value between the restricted sites and the favored sites will seem greater. The developer who seeks a zoning change will be able to show a larger loss in value as the basis for his claim that the zoning restriction, as applied to him, has deprived him of ''property'' without Due Process of Law. No doubt it is pressures such as these, explicitly recognized or not, which lead planners . . . to a less

> restrictive plan, and which encourage lay members of boards and commissions to hasten the invasion of less developed and urbanized areas.[13]

The *Rezone2* model assumes that the business-to-residential-land-price ratio BRLPR (where land prices are averaged across the city) has a strong influence on land rezoning between residential and business use. If a city contains more than enough residential land but a less than adequate supply of business land, then the price of business land relative to residential land may run high. Developers and land speculators will pressure for the rezoning of residential land in order to profit from higher land prices.

9.3 Model Behavior

The behavior of the *Rezone2* model is fully consistent with the *Urban Dynamics* model during both the growth-to-equilibrium simulation run and the standard policy tests performed at equilibrium. Moreover, the additional model structure allows for policy tests beyond the scope of *Urban Dynamics*. The balance of this reading examines the response of the *Rezone2* model to two policy tests: (1) favoring business over residential land use, and (2) a combination policy for urban revival. The primary urban goals that provide the criteria for policy evaluation here are reducing unemployment and raising economic mobility among the underemployed. Both goals can be achieved only in a city with a satisfactory balance between jobs and population. So a secondary goal must be to constrain population growth. Otherwise, new jobs alone may attract so many new urban migrants or commuters that city employment conditions actually worsen. The *Rezone2* model is capable of investigating the feasibility of alternative urban goals. Given a set of achievable goals, the model can then be used to identify specific policies for moving the city toward its unique goals.

A Policy Favoring Business Development (RLRPF2 = 5, BLRPF2 = 0.2). A policy of rezoning land from residential to business use favors business development by providing additional land for industrial expansion and lowering the average price of business land. In Figure 9-7 at year 5, the rate of rezoning land from residential to business use increases by a factor of five, and the rate of rezoning land from business to residential use decreases to one-fifth its original value. The two changes increase the yearly quantity of land rezoned from residential to business use and decrease the land rezoned from business to residential use.

In Figure 9-7, the plotted variables change over a forty-year period from their original equilibrium values toward a new equilibrium in response to the rezoning policy, which transfers unoccupied residential land to land zoned for business use. Figure 9-7a shows that new enterprise NE rises to a peak at about year 25 and falls back to its initial equilibrium level by year 40. Initially, the increased availability of business land permits more business construction. However, as business land fills, new construction tapers off, and the level of new enterprise declines as buildings mature and decline. Figure 9-7a also shows an increase in both labor L and underemployed U, although by year 30 the labor population begins to decline as the initial job boom falters. In Figure 9-7b the underemployed/job ratio UR initially falls (employment conditions improve); but it later turns upward, indicating that early employment gains have been lost. The

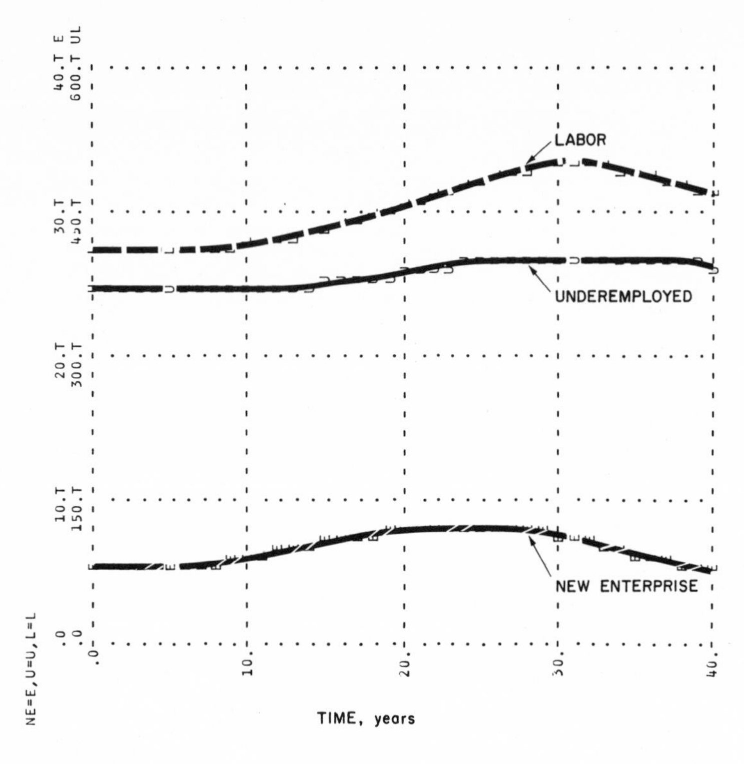
LABOR
UNDEREMPLOYED
NEW ENTERPRISE
TIME, years
NE=E,U=U,L=L

a.

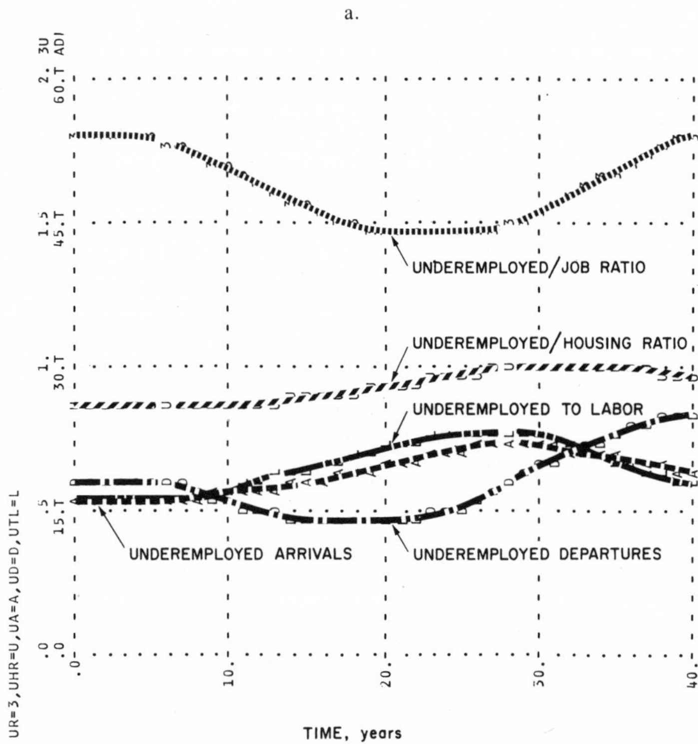
UNDEREMPLOYED/JOB RATIO
UNDEREMPLOYED/HOUSING RATIO
UNDEREMPLOYED TO LABOR
UNDEREMPLOYED ARRIVALS
UNDEREMPLOYED DEPARTURES
TIME, years
UR=3,UHR=U,UA=A,UD=D,UTL=L

b.

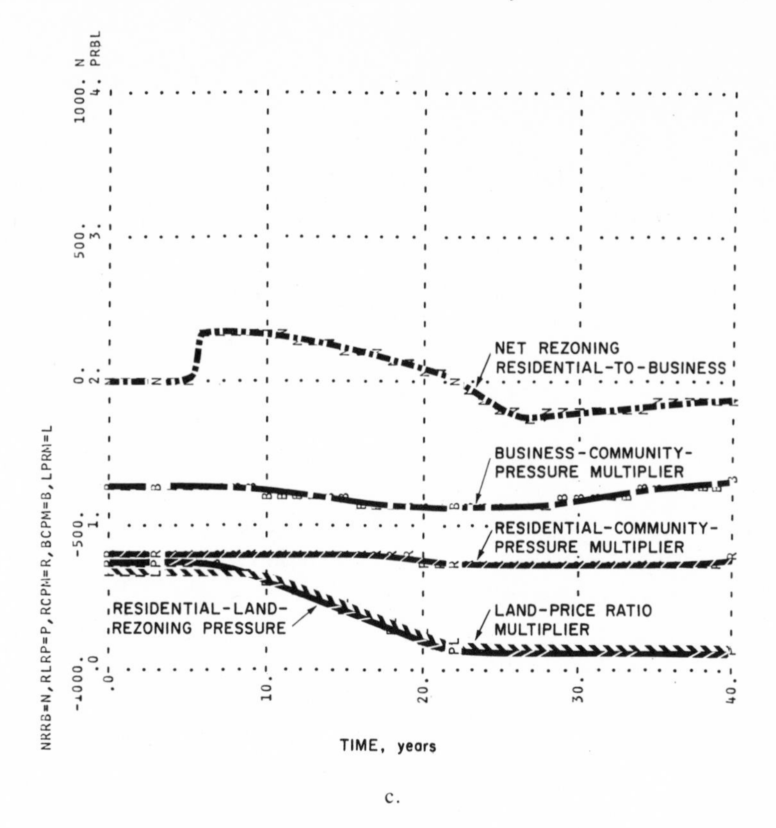

c.

Figure 9-7 The behavior caused by a policy of rezoning land from residential to business use to favor business development

underemployed/housing ratio UHR rises slightly, attesting to a somewhat tighter housing market. At first, underemployed arrivals rise and underemployed departures drop because the increased availability of land promotes new business construction and job creation. After year 30, however, the underemployed migration rates quickly reverse and show a high net out-migration of underemployed. The indicator of socioeconomic advancement is the rate of underemployed to labor UTL. In Figure 9-7b, UTL rises to begin with, but it later falls as the longer-term effects of the policy begin to undermine the more immediate benefits of the construction wave. Counter-pressures, which act in the opposite direction of the rezoning policy, significantly decrease the long-term impact of the proposed policy. The effect of these counterpressures can be seen in Figure 9-7c. As soon as the policy of rezoning residential land for business use begins in year 5, forces begin to oppose the desired policy results. Residential-land-rezoning pressure RLRP decreases in Figure 9-7c, thereby countering the rezoning of residential land for business use. The business-community-pressure multiplier BCPM also falls slightly, thus making the policy less effective in increasing the amount of business land. BCPM (favoring the conversion of residential land to business use) falls because the rezoning policy successfully increases the amount of undeveloped business land and improves employment conditions in the city. Improved business conditions decrease business-group pressures in favor of rezoning for business development. Through the land-price-ratio multiplier LPRM, land developers and homeowners create the major compensation against the desired impact of the rezoning policy in Figure 9-7c. As the price of residential land rises by more than the price of business land, developers and homeowners are assumed to oppose the further rezoning of residential land to business use. Developers exert pressure to rezone lower-valued business land to higher-valued residential land, while homeowners oppose the rezoning of their high-valued residential land to lower-valued business land. The decline in pressures brings about a further decrease in the residential-land-rezoning pressure RLRP, thereby diminishing the impact of the policy with respect to increasing the amount of available business land. The residential-community-pressure multiplier RCPM does not change in Figure 9-7c because the policy creates no housing shortage. If the policy took more undeveloped residential land for business use, the residential-community-pressure multiplier RCPM would rise to oppose the policy's objectives. In Figure 9-7c, the net amount of residential land rezoned for business (NRRB) shows an initial upward jump in year 5, followed by a slow decline. By year 25, more land is being rezoned for residential use than for business use. Clearly the compensating feedback pressures sap the rezoning policy of its long-term vitality.

Before the implementation of the new rezoning policy, pressures in the land-use system are balanced. No net rezoning of land takes place. But the rezoning policy upsets the balance of pressures. The system moves toward a new equilibrium with readjusted internal pressures. The rezoning policy partially compensates for some pressures, such as the business-community-pressure multiplier BCPM. The shift from the internal balancing of pressures to a partial reliance on pressures exerted through the rezoning policy impairs the overall impact of the policy. Counterbalancing pressures then arise to offset the policy. Shifting pressures in a complex system may induce reactions to diminish the policy's overall effectiveness.

A Combination Policy. Combining several individual policies can vastly improve their mutual effectiveness. The policy described here combines four individual policies: land rezoning to favor business development, encouraging additional enterprise expansion, demolishing additional low-quality housing, and reducing worker-housing construction. The changes made in the *Rezone2* model for the combination policy are as follows:

```
C        BLRPF2 = 0.2
C        RLRPF2 = 5
C        SWT13 = 5
C        SWT14 = 5
C        NEEF = 0.01
C        SWT12 = 5
C        WHCCBF = 0.015
C        SWT15 = 5
```

```
C          ACRES = 4,000
C          SWT17 = 5
C          SWT18 = 7
C          TT1 = 5
C          TT2 = 15
```

The combination rezoning policy incorporates an active program for increasing the business-land area in the city. The combination policy has two elements: changing rezoning pressures to increase the amount of business land, and accelerating job expansion through the construction of several industrial parks (requiring 4,300 acres in the 100,000-acre *Rezone2* model) during the first two years of the policy. (This extra industrial land is merely added to the amount of business land in the model by making a change in equation 202.) The policy is designed to transfer about 4.3 percent of the city's residential land to business use within two years. In practical terms, the rezoning policy calls for the city planning commission to review the city's land-use plans. Future planning recommendations should favor increased business use over residential use. Preference should be given to the development of land now adjoining local businesses in order to encourage their expansion and prevent their departure because of a lack of suitable land for expansion. Zoning boards should place the burden of proof of need on any party supporting residential uses. A city must do more than adopt effective land-rezoning policies. Land parceling and predevelopment preparation, tax abatements, advertising campaigns, and other activities help to create an atmosphere that will attract business investment. Since the combination policy encourages more industrial expansion, normal business construction as a fraction of total business increases from 5 percent to 6 percent per year. (In *Urban Dynamics*, the corresponding policy increases business construction from 5 percent to 7 percent per year.) By demolishing low-quality housing, the combination policy increases the amount of land available for new industrial development and decreases the amount of abandoned and excess substandard housing. With less low-quality housing available, the excessive in-migration that would otherwise weaken the land-rezoning policy will be frustrated. A program of increased low-quality-housing demolition can be undertaken in two ways: (1) directly, through the use of eminent domain and demolition, and (2) indirectly, through appropriate changes in city tax policies and building-code enforcement practices or as part of federal-or state-financed urban renewal. The demolition program gradually increases the normal fraction of low-quality housing demolished each year from 2 percent in year 5 to 6 percent in year 15. The increased incentives for housing demolition take effect slowly over the ten-year course of policy application. The unusual form of equation 285 accomplishes this end by combining two RAMP functions: the first begins in year 5 and slowly increases the housing demolition normal by 0.4 percent each year; the second is a negative RAMP of 0.4 percent that begins in year 15 and exactly cancels any further increase in the normal value, which reaches 6 percent at year 15. In *Urban Dynamics*, the corresponding policy change is a STEP increase in housing demolition from 2 percent to 7 percent.

At the beginning of the program, the city has a considerable quantity of low-quality housing. If the demolition program begins at 6 percent per year, a substantial amount of low-quality housing will disappear during the early years of the program. By, instead, gradually increasing demolition from 2 percent to 6 percent per year over ten years, the positive consequences of parallel economic improvement in the city have sufficient time to take root to counter any negative consequences from housing removal. Economic improvement increases employment and upward economic mobility for the underemployed. The underemployed residents should then discover that the disadvantages of a reduced housing supply are more than offset by improved opportunities for employment and upward economic mobility. As economic conditions improve for the underemployed, they can afford better housing; therefore, the demolition policy almost entirely removes *vacant* substandard units rather than poor-quality *occupied* housing. Besides increasing incentives for low-quality housing demolition, the combination policy reduces worker-housing construction. Decreasing worker-housing construction leaves more land available for industrial expansion, discourages the inflow of skilled-labor migrants, and reduces the potential amount of aging substandard housing. Cities can reduce worker-housing construction by issuing fewer building permits, by appropriate tax measures, by not building and extending sewer and power lines, and by restrictive zoning.

General Policy Results. The combination policy induces the behavior shown in Figure 9-8. Figure 9-8a indicates a substantial increase in city business activity. New enterprise NE rises quickly, thereby creating more jobs, yet soon after year 20 declines toward its initial value. As in Figure 9-7a, once city land is consumed by structures, construction inevitably slows. The labor population L increases by approximately 50 percent, while the underemployed population U decreases by about 17 percent. A higher upward economic mobility for the underemployed leads to significant changes in the labor force and in the underemployed population. Many underemployed persons enter the labor category (underemployed to labor UTL increases in Figure 9-8b). Figure 9-8b depicts dramatically improved employment conditions offset by a substantially tighter housing market. As a consequence of both upward economic mobility (decreasing the number of underemployed) and improved employment conditions (providing more underemployed jobs UJ), the underemployed/job ratio UR declines steeply in Figure 9-8b (from approximately 1.8 to 1.0). The drop in the underemployed/job ratio UR translates as a tremendous increase in job opportunities for the underemployed. Figure 9-8b suggests that increased net upward economic mobility reduces the number of underemployed in a city. During the period of policy application, underemployed arrivals UA always exceed underemployed departures UD. Improved economic conditions more than offset the tight housing market, thereby encouraging a slight net in-migration of the underemployed to the city. Figure 9-8c shows the effects of the compensating pressures that counter the land-rezoning policy. After an initial jump to reflect the industrial park creation program, the net amount of land rezoned from residential to business use quickly becomes negative. The compensating pressures continually pull business land into residential use, thereby impairing the long-term strength of the combination policy. In Figures 9-8a through 9-8c, the initial benefits of the combination policy appear to diminish after year 20. The rezoning mechanism tends to counter even the rigorous impact of the industrial expansion and housing limitation implemented in the combination policy.

9.4 Conclusions

Urban Dynamics argues that the relative mix among housing, population, and employment-producing activities significantly affects a city's socioeconomic condition. The natural aging of city structures leads to chronic unemployment. Aging industrial buildings provide less employment opportunities per unit of floor space. However, more people crowd into housing as residential structures age. An imbalance between housing and industrial structures tends to trap lower-income people with inadequate local job opportunities and decaying housing. *Urban Dynamics* suggests that land-rezoning policies aimed at improving the quantity and quality of unoccupied urban business land, rather than residential land, can alter a city's mix of housing and industry and thereby ameliorate urban unemployment. However, the highly aggregated *Urban Dynamics* model cannot explicitly test and evaluate different land-rezoning policies. The behavior of the *Urban Dynamics* model guided the development of the *Rezone2* model. Both models have the same purpose and boundary. Both models address the same problems of central-city unemployment and stagnation. Behavioral differences between the models reflect either different parameter values or a slightly different portrayal of reality in the *Rezone2* model. However, during its development, the *Rezone2* model was constantly compared with the *Urban Dynamics* model to ensure that behavioral differences were clearly caused by improvements in making the land-rezoning sector explicit.

The combination land-rezoning policy improves urban employment conditions in the *Rezone2* model. The combination policy calls for rezoning land to favor business development, encouraging additional enterprise expansion, demolishing more low-quality housing, and reducing worker-housing construction. Most of the benefits of the improvement go to the underemployed population. The increased upward economic mobility of the underemployed furnishes a steady stream of new skilled workers to fill labor jobs. As low-skilled workers acquire skills and can afford improved housing, the city can demolish more old, vacated, substandard housing. The reduced availability of substandard housing discourages the inflow of unskilled workers who might otherwise upset the improved internal balance between jobs and people. All city residents appear to benefit from the combination policy. In particular, the underemployed population benefits from the improved employment conditions and higher upward economic mobility. As more underemployed enter the economic mainstream, city expenditure for welfare should drop. In addition, the crime level may decrease, and blight should dissipate. But perhaps the most penetrating insight into urban behavior is the realization that every policy inevitably produces self-compensating counterpressures. Rezoning, rather than improving the long-term social and economic health of a city, generates very powerful compensating feedback forces that, primarily through the price mechanism, undermine the long-term success of rezoning policies.

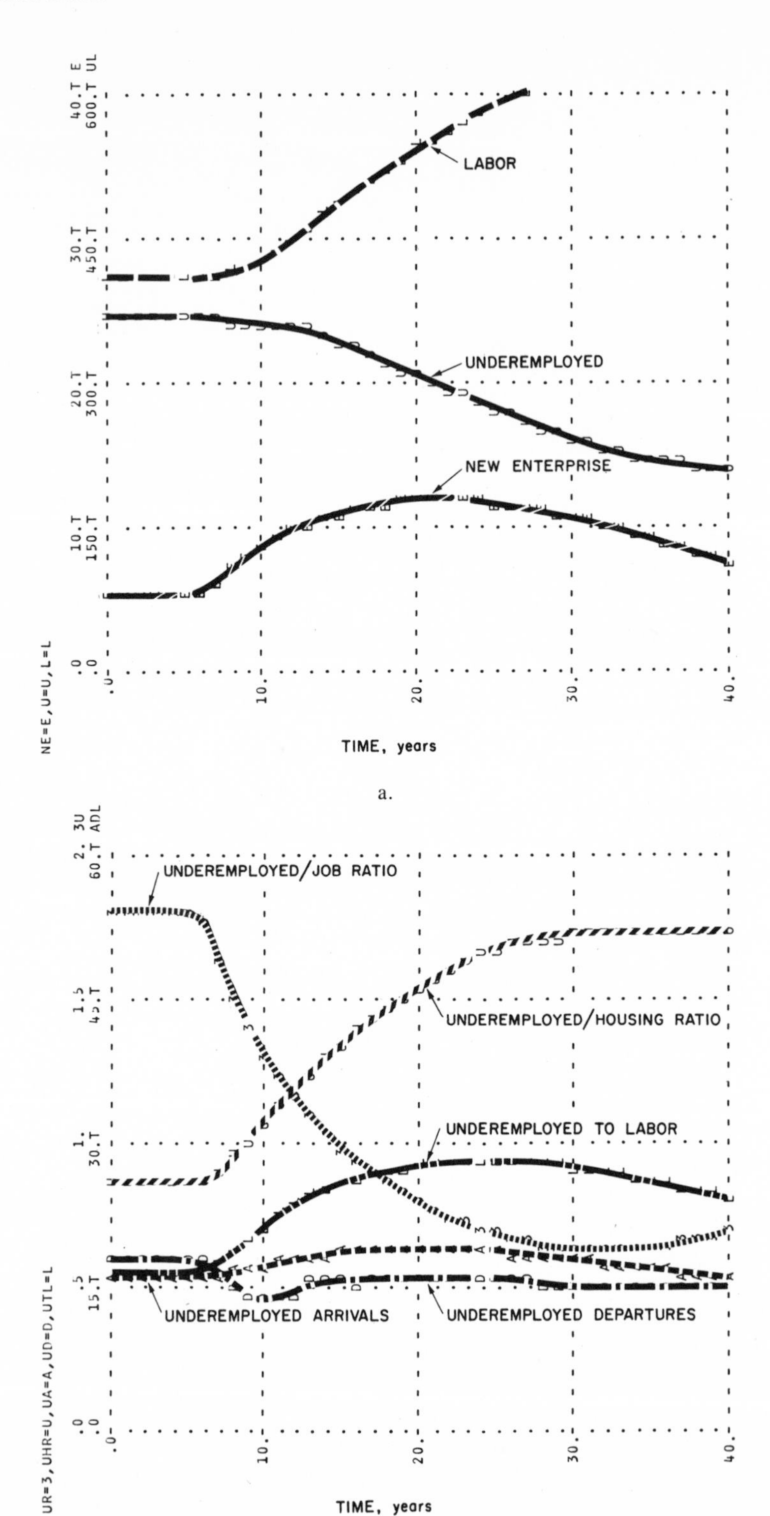
LABOR
UNDEREMPLOYED
NEW ENTERPRISE
TIME, years
UNDEREMPLOYED/JOB RATIO
UNDEREMPLOYED/HOUSING RATIO
UNDEREMPLOYED TO LABOR
UNDEREMPLOYED ARRIVALS
UNDEREMPLOYED DEPARTURES
TIME, years

a.

b.

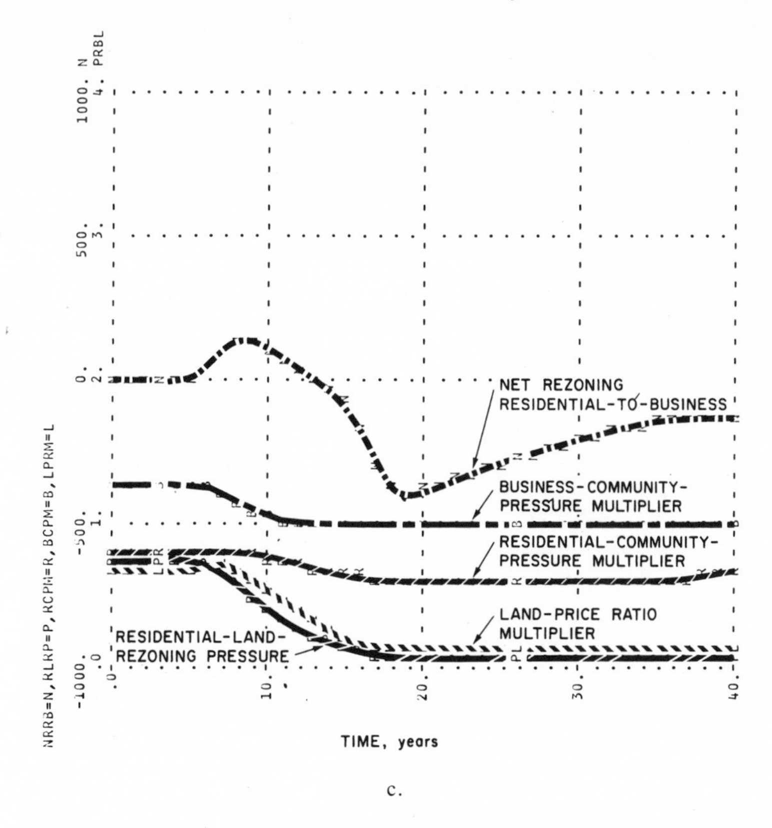

Figure 9-8 The behavior caused by a combination policy to favor business development by rezoning land to business use, additional enterprise expansion, demolishing additional low-quality housing, and reducing worker-housing construction

The rezoning refinement by no means completes the study of land use within an urban area. The *Rezone2* model treats land use at a highly simplified and aggregated level. The aggregation seems justifiable in terms of the broad issues of industrial and housing composition addressed here. The *Rezone2* model does not decide whether a particular piece of urban land should go to residential or business use, nor does it provide a better understanding of the possible role of land-rezoning decisions in managing the urban system. If a real city has important characteristics not adequately portrayed in the *Rezone2* model, some model modifications may be necessary before applying the model. Moreover, the city may have different goals from the *Rezone2* model city's goals of reducing unemployment and raising economic mobility among the urban underemployed. With a better understanding of the overall aspects of urban behavior, more detailed models will be necessary. Residential land and business land could be disaggregated into different categories of use. Service industries, for example, do not offer the same kinds of employment as manufacturing, and otherwise affect a city in different ways. Although it does not supply detailed information, the *Rezone2* model provides an expandable framework for analyzing urban land-use problems.

Notes

1. John S. Miller, "Refinement of the Urban Dynamics Model for Land Rezoning Policy Analysis," Ph.D. dissertation, Massachusetts Institute of Technology, Sloan School of Management, Cambridge, Massachusetts, 1973.

2. Nathaniel J. Mass, "A Dynamic Model of Land Pricing and Urban Land Allocation," in *Readings in Urban Dynamics, vol. 1,* ed. Nathaniel J. Mass (Cambridge, Mass.: Wright-Allen Press, 1974), pp. 175–196.

3. John Stainton, consultant to the Boston Redevelopment Authority, and Bruce Hahl, acting planning director of the Community Development Authority in Lowell, Massachusetts, contributed their knowledge to the *Rezone* refinement.

4. S. J. Makielski, *The Politics of Zoning* (New York: Columbia University Press, 1966), p. 1.

5. Daniel R. Mandelker, *The Zoning Dilemma* (New York: Bobbs-Merrill Co., 1971), p. 23.

6. Ibid., p. 64.

7. Ibid., p. 45.

8. The following 19 equations in the *Rezone2* model were changed or added to the *Urban Dynamics* model: equations 64, 66, 67 (new), 69, 76, 83, 85, 86, 87 (new), 89, 93, 103, 105, 107, 108, 109 (new), 111, 114, 126. To maintain a distinction between the *Urban Dynamics* model and the added sectors, the equation numbering was started at 200 at the beginning of the land rezoning sector.

9. Mass, pp. 175–196.

10. Makielski, p. 143.

11. Mandelker, p. 159.

12. Makielski, p. 141.

13. Mandelker, p. 184.

Appendix: *Rezone2* Model

```
        *       REZONE2
        NOTE
        NOTE    **********UNDEREMPLOYED SECTOR
1       R       UA.KL=(U.K+L.K)(UAN)(AMMP.K)
        C       UAN=.05
2       L       AMMP.K=AMMP.J+(DT/AMMPT)(AMM.J-AMMP.J)
        C       AMMPT=20
3       A       AMM.K=(UAMM.K)(UHM.K)(PEM.K)(UJM.K)(UHPM.K)(AMF)
        C       AMF=1
4       A       UAMM.K=TABHL(UAMMT,UM.K,0,.15,.025)
        T       UAMMT=.3/.7/1/1.2/1.3/1.4/1.5
5       A       UHM.K=TABHL(UHMT,UHR.K,0,2,.25)
        T       UHMT=2.5/2.4/2.2/1.7/1/.4/.2/.1/.05
6       A       UHR.K=(U.K*UFS)/(UH.K*UHPD)
        C       UHPD=12
7       A       PEM.K=TABHL(PEMT,TPCR.K,0,3,.5)
        T       PEMT=.2/.6/1/1.6/2.4/3.2/4
8       A       TPCR.K=((TC.K/P.K)+TPCSP.K)/TPCN
        C       TPCN=250
9       A       P.K=(MP.K)(MPFS)+(L.K)(LFS)+(U.K)(UFS)
        C       MPFS=5
        C       LFS=6
        C       UFS=8
10      A       UJM.K=TABHL(UJMT,UR.K,0,3,.25)
        T       UJMT=2/2/1.9/1.6/1/.6/.4/.3/.2/.15/.1/.05/.02
11      A       UHPM.K=TABHL(UHPMT,UHPR.K,0,.05,.01)
        T       UHPMT=1/1.2/1.5/1.9/2.4/3
12      A       UHPR.K=LCHP.JK/U.K
13      R       UD.KL=(UDN)(U.K)(UDM.K)
        C       UDN=.02
14      A       UDM.K=TABHL(UDMT,1.44*LOGN(AMM.K),-3,3,1)
        T       UDMT=8/4/2/1/.5/.25/.125
15      R       UB.KL=(U.K)(UBR)
        C       UBR=.015
16      L       U.K=U.J+(DT)(UA.JK+UB.JK+LTU.JK-UD.JK-UTL.JK)
        NOTE
        NOTE    **********LABOR SECTOR
17      R       UTL.KL=(UMN)(UW.K)(UMMP.K)+UTP.K
        C       UMN=.1
18      A       UW.K=(U.K)(UFW.K)
19      A       UFW.K=TABHL(UFWT,UR.K,0,4,1)
        T       UFWT=.9/.8/.5/.33/.25
20      L       UTLP.K=UTLP.J+(DT/UTLPT)(UTL.JK-UTLP.J)
        C       UTLPT=10
21      A       UM.K=UTLP.K/U.K
22      L       UMMP.K=UMMP.J+(DT/UMMPT)(UMM.J-UMMP.J)
        C       UMMPT=10
23      A       UMM.K=(LSM.K)(LUM.K)(UEM.K)(UMF)
        C       UMF=1
24      A       LSM.K=TABHL(LSMT,LR.K,0,2,.5)
        T       LSMT=2.4/2/1/.4/.2
25      A       LUM.K=TABHL(LUMT,LUR.K,0,5,1)
        T       LUMT=.2/.7/1/1.2/1.3/1.4
26      A       LUR.K=L.K/U.K
27      A       UEM.K=TABHL(UEMT,TPCR.K,0,3,.5)
        T       UEMT=.2/.7/1/1.3/1.5/1.6/1.7
28      R       LB.KL=(L.K)(LBR)
        C       LBR=.01
29      L       L.K=L.J+(DT)(UTL.JK+LB.JK-LTM.JK+LA.JK-LD.JK-LTU.JK)
30      R       LTU.KL=(L.K)(LLF.K)
31      A       LLF.K=TABHL(LLFT,LR.K,0,2,.5)
        T       LLFT=0/.01/.03/.1/.3
32      R       LTM.KL=(LMN)(L.K)(LMMP.K)+LTPG.K
        C       LMN=.02
33      L       LMMP.K=LMMP.J+(DT/LMMPT)(LMM.J-LMMP.J)
        C       LMMPT=15
34      A       LMM.K=(MSM.K)(MLM.K)(LEM.K)(LMF)
        C       LMF=1
35      A       MSM.K=TABHL(MSMT,MR.K,0,2,.25)
        T       MSMT=2.3/2.2/2/1.6/1/.5/.2/.1/.05
36      A       MR.K=MP.K/MJ.K
37      A       MJ.K=(NE.K)(NEM)+(MB.K)(MBM)+(DI.K)(DIM)
        C       NEM=4
        C       MBM=2
        C       DIM=1
38      A       MLM.K=TABHL(MLMT,MLR.K,0,.2,.05)
        T       MLMT=.2/.7/1/1.2/1.3
```

```
39      A       MLR.K=MP.K/L.K
40      A       LEM.K=TABHL(LEMT,TPCR.K,0,3,.5)
        T       LEMT=.2/.7/1/1.3/1.5/1.6/1.7
41      R       LA.KL=(LAN)(L.K)(LAMP.K)
        C       LAN=.03
42      L       LAMP.K=LAMP.J+(DT/LAMPT)(LAM.J-LAMP.J)
        C       LAMPT=15
43      A       LAM.K=(LAJM.K)(LAUM.K)(LATM.K)(LAHM.K)(LAF)
        C       LAF=1
44      A       LAJM.K=TABHL(LAJMT,LR.K,0,2,.25)
        T       LAJMT=2.6/2.6/2.4/1.8/1/.4/.2/.1/.05
45      A       LAUM.K=TABHL(LAUMT,LUR.K,0,5,1)
        T       LAUMT=.4/.8/1/1.2/1.3/1.3
46      A       LATM.K=TABHL(LATMT,1.44*LOGN(TR.K),-2,4,2)
        T       LATMT=1.2/1/.7/.3
47      A       LAHM.K=TABHL(LAHMT,LHR.K,0,3,.5)
        T       LAHMT=1.3/1.2/1/.5/.2/.1/.05
48      A       LHR.K=(L.K*LFS)/(WH.K*WHPD)
        C       WHPD=6
49      R       LD.KL=(LDN)(L.K)(LDM.K)
        C       LDN=.02
50      A       LDM.K=TABHL(LDMT,1.44*LOGN(LAM.K),-3,3,1)
        T       LDMT=8/4/2/1/.5/.25/.125
        NOTE
        NOTE    **********MANAGERIAL-PROFESSIONAL SECTOR
51      R       MPB.KL=(MP.K)(MPBR)
        C       MPBR=.0075
52      L       MP.K=MP.J+(DT)(LTM.JK+MPB.JK+MA.JK-MD.JK)
53      R       MA.KL=(MAN)(MP.K)(MAMP.K)
        C       MAN=.03
54      L       MAMP.K=MAMP.J+(DT/MAMPT)(MAM.J-MAMP.J)
        C       MAMPT=10
55      A       MAM.K=(MAJM.K)(MAPM.K)(MATM.K)(MAHM.K)(MAF)
        C       MAF=1
56      A       MAJM.K=TABHL(MAJMT,MR.K,0,2,.25)
        T       MAJMT=2.7/2.6/2.4/2/1/.4/.2/.1/.05
57      A       MAPM.K=TABHL(MAPMT,MPR.K,0,.1,.02)
        T       MAPMT=.3/.7/1/1.2/1.3/1.3
58      A       MPR.K=MP.K/(L.K+U.K)
59      A       MATM.K=TABHL(MATMT,1.44*LOGN(TR.K),-2,4,2)
        T       MATMT=1.4/1/.7/.3
60      A       MAHM.K=TABHL(MAHMT,MHR.K,0,3,.5)
        T       MAHMT=1.3/1.2/1/.5/.2/.1/.05
61      A       MHR.K=(MP.K*MPFS)/(PH.K*PHPD)
        C       PHPD=3
62      R       MD.KL=(MDN)(MP.K)(MDM.K)
        C       MDN=.02
63      A       MDM.K=TABHL(MDMT,1.44*LOGN(MAM.K),-3,3,1)
        T       MDMT=8/4/2/1/.5/.25/.125
        NOTE
        NOTE    **********PREMIUM HOUSING SECTOR
64      R       PHC.KL=(PHCD.K)(LCR.K)(RLAC.K)
65      A       PHCD.K=(PHCN)(PH.K)(PHM.K)+PHCP.K
        C       PHCN=.03
66      A       PHM.K=(PHAM.K)(PHLM.K)(PHPM.K)(PHTM.K)(PHEM.K)(PHGM.K)(PHLPM.K)
        X       (PHF)
        C       PHF=1
67      A       PHLPM.K=TABHL(PHLPMT,RLRPA.K,0,3,.5)
        T       PHLPMT=1.2/1.1/1/.9/.7/.5/.3
68      A       PHAM.K=TABHL(PHAMT,MHR.K,0,2,.25)
        T       PHAMT=0/.001/.01/.2/1/3/4.6/5.6/6
69      A       PHLM.K=TABHL(PHLMT,RLFO.K,0,1,.1)
        T       PHLMT=.4/.9/1.3/1.6/1.8/1.9/1.9/1.8/1.4/.7/.2
70      A       LFO.K=(HUT.K*LPH+PUT.K*LPP)/AREA
        C       LPH=.1
        C       LPP=.2
        C       AREA=100000
71      A       HUT.K=PH.K+WH.K+UH.K
72      A       PUT.K=NE.K+MB.K+DI.K
73      A       PHPM.K=TABHL(PHPMT,MPR.K,0,.1,.02)
        T       PHPMT=.3/.7/1/1.2/1.3/1.3
74      A       PHTM.K=TABHL(PHTMT,1.44*LOGN(TR.K),-2,4,2)
        T       PHTMT=1.2/1/.7/.3
75      A       PHEM.K=TABHL(PHEMT,NEGR.K,-.1,.15,.05)
        T       PHEMT=.2/.6/1/1.4/1.8/2.2
76      A       PHGM.K=TABHL(PHGMT,PHGR.K,-.1,.15,.05)
        T       PHGMT=.6/.8/1/1.2/1.4/1.6
77      A       PHGR.K=(PH.K-PHA.K)/(PH.K*PHAT)
```

```
78    L     PHA.K=PHA.J+(DT/PHAT)(PH.J-PHA.J)
      N     PHA=PH-(PHGRI)(PHAT)(PH)
      C     PHAT=10
79    L     PH.K=PH.J+(DT)(PHC.JK-PHO.JK)
80    R     PHO.KL=(PHON)(PH.K)(PHOM.K)
      C     PHON=.03
81    A     PHOM.K=TABHL(PHOMT,1.44*LOGN(PHM.K),-3,3,1)
      T     PHOMT=2.8/2.6/2/1/.5/.3/.2
      NOTE
      NOTE  **********WORKER HOUSING SECTOR
82    L     WH.K=WH.J+(DT)(PHO.JK+WHC.JK-WHO.JK)
83    R     WHC.KL=(WHCD.K)(LCR.K)(RLAC.K)
84    A     WHCD.K=(WHCN.K)(WH.K)(WHM.K)+WHCP.K
85    A     WHCN.K=.03-WHCCB.K
86    A     WHM.K=(WHAM.K)(WHLM.K)(WHUM.K)(WHTM.K)(WHEM.K)(WHGM.K)(WHLPM.K)
      X     (WHF)
      C     WHF=1
87    A     WHLPM.K=TABHL(WHLPMT,RLRPA.K,0,3,.5)
      T     WHLPMT=1.2/1.1/1/.9/.7/.5/.3
88    A     WHAM.K=TABHL(WHAMT,LHR.K,0,2,.25)
      T     WHAMT=0/.05/.1/.3/1/1.8/2.4/2.8/3
89    A     WHLM.K=TABHL(WHLMT,RLFO.K,0,1,.1)
      T     WHLMT=.4/.9/1.3/1.6/1.8/1.9/1.9/1.8/1.4/.7/.2
90    A     WHUM.K=TABHL(WHUMT,LUR.K,0,5,1)
      T     WHUMT=.5/.8/1/1.2/1.3/1.3
91    A     WHTM.K=TABHL(WHTMT,1.44*LOGN(TR.K),-2,4,2)
      T     WHTMT=1.2/1/.7/.3
92    A     WHEM.K=TABHL(WHEMT,NEGR.K,-.2,.3,.1)
      T     WHEMT=.3/.7/1/1.2/1.3/1.4
93    A     WHGM.K=TABHL(WHGMT,WHGR.K,-.1,.15,.05)
      T     WHGMT=.6/.8/1/1.2/1.4/1.6
94    A     WHGR.K=(WH.K-WHA.K)/(WH.K*WHAT)
95    L     WHA.K=WHA.J+(DT/WHAT)(WH.J-WHA.J)
      N     WHA=WH-(WHGRI)(WHAT)(WH)
      C     WHAT=10
96    R     WHO.KL=(WHON)(WH.K)(WHOM.K)
      C     WHON=.02
97    A     WHOM.K=TABHL(WHOMT,1.44*LOGN(WHM.K),-3,3,1)
      T     WHOMT=2.2/2/1.6/1/.7/.5/.4
      NOTE
      NOTE  **********UNDEREMPLOYED HOUSING SECTOR
98    L     UH.K=UH.J+(DT)(WHO.JK-SHD.JK+LCHP.JK)
99    R     SHD.KL=(SHDN.K)(UH.K)(SHDM.K)+SHDP.K
100   A     SHDN.K=.02+SHDDP.K
101   A     SHDM.K=(SHAM.K)(SHLM.K)(SHDF)
      C     SHDF=1
102   A     SHAM.K=TABHL(SHAMT,UHR.K,0,2,.5)
      T     SHAMT=3.6/2/1/.6/.4
103   A     SHLM.K=TABHL(SHLMT,RLFO.K,.8,1,.05)
      T     SHLMT=1/1.2/1.4/1.8/2
      NOTE
      NOTE  **********NEW ENTERPRISE SECTOR
104   L     NE.K=NE.J+(DT)(NEC.JK-NED.JK)
105   R     NEC.KL=(NECD.K)(LCR.K)(BLAC.K)
106   A     NECD.K=(NECN.K)(NECF*NE.K+MBCF*MB.K+DICF*DI.K)(EM.K)+NECP.K
      C     NECF=1
      C     MBCF=.5
      C     DICF=.3
107   A     NECN.K=.05+NECE.K
108   A     EM.K=(EMM.K)(ELM.K)(ELJM.K)(ETM.K)(EGM.K)(ELPM.K)(EF)
      C     EF=1
109   A     ELPM.K=TABHL(ELPMT,BLPR.K,0,3,.5)
      T     ELPMT=1.6/1.3/1.1/1/.9/.85/.8
110   A     EMM.K=TABHL(EMMT,MR.K,0,2,.25)
      T     EMMT=.1/.15/.3/.5/1/1.4/1.7/1.9/2
111   A     ELM.K=TABHL(ELMT,BLFO.K,0,1,.1)
      T     ELMT=1/1.15/1.3/1.4/1.45/1.4/1.3/1.25/1/.7/.4
112   A     ELJM.K=TABHL(ELJMT,LRP.K,0,2,.25)
      T     ELJMT=0/.05/.15/.4/1/1.5/1.7/1.8/1.8
113   A     ETM.K=TABHL(ETMT,1.44*LOGN(TR.K),-2,4,1)
      T     ETMT=1.3/1.2/1/.8/.5/.25/.1
114   A     EGM.K=TABHL(EGMT,NEGR.K,-.1,.15,.05)
      T     EGMT=.6/.8/1/1.2/1.4/1.6
115   A     NEGR.K=(NE.K-NEA.K)/(NE.K*NEAT)
116   L     NEA.K=NEA.J+(DT/NEAT)(NE.J-NEA.J)
      N     NEA=NE-(NEGRI)(NEAT)(NE)
      C     NEAT=10
      NOTE
```

```
        NOTE    **********MATURE BUSINESS SECTOR
117     R       NED.KL=(NEDN)(NE.K)(EDM.K)
        C       NEDN=.08
118     A       EDM.K=TABHL(EDMT,1.44*LOGN(EM.K),-3,3,1)
        T       EDMT=2/1.8/1.5/1/.7/.5/.5
119     L       MB.K=MB.J+(DT)(NED.JK-MBD.JK)
120     R       MBD.KL=(MBDN)(MB.K)(BDM.K)
        C       MBDN=.05
121     A       BDM.K=TABHL(BDMT,1.44*LOGN(EM.K),-3,3,1)
        T       BDMT=2/1.8/1.5/1/.7/.5/.4
        NOTE
        NOTE    **********DECLINING INDUSTRY SECTOR
122     L       DI.K=DI.J+(DT)(MBD.JK-DID.JK)
123     R       DID.KL=(DIDN)(DI.K)(DIDM.K)+DIDP.K
        C       DIDN=.03
124     A       DIDM.K=(DIEM.K)(DILM.K)(DIDF)
        C       DIDF=1
125     A       DIEM.K=TABHL(DIEMT,1.44*LOGN(EM.K),-3,3,1)
        T       DIEMT=.4/.5/.7/1/1.6/2.4/4
126     A       DILM.K=TABHL(DILMT,BLFO.K,.8,1,.05)
        T       DILMT=1/1.2/1.4/1.6/2
        NOTE
        NOTE    **********TAX SECTOR
127     A       TC.K=(AV.K)(TAN)(TR.K)
        C       TAN=50
128     A       TR.K=TABHL(TRT,1.44*LOGN(TRNP.K),-2,4,1)
        T       TRT=.3/.5/1/1.8/2.8/3.6/4
129     L       TRNP.K=TRNP.J+(DT/TRNPT)(TRN.J-TRNP.J)
        N       TRNP=TRN
        C       TRNPT=30
130     A       TRN.K=TAI.K/TAN
131     A       TAI.K=TN.K/AV.K
132     A       TN.K=(TMP*MPFS*MP.K+TLP*LFS*L.K+TUP*UFS*U.K)(TCM.K)
        C       TMP=150
        C       TLP=200
        C       TUP=300
133     A       TCM.K=TABHL(TCMT,LUR.K,0,3,.5)
        T       TCMT=2/1.6/1.3/1.1/1/.9/.8
134     A       AV.K=(HAV.K+BAV.K)
135     A       HAV.K=PHAV*PH.K+WHAV*WH.K+UHAV*UH.K
        C       PHAV=30
        C       WHAV=15
        C       UHAV=5
136     A       BAV.K=NEAV*NE.K+MBAV*MB.K+DIAV*DI.K
        C       NEAV=500
        C       MBAV=300
        C       DIAV=100
        NOTE
        NOTE    **********JOB SECTOR
137     A       LDC.K=PHCD.K*PHCL+WHCD.K*WHCL+NECD.K*NECL+LCHCD.K*LCHCL
        C       PHCL=2
        C       WHCL=1
        C       NECL=20
        C       LCHCL=.6
138     A       LDI.K=NE.K*NEL+MB.K*MBL+DI.K*DIL
        C       NEL=20
        C       MBL=15
        C       DIL=10
139     A       LJ.K=LDC.K+LDI.K
140     A       LR.K=L.K/LJ.K
141     A       ULJR.K=TABHL(ULJRT,LR.K,0,2,.5)
        T       ULJRT=1.15/.8/.5/.25/.1
142     A       UJ.K=LJ.K*ULJR.K+UJP.K
143     A       UR.K=U.K/UJ.K
144     A       LCR.K=TABHL(LCRT,LR.K,0,2,.5)
        T       LCRT=0/.5/.9/1.1/1.15
145     L       LRP.K=LRP.J+(DT/LRPT)(LR.J-LRP.J)
        C       LRPT=5
        NOTE
        NOTE    **********LAND REZONING ELABORATION
200     L       RL.K=RL.J+(DT)(BLR.JK-RLR.JK)
        N       RL=AREA-BL
201     L       BL.K=BL.J+(DT)(RLR.JK-BLR.JK)
        N       BL=AREA*BLFI
        C       BLFI=0.05
202     R       RLR.KL=(RL.K)(RLFR.K)(RLRPF.K)+RLRD.K
203     R       BLR.KL=(BL.K)(BLFR.K)(BLRPF.K)
204     A       RLFR.K=(RLRN)(RLAM.K)(RLRM.K)
        C       RLRN=.002
```

```
205     A     BLFR.K=(BLRN)(BLAM.K)(BLRM.K)
        C     BLRN=.015
206     A     RLAM.K=TABHL(RLAMT,RLFO.K,0,1,.2)
        T     RLAMT=.4/.38/.35/.32/.29/.25
207     A     BLAM.K=TABHL(BLAMT,BLFO.K,0,1,.2)
        T     BLAMT=.4/.38/.35/.3/.2/.1
208     A     RLFO.K=RLO.K/RL.K
209     A     RLO.K=HUT.K*LPH
210     A     RLU.K=RL.K-RLO.K
211     A     BLFO.K=BLO.K/BL.K
212     A     BLO.K=PUT.K*LPP
213     A     BLU.K=BL.K-BLO.K
214     A     RLRM.K=TABHL(RLRMT,RLRPA.K,0,6,1)
        T     RLRMT=0/1/3/5.5/8/15/25
215     A     BLRM.K=TABHL(BLRMT,1.44*LOGN(RLRPA.K),-3,3,1)
        T     BLRMT=30/8/3/1/.5/.25/0
216     A     RLRPA.K=SMOOTH(RLRP.K,RLRPAT)
        N     RLRPA=1
        C     RLRPAT=2
217     A     RLRP.K=(RCPM.K)(BCPM.K)(LPRM.K)
218     A     RCPM.K=TABHL(RCPMT,HSI.K,0,2,.5)
        T     RCPMT=1/1/.8/.55/.3
219     A     HSI.K=(WSP.K)/(WSAH.K)
220     A     WSP.K=(MP.K*MPFS*MIW)+(L.K*LFS*LIW)+(U.K*UFS*UIW)
221     A     WSAH.K=(PH.K*PHPD*MIW)+(WH.K*WHPD*LIW)+(UH.K*UHPD*UIW)
        C     MIW=3
        C     LIW=2
        C     UIW=1
222     A     BCPM.K=TABHL(BCPMT,JSI.K,0,2,.5)
        T     BCPMT=1/1/1/1.5/2
223     A     JSI.K=(MP.K+L.K+U.K)/(MJ.K+LJ.K+UJ.K)
224     A     LPRM.K=TABHL(LPRMT,1.44*LOGN(BRLPR.K),-4,2,1)
        T     LPRMT=.125/.167/.33/.6/1/3/6
225     A     BRLPR.K=BLPR.K/RLPR.K
226     S     NRRB.K=RLR.JK-BLR.JK
        NOTE
        NOTE  **********LAND PRICING ELABORATION
        NOTE
        NOTE  **********BUSINESS LAND PRICE SECTOR
227     L     BLP.K=BLP.J+(DT)(BLPC.JK)
        N     BLP=BLPI
228     R     BLPC.KL=BLP.K*BLFPC.K
229     A     BLFPC.K=TABHL(BLFPCT,1.44*LOGN(BLD.K/BLS.K),-3,3,1)
        T     BLFPCT=-.2/-.18/-.1/0/.15/.35/.4
230     A     BLDNC.K=(NECD.K)(LPP)
231     A     BLDS.K=(BLDNC.K)(BLSN)(BLDSM.K)
        C     BLSN=.25
232     A     BLDSM.K=TABHL(BLDSMT,BLSI.K,0,6,1)
        T     BLDSMT=.7/1/1.3/1.75/2.25/3/4
233     A     BLSI.K=TABHL(BLSIT,BLPGR.K,-.3,.5,.1)
        T     BLSIT=.5/.6/.75/1/1.3/1.65/2/2.5/3
234     L     BLPA.K=BLPA.J+(DT/BLPAT)(BLP.J-BLPA.J)
        N     BLPA=BLP
        C     BLPAT=5
235     A     BLPGR.K=(BLP.K-BLPA.K)/(BLP.K*BLPAT)
236     A     BLS.K=((BLU.K*BLLF.K)/BLHTN)(BLSTM.K)(BLSPM.K)(BLSSM.K)
237     A     BLLF.K=TABHL(BLLFT,BLFO.K,0,1,.2)
        T     BLLFT=.02/.3/.6/.9/1/1
        C     BLHTN=14
238     A     BLSTM.K=TABHL(BLSTMT,1.44*LOGN(TR.K),-2,2,1)
        T     BLSTMT=.5/.6/1/1.2/1.28
239     A     BLSPM.K=TABHL(BLSPMT,BLP.K/BLPPA.K,0,3,.5)
        T     BLSPMT=0/.5/1/1.2/1.3/1.35/1.4
240     A     BLPPA.K=SMOOTH(BLP.K,BLHT.K)
241     A     BLHT.K=(BLU.K*BLLF.K)/BLT.K
242     A     BLPR.K=BLP.K/BLPN
        C     BLPN=5000
243     A     BLSSM.K=TABHL(BLSSMT,BLSI.K,0,6,1)
        T     BLSSMT=1.4/1/.75/.65/.55/.5/.5
244     A     BLT.K=BLS.K*BLTM.K
245     A     BLTM.K=TABHL(BLTMT,BLS.K/BLD.K,0,6,1)
        T     BLTMT=1.2/1/.55/.35/.25/.2/.167
246     A     BLAC.K=BLT.K/BLD.K
247     A     BLD.K=BLDNC.K+BLDS.K
        NOTE
        NOTE  **********RESIDENTIAL LAND PRICE SECTOR
248     L     RLP.K=RLP.J+(DT)(RLPC.JK)
        N     RLP=RLPI
```

```
249    R     RLPC.KL=RLP.K*RLFPC.K
250    A     RLFPC.K=TABHL(RLFPCT,1.44*LOGN(RLD.K/RLS.K),-3,3,1)
       T     RLFPCT=-.18/-.15/-.08/0/.12/.28/.35
251    A     RLDNC.K=(PHCD.K+WHCD.K)(LPH)
252    A     RLDS.K=(RLDNC.K)(RLSN)(RLDSM.K)
       C     RLSN=.25
253    A     RLDSM.K=TABHL(RLDSMT,RLSI.K,0,6,1)
       T     RLDSMT=.7/1/1.3/1.75/2.25/3/4
254    A     RLSI.K=TABHL(RLSIT,RLPGR.K,-.3,.5,.1)
       T     RLSIT=.5/.6/.75/1/1.3/1.65/2/2,5/3
255    L     RLPA.K=RLPA.J+(DT/RLPAT)(RLP.J-RLPA.J)
       N     RLPA=RLP
       C     RLPAT=5
256    A     RLPGR.K=(RLP.K-RLPA.K)/(RLP.K*RLPAT)
257    A     RLS.K=((RLU.K*RLLF.K)/RLHTN)(RLSTM.K)(RLSPM.K)(RLSSM.K)
258    A     RLLF.K=TABHL(RLLFT,RLFO.K,0,1,.2)
       T     RLLFT=.02/.3/.6/.9/.95/1
       C     RLHTN=14
259    A     RLSTM.K=TABHL(RLSTMT,1.44*LOGN(TR.K),-2,2,1)
       T     RLSTMT=.5/.6/1/1.1/1.15
260    A     RLSPM.K=TABHL(RLSPMT,RLP.K/RLPPA.K,0,3,.5)
       T     RLSPMT=0/.5/1/1.2/1.3/1.35/1.4
261    A     RLPPA.K=SMOOTH(RLP.K,RLHT.K)
262    A     RLHT.K=(RLU.K*RLLF.K)/RLT.K
263    A     RLPR.K=RLP.K/RLPN
       C     RLPN=4000
264    A     RLSSM.K=TABHL(RLSSMT,RLSI.K,0,6,1)
       T     RLSSMT=1.4/1/.75/.65/.55/.5/.5
265    A     RLT.K=RLS.K*RLTM.K
266    A     RLTM.K=TABHL(RLTMT,RLS.K/RLD.K,0,6,1)
       T     RLTMT=1.2/1/.55/.35/.25/.2/.167
267    A     RLAC.K=RLT.K/RLD.K
268    A     RLD.K=RLDNC.K+RLDS.K
       NOTE
       NOTE  **********CITY DEVELOPMENT PROGRAMS
269    A     UTP.K=UTR*U.K*CLIP(0,1,SWT1,TIME.K)
       C     UTR=0
       C     SWT1=0
270    A     LTPG.K=LTR*L.K*CLIP(0,1,SWT2,TIME.K)
       C     LTR=0
       C     SWT2=0
271    A     PHCP.K=PHCR*PH.K*PHLM.K*CLIP(0,1,SWT3,TIME.K)
       C     PHCR=0            NOTE LAND MULTIPLIER TERM
       C     SWT3=0
272    A     WHCP.K=WHCR*HUT.K*WHLM.K*CLIP(0,1,SWT4,TIME.K)
       C     WHCR=0            NOTE LAND MULTIPLIER TERM
       C     SWT4=0
273    A     SHDP.K=SHDR*UH.K*CLIP(0,1,SWT5,TIME.K)
       C     SHDR=0
       C     SWT5=0
274    A     NECP.K=NECR*PUT.K*ELM.K*CLIP(0,1,SWT6,TIME.K)
       C     NECR=0             NOTE LAND MULTIPLIER TERM
       C     SWT6=0
275    A     DIDP.K=DIDR*DI.K*CLIP(0,1,SWT7,TIME.K)
       C     DIDR=0
       C     SWT7=0
276    A     TPCSP.K=TPCS*CLIP(0,1,SWT8,TIME.K)
       C     TPCS=0
       C     SWT8=0
277    A     UJP.K=UJPC*U.K*CLIP(0,1,SWT9,TIME.K)
       C     UJPC=0
       C     SWT9=0
278    R     LCHP.KL=(LCHCD.K)(LCR.K)
279    A     LCHCD.K=LCHPC*U.K*WHLM.K*CLIP(0,1,SWT10,TIME.K)
       C     LCHPC=0
       C     SWT10=0
       NOTE
       NOTE     ******NEW LAND REZONING PROGRAMS
280    A     NECE.K=NEEF*CLIP(0,1,SWT12,TIME.K)
       C     NEEF=0
       C     SWT12=0
281    A     RLRPF.K=CLIP(RLRPF1,RLRPF2,SWT13,TIME.K)
       C     RLRPF1=1
       C     RLRPF2=1
       C     SWT13=0
282    A     BLRPF.K=CLIP(BLRPF1,BLRPF2,SWT14,TIME.K)
       C     BLRPF1=1
       C     BLRPF2=1
       C     SWT14=0
```

```
283     A       WHCCB.K=WHCCBF*CLIP(0,1,SWT15,TIME.K)
        C       WHCCBF=0
        C       SWT15=0
284     A       RLRD.K=ACRES*CLIP(0,1,SWT17,TIME.K)-ACRES*CLIP(0,1,SWT18,
        X       TIME.K)
        C       ACRES=0
        C       SWT17=0
        C       SWT18=0
285     A       SHDDP.K=RAMP(.004,TT1)-RAMP(.004,TT2)
        C       TT1=0
        C       TT2=0
        NOTE
        NOTE    CONTROL CARDS
        NOTE
        C       DT=.5
        C       LENGTH=50
        N       TIME=-500
286     A       PLTPER.K=CLIP(PLTMIN,PLTMAX,PLTCT,TIME.K)
        C       PLTMIN=0
        C       PLTMAX=0
        C       PLTCT=-.5
287     A       PRTPER.K=CLIP(PRTMIN,PRTMAX,PRTCT,TIME.K)
        C       PRTMIN=0
        C       PRTMAX=0
        C       PRTCT=-.5
288     S       UTLN.K=UTL.JK-LTU.JK
        PLOT    NE=E(0,40E3)/U=U,L=L(0,600E3)
        PLOT    UR=3,UHR=U(0,2)/UA=A,UD=D,UTL=L(0,60E3)
        PLOT    NRRB=N(-1E3,1E3)/RLRP=P,RCPM=R,BCPM=B,LPRM=L(0,4)
        NOTE       INITIAL VALUES FOR CITY2G
        N       NE=200
        N       MB=1000
        N       DI=100
        N       PH=5000
        N       WH=21000
        N       UH=1100
        N       MP=3900
        N       L=14000
        N       U=1200
        N       AMMP=1
        N       UTLP=75
        N       UMMP=1
        N       LMMP=1
        N       LAMP=1
        N       MAMP=1
        N       LRP=1
        N       PHGRI=.03
        N       WHGRI=.03
        N       NEGRI=.03
        N       BLPI=40
        N       RLPI=40
        RUN     EQULIBRIUM TEST
        C       BLRPF2=.2
        C       RLRPF2=5
        C       SWT13=5
        C       SWT14=5
        C       PLTMIN=50
        C       PLTMAX=1
        RUN     FIGURE 9-7
        C       BLRPF2=.2
        C       RLRPF2=5
        C       SWT13=5
        C       SWT14=5
        C       NEEF=.01
        C       SWT12=5
        C       WHCCBF=.015
        C       SWT15=5
        C       ACRES=4000
        C       SWT17=5
        C       SWT18=7
        C       TT1=5
        C       TT2=15
        C       SHDR=.04
        C       SWT5=5
        C       PLTMIN=50
        C       PLTMAX=1
        RUN     FIGURE 9-8
```

10

Urban Dynamics and Housing Abandonment

Walter W. Schroeder III

Housing abandonment is a serious and growing problem in mature American cities. The exodus of middle- and upper-income families from the central city has created a socioeconomic vacuum in which the poor, the least equipped to combat housing abandonment, suffer most severely. Abandonment continually worsens city conditions, frustrates attempts to eradicate poverty, and drains a city's economic strength.

This reading presents a broad-based analysis of the housing-abandonment problem. Changes are made in the Urban Dynamics *model to represent explicitly the abandonment structure and how it relates to the rest of the urban system. The refinement also permits a test of urban policies for their potential impact on the level of abandoned housing. For example, the refined model is used to simulate and evaluate the demolition of abandoned housing. Demolition offers older cities the opportunity to clear more land in their stagnant central cores for job-intensive industrial development, thereby attracting the employment opportunities without which revival cannot be sustained.*

10
Urban Dynamics and Housing Abandonment

10.1 Introduction

Many experts believe that housing abandonment comes about primarily as a result of local interactions among urban housing and economic and social influences.[1] If so, the *Urban Dynamics* model should be particularly well suited for studying the problem of housing abandonment, for it focuses on local socioeconomic interactions and the effects of present conditions on future conditions. The model also offers a promising perspective for designing policies aimed at controlling abandonment. This reading describes and explains a set of modifications to the *Urban Dynamics* model. The aim of the modifications is to represent specifically the process of housing abandonment in our cities. The *Urban Dynamics* model reproduces many forces that tend, over time, to drive upper-income families away from a city; it also contains an explicit representation of over- or under-utilized residential properties. Therefore, the model provides a useful framework for an analysis of abandonment. The observed causes and consequences of abandonment are added to the *Urban Dynamics* model in this reading. Since the highly aggregated structure of that model subsumes a great many real-city elements, and the model behavior appears to correspond accurately to observed urban processes, the abandonment refinement should not significantly alter the model's behavior. The disaggregation of the housing sector to make an explicit representation of abandoned housing, however, has several advantages over the aggregated *Urban Dynamics* model.

First, the separation of underemployed housing into occupiable and abandoned housing provides a more realistic representation. The *Urban Dynamics* model, by aggregating occupiable and abandoned structures in one level, combines both abandoned and underemployed housing as influences in attracting potential underemployed residents. A disaggregated model structure can display occupiable and abandoned housing as two separate levels. Only occupiable housing directly influences migration. Second, the *Urban Dynamics* model's ability to describe medium-term (six to ten years) responses to policy alternatives improves through disaggregation. The refinement breaks three relatively long delays (corresponding to the normal lifetime of each housing category in the original model) into four delays. The shorter average delays sharpen the model's short-term response. Third, disaggregation adds to the *Urban Dynamics* model by permitting an examination of the effects of various policies on abandoned housing in an urban area. An abandoned-housing-demolition program, for example, cannot be clearly investigated with the *Urban Dynamics* model, which does not distinguish between demolishing abandoned housing and demolishing low-quality, but still occupiable, housing. The abandonment refinement serves as an improved basis for urban policy analysis. A properly constructed abandonment sector not only allows for a more detailed examination of housing-demolition programs but can also help to evaluate how other city policies indirectly affect housing abandonment.

10.2 Real-World System Structure Surrounding Abandonment

Abandoned housing is removed from the urban system either through demolition or through upgrading. By definition, the upgrading process consists of partial demolition as well as reconstruction. Representing the upgrading process through the demolition-construction rates in the model is technically sound, and it permits an effective concentration on just one rate of removal of abandoned housing: demolition. Cities demolish abandoned housing in an attempt to reduce the amount of abandoned and blighted property. The abandonment refinement should be able to test whether a program of accelerated demolition of abandoned housing provides an appropriate strategy for improving overall conditions in a city. Many urban models cannot fully address such a large-scale question because the analysis must include not only the urban housing market but also the interrelationships between the housing market and the rest of the urban system. If a program directly or indirectly affects many elements of the urban system, a model that contains only one or a few of the elements cannot make a complete policy evaluation. The following analysis helps to identify the relationships that tie the housing-abandonment subsystem to the rest of the urban system. If the important causal ties can be properly identified and represented in an urban dynamics model, then public officials will have a better means of evaluating programs aimed at combatting the effects of abandonment. Two rates, abandoned-housing demolition and abandonment, directly influence the amount of abandoned housing within the urban system. Figure 10-1 illustrates the abandonment subsystem and shows how the two rates modulate the level of abandoned housing in a city. Because the two rates operate independently in Figure 10-1, neither rate totally controls the level. The demolition rate can influence, but not govern, the level of abandoned housing. A full analysis of the consequences of an abandoned-housing demolition program must also take into account any forces that influence the rate of abandonment.

In normal circumstances, demolishing abandoned housing immediately reduces the level of abandoned houses in a city. But the reduced level of abandoned houses may induce future change in the rate of abandonment. If the abandonment rate increases as a

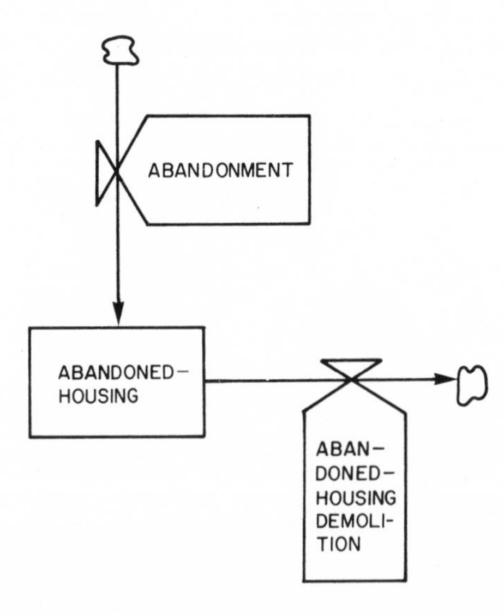

Figure 10-1 The abandonment subsystem: two rates affect the level of abandoned housing

consequence of the demolition program, then the system has compensated against the program, and the level of abandoned houses may ultimately decline only slightly. If the abandonment rate decreases, however, then the two rates reinforce one another in reducing the abandoned-housing level. Therefore, whether the demolition program activates a self-reinforcing or a self-compensating set of reactions is an important policy question.

Figure 10-2 diagrams one possible self-compensating feedback loop. As the demolition program removes abandoned houses, more land becomes available for new housing construction. New construction increases the supply of good-quality housing, but it may also increase the rate of filter-down of housing into the older, low-quality category. As the pool of low-quality housing grows, abandonment also becomes more likely. The self-compensating loop tends to diminish the effectiveness of the demolition program by increasing the rate of abandonment. Conversely, the feedback loop shown in Figure 10-3 reduces the rate of abandonment as a consequence of the demolition program. The reinforcing loop tends to preserve neighborhood conditions by removing the threat of blight, thus reducing the incentives for abandonment. The loop

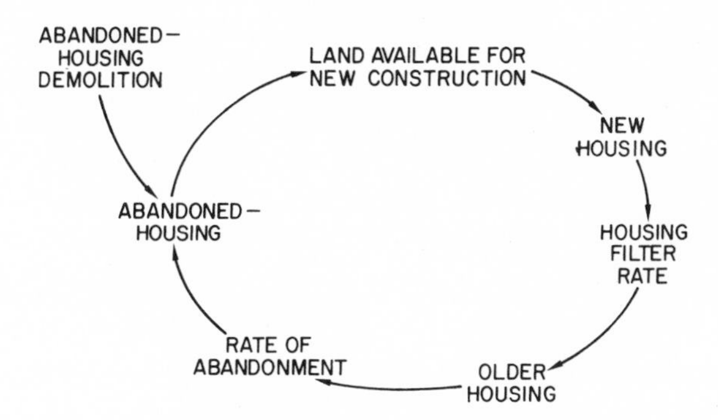

Figure 10-2 A compensating feedback loop that can diminish the effects of the demolition program

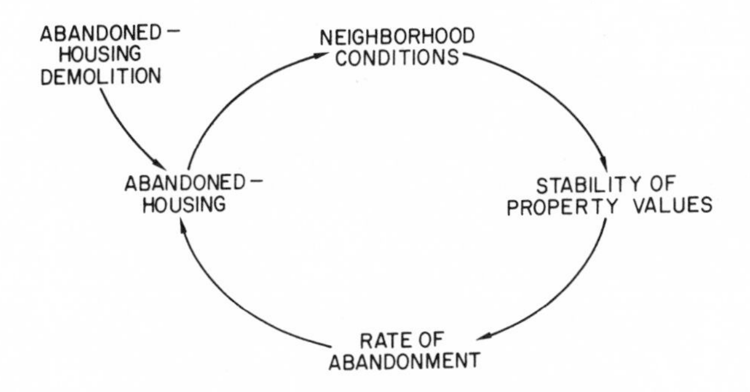

Figure 10-3 A reinforcing feedback loop that augments the effects of the demolition program

has a supportive effect relative to the demolition program. Reducing the level of abandoned housing tends to protect neighborhood conditions and property values. Given stable property values, landlords less often resort to abandonment. With a decreased rate of abandonment and increased demolition, the level of abandoned housing falls.

Financial considerations normally constitute the primary constraint on demolishing abandoned housing. The analysis presented here assumes the availability of adequate finances from external sources. For example, it assumes that the city uses a portion of its community development revenues for housing demolition. Lack of public enthusiasm or interest in demolition imposes another more subtle constraint. Most city officials prefer to associate themselves with ambitious construction programs rather than with demolition activity. Consequently, a model capable of illustrating the long-range consequences of demolition can serve as a public educational device. If demolition can benefit a city, a program of public education may help remove the current constraint of disinterest.

10.3 Structure of the Abandonment Refinement

A DYNAMO flow diagram of the structural additions to the *Urban Dynamics* model to incorporate the abandonment refinement appears in Figure 10-4. The level of abandoned housing AH originates from the level of underemployed housing UH. Underemployed housing can undergo either demolition, through the underemployed-housing demolition rate UHD, or abandonment, through the rate of underemployed-housing abandonment UHA. Figure 10-4 displays three local influences on the rate of underemployed-housing abandonment UHA. Two influences on the rate of abandoned-housing demolition AHD also appear. The upper right-hand portion of Figure 10-4 contains variables that affect the rate of underemployed-housing demolition UHD. Finally, the upper left-hand portion of Figure 10-4 deals with the effect of abandonment on the rate of worker-housing obsolescence WHO. The numbers next to or below each variable in Figure 10-4 are the equation numbers appearing in the documentor listing of the refined model. For example, equation 200 in the refined model defines the level of abandoned housing AH. Equation numbers beginning with 200 correspond to new or altered variables. Equation numbers below 200 correspond to variables unchanged from the *Urban Dynamics* model. (A documentor listing of the abandonment sector appears as the appendix to this reading.)

Refining the model structure and parameters involves four important steps:

1. representing the rate of underemployed-housing abandonment UHA,
2. representing the rate of abandoned-housing demolition AHD,
3. readjusting the rate of underemployed-housing demolition UHD, and
4. altering the rates of premium-housing and worker-housing obsolescence (PHO and WHO) to reflect the spread of blight.

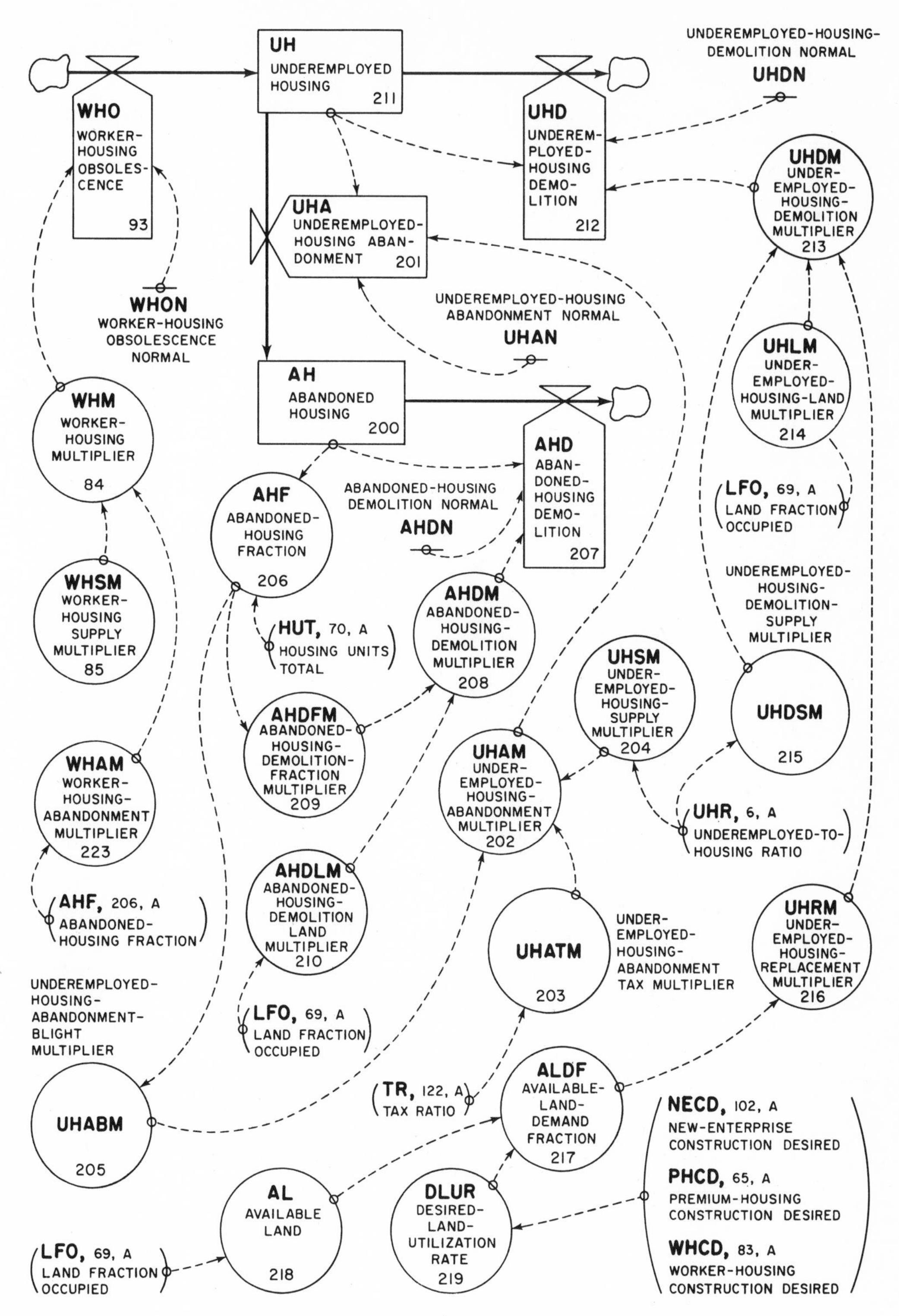

Figure 10-4 Flow diagram of the housing-abandonment refinement

Underemployed-Housing Abandonment UHA. The *National Survey of Housing Abandonment* defines abandonment as:

> the end of a historical process which has less to do with housing quality than with who lives in it, who owns it, and the willingness of investment capital to remain engaged. . . Abandonment is highest in areas with. . . economically unstable tenants.[2]

The definition suggests that abandoned housing has a close relationship with underemployed housing UH in the *Urban Dynamics* model. The levels of housing in that model are defined in terms of their age and the socioeconomic status of their inhabitants. Underemployed housing is older and most often occupied by lower-income families. Abandonment can reasonably be modeled as a potential final stage in the aging of a house, for it seldom occurs when housing inhabited by upper-income families suddenly becomes vacant.[3] Housing qualifies for the abandoned category only after habitation by "economically unstable tenants." In the *Urban Dynamics* model, underemployed housing includes all housing inhabited by economically unstable tenants. Modeling abandoned housing as a level originating from the level of underemployed housing therefore seems to be consistent with most expert opinions. In Figure 10-4, four primary forces influence the rate of abandonment. One influence is the level of underemployed housing UH. The other three influences, arising from conditions other than the amount of housing alone, modulate the normal rate of abandonment (underemployed-housing-abandonment normal UHAN) through the underemployed-housing-abandonment multiplier UHAM. The first influence on the rate of underemployed-housing abandonment UHA is the level of underemployed housing. As entire urban communities fill with lower-income families, housing becomes more prone to abandonment. Banks and loan agencies often refuse home-improvement loans and new mortgages to residents of economically depressed neighborhoods.[4] The *Urban Dynamics* model can represent a city's tendency to have more "economically unstable" neighborhoods as underemployed housing increases. If the amount of underemployed housing increases, the rate of underemployed-housing abandonment in the refined model (measured in structures per year) should also tend to rise. Figure 10-5, which reproduces the relevant portion of Figure 10-4, contains a causal connection (dotted line) showing the relationship between the level of underemployed housing and underemployed-housing abandonment. Equations 200 and 201 describe housing aban-

```
AH.K=AH.J+(DT)(UHA.JK-AHD.JK-AHDP.JK)                    200, L
AH=0                                                     200.1, N
    AH      - ABANDONED HOUSING (HOUSING UNITS)
    UHA     - UNDEREMPLOYED-HOUSING ABANDONMENT (HOUSING
                UNITS/YEAR)
    AHD     - ABANDONED-HOUSING DEMOLITION (HOUSING
                UNITS/YEAR)
    AHDP    - ABANDONED-HOUSING-DEMOLITION PROGRAM
                (HOUSING UNITS/YEAR)

UHA.KL=(UH.K)(UHAN)(UHAM.K)                              201, R
UHAN=.005                                                201.1, C
    UHA     - UNDEREMPLOYED-HOUSING ABANDONMENT (HOUSING
                UNITS/YEAR)
    UH      - UNDEREMPLOYED HOUSING (HOUSING UNITS)
    UHAN    - UNDEREMPLOYED-HOUSING-ABANDONMENT NORMAL
                (FRACTION/YEAR)
    UHAM    - UNDEREMPLOYED-HOUSING-ABANDONMENT
                MULTIPLIER (DIMENSIONLESS)
```

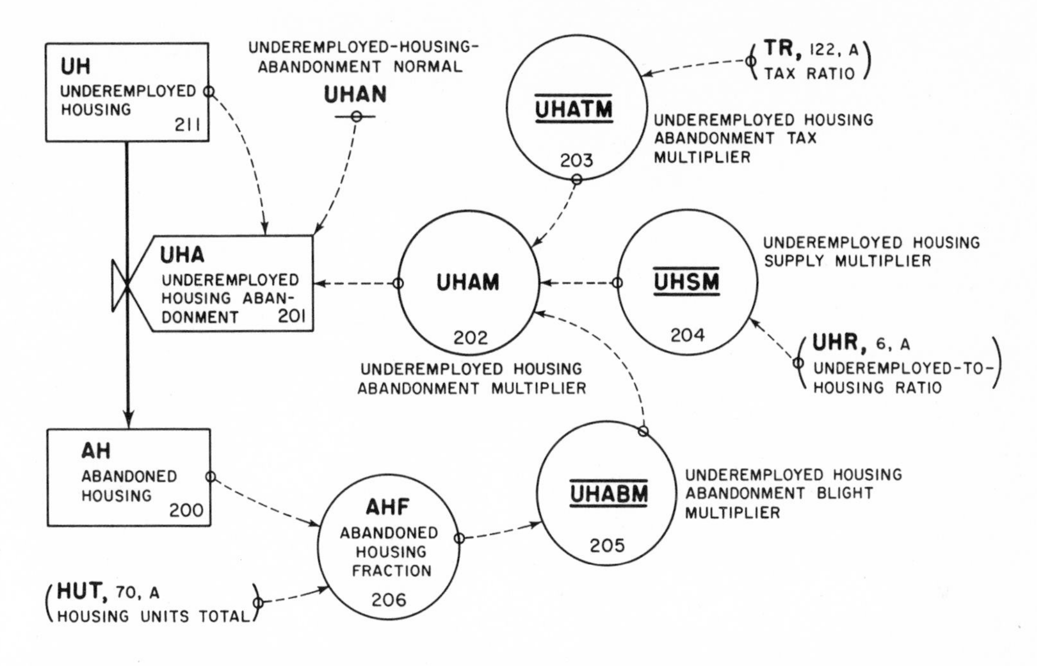

Figure 10-5 Influences on the rate of underemployed-housing abandonment UHA

donment as a level variable, increased by the rate of underemployed-housing abandonment. The normal annual rate of abandonment in the refined model, by definition, is 0.005 of the underemployed housing level. As underemployed housing increases, underemployed-housing abandonment also tends to increase, thereby completing a feedback loop in Figure 10-5. The 0.005 normal figure comes from the assumption that landlords normally demolish three quarters (75 percent) of a city's underemployed-housing units as they become economically and physically nonviable, and normally abandon only about one quarter (25 percent) of the stock. The observed rate in a real city might run substantially higher or lower than 0.005 per year, depending upon the value of the particular local housing-abandonment multiplier.

In equation 202, three variables, representing the other basic influences on abandonment, relate the likelihood of abandonment to

1. the local property tax rate (UHATM),
2. the relative supply and demand for underemployed housing (UHSM), and
3. the physical condition of the community (UHABM).

The variables combine to determine the underemployed-housing-abandonment multiplier UHAM. Although a simplification of real-world forces, the variables entering the

```
UHAM.K=(UHATM.K)(UHSM.K)(UHABM.K)                    202, A
    UHAM    - UNDEREMPLOYED-HOUSING-ABANDONMENT
                MULTIPLIER (DIMENSIONLESS)
    UHATM   - UNDEREMPLOYED-HOUSING-ABANDONMENT TAX MULT.
                (DIMENSIONLESS)
    UHSM    - UNDEREMPLOYED-HOUSING-SUPPLY MULTIPLIER
                (DIMENSIONLESS)
    UHABM   - UNDEREMPLOYED-HOUSING-ABANDONMENT-BLIGHT
                MULT. (DIMENSIONLESS)
```

underemployed-housing-abandonment multiplier do encompass a range of factors threatening the value of marginal housing in a community.

In a typical setting, a financial loss by property owners provides the major stimulus for abandonment. As building maintenance expenses and operating costs rise faster than income, a landlord has little incentive to preserve his building. When costs exceed income, the landlord faces a choice: upgrade, demolish, or abandon. Where the socioeconomic health of the neighborhood has already faltered, the landlord is unlikely to upgrade, given his limited income potential. Nor can the community count on owners to spend their own funds on demolition. The less healthy the neighborhood and its surrounding community, the more often landlords abandon, rather than upgrade, their aging property.[5] Rising taxes impose a direct cost increase on landlords. As taxes and other costs rise, a landlord's ability to maintain his building often diminishes. The quality of his building may rapidly deteriorate to the point where he must upgrade, demolish, or abandon. As the tax ratio rises, profits and maintenance expenditures decrease, and the likelihood of abandonment increases. Equation 203 contains the relationship described in Figure 10-6, in which a rising tax ratio TR drives up the underemployed-housing-abandonment multiplier UHAM.

The relative supply of and demand for underemployed housing also impinges on maintenance costs. Given a strong demand for housing, rents tend to stay relatively

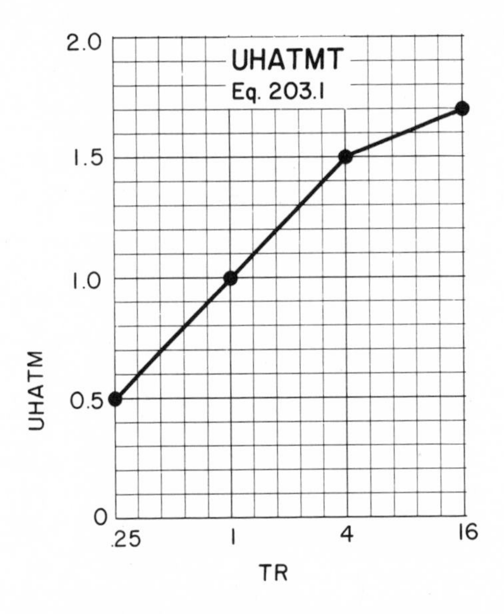

Figure 10-6 Underemployed-housing-abandonment tax multiplier table UHATMT: rising taxes tend to increase the likelihood of abandonment

```
UHATM.K=TABLE(UHATMT,1.44*LOGN(TR.K),-2,4,2)          203, A
UHATMT=.5/1/1.5/1.7                                    203.1, T
    UHATM   - UNDEREMPLOYED-HOUSING-ABANDONMENT TAX MULT.
                (DIMENSIONLESS)
    UHATMT  - UNDEREMPLOYED-HOUSING-ABANDONMENT TAX
                MULTIPLIER TABLE
    TR      - TAX RATIO (DIMENSIONLESS)
```

high; higher rents generally mean greater profits and therefore less incentive for abandonment. Conversely, given relatively abundant housing, vacancies are more extensive and rents usually fall; and lower rents and lower profits increase the potential for abandonment. The *Urban Dynamics* model contains a variable labeled the underemployed/housing ratio UHR, which indicates the relative demand for and supply of underemployed housing. A UHR greater than 1.0 suggests an increasingly tight housing market; a UHR of less than 1.0 means more vacancies and a looser market. UHR therefore indirectly reflects pressures for either rising or falling rent levels. The rent level in turn substantially determines landlord incomes. As UHR increases, the rate of underemployed-housing abandonment UHA decreases. Equation 204 incorporates the effect of the underemployed/housing ratio UHR on the underemployed-housing-supply multiplier UHSM, which in turn modulates the rate of underemployed-housing abandonment UHA. As illustrated in Figure 10-7, a tight housing market (UHR greater than 1.0), causes abandonment to occur less frequently; but when housing becomes more abundant, more landlords begin to abandon their marginal housing structures.

A landlord's ability to maintain his building also directly depends upon the social stability of the community in which the property stands. In communities where only lower-income families live, vandalism and other crimes are common, and the cost of fire and crime insurance tends to run disproportionately high.[6] The ratio of abandoned housing AH to housing units total HUT provides a measure of community quality. The higher the ratio of AH/HUT (or the abandoned-housing fraction AHF), the more the

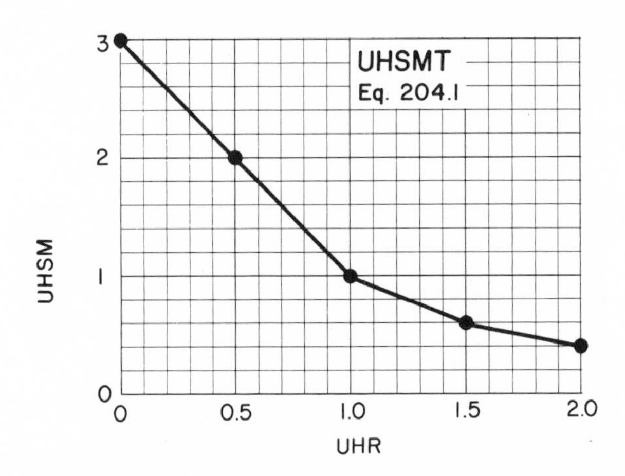

Figure 10-7 Underemployed-housing-supply multiplier table UHSMT: abandonment tends to increase as the demand for housing falls relative to supply

```
UHSM.K=TABLE(UHSMT,UHR.K,0,2,.5)                          204, A
UHSMT=3/2/1/.6/.4                                         204.1, T
     UHSM     - UNDEREMPLOYED-HOUSING-SUPPLY MULTIPLIER
                   (DIMENSIONLESS)
     UHSMT    - UNDEREMPLOYED-HOUSING-SUPPLY MULTIPLIER
                   TABLE
     UHR      - UNDEREMPLOYED/HOUSING RATIO (DIMENSIONLESS)
```

community resembles a crisis ghetto. The measure of quality of the surrounding community encompasses both the visual condition of a community and the perception of lending institutions of the probable failure rate of loans extended in that area. As the abandoned-housing fraction in a community increases, the propensity for disinvestment in the area increases. Rather than pay increasing costs and repair frequent damages to his property, a landlord in a declining community will save his cash and "milk" his property.

> When an owner of a house fails to replace worn mechanical or structural elements or to modernize periodically, he is "using up" his investment; he is also spending elsewhere the money that is normally set aside for maintenance and replacement and is thus disinvesting in his house.[7]

Disinvestment is a critical step toward abandonment. Since the abandoned-housing fraction is proportional to the likelihood of disinvestment, AHF is intimately related to the rate of underemployed-housing abandonment. Figure 10-8 shows how the abandoned-housing fraction affects the underemployed-housing-abandonment-blight

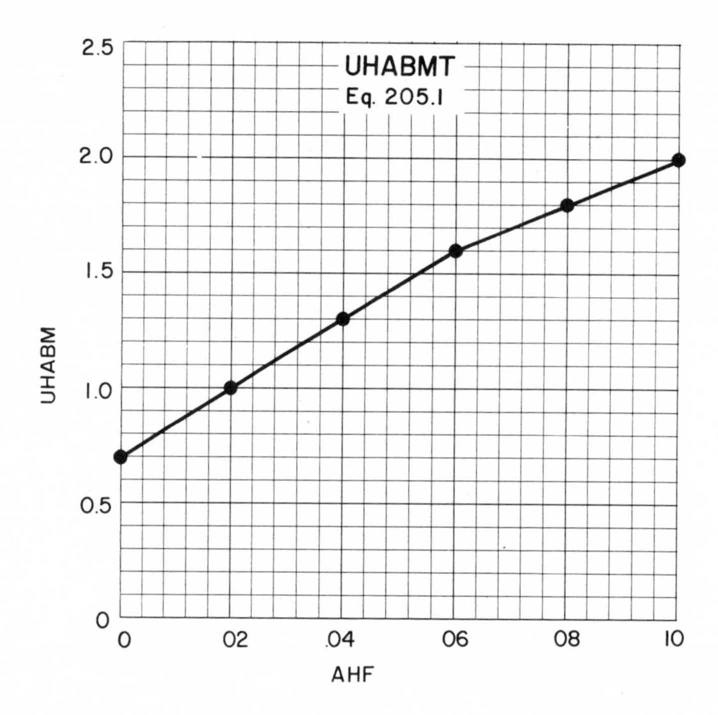

Figure 10-8 Underemployed-housing-abandonment-blight multiplier table (UHABMT): the rate of underemployed housing abandonment increases as conditions of blight worsen

```
UHABM.K=TABLE(UHABMT,AHF.K,0,.1,.02)                      205, A
UHABMT=.7/1/1.3/1.6/1.8/2                                  205.1, T
     UHABM   - UNDEREMPLOYED-HOUSING-ABANDONMENT-BLIGHT
                  MULT. (DIMENSIONLESS)
     UHABMT  - UNDEREMPLOYED-HOUSING-ABANDONMENT-BLIGHT
                  MULTIPLIER TABLE
     AHF     - ABANDONED-HOUSING FRACTION (DIMENSIONLESS)
```

```
AHF.K=AH.K/HUT.K                                          206, A
   AHF    - ABANDONED-HOUSING FRACTION (DIMENSIONLESS)
   AH     - ABANDONED HOUSING (HOUSING UNITS)
   HUT    - HOUSING UNITS TOTAL (HOUSING UNITS)
```

multiplier UHABM, which in turn influences the rate of underemployed-housing abandonment UHA. In Figure 10-8, abandonment accelerates as blight worsens.

Abandoned-Housing Demolition AHD. Figure 10-4 illustrated three forces influencing the abandoned-housing demolition rate. One influence comes directly from the level, or amount, of abandoned housing in the system. The other two influences modulate the normal rate of demolition through the abandoned-housing-demolition multiplier AHDM. The observed rate of abandoned-housing demolition AHD (measured in units per year) is roughly proportional to the amount of abandoned housing. In general, an abandoned house undergoes demolition five to ten years after abandonment. As much as five years may go by before a city can clear the necessary legal and financial details to acquire title to abandoned property—a prerequisite for public demolition.[8] In equation 207 the normal rate of abandoned-housing demolition AHDN equals 12.5 percent per year of the abandoned stock. At a rate of 12.5 percent per year, the average delay before demolition is eight years. In Figure 10-4 and equation 208, two factors influenced the rate of abandoned-housing demolition through the abandoned-housing-demolition multiplier AHDM: (1) the fraction of city housing that is abandoned (through AHDFM), and (2) the scarcity of land (through AHDLM).

```
AHD.KL=(AH.K)(AHDN)(AHDM.K)                               207, R
AHDN=.125                                                 207.1, C
   AHD    - ABANDONED-HOUSING DEMOLITION (HOUSING
               UNITS/YEAR)
   AH     - ABANDONED HOUSING (HOUSING UNITS)
   AHDN   - ABANDONED-HOUSING-DEMOLITION NORMAL
               (FRACTION/YEAR)
   AHDM   - ABANDONED-HOUSING-DEMOLITION MULTIPLIER
               (DIMENSIONLESS)
```

The ratio of abandoned housing to total housing (AHF) indicates the extent of blight in a community. The higher the fraction, the greater a city's abandonment problem. St. Louis, New York, Philadelphia, and Cleveland, with a relatively high (over 3 percent) abandoned-housing fraction, have experienced a widespread public reaction to the abandonment problem.[9] The reaction includes a great deal of community pressure to eliminate abandoned housing through demolition. Equation 209 describes an assumed relationship between the abandoned-housing fraction AHF and the rate of abandoned-housing demolition AHD. This relationship is depicted in Figure 10-9. Labeled the abandoned-housing-demolition-fraction multiplier AHDFM, the relationship generates an increasing demolition rate through a rise in the abandoned-housing-demolition multiplier AHDM as AHF increases.

As unused land in a community becomes scarce, demolition tends to increase. Some amount of demolition usually must precede any further construction of roads, schools, playgrounds, theaters, or new housing in an older city. Abandoned structures are a prime target for demolition, since the cost of acquisition is generally small and the

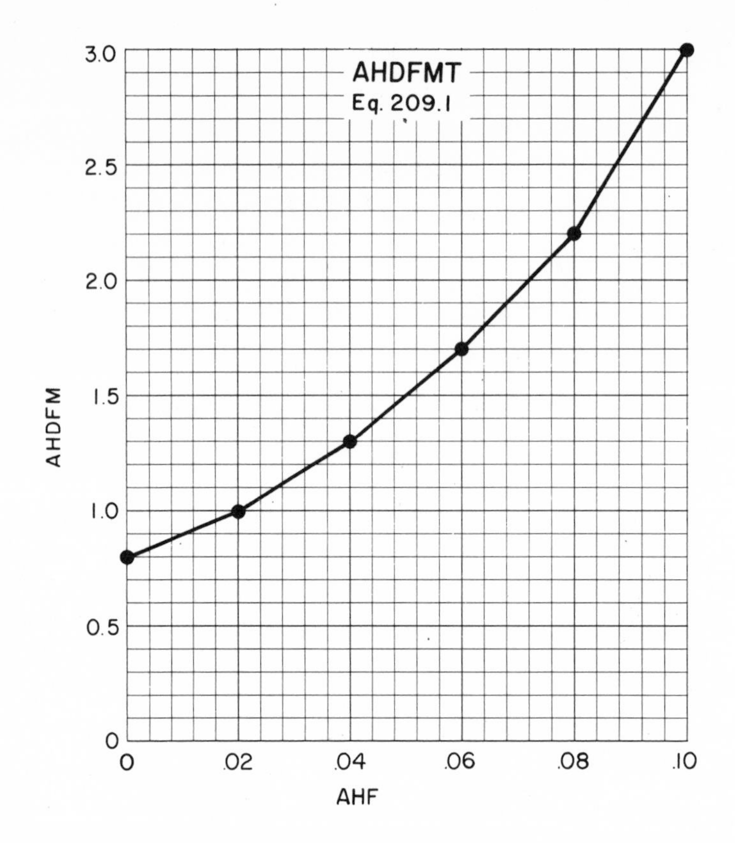

Figure 10-9 Abandoned-housing-demolition-fraction multiplier table AHDFMT: community pressures for demolition rise as AHF increases

```
AHDM.K=(AHDLM.K)(AHDFM.K)                                    208, A
    AHDM    - ABANDONED-HOUSING-DEMOLITION MULTIPLIER
                (DIMENSIONLESS)
    AHDLM   - ABANDONED-HOUSING-DEMOLITION-LAND MULT.
                (DIMENSIONLESS)
    AHDFM   - ABANDONED-HOUSING-DEMOLITION-FRACTION
                MULTIPLIER (DIMENSIONLESS)

AHDFM.K=TABLE(AHDFMT,AHF.K,0,.1,.02)                         209, A
AHDFMT=.8/1/1.3/1.7/2.2/3.0                                  209.1, T
    AHDFM   - ABANDONED-HOUSING-DEMOLITION-FRACTION
                MULTIPLIER (DIMENSIONLESS)
    AHDFMT  - ABANDONED-HOUSING-DEMOLITION-FRACTION
                MULTIPLIER TABLE
    AHF     - ABANDONED-HOUSING FRACTION (DIMENSIONLESS)
```

city does not have to pay for family relocation. The scarcity of land in the refined model is directly dependent upon the land fraction occupied LFO. In equation 210 the rate of abandoned-housing demolition AHD increases as LFO increases. LFO modulates AHD through the abandoned-housing-demolition-land multiplier AHDLM, which increases the abandoned-housing-demolition multiplier AHDM when LFO increases. Figure 10-10 illustrates the relationship between LFO and the abandoned-housing-demolition-land multiplier AHDLM.

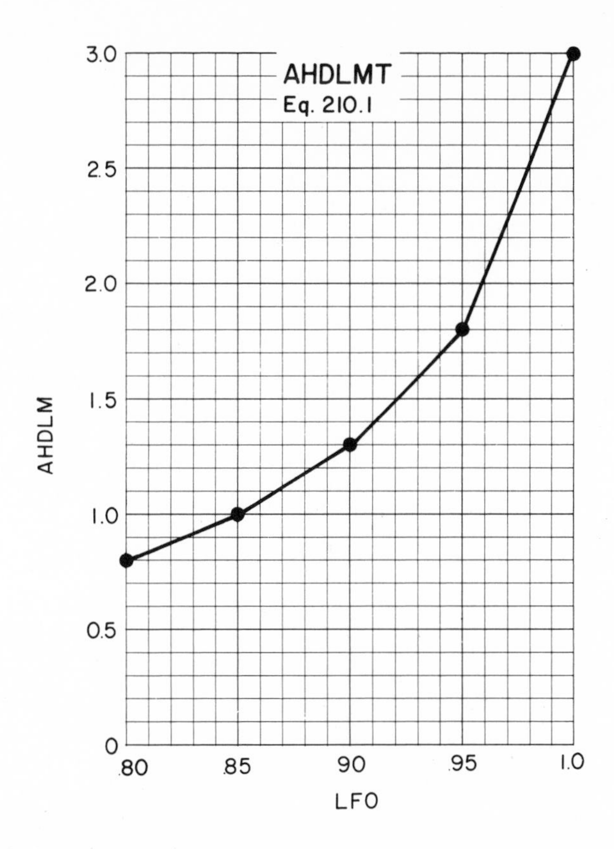

Figure 10-10 Abandoned-housing-demolition-land multiplier table AHDLMT: the demolition of abandoned houses rises as land becomes scarcer

```
AHDLM.K=TABHL(AHDLMT,LFO.K,.8,1,.05)                        210, A
AHDLMT=.8/1/1.3/1.8/3                                       210.1, T
     AHDLM   - ABANDONED-HOUSING-DEMOLITION-LAND MULT.
                 (DIMENSIONLESS)
     AHDLMT  - ABANDONED-HOUSING-DEMOLITION-LAND
                 MULTIPLIER TABLE
     LFO     - LAND FRACTION OCCUPIED (FRACTION)
```

Readjusting Underemployed-Housing Demolition UHD. Adding new variables to an urban dynamics model involves (1) identifying new system equations and (2) altering the original equations and parameters to preserve consistency between the original and new models. Consider, for example, the treatment of underemployed housing in the *Urban Dynamics* model, which subsumes both abandoned and occupiable housing in one level: underemployed housing. Only one rate of flow demolition depletes the level of underemployed housing. But the abandonment refinement creates a second level of low-quality housing and a second means by which housing can leave the urban system. At any point in time, the new level of abandoned housing added to the new level of underemployed housing should equal the total level of underemployed housing in the *Urban Dynamics* model. To avoid substantially different model behavior, the *Urban Dynamics* model's demolition rate must be reformulated in the refined model. The normal demolition rate for underemployed housing in the *Urban Dynamics* model should equal the sum of the normal demolition rates for underemployed housing and abandoned housing in the refined model. Therefore, the *Urban Dynamics* model structure and parameters must change to keep the respective sums of the housing levels and demolition rates equal in the original and refined models. As shown in Figure 10-4, underemployed-housing demolition UHD in the refined model replaces slum-housing demolition SHD in the *Urban Dynamics* model. In both models, the demolition rate represents the removal of underemployed housing from the system. But "slum housing" is not specific enough for the abandonment refinement, because that term could refer to either underemployed or abandoned housing, or both. "Slum-housing demolition" is unsatisfactory for the same reason, but changing the term to "underemployed-housing demolition," as in equation 212, clarifies the variable's specific role within the refined model. The value of the parameter for the underemployed-housing-demolition normal UHDN must be less in the refined model than in the *Urban Dynamics* model, where 2 percent of the underemployed housing undergoes demolition each year. In the refined model, 2 percent of the underemployed housing should still be removed each year. But, as Figure 10-11 indicates, a second flow rate depletes the level of underemployed housing in the refined model. If some underemployed housing is abandoned each year in the refined model, then the normal demolition rate must be less than in the *Urban Dynamics* model. Otherwise, the new normal rate of outflow (demolition plus abandonment) would exceed 2 percent per year. Normal conditions in the *Urban Dynamics* model apply to a city near the end of its growth phase. When growth begins to taper off, a city normally contains a relatively small amount of abandoned housing. Therefore, in the *Urban Dynamics* model, the amount of abandoned housing is small relative to underemployed housing. To behave in a manner consistent with all normal conditions defined in the *Urban Dynamics* model, the refined model must have approximately the same amount of underemployed housing as the original model near the end of the growth phase. The amount of underemployed housing can remain about the same only if the value of

```
UH.K=UH.J+(DT)(WHO.JK-UHD.JK-UHA.JK+LCHP.JK)          211, L
UH=1100                                                211.1, N
    UH      - UNDEREMPLOYED HOUSING (HOUSING UNITS)
    WHO     - WORKER-HOUSING OBSOLESCENCE (HOUSING UNITS/
                YEAR)
    UHD     - UNDEREMPLOYED-HOUSING DEMOLITION (HOUSING
                UNITS/YEAR)
    UHA     - UNDEREMPLOYED-HOUSING ABANDONMENT (HOUSING
                UNITS/YEAR)
    LCHP    - LOW-COST-HOUSING PROGRAM (HOUSING UNITS/
                YEAR)

UHD.KL=(UHDN)(UH.K)(UHDM.K)+SHDP.K                      212, R
UHDN=.015                                               212.1, C
    UHD     - UNDEREMPLOYED-HOUSING DEMOLITION (HOUSING
                UNITS/YEAR)
    UHDN    - UNDEREMPLOYED-HOUSING-DEMOLITION NORMAL
                (FRACTION/YEAR)
    UH      - UNDEREMPLOYED HOUSING (HOUSING UNITS)
    UHDM    - UNDEREMPLOYED-HOUSING-DEMOLITION MULTIPLIER
                (DIMENSIONLESS)
    SHDP    - SLUM-HOUSING-DEMOLITION PROGRAM (HOUSING
                UNITS/YEAR)
```

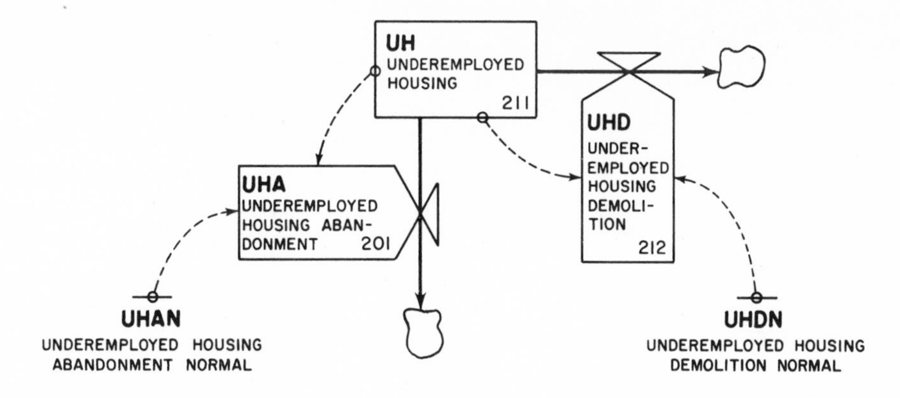

Figure 10-11 The total normal outflow rate from underemployed housing UH is 2 percent—the same as in the *Urban Dynamics* model

underemployed-housing-demolition normal UHDN in the new model drops by an amount exactly equal to the value of underemployed-housing-abandonment normal UHAN. If the sum of the two normal values in the refined model equals the *Urban Dynamics* model's slum-housing-demolition normal SHDN (0.02), as in Figure 10-11, the amount of underemployed housing at the end of the growth phase should not change significantly. The values of UHDN and UHAN (0.015 and 0.005, respectively) sum to the value of SHDN in the *Urban Dynamics* model (0.02). During normal conditions in the refined model, one of every four landlords abandons, rather than voluntarily demolishes, an unprofitable building in need of major repairs. The underemployed-housing-demolition multiplier UHDM in equation 213 modulates the normal rate of underemployed-housing demolition. In Figure 10-4, UHDM has three inputs: (1) the underemployed-housing-land multiplier UHLM, (2) the underemployed-housing-demolition-supply multiplier UHDSM, and (3) the underemployed-housing-replacement multiplier UHRM. UHLM and UHDSM are equivalent to the respective factors that influence the *Urban Dynamics* model's rate of underemployed-housing demolition: the underemployed-housing-land multiplier UHLM in equation 214 and the underemployed-housing-demolition-supply multiplier UHDSM in equation 215.

```
UHDM.K=(UHRM.K)(UHLM.K)(UHDSM.K)(SHDF)                213, A
SHDF=1                                                213.1, C
    UHDM    - UNDEREMPLOYED-HOUSING-DEMOLITION MULTIPLIER
                (DIMENSIONLESS)
    UHRM    - UNDEREMPLOYED-HOUSING-REPLACEMENT
                MULTIPLIER (DIMENSIONLESS)
    UHLM    - UNDEREMPLOYED-HOUSING-LAND MULTIPLIER
                (DIMENSIONLESS)
    UHDSM   - UNDEREMPLOYED-HOUSING-DEMOLITION-SUPPLY
                MULTIPLIER (DIMENSIONLESS)
    SHDF    - SLUM-HOUSING-DEMOLITION FACTOR
                (DIMENSIONLESS)

UHLM.K=TABHL(UHLMT,LFO.K,.8,1,.05)                    214, A
UHLMT=1/1.2/1.6/2.2/6                                 214.1, T
    UHLM    - UNDEREMPLOYED-HOUSING-LAND MULTIPLIER
                (DIMENSIONLESS)
    UHLMT   - UNDEREMPLOYED-HOUSING-LAND MULTIPLIER TABLE
    LFO     - LAND FRACTION OCCUPIED (FRACTION)
```

```
UHDSM.K=TABLE(UHDSMT,UHR.K,0,2,.5)                      215, A
UHDSMT=1.2/1.1/1/.8/.7                                  215.1, T
    UHDSM   - UNDEREMPLOYED-HOUSING-DEMOLITION-SUPPLY
                MULTIPLIER (DIMENSIONLESS)
    UHDSMT  - UNDEREMPLOYED-HOUSING-DEMOLITION-SUPPLY
                MULTIPLIER TABLE
    UHR     - UNDEREMPLOYED/HOUSING RATIO (DIMENSIONLESS)
```

The new underemployed-housing-replacement multiplier UHRM explicitly represents the rising pressure for demolition as a city runs out of open land for new development. UHRM is derived in equations 216 and 217 from a comparison of available land with the amount of land currently desired for construction. Figure 10-12 illustrates the relationship between UHRM and the ratio of available land AL (equation 218) to the desired-land-utilization rate DLUR (equation 219). Equations 220 and 221 are supplemental equations that calculate slum housing SHT and slum-housing demolition SHD.

```
UHRM.K=TABLE(UHRMT,ALDF.K,0,.2,.025)                    216, A
UHRMT=.7/1/1.3/1.7/2.2/2.5/2.7/2.9/3                    216.1, T
    UHRM    - UNDEREMPLOYED-HOUSING-REPLACEMENT
                MULTIPLIER (DIMENSIONLESS)
    UHRMT   - UNDEREMPLOYED-HOUSING-REPLACEMENT
                MULTIPLIER TABLE
    ALDF    - AVAILABLE-LAND-DEMAND FRACTION
                (DIMENSIONLESS)

ALDF.K=DLUR.K/AL.K                                      217, A
    ALDF    - AVAILABLE-LAND-DEMAND FRACTION
                (DIMENSIONLESS)
    DLUR    - DESIRED-LAND UTILIZATION RATE (ACRES)
    AL      - AVAILABLE LAND (ACRES)
```

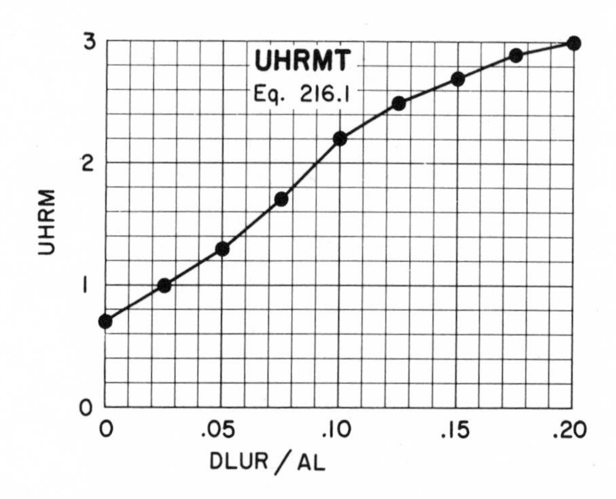

Figure 10-12 Underemployed-housing-replacement multiplier table UHRMT: voluntary demolition rises when land for new construction is in short supply

```
AL.K=(1-LFO.K)(AREA)                                    218, A
    AL      - AVAILABLE LAND (ACRES)
    LFO     - LAND FRACTION OCCUPIED (FRACTION)
    AREA    - LAND AREA (ACRES)
```

```
DLUR.K=NECD.K*LPP+(PHCD.K+WHCD.K)*LPH                     219, A
    DLUR    - DESIRED-LAND UTILIZATION RATE (ACRES)
    NECD    - NEW-ENTERPRISE-CONSTRUCTION DESIRED
                (PRODUCTION UNITS/YEAR)
    LPP     - LAND PER PRODUCTION UNIT (ACRES/PRODUCTION
                UNIT)
    PHCD    - PREMIUM-HOUSING CONSTRUCTION DESIRED
                (HOUSING UNITS/YEAR)
    WHCD    - WORKER-HOUSING CONSTRUCTION DESIRED
                (HOUSING UNITS/YEAR)
    LPH     - LAND PER HOUSE (ACRES/HOUSING UNIT)

SHT.K=UH.K+AH.K                                           220, S
    SHT     - SLUM HOUSING, TOTAL (HOUSING UNITS)
    UH      - UNDEREMPLOYED HOUSING (HOUSING UNITS)
    AH      - ABANDONED HOUSING (HOUSING UNITS)

SHD.K=UHD.JK+AHD.JK                                       221, S
    SHD     - SLUM HOUSING DEMOLITION (HOUSING UNITS/
                YEAR)
    UHD     - UNDEREMPLOYED-HOUSING DEMOLITION (HOUSING
                UNITS/YEAR)
    AHD     - ABANDONED-HOUSING DEMOLITION (HOUSING
                UNITS/YEAR)
```

Altering the Premium-Housing and Worker-Housing Sectors. Spreading abandonment tends to erode property values and discourage new housing construction in a city. Landlords and homeowners, sensitive to local blight, begin to sell their property and move to the suburbs or other cities where the socioeconomic environment seems more stable. The departing more affluent citizenry leaves behind a city where remaining housing may deteriorate even more rapidly. Worsening decay then discourages further residential construction.

Evidence that blight and abandonment affect local property values is cited in *Urban Decay in St. Louis:*

> The physical starting point of blight is abandonment. . . . Although it is an areal manifestation, it can begin with a single house on a single block, for its most outstanding characteristics are that it is at once highly virulent and highly contagious. In its cumulative nature it is highly productive of neighborhood transiency. (pp. 63–64)

The process of neighborhood decline can be very rapid:

> . . . the process of blight is a process of wastage, an economic consequence of poverty coexistent with affluence in which the desire of the poor for decent housing is met through the exhaustion, the simple using-up, of an oversupply of devalued housing stock.
>
> The deterioration practices ensuing from devaluation and lower-level use lead to a loss of confidence on the part of insurance companies and lenders, who fear that the value of housing will decline faster than the value of mortgages (as is often the case), and this produces a cumulative effect. First on a selective basis—particular houses, certain blocks on certain streets—then areawide by blanket "red-lining" insurance is refused and conventional financing is withdrawn.[11]

If the *Urban Dynamics* model implicitly subsumes the phenomenon of housing abandonment, then the effect of abandonment on housing construction and housing obsolescence should also be embedded within the original model. Six factors in the *Urban Dynamics* model determine the premium-housing and worker-housing multipliers PHM and WHM. Which of the six factors best accounts for the influence of abandonment? The question must be answered because, before explicitly adding the effect of abandonment as a seventh influence on PHM and WHM, the modeler must explicitly remove its former implicit effect from the other six influences to prevent a double-counting error. The definition and function of the premium-housing-population multiplier PHPM in the *Urban Dynamics* model imply that PHPM already accounts for the primary influence of abandonment. PHPM relates the rates of premium-housing construction and maintenance to the current population composition of the community. PHPM implicitly assumes that, as the ratio of upper-income population to total population falls, the attractiveness of the city for upper-income-housing construction also falls. Figure 10-13 shows the original relationship between the manager-to-population ratio MPR and the propensity to construct premium housing. As the manager-to-population ratio MPR falls, incentives for construction (PHPM) fall as well.

Figure 10-13 implicitly incorporates the effect of abandonment on premium-housing construction PHC: as abandonment increases in a community, the socioeconomic balance tends to shift toward the lower-income population. The left-hand portion of the figure portrays both a low manager-to-population ratio and an unhealthy local housing condition. The implicit effect of abandonment in Figure 10-13 has been carried over into the abandonment refinement as an explicit influence. In the refined model, a seventh multiplier, the premium-housing-abandonment multiplier PHABM, enters equation 66, which computes the premium-housing multiplier PHM.

Figure 10-14 is a modified version of the premium-housing-population multiplier PHPM curve. PHPM has been modified to account for a new curve, shown in Figure 10-15, relating the premium-housing-abandonment multiplier PHABM to the

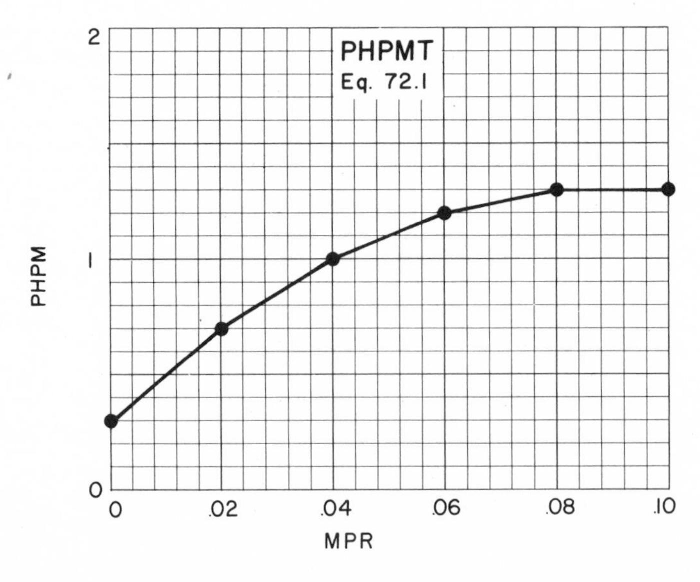

Figure 10-13 Premium-housing-population multiplier table PHPMT: the attractiveness for premium-housing construction falls as the population mix shifts toward a predominance of lower-income families

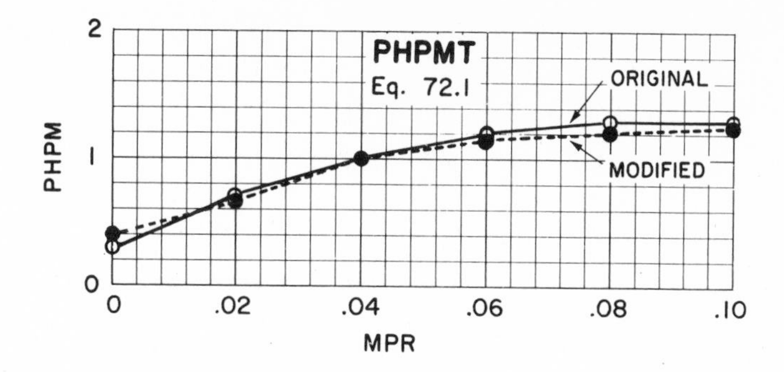

Figure 10-14 Removing the effect of abandonment from the premium-housing-population multiplier PHPM curve

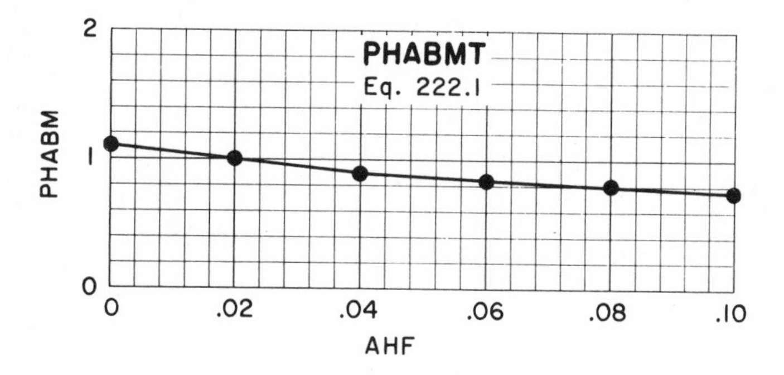

Figure 10-15 Premium-housing-abandonment multiplier table PHABMT: construction declines as abandonment increases in the community

```
PHM.K=(PHAM.K)(PHLM.K)(PHPM.K)(PHTM.K)(PHEM.K)          66, A
  (PHGM.K)(PHABM.K)(PHF)
PHF=1                                                   66.2, C
     PHM     - PREMIUM-HOUSING MULTIPLIER (DIMENSIONLESS)
     PHAM    - PREMIUM-HOUSING-ADEQUACY MULTIPLIER
                 (DIMENSIONLESS)
     PHLM    - PREMIUM-HOUSING LAND MULTIPLIER
                 (DIMENSIONLESS)
     PHPM    - PREMIUM-HOUSING POPULATION MULTIPLIER
                 (DIMENSIONLESS)
     PHTM    - PREMIUM-HOUSING TAX MULTIPLIER
                 (DIMENSIONLESS)
     PHEM    - PREMIUM-HOUSING ENTERPRISE MULTIPLIER
                 (DIMENSIONLESS)
     PHGM    - PREMIUM-HOUSING-GROWTH MULTIPLIER
                 (DIMENSIONLESS)
     PHABM   - PREMIUM-HOUSING-ABANDONMENT MULTIPLIER
                 (DIMENSIONLESS)
     PHF     - PREMIUM-HOUSING FACTOR (DIMENSIONLESS)

PHAM.K=TABLE(PHAMT,MHR.K,0,2,.25)                       67, A
PHAMT=0/.001/.01/.2/1/3/4.6/5.6/6                       67.1, T
     PHAM    - PREMIUM-HOUSING-ADEQUACY MULTIPLIER
                 (DIMENSIONLESS)
     PHAMT   - PREMIUM-HOUSING-ADEQUACY MULTIPLIER TABLE
                 (DIMENSIONLESS)
     MHR     - MANAGER/HOUSING RATIO (DIMENSIONLESS)
```

abandoned-housing fraction AHF. PHABM, defined in equation 222, becomes a new component of the overall premium-housing multiplier PHM. Equivalent changes to those in the premium-housing sector were also made in the worker-housing sector.

```
PHABM.K=TABLE(PHABMT,AHF.K,0,.1,.02)                    222, A
PHABMT=1.1/1.0/.9/.85/.8/.75                            222.1, T
    PHABM  - PREMIUM-HOUSING-ABANDONMENT MULTIPLIER
               (DIMENSIONLESS)
    PHABMT - PREMIUM-HOUSING-ABANDONMENT MULTIPLIER
               TABLE
    AHF    - ABANDONED-HOUSING FRACTION (DIMENSIONLESS)
```

10.4 Behavior of the Refined Model

Figures 10-16 and 10-17 exhibit the growth and decline of the same nine major levels in the *Urban Dynamics* model and in the model refined to include the dynamics of abandonment. In Figure 10-17, the process and consequences of housing abandonment stand out most clearly during the late stages of urban evolution. For example, abandoned housing AH grows rapidly after the year 120 as a result of the large increase in underemployed housing (see Figure 10-17 beginning around year 100). As underemployed houses age and as community-wide problems of decay become more intense, the rate of underemployed-housing abandonment increases.

Figure 10-17 shows how the effects of (1) rising taxes (a rising underemployed-housing-abandonment tax multiplier UHATM), (2) a decreasing demand for underemployed housing relative to supply (a rising underemployed-housing-supply multiplier UHSM), and (3) increasing neighborhood blight (a rising underemployed-housing-abandonment-blight multiplier UHABM) all combine to encourage the abandonment of marginal housing structures after about year 100. During years 110 to 150 the fraction of abandoned housing AHF (not explicitly plotted) rises from less than 0.004 to over 0.03.

The level of abandoned housing peaks at year 150. An impressive amount of abandonment has created extraordinary community pressure for demolition. The subsequently increasing demolition rate removes abandoned houses faster than they are generated, so the number of abandoned houses declines. During years 150 to 190 the fraction of total housing that is abandoned falls from over 3 percent to less than 3 percent. By year 190 the reduced level of abandoned structures has lessened the pressure for demolition to the point where the demolition and abandonment rates are approximately equal. After year 190 the level of abandoned structures stays nearly constant, at about 2.5 percent of the total city housing stock. The 2.5 percent value falls well within the range of observed real-world conditions. In St. Louis, for example, over 3.5 percent of the total housing supply is abandoned. In Newark, the current total figure also exceeds 3 percent. But the level of abandoned housing in St. Louis and Newark may somewhat exceed the amount in other cities. Experts on abandonment place the normal abandonment figure for older cities in the 1–3 percent region.[12] Several aspects of the abandonment process in St. Louis provide a qualitative behavioral test of the refined model. Proliferating abandonment in St. Louis has been accompanied by

1. A decreasing population.
2. An increase in the proportion of lower-income, as compared to middle-income, families.
3. A depressed housing market:

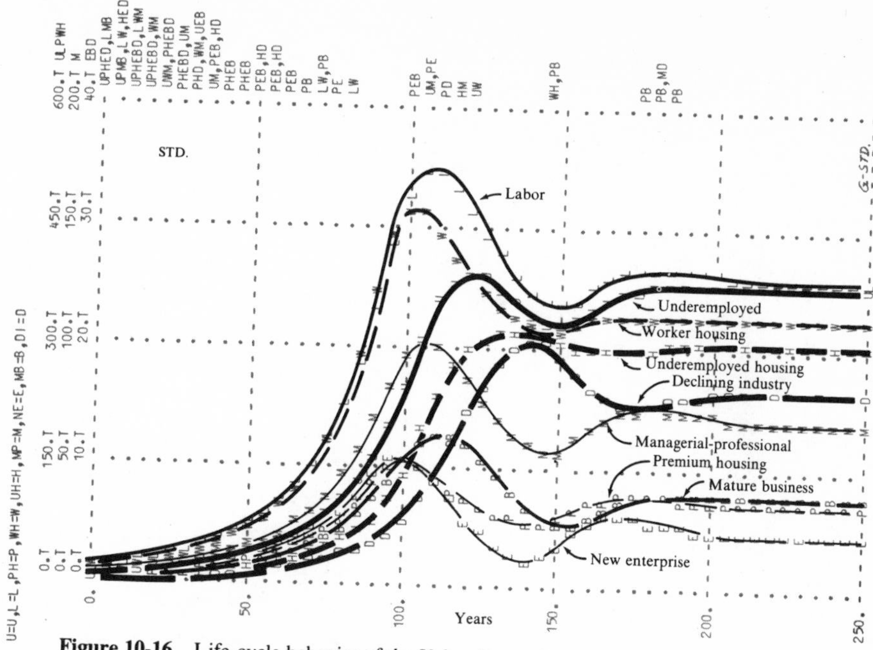

Figure 10-16 Life-cycle behavior of the *Urban Dynamics* model; plot of major system levels

Source: Reprinted from *Urban Dynamics* by Jay W. Forrester by permission of The MIT Press, Cambridge, Massachusetts, Figure 3-1.

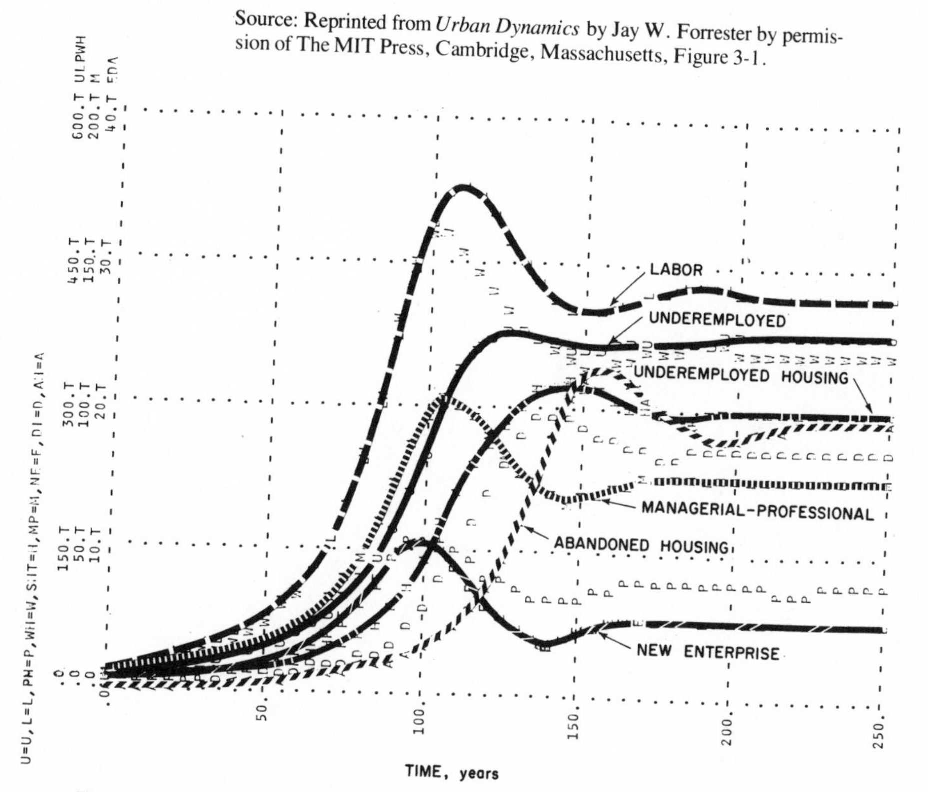

Figure 10-17 Life-cycle behavior of the *Urban Dynamics* model refined to include abandonment; plot of major system levels

> During the period from 1960 to 1970, the City of St. Louis experienced the largest population loss of any major American city, approximately 106,000 persons left the city. Today, the population of St. Louis is less than three fourths of what it was in 1950, and the decline is forecast to continue through 1972.
>
> The tragedy [of the outward migration of upper- and middle-class residents from St. Louis] is that once the exodus began, the poor themselves became caustive agents for further abandonment, and the neighborhoods into which they moved crumbled about them. . . . The community-at-large also is unprepared to accept these people on class or race terms; the result is a flight of whites and middle-income persons of both races to other areas.
>
> The net decrease in total housing units in St. Louis has been more than compensated for by the even larger population loss experienced by the city; there has been a decrease in the average number of persons per unit.[13]

The behavior of the refined model clearly reflects the features of abandonment in St. Louis. Figure 10-17 shows a sharp decline in the number of middle-income and upper-income residents during the thirty-year span from year 110 to year 140. As in St. Louis, the total population decline is within the 20–30 percent range.

In Figure 10-17 the ratio of middle-income (labor) families to lower-income (underemployed) families decreases from about 1.6 (510,000/320,000) to 1.0 (375,000/375,000) during years 110 to 135. The declining ratio reflects the unbalanced socioeconomic trend already experienced by many older American cities. Figure 10-17 also shows a change, similarly exemplified by St. Louis, in the lower-quality housing market. In year 110 the ratio of underemployed families to underemployed housing (1.6, or 340,000/210,000), indicates a relatively high level of crowding and few vacancies. By year 140 the fallen ratio (1.1, or 330,000/310,000) reflects a far looser housing market. Correlations between model behavior and observed urban behavior can never absolutely validate a model. However, such comparisons do increase confidence in a model. The behavior of the refined model apparently captures the essential dynamic features of abandonment in real cities.

10.5 Comparing the Behavior of the Refined Model and the Urban Dynamics Model

The abandonment refinement should clarify, without substantially altering, the behavior of the *Urban Dynamics* model. The following analysis compares the behavior of the refined model (Figure 10-17) and the *Urban Dynamics* model (Figure 10-16).

Figures 10-16 and 10-17 have strong similarities. Growth rates, peaks, and equilibria of the variables are nearly identical in both figures. Of equal importance, the sequence of events (including peaks and declines) also matches. For example, the number of labor families L and the number of managerial-professionals MP obviously remain the same in the two runs. Overall, the *Urban Dynamics* model and the refined model have nearly identical behavior. Both models reproduce the evolution of a city from growth to decline and from relative prosperity into a less desirable situation characterized by economic decline, unemployment, and socioeconomic imbalance.

The abandonment refinement disaggregates the original underemployed-housing level into two separate levels of underemployed and abandoned housing. Figure 10-18

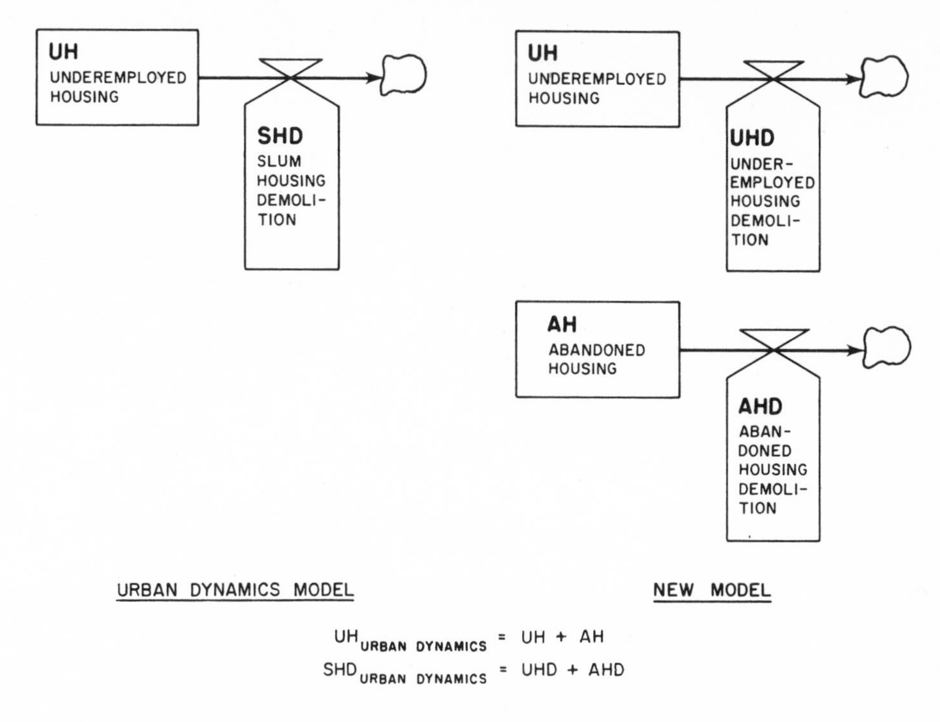

Figure 10-18 The original level should equal the sum of the new levels; the original outflow rate should equal the sum of the new outflow rates

summarizes the model disaggregation and the technical requirements for disaggregation. Since the *Urban Dynamics* model subsumes abandonment, the total amount of abandoned and underemployed housing in the refined model should equal the total amount of underemployed housing in the *Urban Dynamics* model. Similarly, the rate of demolition of underemployed housing (SHD) in the *Urban Dynamics* model should correspond to the combined rates of underemployed-housing demolition UHD and abandoned-housing demolition AHD in the refined model. Figures 10-19 and 10-20 provide a test of whether the disaggregation requirements outlined in Figure 10-18 are met in the refined model. Figure 10-19 compares two curves: underemployed housing in the *Urban Dynamics* model, and slum housing, total SHT (the sum of abandoned housing AH and underemployed housing UH in the refined model). As Figure 10-19 illustrates, slum housing, total SHT grows, peaks, and stabilizes at nearly the same values as the level of underemployed housing in the *Urban Dynamics* model. Given the correspondence between $\text{UH}_{\textit{Urban Dynamics}}$ and SHT, does the sum of the rates of abandoned-housing demolition AHD and underemployed-housing demolition UHD in the refined model correspond to the rate of underemployed-housing demolition (slum-housing demolition SHD) in the *Urban Dynamics* model? In Figure 10-20 one curve represents slum-housing demolition (UHD + AHD) from the refined model. The other curve reproduces the behavior of SHD from the *Urban Dynamics* model. The two curves grow similarly and have closely matching final values. Therefore, the joint effect of the normal demolition rates in the refined model corresponds well with the

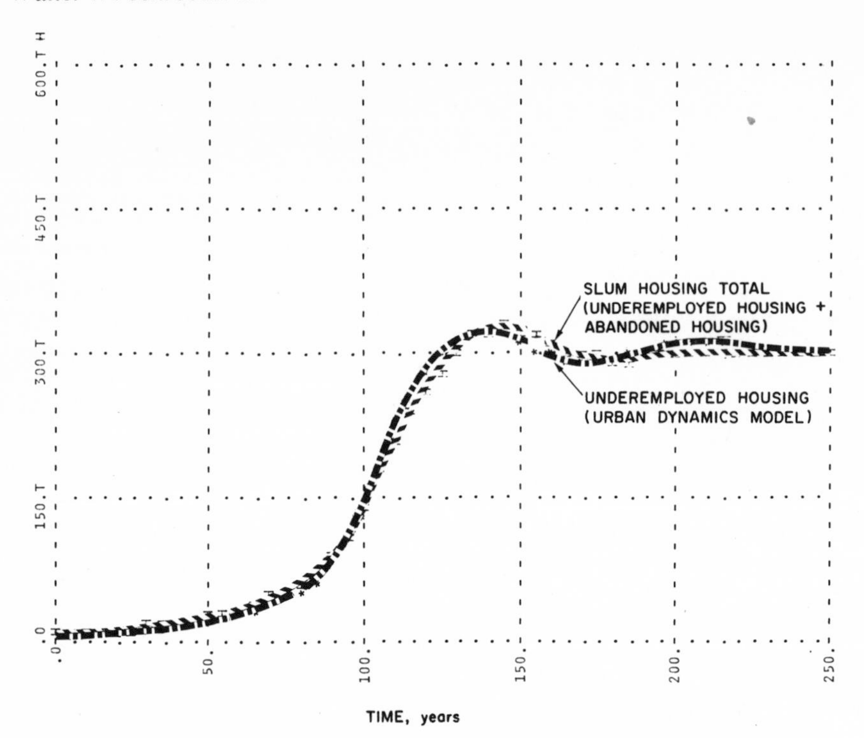

Figure 10-19 A comparison of the behavior of underemployed housing UH in the *Urban Dynamics* model and underemployed housing plus abandoned housing (UH + AH) in the refined model

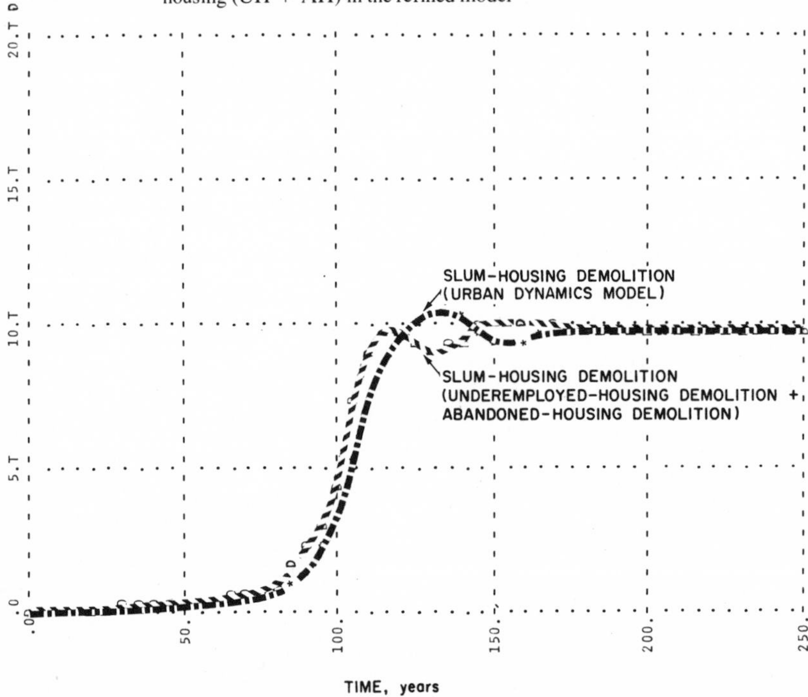

Figure 10-20 A comparison of the behavior of slum-housing demolition SHD in the *Urban Dynamics* model and underemployed-housing demolition plus abandoned-housing demolition (UHD + AHD) in the refined model

effect of the equivalent rate in the *Urban Dynamics* model. The disaggregation produces no unanticipated changes in model behavior.

10.6 Response to Policy Alternatives

A comparison based on the behavioral responses to the same policy changes cannot guarantee that the *Urban Dynamics* model and the refined model are properly consistent. However, such a comparison can ensure that any differences in policy response are reasonable and consistent with alterations in the refined model. Two policy tests not directly involving abandoned-housing demolition were carried out on the refined model and then compared with the same tests on the *Urban Dynamics* model. The two policies are low-cost-housing construction and underemployed-housing demolition, coupled with new-enterprise encouragement.

Low-Cost-Housing Construction. Forrester tested a policy of constructing low-cost housing for the urban underemployed in *Urban Dynamics* (p. 65). The policy consisted of housing construction for 5 percent of the underemployed population each year. Figure 10-21 plots the response of the refined model to the identical policy test. Column 3 of Figure 10-22 is a tabulated summary of the effect of a low-cost-housing program on the refined model. Column 4, taken from *Urban Dynamics*, tabulates the

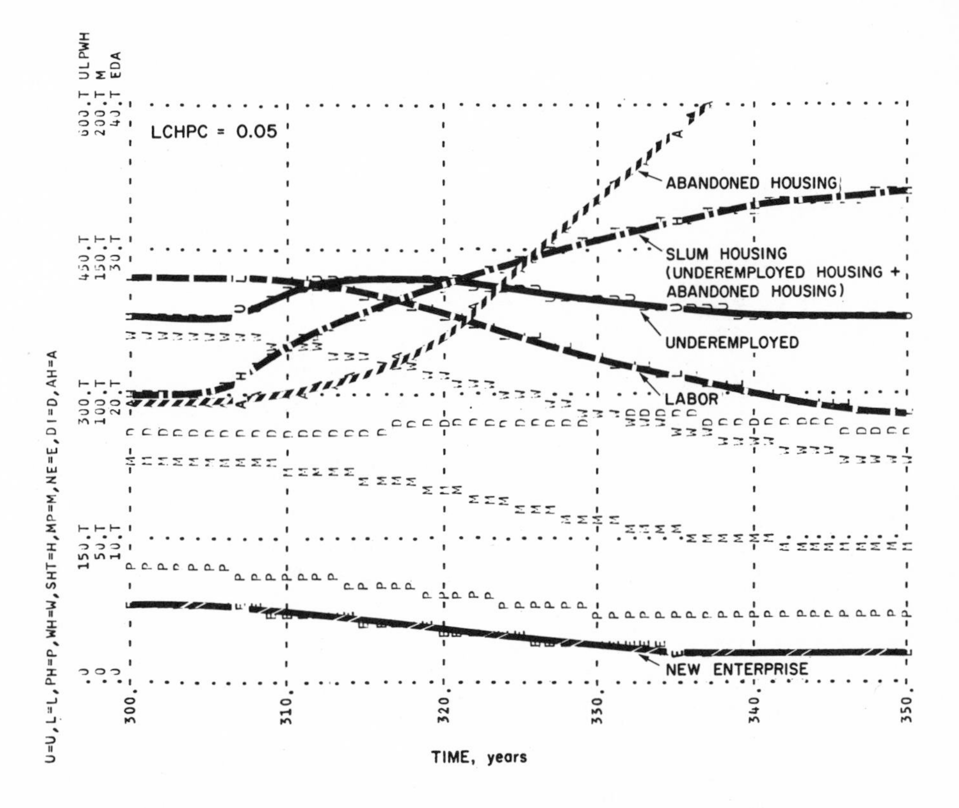

Figure 10-21 Plot of major system levels in response to a low-cost-housing construction program

(1) Variable Name	(2) Symbol	(3) Change (%)	(4) Change in *Urban Dynamics* (%)	(5) Difference (Column 3 − Column 4)
1. New enterprise	NE	−57	−49	−8
2. Mature business	MB	−52	−45	7
3. Declining industry	DI	−2	−6	+4
4. Premium housing	PH	−42	−34	−8
5. Worker housing	WH	−37	−31	−6
6. Slum housing total	SHT	+61	+45	+16
7. Abandoned housing	AH	+138	—	—
8. Managerial-professional	MP	−39	−34	−5
9. Labor	L	−34	−30	−4
10. Underemployed	U	−1	−1	0
11. Manager/housing ratio	MHR	+6	0	+6
12. Labor/housing ratio	LHR	+5	+1	+4
13. Underemployed/housing ratio	UHR	−38	−32	−6
14. Manager/job ratio	MR	+13	0	+13
15. Labor/job ratio	LR	−5	−4	−1
16. Underemployed/job ratio	UR	+34	+30	+4
17. Tax ratio needed	TRN	+46	+36	+10
18. Underemployed to labor net	UTLN	−34	−31	−3

Figure 10-22 Changes caused by a low-income-housing program (LCHPC = 0.05) on the refined model and comparison with the same run from *Urban Dynamics* (p.70)

effect of the same policy on the *Urban Dynamics* model. Column 5 computes the differences between columns 3 and 4. Any differences are caused solely by the abandonment refinement.

When comparing columns 3 and 4 of Figure 10-22, keep in mind the structural differences between the two models. The *Urban Dynamics* model contains a level of underemployed housing disaggregated into two levels of underemployed housing and abandoned housing in the refined model. To facilitate a comparison of the behavior of underemployed housing over time, Figure 10-21 shows the plot of SHT—the sum of underemployed housing UH and abandoned housing AH in the refined model. Overall, the two models respond to low-cost-housing construction in a strongly similar fashion. However, additional variables, such as the level of abandoned housing AH, provide new insights into the refined model's response to low-cost housing construction. AH points to a marked increase in the level of abandoned housing, from 20,000 to over 40,000 units, as the pool of underemployed housing increases after the construction program begins. The level of abandoned housing increases as the expanding supply

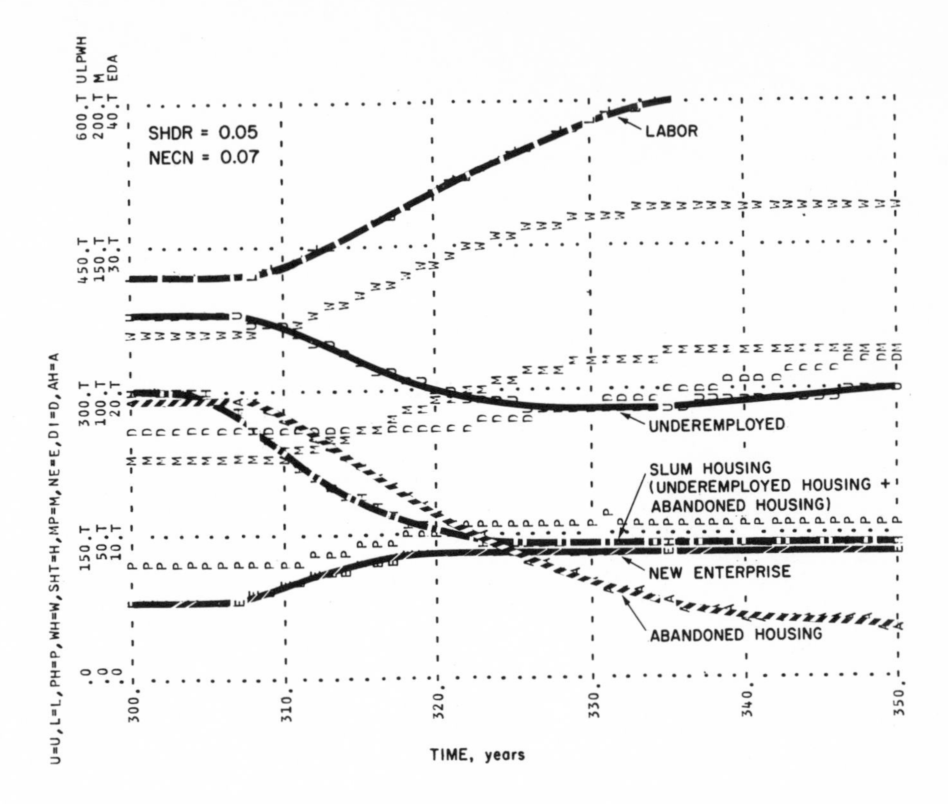

Figure 10-23 Plot of major system levels in response to the *Urban Dynamics* revival program

of low-cost housing loosens the bottom end of the housing market. With more vacancies, profits fall, making landlords more likely to abandon marginal housing. Because the overall economy of the city has not improved, incentives for voluntary demolition remain low. Consequently, the rate of underemployed-housing abandonment and the level of abandoned houses tend to increase. Whether or not the same situation develops in a real city depends both on the magnitude of the low-cost housing program and on the overall condition of the city's economy.[14] Testing the low-cost housing program on the refined model illustrates one major advantage of disaggregation. The refined model permits a test of how programs not directly related to abandonment affect the abandonment problem.

Urban Revival. The program found to be most effective in *Urban Dynamics* consists of simultaneously demolishing underemployed housing and providing incentives for new enterprise. Figure 10-23 reproduces the behavioral consequences in the refined model when 5 percent of the underemployed housing annually undergoes demolition and 40 percent more industrial construction takes place. Figure 10-24 is the tabulated summary of the same run.

Figure 10-24 indicates that, once again, the refined model behaves similarly to the *Urban Dynamics* model. Some slight differences between the two model runs deserve brief examination, however. Column 5 of Figure 24 indicates that the *Urban Dynamics*

(1) Variable Name	(2) Symbol	(3) Change (%)	(4) Change in *Urban Dynamics* (%)	(5) Difference (Column 3 – Column 4)
a. Slum-housing demolition total rate	SHD	+33	+36	−3
b. New enterprise construction	NEC	+78	+80	−2
1. New enterprise	NE	+66	+63	+3
2. Mature business	MB	+58	+64	−6
3. Declining industry	DI	+28	+35	−7
4. Premium housing	PH	+37	+38	−1
5. Worker housing	WH	+36	+34	+2
6. Slum housing total	SHT	−51	−43	−8
7. Abandoned housing	AH	−83	—	—
8. Managerial-professional	MP	+51	+53	−2
9. Labor	L	+56	+53	+3
10. Underemployed	U	−21	−11	−10
11. Manager/housing ratio	MHR	+10	+11	−1
12. Labor/housing ratio	LHR	+11	+14	−3
13. Underemployed/housing ratio	UHR	+61	+58	+3
14. Manager/job ratio	MR	−1	−1	0
15. Labor/job ratio	LR	+2	+1	+1
16. Underemployed/job ratio	UR	−58	−41	−17
17. Tax ratio needed	TRN	−40	−33	−7
18. Underemployed to labor net	UTLN	+31	+67	−36

Figure 10-24 Changes caused by the revival program (SHDR = 0.05, NECN = 0.07) on the refined model and comparison with the same run from *Urban Dynamics* (p.101)

model contains somewhat more underemployed housing UH and underemployed U than the refined model. The difference stems primarily from the tendency of the revival program to reduce the amount of abandoned housing by 83 percent. Because the abandoned-housing fraction AHF also drops by about 80 percent, property values remain more stable, and the obsolescence rates of premium housing and worker housing slow down. The *Urban Dynamics* model does not so fully exhibit this reinforcing effect of the revival program on housing quality. In the refined model, the revival policy reduces the flow of housing *into* the underemployed housing category and annually *removes* an extra 5 percent of the underemployed housing. A reduced inflow to and increased outflow from the level of underemployed housing UH lead to a lower equilibrium value of UH in the refined model. The lower level of UH at equilibrium in the refined model means a somewhat more limited housing capacity and therefore a lower level of underemployed population than in the original revival runs in *Urban Dynamics*. The revival program shows even greater promise when tested on the refined model. As a final difference, in Figure 10-23, a substantial decline in the level of abandoned structures is indicated. Because the *Urban Dynamics* model has no specific and separate abandoned-housing variable, a decline in abandoned housing can only be inferred in *Urban Dynamics*. The refined model containing an abandonment subsector remains consistent with the *Urban Dynamics* model from a policy viewpoint. A policy that improves the city in the *Urban Dynamics* model still improves the city in the refined model. An unrewarding policy gets equally bad marks from both models. The model refinement does, however, allow for a more complete policy analysis, since housing abandonment is specifically represented in the refinement. But differences in policy responses in the two models seem to be consistent with the changes made to incorporate the dynamics of abandonment.

10.7 Demolition of Abandoned-Housing Structures

Figure 10-25 depicts the response of the refined model to an annual demolition of 20 percent of the city's abandoned housing. No attempt is made to determine whether the demolition program is desirable or undesirable; instead, the analysis focuses on whether the refined model responds credibly to the demolition program. Tests for credible responses to policy changes form a valuable part of model evaluation and model refinement. Watching a model react to previously untested but conceptually plausible policies can help to ensure that the refined model accurately corresponds to our understanding of the real-world system.

Perhaps the most obvious feature of Figure 10-25 is that relatively little change takes place. For example, the levels of population, enterprise, and housing change insignificantly. Only the level of abandoned housing AH changes substantially, decreasing from about 20,000 to about 6,000 structures, or 70 percent. The removal of abandoned housing seems to neither attract new enterprise nor improve the balance between people and jobs. Because the levels do not change substantially, the underemployed/housing ratio UHR and the tax ratio needed TRN are also essentially unchanged. As a result of the 70 percent decline in abandoned structures, the abandoned-housing fraction AHF falls from about 2.5 percent to less than 1 percent. The abandoned-housing demolition program thereby successfully improves the overall housing condition in the city.

The model behavior shown by Figure 10-25 does not conflict with the views of urban experts who argue that a program of demolishing abandoned housing can help to reduce the level of abandonment but probably cannot alone improve the overall condition of a city.[15] Unemployment, high taxes, and an oversupply of low-quality housing do not come about solely through abandonment. In fact, abandonment seems to be far more symptomatic than causal of urban decay. The *Urban Dynamics* model, when modified to incorporate the dynamics of abandonment, tends to support the view that abandonment is a later-stage feature of socioeconomic decline in a city. Figure 10-23 showed how abandonment diminishes when the overall economy of the city improves; Figure 10-25 showed how a program to alleviate the abandonment problem does not induce any major improvements elsewhere in the urban system. Figure 10-25 does not

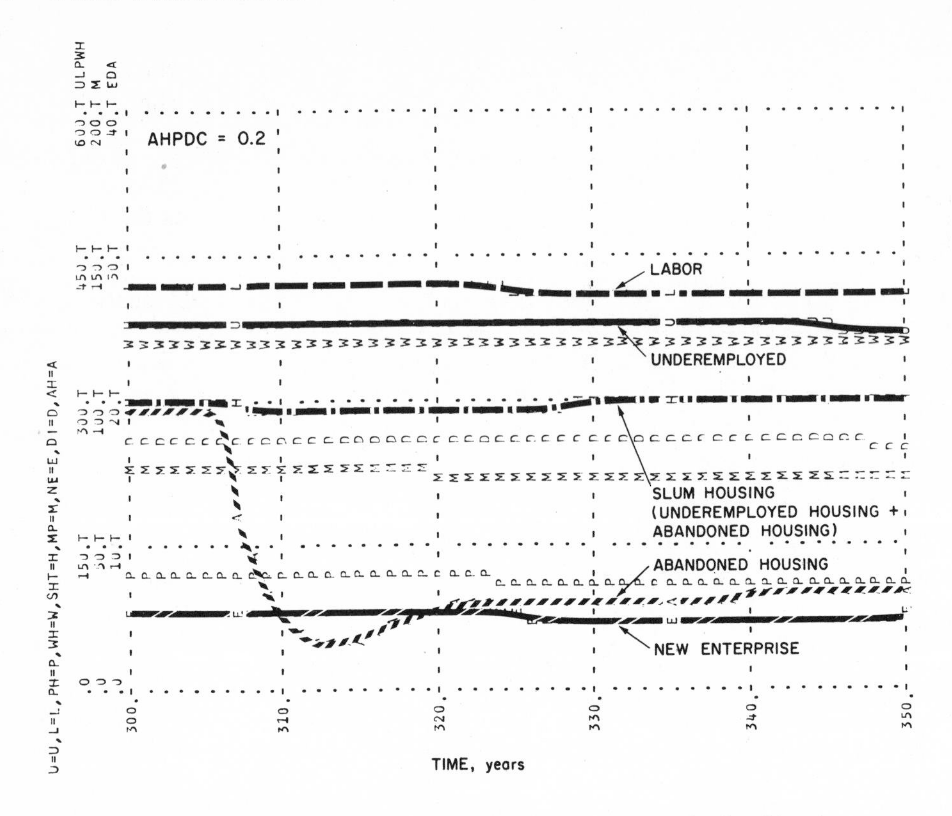

Figure 10-25 Plot of major system levels in response to an abandoned-housing-demolition program

validate the formulation of the abandonment process in the model, but it does show that the abandonment subsector produces both interesting and reasonable behavior—an important test of both usefulness and confidence for any model or model refinement.

10.8 Conclusions

The *Urban Dynamics* model seems to offer a promising point of departure for studying housing abandonment because it simultaneously interrelates many parts of the urban system, and therefore should be able to show whether abandonment results from past and present decisions made within the city. If the causes of abandonment are internal to the city, then so, too, must be the solutions. When tested against observed urban behavior, the refined model portrays housing abandonment as a phenomenon of the late stages of urban evolution. The amount of abandoned housing AH remains fairly small (less than 0.4 percent of the city's total housing stock) until year 110 of the model city's 250-year life cycle. Between years 110 and 150, the amount of abandoned housing rises dramatically to constitute over 3 percent of the total city housing stock. After year 150, the abandonment problem diminishes slightly, then stabilizes near year 200 with approximately 2.5 percent of the city housing stock abandoned. The 2.5 percent value falls within the currently observed range for actual cities. The behavior of the refined model has been compared with the behavior of the *Urban Dynamics* model.

Both models exhibit extremely similar behavior. The abandonment disaggregation adds detail to the original model, but the basic conclusions from *Urban Dynamics* remain intact. A low-cost housing program tested on the refined model still aggravates urban conditions overall (Figure 10-21). The revival program proposed in *Urban Dynamics* still produces substantial economic revitalization, as well as a sharp reduction in the amount of abandonment, in the refined model (Figure 10-23). Finally, a program of abandoned-housing demolition in the refined model seems to lessen the abandonment problem but generates little or no other improvement. Unemployment, high taxes, and socioeconomic decay do not measurably improve. Such results imply that abandonment is more of a symptom than a cause of urban decay. Programs aimed at directly reducing abandonment may ultimately have far less effect in removing the causes of abandonment than other programs designed to improve the overall economy of a city.

Notes

1. Linton, Mields, and Coston, Inc., *A Study of the Problems of Abandoned Housing*, report prepared for the U.S. Department of Housing and Urban Development (HUD), November 1971.

2. *National Survey of Housing Abandonment* (New York: National Urban League, Center for Community Change, April 1971), p. 15.

3. Ibid., p. 3.

4. The practice, known as "red-lining," of refusing a loan application on the basis of physical location has become quite common in American cities. Red-lining may be one of the major causes of a neighborhood's economic stagnation and therefore a direct encouragement of large-scale abandonment. See ibid., p. 15.

5. George Sternlieb, *The Urban Housing Dilemma: The Dynamics of New York City's Rent Controlled Housing* (New York: New York City Housing Development Administration, 1972). Sternlieb offers detailed accounts of how financial pressures on landlords create a climate conducive to abandonment.

6. *National Survey*, p. 5.

7. Ibid., p. 14.

8. The five-year estimate is the personal view of David Moore, Office of Research and Technology, HUD.

9. *National Survey*, pp. 8–13.

10. *Urban Decay in St. Louis* (New York: National Urban League, Center for Community Change, April 1971), pp. 63–64.

11. Ibid., pp. 56–57.

12. *National Survey*, p. 16.

13. Linton, Mields, and Coston; for quotations, see pp. 78, 79, and 93, respectively.

14. The various actions involved in acquiring abandoned property are discussed in greater detail in Reading 3 of this volume.

15. For example, Professor George Sternlieb of the Center for Urban Policy Research at Rutgers University has observed that housing removal and land clearance are often insufficient to stimulate redevelopment (personal communication, August 2, 1973).

Appendix: Documentor Listing

```
**********A HOUSING ABANDONMENT MODEL
**********ABANDONED HOUSING SECTOR

AH.K=AH.J+(DT)(UHA.JK-AHD.JK-AHDP.JK)                    200, L
AH=0                                                     200.1, N
     AH     - ABANDONED HOUSING (HOUSING UNITS)
     UHA    - UNDEREMPLOYED-HOUSING ABANDONMENT (HOUSING
                UNITS/YEAR)
     AHD    - ABANDONED-HOUSING DEMOLITION (HOUSING
                UNITS/YEAR)
     AHDP   - ABANDONED-HOUSING-DEMOLITION PROGRAM
                (HOUSING UNITS/YEAR)

UHA.KL=(UH.K)(UHAN)(UHAM.K)                              201, R
UHAN=.005                                                201.1, C
     UHA    - UNDEREMPLOYED-HOUSING ABANDONMENT (HOUSING
                UNITS/YEAR)
     UH     - UNDEREMPLOYED HOUSING (HOUSING UNITS)
     UHAN   - UNDEREMPLOYED-HOUSING-ABANDONMENT NORMAL
                (FRACTION/YEAR)
     UHAM   - UNDEREMPLOYED-HOUSING-ABANDONMENT
                MULTIPLIER (DIMENSIONLESS)

UHAM.K=(UHATM.K)(UHSM.K)(UHABM.K)                        202, A
     UHAM   - UNDEREMPLOYED-HOUSING-ABANDONMENT
                MULTIPLIER (DIMENSIONLESS)
     UHATM  - UNDEREMPLOYED-HOUSING-ABANDONMENT TAX MULT.
                (DIMENSIONLESS)
     UHSM   - UNDEREMPLOYED-HOUSING-SUPPLY MULTIPLIER
                (DIMENSIONLESS)
     UHABM  - UNDEREMPLOYED-HOUSING-ABANDONMENT-BLIGHT
                MULT. (DIMENSIONLESS)

UHATM.K=TABLE(UHATMT,1.44*LOGN(TR.K),-2,4,2)             203, A
UHATMT=.5/1/1.5/1.7                                      203.1, T
     UHATM  - UNDEREMPLOYED-HOUSING-ABANDONMENT TAX MULT.
                (DIMENSIONLESS)
     UHATMT - UNDEREMPLOYED-HOUSING-ABANDONMENT TAX
                MULTIPLIER TABLE
     TR     - TAX RATIO (DIMENSIONLESS)

UHSM.K=TABLE(UHSMT,UHR.K,0,2,.5)                         204, A
UHSMT=3/2/1/.6/.4                                        204.1, T
     UHSM   - UNDEREMPLOYED-HOUSING-SUPPLY MULTIPLIER
                (DIMENSIONLESS)
     UHSMT  - UNDEREMPLOYED-HOUSING-SUPPLY MULTIPLIER
                TABLE
     UHR    - UNDEREMPLOYED/HOUSING RATIO (DIMENSIONLESS)

UHABM.K=TABLE(UHABMT,AHF.K,0,.1,.02)                     205, A
UHABMT=.7/1/1.3/1.6/1.8/2                                205.1, T
     UHABM  - UNDEREMPLOYED-HOUSING-ABANDONMENT-BLIGHT
                MULT. (DIMENSIONLESS)
     UHABMT - UNDEREMPLOYED-HOUSING-ABANDONMENT-BLIGHT
                MULTIPLIER TABLE
     AHF    - ABANDONED-HOUSING FRACTION (DIMENSIONLESS)

AHF.K=AH.K/HUT.K                                         206, A
     AHF    - ABANDONED-HOUSING FRACTION (DIMENSIONLESS)
     AH     - ABANDONED HOUSING (HOUSING UNITS)
     HUT    - HOUSING UNITS TOTAL (HOUSING UNITS)

AHD.KL=(AH.K)(AHDN)(AHDM.K)                              207, R
AHDN=.125                                                207.1, C
     AHD    - ABANDONED-HOUSING DEMOLITION (HOUSING
                UNITS/YEAR)
     AH     - ABANDONED HOUSING (HOUSING UNITS)
     AHDN   - ABANDONED-HOUSING-DEMOLITION NORMAL
                (FRACTION/YEAR)
     AHDM   - ABANDONED-HOUSING-DEMOLITION MULTIPLIER
                (DIMENSIONLESS)

AHDM.K=(AHDLM.K)(AHDFM.K)                                208, A
     AHDM   - ABANDONED-HOUSING-DEMOLITION MULTIPLIER
                (DIMENSIONLESS)
```

```
    AHDLM  - ABANDONED-HOUSING-DEMOLITION-LAND MULT.
               (DIMENSIONLESS)
    AHDFM  - ABANDONED-HOUSING-DEMOLITION-FRACTION
               MULTIPLIER (DIMENSIONLESS)

AHDFM.K=TABLE(AHDFMT,AHF.K,0,.1,.02)                    209, A
AHDFMT=.8/1/1.3/1.7/2.2/3.0                             209.1, T
    AHDFM  - ABANDONED-HOUSING-DEMOLITION-FRACTION
               MULTIPLIER (DIMENSIONLESS)
    AHDFMT - ABANDONED-HOUSING-DEMOLITION-FRACTION
               MULTIPLIER TABLE
    AHF    - ABANDONED-HOUSING FRACTION (DIMENSIONLESS)

AHDLM.K=TABHL(AHDLMT,LFO.K,.8,1,.05)                    210, A
AHDLMT=.8/1/1.3/1.8/3                                   210.1, T
    AHDLM  - ABANDONED-HOUSING-DEMOLITION-LAND MULT.
               (DIMENSIONLESS)
    AHDLMT - ABANDONED-HOUSING-DEMOLITION-LAND
               MULTIPLIER TABLE
    LFO    - LAND FRACTION OCCUPIED (FRACTION)

**********THE REVISED UNDEREMPLOYED HOUSING SECTOR

UH.K=UH.J+(DT)(WHO.JK-UHD.JK-UHA.JK+LCHP.JK)            211, L
UH=1100                                                 211.1, N
    UH     - UNDEREMPLOYED HOUSING (HOUSING UNITS)
    WHO    - WORKER-HOUSING OBSOLESCENCE (HOUSING UNITS/
               YEAR)
    UHD    - UNDEREMPLOYED-HOUSING DEMOLITION (HOUSING
               UNITS/YEAR)
    UHA    - UNDEREMPLOYED-HOUSING ABANDONMENT (HOUSING
               UNITS/YEAR)
    LCHP   - LOW-COST-HOUSING PROGRAM (HOUSING UNITS/
               YEAR)

UHD.KL=(UHDN)(UH.K)(UHDM.K)+SHDP.K                      212, R
UHDN=.015                                               212.1, C
    UHD    - UNDEREMPLOYED-HOUSING DEMOLITION (HOUSING
               UNITS/YEAR)
    UHDN   - UNDEREMPLOYED-HOUSING-DEMOLITION NORMAL
               (FRACTION/YEAR)
    UH     - UNDEREMPLOYED HOUSING (HOUSING UNITS)
    UHDM   - UNDEREMPLOYED-HOUSING-DEMOLITION MULTIPLIER
               (DIMENSIONLESS)
    SHDP   - SLUM-HOUSING-DEMOLITION PROGRAM (HOUSING
               UNITS/YEAR)

UHDM.K=(UHRM.K)(UHLM.K)(UHDSM.K)(SHDF)                  213, A
SHDF=1                                                  213.1, C
    UHDM   - UNDEREMPLOYED-HOUSING-DEMOLITION MULTIPLIER
               (DIMENSIONLESS)
    UHRM   - UNDEREMPLOYED-HOUSING-REPLACEMENT
               MULTIPLIER (DIMENSIONLESS)
    UHLM   - UNDEREMPLOYED-HOUSING-LAND MULTIPLIER
               (DIMENSIONLESS)
    UHDSM  - UNDEREMPLOYED-HOUSING-DEMOLITION-SUPPLY
               MULTIPLIER (DIMENSIONLESS)
    SHDF   - SLUM-HOUSING-DEMOLITION FACTOR
               (DIMENSIONLESS)

UHLM.K=TABHL(UHLMT,LFO.K,.8,1,.05)                      214, A
UHLMT=1/1.2/1.6/2.2/6                                   214.1, T
    UHLM   - UNDEREMPLOYED-HOUSING-LAND MULTIPLIER
               (DIMENSIONLESS)
    UHLMT  - UNDEREMPLOYED-HOUSING-LAND MULTIPLIER TABLE
    LFO    - LAND FRACTION OCCUPIED (FRACTION)

UHDSM.K=TABLE(UHDSMT,UHR.K,0,2,.5)                      215, A
UHDSMT=1.2/1.1/1/.8/.7                                  215.1, T
    UHDSM  - UNDEREMPLOYED-HOUSING-DEMOLITION-SUPPLY
               MULTIPLIER (DIMENSIONLESS)
    UHDSMT - UNDEREMPLOYED-HOUSING-DEMOLITION-SUPPLY
               MULTIPLIER TABLE
    UHR    - UNDEREMPLOYED/HOUSING RATIO (DIMENSIONLESS)

UHRM.K=TABLE(UHRMT,ALDF.K,0,.2,.025)                    216, A
UHRMT=.7/1/1.3/1.7/2.2/2.5/2.7/2.9/3                    216.1, T
```

```
    UHRM    - UNDEREMPLOYED-HOUSING-REPLACEMENT
                MULTIPLIER (DIMENSIONLESS)
    UHRMT   - UNDEREMPLOYED-HOUSING-REPLACEMENT
                MULTIPLIER TABLE
    ALDF    - AVAILABLE-LAND-DEMAND FRACTION
                (DIMENSIONLESS)

ALDF.K=DLUR.K/AL.K                                        217, A
    ALDF    - AVAILABLE-LAND-DEMAND FRACTION
                (DIMENSIONLESS)
    DLUR    - DESIRED-LAND UTILIZATION RATE (ACRES)
    AL      - AVAILABLE LAND (ACRES)

AL.K=(1-LFO.K)(AREA)                                      218, A
    AL      - AVAILABLE LAND (ACRES)
    LFO     - LAND FRACTION OCCUPIED (FRACTION)
    AREA    - LAND AREA (ACRES)

DLUR.K=NECD.K*LPP+(PHCD.K+WHCD.K)*LPH                     219, A
    DLUR    - DESIRED-LAND UTILIZATION RATE (ACRES)
    NECD    - NEW-ENTERPRISE-CONSTRUCTION DESIRED
                (PRODUCTION UNITS/YEAR)
    LPP     - LAND PER PRODUCTION UNIT (ACRES/PRODUCTION
                UNIT)
    PHCD    - PREMIUM-HOUSING CONSTRUCTION DESIRED
                (HOUSING UNITS/YEAR)
    WHCD    - WORKER-HOUSING CONSTRUCTION DESIRED
                (HOUSING UNITS/YEAR)
    LPH     - LAND PER HOUSE (ACRES/HOUSING UNIT)

SHT.K=UH.K+AH.K                                           220, S
    SHT     - SLUM HOUSING, TOTAL (HOUSING UNITS)
    UH      - UNDEREMPLOYED HOUSING (HOUSING UNITS)
    AH      - ABANDONED HOUSING (HOUSING UNITS)

SHD.K=UHD.JK+AHD.JK                                       221, S
    SHD     - SLUM HOUSING DEMOLITION (HOUSING UNITS/
                YEAR)
    UHD     - UNDEREMPLOYED-HOUSING DEMOLITION (HOUSING
                UNITS/YEAR)
    AHD     - ABANDONED-HOUSING DEMOLITION (HOUSING
                UNITS/YEAR)

**********ALTERED PREMIUM HOUSING SECTOR

PHABM.K=TABLE(PHABMT,AHF.K,0,.1,.02)                      222, A
PHABMT=1.1/1.0/.9/.85/.8/.75                              222.1, T
    PHABM   - PREMIUM-HOUSING-ABANDONMENT MULTIPLIER
                (DIMENSIONLESS)
    PHABMT  - PREMIUM-HOUSING-ABANDONMENT MULTIPLIER
                TABLE
    AHF     - ABANDONED-HOUSING FRACTION (DIMENSIONLESS)

**********ALTERED WORKER HOUSING SECTOR

WHABM.K=TABLE(WHABMT,AHF.K,0,.1,.02)                      223, A
WHABMT=1.1/1/.9/.85/.8/.75                                223.1, T
    WHABM   - WORKER-HOUSING-ABANDONMENT MULTIPLIER
                (DIMENSIONLESS)
    WHABMT  - WORKER-HOUSING-ABANDONMENT MULTIPLIER TABLE
    AHF     - ABANDONED-HOUSING FRACTION (DIMENSIONLESS)

PLOT  U=U,L=L,PH=P,WH=W,SHT=H(0,600E3)/MP=M(0,200E3)/NE=E,DI=D,AH=A(0,40
X       E3)
RUN   FIGURE 10-17
PLOT  SHT=H(0,600E3)
RUN   FIGURE 10-19
PLOT  SHD=D(0,20E3)
RUN   FIGURE 10-20
PLOT  U=U,L=L,PH=P,WH=W,SHT=H(0,600E3)/MP=M(0,200E3)/NE=E,DI=D,AH=A(0,40
X       E3)
CP    LENGTH=350
CP    PLTCT=299
CP    PLTMIN=0
CP    PLTMAX=1
C     LCHPC=.05
C     SWT10=299
```

```
RUN     FIGURE 10-21
C       SHDR=.05
C       SWT5=299
C       NECR=.07
C       SWT6=299
RUN     FIGURE 10-23
C       AHDPC=.2
C       SWT12=299
RUN     FIGURE 10-25
```

11

Urban Dynamics Applied to an Old Industrial City

Louis Edward Alfeld

Lowell, Massachusetts, is the site of the first application of urban dynamics to the problems of a real city. Lowell, the first American city to experience the Industrial Revolution of the early nineteenth century, suffers from chronic unemployment and economic stagnation. Because Lowell is typical of many old industrial cities, the lessons learned from applying urban dynamics in Lowell should be transferable to other old cities. To alleviate unemployment, the balance between jobs and people must be reestablished. A city that wants to improve employment conditions for its current residents must increase the number of jobs, discourage "outside" competition by restricting in-migration and commuting, and attract jobs that foster upward socioeconomic mobility. Local housing policies, which directly influence migration rates, must complement local employment policies. A combination of policies to encourage business expansion and remove excess housing can stimulate and sustain the revival in old industrial cities.

11
Urban Dynamics Applied to an Old Industrial City

11.1 Urban Dynamics and Lowell in Perspective

Urban dynamics is a management tool for urban policy analysis. An urban dynamics model permits computer simulation of alternative policies to improve city management. Policy testing can help to achieve goals for growing cities and to revive declining cities. Simulation reveals why some past policies have failed and why alternative policies may succeed. For older cities with high unemployment, urban dynamics implies a need for policies that balance jobs and people in a more viable social and economic proportion. Decision makers in many cities responded with great interest to *Urban Dynamics*, even though the book does not translate its broad policy guidelines into specific management actions for mayors and city council members. The gap between theory and recommendations for day-to-day decision making in the book left the public unsure of urban dynamics applications. A fuller understanding of how to use urban dynamics awaited additional modeling and the analysis of policies in a specific city. Lowell, Massachusetts, is the site of the first formal application of urban dynamics modeling to a real city's problems. The modeling process proved useful in developing more feasible policies for Lowell, and the procedure should be applicable to many old industrial cities. In the early 1800s, the construction of Lowell's huge textile mills gave birth to the Industrial Revolution in the United States. Rapid growth, maturity, and decline, similar to the life cycle in the *Urban Dynamics* model, has characterized Lowell's history. Since 1950 the city has exhibited persistent unemployment, excess low-quality housing, and a large percentage of unskilled and underemployed residents. Because its history resembles that of many industrial cities, Lowell was an ideal city for testing urban dynamics.[1]

The general management guidelines that follow illustrate how decision makers in a city such as Lowell might better coordinate urban policies using urban dynamics. Other cities can also benefit from the policy analysis process, if not the specific recommendations.

11.2 To Balance Jobs and People

Urban Dynamics shows how the structural mechanisms common to all cities produce unemployment in older cities by creating an imbalance between jobs and population. The common forces creating the imbalance include a lack of clear and feasible goals, which leads to inconsistencies in local policies. In older cities faced with the problems of a declining job base in manufacturing and a rising population of less-skilled and underemployed workers, urban policy usually aims to increase employment, improve housing, and increase revenues to meet financial needs. However, because many urban conditions are tightly interlocked, an array of policies that pursue different goals can be self-defeating. Some goals are mutually incompatible. Therefore, city residents must often make difficult choices among achievable goals. A consistent combination of policies for achieving those goals must be structured to prevent unforeseen deleterious reactions.

Improved Employment Conditions. The goal of improved employment often dominates trade-offs in older cities such as Lowell. To attain the goal, policy makers must pursue a better balance between jobs and people. However, "balance" implies actions both to create jobs *and* to manage population increases. Otherwise, job creation may attract so many new residents that city employment conditions actually worsen. For example, New Mexico Governor Bruce King told a U.S. Senate Committee that every time Albuquerque gets any new industry, the city's unemployment rate rises slightly, and the population of the surrounding countryside drops proportionately.[2] Unemployment also increased in Detroit following the creation of 50,000 new jobs in the city after a period of rioting.[3] The goal of improved urban employment conditions must guide *all* city policies, not just employment policies.

Benefit Present Residents. A city's first responsibility is to its own residents. If each city solves its own problems, then a nation of healthy cities can prosper. Therefore, city policies to improve employment conditions should first benefit current city residents. Potential job gains for residents tend to erode if commuters or new residents fill most new job openings. No city can create enough jobs to satisfy unemployed in-migrants from all other places. The creation of new jobs without controls on in-migration may only worsen crowding and further overload services in a city. Better employment conditions and correspondingly greater upward socioeconomic mobility for current residents depend upon preventing a faster inflow of newcomers than the city can absorb. Achieving a balance between jobs and people in a city with excessive unemployment requires both more jobs and constraints on further in-migration and commuting. A city should encourage the creation of jobs that will increase the upward mobility of city residents.

The encouragement of job expansion can take many forms. Tax incentives, zoning variances, and site clearance attract new industry to a city. Given proper encouragement, many small firms already in the city may decide to hire more workers. For example, a local printing firm already employing twenty people might hire five more employees if the parking space for two additional delivery trucks were available. City assistance in resolving this parking problem could produce more jobs. Job expansion should focus on industries that offer an internal ladder of economic advancement and require low entry skills. To the average resident, a small printing firm offers more relief from city unemployment than a law office employing the same number of people. Policies to encourage job expansion should not only concentrate on attracting new employment opportunities but also nurture existing industries.

The discouragement of rapid additional in-migration improves the balance between jobs and people by limiting potential increases in a city's population to a rate readily absorbed by local industry. With fewer newcomers, present residents can compete for new jobs more successfully. The city may also have to institute supplemental programs to train the unskilled, to place prospective employees for on-the-job training, and to match underemployed city residents with job openings. Such programs can help current residents compete for jobs. Policies to discourage in-migration counterbalance the attraction for outsiders of improved employment conditions. Therefore, city population growth does not accelerate to nullify the expansion of local employment opportunities. Commuters also decrease the effectiveness of a job-expansion policy by filling jobs that would otherwise be available to city residents. For example, Boston's director of manpower and development acknowledged the detrimental impact of commuting on job availability for city residents by requiring the tenants of a proposed industrial park to provide local notification of job openings before advertising in the metropolitan Boston area.[4] Payroll taxes on city jobs held by commuters and other innovative policies further encourage local firms to hire local labor. Policy makers must strive to ensure that commuters do not fill all the new jobs. City employment policies benefit residents most when new jobs also generate upward socioeconomic mobility for residents. Since the mix of job skills in the population changes in response to city conditions, employment policies should create conditions that upgrade average resident job skills. For city residents, increased upward mobility induced by better job opportunities depends upon giving residents a competitive edge by constraining in-migration and commuting. Young, unskilled factory workers seldom advance to foremen if their employer can more easily hire outsiders than upgrade the skills of his present labor force. Reduced upward mobility also discourages self-advancement. The lack of personal incentives leads to poor work habits, unstable employment records, and a permanently low position on the social ladder. Children of the urban poor may sense the futility of pursuing legitimate economic achievement, give up hope, and turn to welfare or crime. To remain socially and economically healthy, a city must generate upward mobility among its residents. Improved employment opportunities for city residents and constraints on excess in-migration require negative city features to counterbalance the attractiveness of new jobs. No city can improve all its features without suffering destructive excess in-migration by the great numbers of people who would indubitably find a "perfect" city extremely attractive. Housing policy provides one possible leverage point for influencing in-migration.

Constraining In-migration. A shortage of housing can deter potential excess in-migration to a city. Several strategies can reduce housing availability: the immediate removal of vacant excess housing from the market, the strict enforcement of building and occupancy codes, active housing demolition programs, a limit on new housing construction, and the limiting of residential densities. Housing policies that constrain population increases help to improve the local balance between jobs and people. A city's first obligation must be to its own residents. Only when a city is able to sustain its current residents with adequate employment and opportunities for advancement should a city undertake to upgrade the socioeconomic status of underemployed in-migrants. Housing restrictions should serve not as a weapon of discrimination but as a device for preventing potentially even greater poverty if in-migrants can move into the reviving city at will. When a once stagnant city succeeds in changing the fortunes of its current residents, the city can admit a larger stream of in-migrants than was possible before revival. But even then, its housing policy should continue to function as a regulator of increased in-migration.

Meeting Residents' Needs. Housing policies should not create unnecessary hardships for city residents. A restricted city housing supply usually raises costs and decreases choices. However, increased job availability should raise resident incomes and offset higher housing costs. A clear trade-off exists between jobs and housing for residents; if present housing problems result primarily from inadequate incomes, then raising incomes through expanded employment opportunities makes better housing financially feasible for city residents. Special programs should meet the housing needs of elderly or infirm residents, who are unlikely to benefit from new jobs; no current resident should have to leave the city because of an induced housing shortage. To sustain improved employment conditions and resulting income gains, housing officials must continually monitor the city's housing supply to maintain adequate housing for current residents, while enforcing a tight housing market for potential in-migrants.

11.3 Policy Interpretation

Extensive refinements of the *Urban Dynamics* model have gradually led to a better understanding of how specific urban policies might further rebalance jobs and people in a city. Some combinations of urban policies strongly affect a city while, individually, they hardly change urban conditions. The policy recommendations presented here reflect the results of many tests of both individual and combined policy alternatives.[5] Of course, further model refinements might yield additional policy details. The following recommendations merely illustrate how one specific combination of policies rebalances jobs and people, benefits city residents by improving city employment conditions, and encourages greater upward socioeconomic mobility. A combination of the following policy recommendations should improve conditions in Lowell and other old industrial cities. By mutually reinforcing one another's strengths and compensating for weaknesses, the interacting policies produce pressures to improve city conditions. The recommended policies are:

1. encourage business over residential development,
2. encourage demolition or rehabilitation of underused buildings,
3. control the density of new development,
4. reduce housing construction, and
5. improve transportation access for commercial and retail activity but not for commuters.

Encourage Business over Residential Development. The city planning commission and zoning board should rezone residential land for business uses. Such a rezoning policy tends to (1) restrict housing expansion by reducing the supply of residential land and (2) encourage new business construction by increasing the supply of business land. The policy also benefits city residents because the recommended change in land-use patterns encourages job expansion without also furthering population growth. However, to protect residential values, zoning authorities should respect neighborhood integrity. The city planning commission should review established zoning laws and recommend changes to the city council. Future plans should favor land development for business rather than residences. (The redesignation of Lowell's forty-four-acre Hale-Howard Redevelopment Area from residential to industrial use is a real-world example of such a healthy shift in land use.)[6] The zoning board should also adopt variance review procedures that favor business uses of land. Moreover, the city should prevent zoning changes that would increase present housing densities and should rigidly enforce present occupancy codes to prevent a short-run expansion of the housing supply. A policy of favoring business over residential uses tends to shift urban land-use patterns and thereby sustain a healthier balance between jobs and people. Increased efforts to promote business expansion should help in generating new jobs. City officials should encourage established industries to relocate locally and should provide local industries with special inducements for permanent establishment or expansion. The aging city needs new jobs offering wage scales that are competitive with present welfare and unemployment compensation to encourage residents to learn skills and thereby advance themselves. The city should provide business advice, financial aid, employee training and placement, real-estate guidance, and management assistance to local industries. Businesses that hire, train, and offer advancement to less-skilled workers should receive special attention.

Encourage Demolition or Rehabilitation of Underused Buildings. An aggressive program to demolish abandoned and excess low-quality housing should tend to (1) reduce the city's housing capacity and (2) aid the conversion of cleared residential land to potential business sites. Carefully planned demolition of excess housing should not force current residents out of the city but should instead constrain outsiders from moving in beyond the capacity of the city to provide jobs. Demolition can also provide low-skill job opportunities, particularly for neighborhood teenagers. The lack of adequate public funds for demolition may necessitate tax incentives and the enforcement of building and occupancy codes to encourage demolition. Cleared sites inappropriate for business uses should be designated for such other nonresidential uses as parks and playgrounds. As current residents benefit from socioeconomic gains and begin to move to better housing, the demolition of vacated low-quality housing left behind should deter excessive in-migration without causing a housing shortage for the city's current poor.

Control the Density of New Development. Most cities are moving consistently in the direction of high-density rental apartment living. For example, Lowell's downtown section has become nearly 100 percent renter occupied. Apartments offer different benefits and drawbacks from lower-density privately owned homes. Cities must recognize the differences and decide whether to encourage apartment construction.

High-density living permits the city's land to support a larger population. The larger population, if not accompanied by job growth, can create an environment ripe for increased unemployment and congestion. An increase in the number of moderately priced apartments may attract even more families to declining cities and aggravate the very problems of most concern to their residents. Moreover, the socioeconomic stability of the city may lessen as apartments gain in relation to private homes. Unlike homeowners, apartment dwellers have no equity invested in their city and can freely move out if conditions worsen. Homeowners cannot afford to ignore their city's problems and can be depended upon to combat the forces of blight and decay more ambitiously.

Reduce Housing Construction. City officials should try to cut the rate of housing construction by 50 percent. Rigid standards and reviews for granting residential building permits and strict enforcement of all building codes should discourage some residential development. Limiting construction in order to restrict housing availability discourages in-migration of skilled labor that might otherwise deny jobs to current residents and prevent the promotion of less-skilled city residents to skilled positions. A tighter housing market also tends to reduce the rate of filter-down, so that the demolition of low-quality housing more effectively removes excess housing from the market. The continued construction of some premium housing should increase the filter-down of some high-quality housing to the middle-income market. Higher-quality housing and less choice should drive up housing costs, a necessary trade-off for sustaining improved economic opportunities. An overall reduction in housing construction can influence housing-market pressures to rebalance housing, population, and jobs.

Improve Transportation Access for Commercial and Retail Activity but Not for Commuters. A policy to discourage commuting can reduce outside competition for jobs intended for current city residents. City officials should deemphasize transportation access between the city and its suburbs by rescheduling public transportation to less convenient commuting times or routes and by restricting automobile access. In-town commuter parking should be constrained by either raising prices or removing parking to less convenient locations. However, the commuter policies should avoid forcing existing industry and stores out of the city. City transportation should maximize the accessibility of local jobs to current residents. As total employment increases in response to policy changes, pressures preventing increases in commuter traffic should tend to draw more local residents into local jobs. Anti-commuting pressures also tend to discourage new upwardly mobile families from moving to the suburbs and commuting to city jobs.

Urban dynamics analysis can help in explaining the overall logic and consistency of the above policy recommendation. The city-suburb model described in Reading 12 of this collection can be readily used to analyze and project the effect of these recommendations on Lowell and its metropolitan region. Basically five model parameters were altered to incorporate the above policy changes in the city suburb model:

1. 20 percent acceleration in new-business construction,
2. demolition of 5 percent of the lowest-quality housing,
3. demolition of 5 percent of the most underused industrial property,
4. one-third less upper-income-housing construction,
5. 50 percent greater resistance to extending commuter-oriented transportation facilities.[7]

These changes are implemented in 1975, and the model projects the consequences through the year 2000 (Figures 11-1 to 11-5).

Figure 11-1 shows that the recommended policies simulated in the city-suburb model can produce greatly improved employment conditions for lower-income resi-

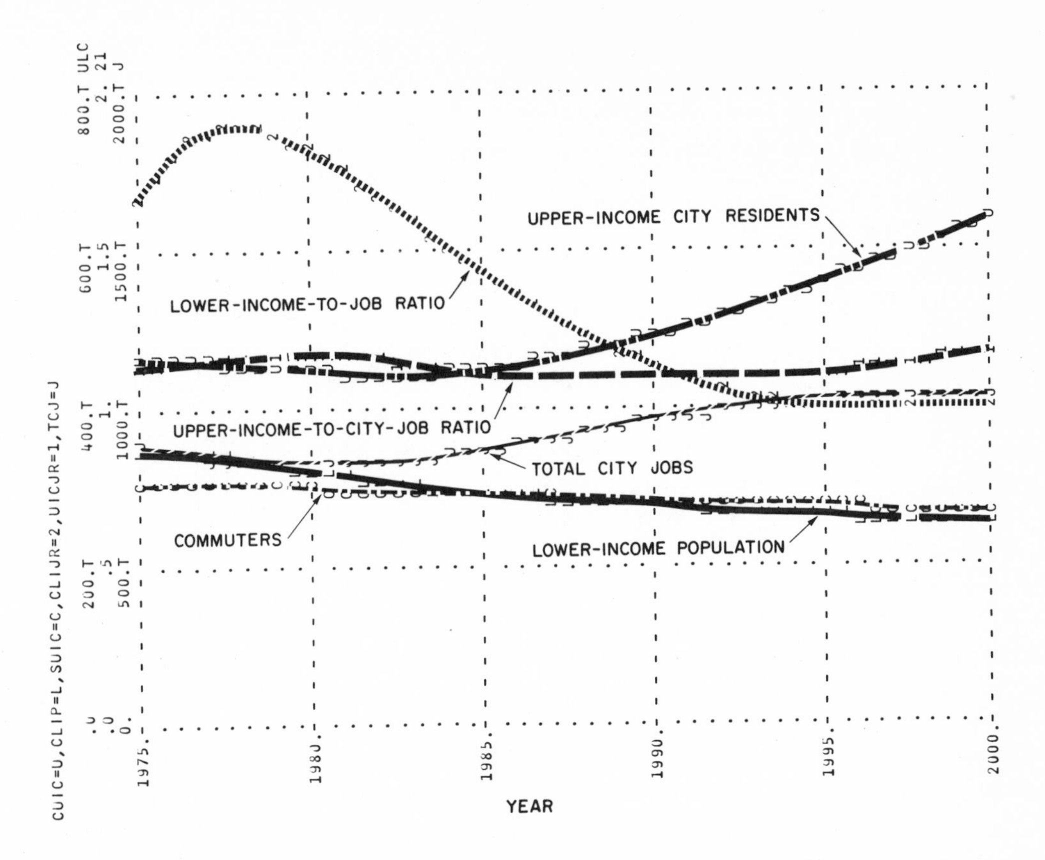

Figure 11-1 The effects of recommended policies on employment conditions

dents and a substantial increase in jobs for both lower and upper-income workers. The most noticeable improvement, a decreased lower-income-to-job ratio, results from a much better balance between the lower-income workforce (which decreases due to accelerated upward economic mobility) and job availability. The upper-income-to-job ratio improves (drops) slightly during the first fifteen years between 1975 and 1990 and then returns to about its original value due to a substantial increase in the number of upper-income city residents. Upper-income families increase due to (1) in-migration from outside the region, (2) increased upward mobility of lower-income residents, and (3) a net reduction of commuters, many of whom have chosen to move back to the city. The city appears stronger both in terms of its employment picture and a more healthy socio-economic population mix that encourages some upper-income population to return to the city. Figure 11-2 shows the improved mix among types of city housing that results from the recommended policies. Total city housing remains fairly constant. A decrease in lower-income housing balances an increase in upper-income housing. The gap between lower-income housing demolition and upper-income housing construction between 1975 and 1985 attests to a net loss of housing. Beyond 1985, construction exceeds demolition and produces a net housing gain. Despite a policy of reducing housing construction by one-third, the level of good-quality (upper-income) housing is

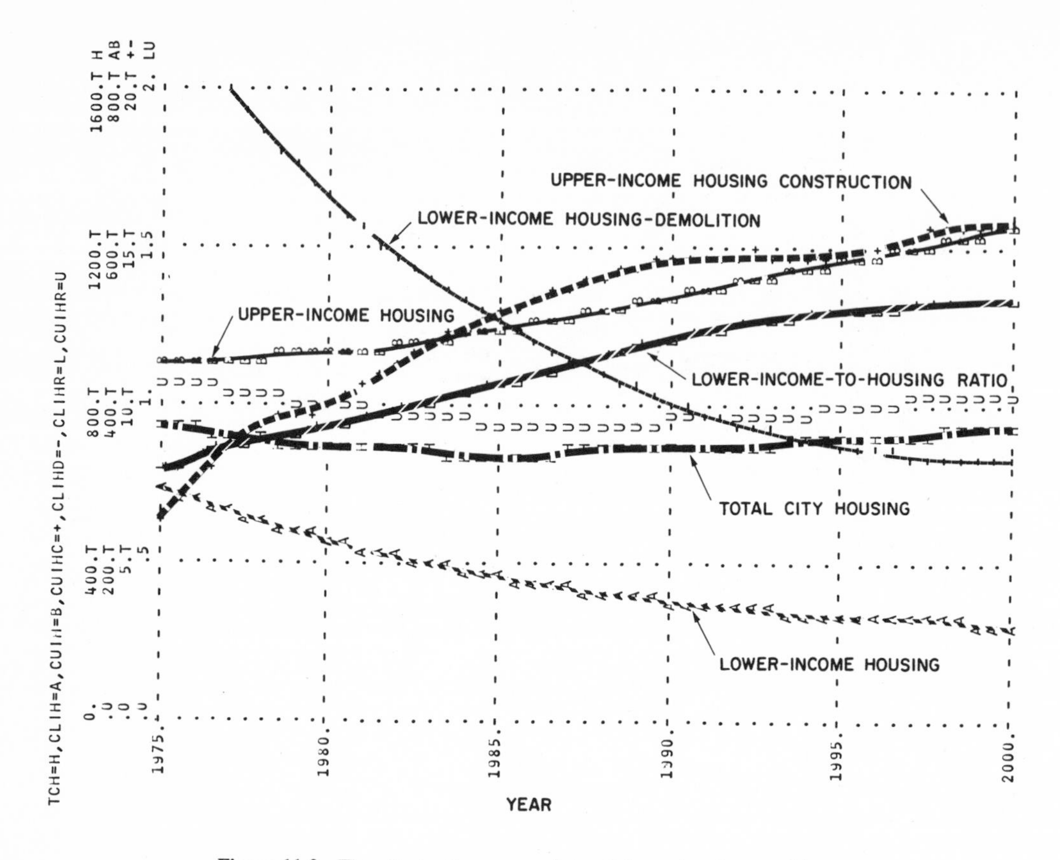

Figure 11-2 The effects of recommended policies on housing conditions

never less than its original amount. Pressures to decrease housing construction encounter rising pressures for more good-quality middle-income housing as lower-income families advance to the upper-income category. The induced housing shortage, by deterring the in-migration of skilled labor, aids upward mobility for the urban poor. The changed composition of the housing stock encourages a more favorable socioeconomic mix of city residents.

For unskilled lower-income city residents, the benefits from the recommended policies include better employment conditions and a more rapid upward socioeconomic mobility. Figure 11-3 shows both a rising number of upper-income city residents and a decreasing lower-income population. The socioeconomic mix in the city population improves because the rate of upward economic advancement from lower income to upper income increases substantially. The lower-income population decreases, not because they must leave the city but because they move up into a higher economic category. The stability of lower-income arrivals and the long-term decrease in lower-income departures reflect improved internal conditions for lower-income population. The lower-income-to-housing ratio rises as the housing market tightens. Decreased housing availability counterbalances the advantages offered by increased job availability and a doubling of net upward economic mobility. The fraction of lower-income

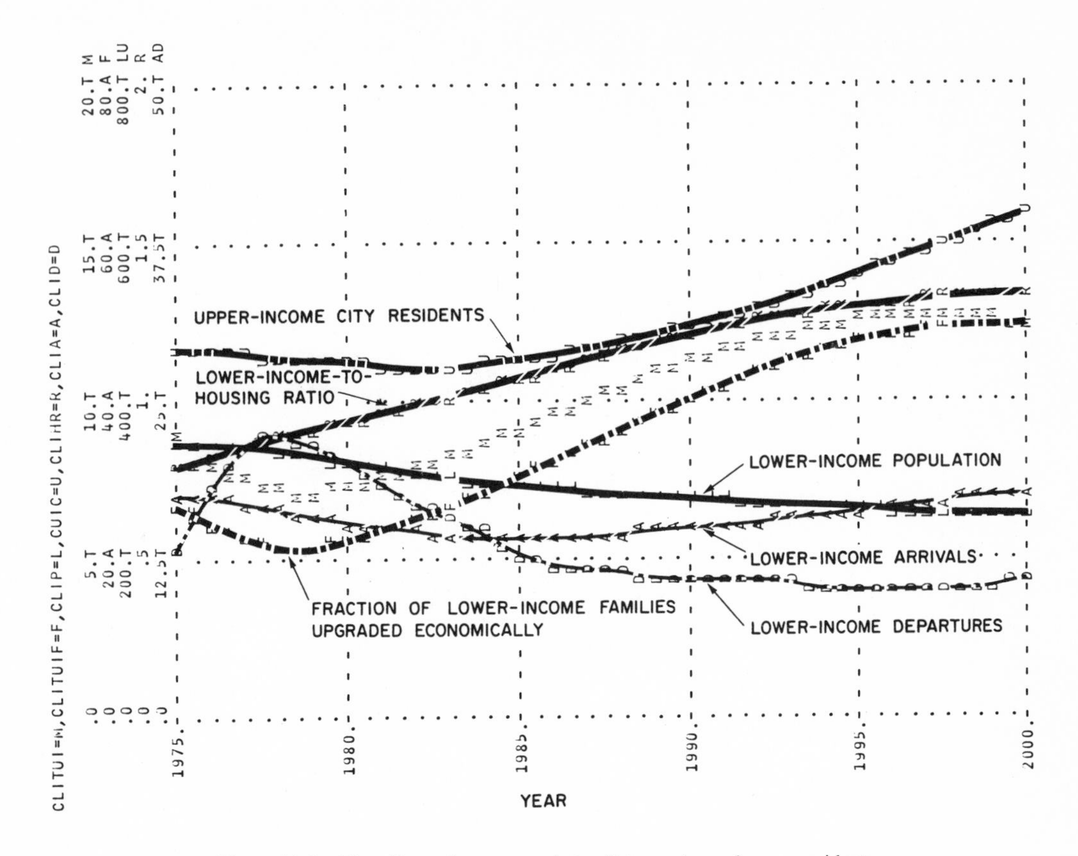

Figure 11-3 The effects of recommended policies on lower-income residents

families economically upgraded every year rises from less than 3 percent to 5 percent. The recommended policies benefit lower-income population and relieve conditions of poverty in the city. Because the recommended policies tend to remove older, underused structures and replace them with newer buildings, the city's economic and tax bases are strengthened. Figure 11-4 shows that the total stock of city new-business structures increases significantly during the years 1975 to 1995. The industrial demolition program causes the total stock of city older-business structures to drop considerably. However the net effect is an increase in total jobs (Figure 11-1). An additional consequence is higher city assessed value. A higher rate of city new-business-structures construction also ensures a more diverse industrial base that offers modern, well-paying jobs. The city's improved economic base narrows the gap between needs and resources. The tax ratio drops slightly as the city's tax base expands. The policy recommendations, by encouraging demolition and clearing land, permit increased construction that benefits both developers and city residents.

Changes in suburban conditions result from natural system "reactions" to the changing city. Figure 11-5 indicates that improvements in city conditions do not come at the expense of the suburb but instead create a healthier metropolitan region. For example, total metropolitan assessed value rises steadily from 1975 on. As city busi-

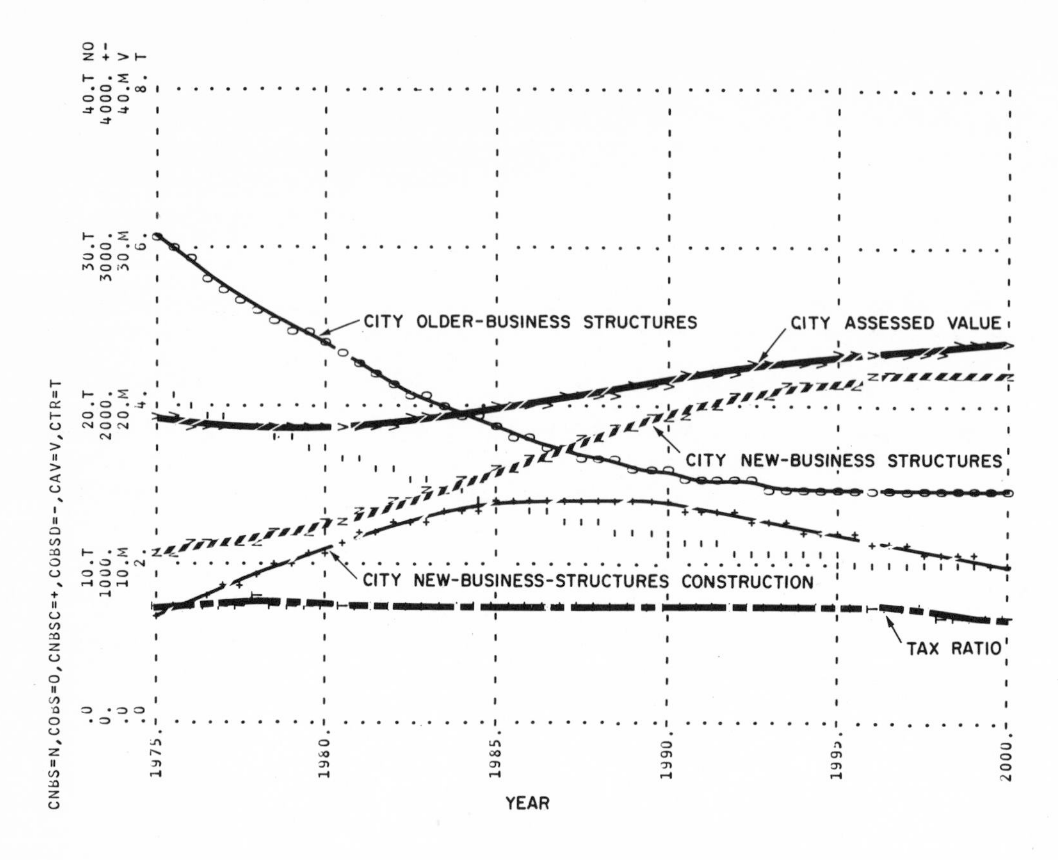

Figure 11-4 The effects of recommended policies on the city's economic base

ness structures (and activity) increase, some additional firms attracted to the region's growing industrial base choose to locate in the suburbs. After the year 1980, the rate of suburban new-business structures construction increases slightly. The consequent increase in suburban jobs makes commuting less necessary. The decline in the number of commuters between 1980 and 2000 in Figure 11-5 indicates that the suburbs have become self-sufficient. Moreover, because the entire region's economic base has expanded, the outlook for continued prosperity in the region is favorable. Suburban families move back to the city in greater numbers between 1985 and 2000. As the urban population mix and housing market improve, the city becomes a more attractive place in which to live. In a sense, the incentives for commuting (to avoid the problems of urban living) diminish. The urban system reverts to a condition in which more families live and work inside the city. In short, both the city and its suburbs gain from the recommended policies. These policies should provide the city's current population with higher incomes through increased employment and sustain the improvement by altering the housing supply to reinforce a new balance in the socioeconomic composition of the city's population. Current unskilled and underemployed residents should benefit from the upgrading of their socioeconomic status. Internal policies that trade excess housing for more jobs advance the city's goal of improved employment conditions.

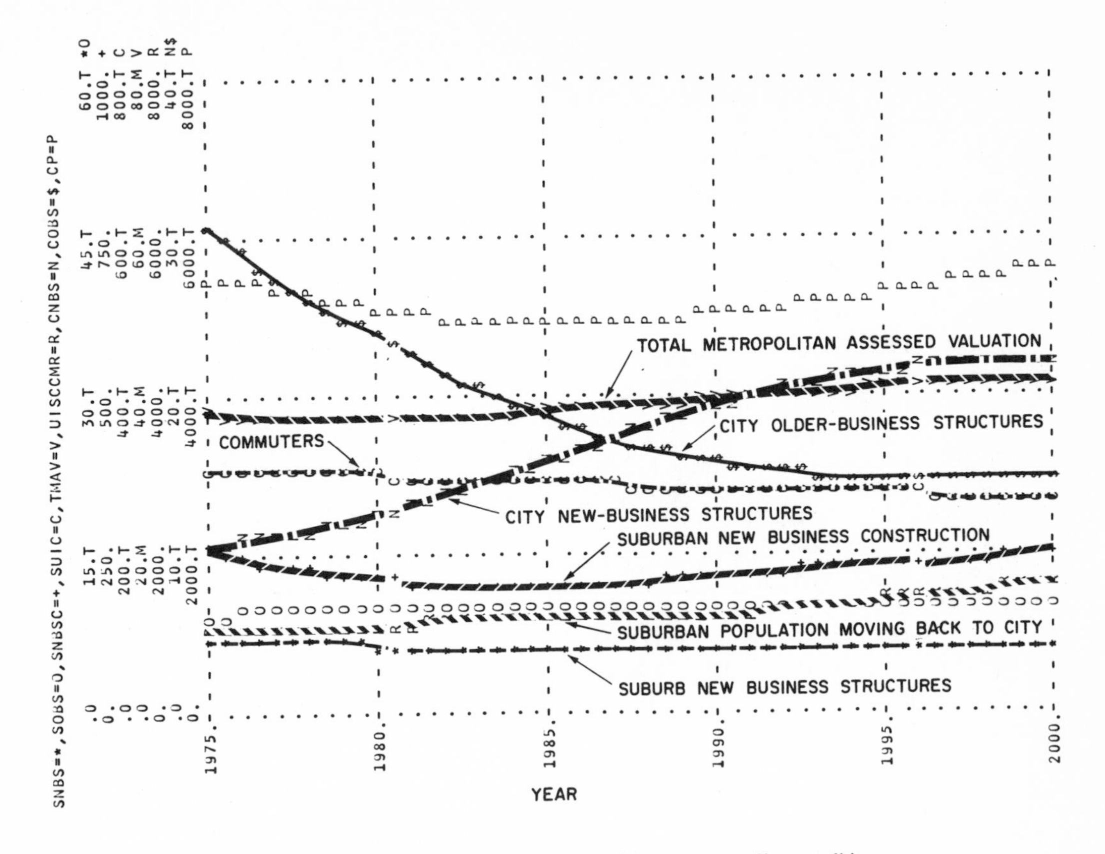

Figure 11-5 The effects of recommended policies on metropolitan conditions

11.4 Transferability of Results

The application of urban dynamics involves adapting a model to a specific city and demonstrating how to analyze specific policies with that model. Adjusting urban dynamics models to fit other cities always requires an alteration of model parameters. The refinement of a model's structure to permit the representation of specific policy alternatives permits the evaluation of policy alternatives previously outside the scope of the original model. An increased sophistication in the application of feedback-control theory through urban dynamics models should improve the design of specific urban policies. For example, the continuous monitoring of city conditions can directly lead to readjustments in policy and the proper phasing of policy implementation.

Lowell was chosen for urban dynamics research because the city is typical of urban areas in New England. Policy recommendations to improve conditions in Lowell should also improve conditions in other American cities where goals and circumstances are similar. Because the suggested policies depend only upon internal urban-management actions for implementation, other cities can adopt and mold the policy recommendations to fit local customs, politics, and conditions. Cities that adopt such policies should become better socioeconomic converters for the underemployed by drawing in and upgrading the poor into the labor class. If judiciously applied to enough other cities, the policy recommendations should generally improve employment conditions and increase the national standard of living. System dynamics models can improve national urban policy design by identifying essential trade-offs within urban systems and by helping to define realistic goals for American cities. Many national policies have unwittingly promoted concentrations of the urban poor beyond the capacity of urban systems to provide corresponding economic opportunities. Some policies to support the urban poor have worsened urban poverty by further disturbing the balance between jobs and population. System dynamics can help to avoid the frustrating, unforeseen reactions to a wide range of policies affecting urban employment, transportation, housing, and education.

Notes

1. See Walter W. Schroeder III and John E. Strongman, "Adapting *Urban Dynamics* to Lowell," and Walter W. Schroeder III, "Lowell Dynamics: Preliminary Applications of the Theory of *Urban Dynamics*," in *Readings in Urban Dynamics*, vol. 1, ed. Nathaniel J. Mass (Cambridge, Mass.: Wright-Allen Press, 1974), Readings 16 and 20, respectively.

2. Reported by Robert Cassidy, "America Outside the Cities and Suburbs," *Planning*, vol. 39, no. 7 (August 1973), p. 9.

3. "Hard-core Program in Detroit May Be Backfiring," *Wall Street Journal*, February 9, 1968, p. 6.

4. "BEDIC—Getting Jobs to Neighborhoods," *Boston Globe*, August 12, 1973, p. A57.

5. Walter W. Schroeder III and John S. Miller contributed significantly to Section 11.3 of this reading.

6. "HUD Approves Hale-Howard Plan," *Lowell* (Massachusetts) *Sun*, December 11, 1972, p. 9.

7. The following five parameters were changed:

Variable Name	Symbol	Original Value	Altered Value
1. City new-business-structures construction rate	CNBSCR	0	0.2
2. City lower-income housing-demolition rate	CLIHDR	0	0.05
3. City older-business-structures demolition rate	COBSDR	0	0.05
4. City upper-income-housing construction normal	CUIHCN	0.03	0.02
5. Regional transportation expansion policy	RTRANPS	1.0	0.5

In addition, the following switches, plot cards, etc. were used to start the model in equilibrium and obtain the computer runs given in Figures 11-1, 11-2, 11-4, and 11-5:

```
A       PRTPER.K=CLIP(PRTMIN,PRTMAX,PRTCT,TIME.K)
C       PRTMIN=100
C       PRTMAX=0
C       PRTCT=500
PLOT    CUIC=U,CLIP=L,SUIC=C(0,800E3)/CLIJR=2,UICJR=1(0,2)/TCJ=J(0,2E
X       6)
PLOT    TCH=H(0,1600E3)/CLIH=A,CUIH=B(0,800E3)/CUIHC=+,CLIHD=-(0,20E3
X       )/CLIHR=L,CUIHR=U(0,2)
PLOT    CLITUI=M(0,20E3)/CLITUIF=F(0,.08)/CLIP=L,CUIC=U(0,800E3)/CLIHR=
X       R(0,2)/CLIA=A,CLID=D(0,50E3)
PLOT    CNBS=N,COBS=O(0,40E3)/CNBSC=+,COBSD=-(0,4E3)/CAV=V(0,40E6)/CTR=
X       T(0,8)
PLOT    SNBS=*,SOBS=O(0,60E3)/SNBSC=+(0,1E3)/SUIC=C(0,800E3)/TMAV=V(0,8
X       0E6)/UISCCMR=R(0,8E3)
```

```
X         CNBS=N,COBS=$(0,40E3)/CP=P(0,8E6)
RUN       STD.
C         LENGTH=325
C         TIMEI=1675
C         PLTCT=1974.5
C         PLTMIN=0
C         PLTMAX=0.5
C         SWT4=1974.5
C         SWT5=1974.5
C         SWT6=1974.5
C         SWT10=1974.5
C         SWT11=1974.5
RUN       FIGURE 11-1 11-2 11-3 11-4 11-5
```

For complete technical details of the model and variable definitions, etc. the reader is referred to the definition file and the documentor listing of the city-suburb model given in the Appendixes of Reading 12. To keep this paper non-technical, somewhat simplified variable definitions, different from those given in Chapter 12, have been used to describe the computer runs. The reader interested in the technical details as to which exact model variables are being described or referred to is advised to follow the variables by their letter groups, indicated on the left hand side of the computer runs.

12

Urban Dynamics and the Suburbs

Walter W. Schroeder III

A frequently raised criticism of Urban Dynamics *is that the* Urban Dynamics *model fails to account for the impact of suburbs on urban problems. The initial responses to this criticism emphasized that suburbs are more a consequence than a cause of urban distress. Suburbs tend to grow as the affluent flee the decaying core-city area. Since suburbs are not fundamental causal agents of urban change,* Urban Dynamics *places the suburbs outside the model boundary. However, urban officials have a deep interest in metropolitan or regional issues that cross the boundary between city and suburb, and an analysis of city-suburb interactions seems desirable.*

This reading examines the treatment of city-suburb relationships. By interfacing two urban dynamics models, a city-suburb model containing an explicit suburban structure has been developed. A variety of tests demonstrate that the behavior of the city-suburb model substantially reaffirms the policy recommendations presented in Urban Dynamics.

12
Urban Dynamics and the Suburbs

12.1 Introduction

One of the most difficult but important issues raised in the reviews of *Urban Dynamics* is whether an urban policy model must deal explicitly with interactions between suburbs and central cities.[1] Despite a prominent trend to redefine urban problems as *metropolitan* problems involving both city and suburb, the *Urban Dynamics* model expressly focuses on one piece of a metropolitan system: the central city.

> The [geographical] area treated here would be only a part of our larger cities. The appropriate area is small enough so that cultural, economic, and educational interchange is possible between its component populations. It could be a suburban area or the core area of a city but probably not an area containing both. [*Urban Dynamics*, p. 2]

The *Urban Dynamics* model treats suburbs as part of the external environment surrounding the city. Reviewers of the book who were troubled by this treatment of suburbs maintain that interactions between a city and its suburbs are stronger and more extensive than interactions between a city and its larger environment. They conclude that an explicit suburb representation is needed to account for commuters, who occupy city jobs but provide no direct property-tax revenues. Interactions between city and suburb also include suburban demands for services, the cost of which may be borne disproportionately by the city. Transportation interactions, including mass transit extensions financed from general revenues, may yield greater advantage to suburban users than to urban residents.

12.2 Model Purpose and Model Boundary

Whether suburbs require explicit treatment in an urban dynamics model is really a boundary issue. The boundary of a dynamic model, in turn, must suit the model's purpose. Therefore, the discussion of suburbs in the *Urban Dynamics* model must begin with a discussion of that model's purpose. The *Urban Dynamics* model was designed to re-create the observed life cycle of cities—growth, maturation, and decline—and to evaluate alternative policies for urban revival. To re-create historical patterns of urban behavior, the model boundary was drawn to incorporate all the dominant feedback forces that govern city growth and decline. The model was built upon the fundamental premise that internal feedback forces, rather than external forces, govern the urban life cycle.

> The aging of the city is here conceived as an internal process, like the aging of a person. Aging is not a series of changes generated and imposed primarily by the outside environment, although changes from the outside might hasten or retard the process. [*Urban Dynamics*, p. 17]

A model that accurately reproduces the major forces governing urban growth and decline could have great value for policy makers because a model that contains the forces *creating* a problem also frequently contains the forces that must be harnessed to *relieve* the problem. The *Urban Dynamics* model satisfies these desired characteristics and can, in theory, be extended to address any specific urban issue. The city-suburb controversy centers on the *Urban Dynamics* model's capability to address questions of urban policy. Other dynamic models may be designed to address metropolitan and national policy alternatives, but the *Urban Dynamics* model is intentionally limited to analyzing local urban decision-making alternatives. One purpose of the *Urban Dynamics* model is to investigate the causes of urban decay. Therefore, the major forces governing urban growth and decline must lie within the model boundary. Because the model deals exclusively with feedback relationships, the city-suburb issue will be treated here as a question of whether any strong feedback effects extend beyond the city to its suburbs, thereby violating the model boundary. The hypothetical city in the model is a dynamic system defined by its condition relative to an average of all other cities in its surrounding, "limitless environment." The limitless environment beyond the boundary includes the city's suburbs. Migrants and new industries enter from and leave the city for the limitless environment. The model boundary assumes no city-suburb feedback relationships of critical importance either for urban behavior or for urban policy decisions. But many reviewers have questioned this assumption. Figure 12-1 diagrams a hypothetical simple feedback link between city and suburb. In the illustrated feedback relationship, conditions in the city (called A) influence conditions in the suburb (called B), and conditions in the suburb (B) in turn influence conditions in the city (A).

Figure 12-1 raises two important questions about city-suburb relationships. First, does any feedback between city and suburb help to explain the urban life cycle of growth, maturation, and decline? Second, does any feedback between city and suburb call into question the policy conclusions in *Urban Dynamics*?

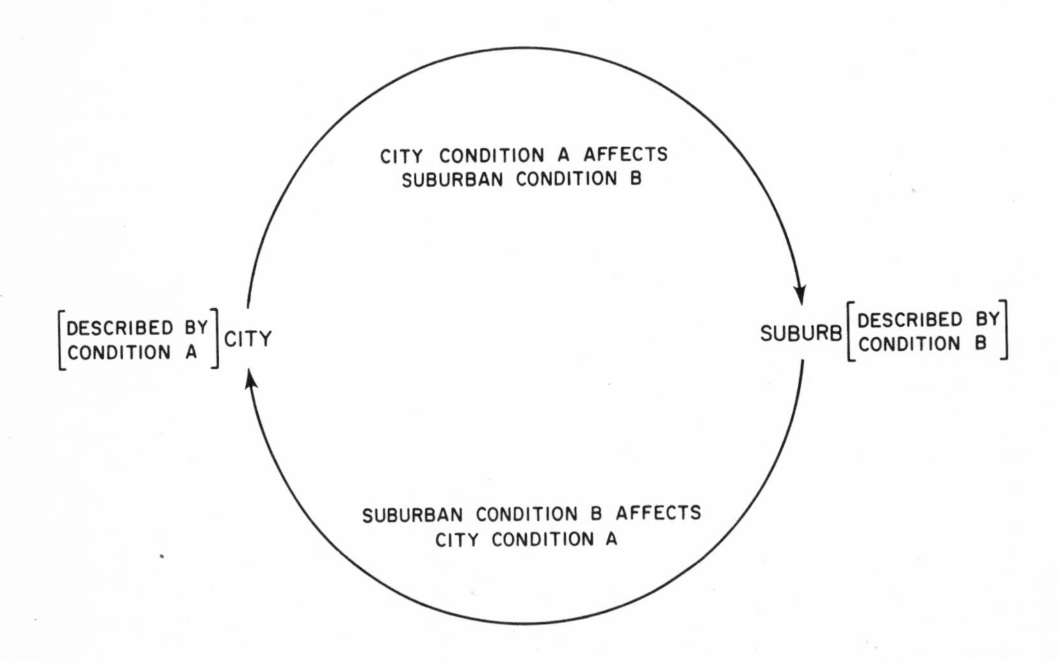

Figure 12-1 A city-suburb feedback relationship

The preliminary responses to the city-suburb issue emphasized urban congestion and decline as causes of suburban development and argued that solutions to urban problems must therefore come from within cities themselves.[2] The argument that suburbs are a symptom, rather than a cause, of urban decline is an interesting theoretical matter, but it is not sufficiently precise to resolve the issue. To respond to the complex practical concerns of local and regional decision makers, the System Dynamics Group at M.I.T. began constructing a city-suburb model in early 1974. Officials from Lowell, Massachusetts, provided valuable assistance in formulating and testing the model. This reading describes the city-suburb model, emphasizing its formulation and basic behavior characteristics. The same model was used to develop the policy recommendations presented in Reading 11.

12.3 The Basic Model Structure

The first task in constructing the city-suburb model was to develop a structure of interactions consistent with the *Urban Dynamics* model but containing a second geographical area (suburb). The appropriate substructure for each of the two areas (city and suburb) had to be roughly identical because construction activity and population movements give both areas their basic behavioral characteristics. In fact, Forrester (see quotation in Section 12.1), suggests that a city-suburb model should consist of two parallel but separate sectors, each based upon the structure of the *Urban Dynamics* model. Figure 12-2 depicts a two-sector model. One sector is the central city. The other sector is the suburban ring. The city and suburb sectors together represent a metropolitan system. The flows of population and construction activity into both sectors and the population flows between city and suburb represent the interface.

Interconnecting the two models required a complicated interface. The *Urban Dynamics* model alone contains nine major levels. But with a suburb sector added, for example, both managerial-professionals MP and labor L might live in one sector but work in the other. Well over 100 equations would be required to properly connect two *Urban Dynamics* models; the resultant two-sector model would contain approximately 400 equations, nearly three times as many as the original model. To simplify the overall city-suburb model, each sector is based upon an aggregated *Urban Dynamics* model structure containing only six major levels (see the shaded regions in figure 12-2). Both the city and the suburb contain two population, two housing, and two business-structure categories, instead of three. A city-suburb model, by definition, has a broader focus than a central-city model. Accordingly, neither sector of the city-suburb model need be as detailed as the *Urban Dynamics* model. The details of population composition or the city's housing market are more critical to the purpose of a central-city model than to a model of metropolitan interactions. Such differences in purpose permit different levels of aggregation. Just as a neighborhood model must have more microlevel structure than an overall city model, the city model requires more city-specific details than a metropolitan model. The city sector of the city-suburb model should be fully consistent in behavior with the *Urban Dynamics* model, but it can be operated at a higher level of aggregation. The urban dynamics modeling process actually entails a hierarchy or sequence of models, each corresponding to a different

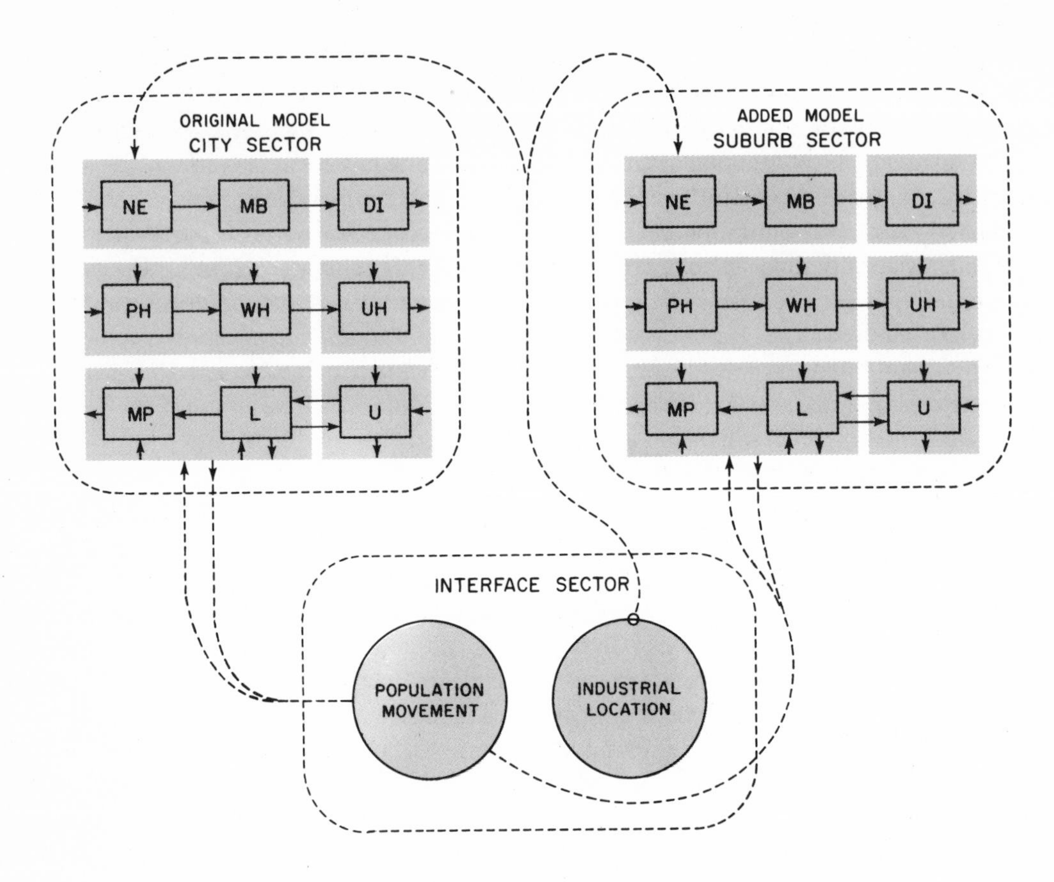

Figure 12-2 The overall structure of the city-suburb model. Two parallel sectors are linked by an interface that (1) determines industrial location within the region and (2) controls flows of people between the two sectors.

level of urban analysis. The *Urban Dynamics* model addresses urban housing, population, and jobs in greater detail than the city-suburb model. The latter, corresponding to a geographically larger system, might address a narrower range of interactions within the city but can also address interactions between the city and its surrounding suburbs. The key to building a useful model is to make the model only as complicated as necessary. Any unnecessary detail tends to confuse rather than clarify the forces generating a system's behavior. But there are clear limits on the degree to which a model can be simplified without losing its basic characteristics. For example, the *Urban Dynamics* model portrays a housing market that distinguishes new houses from old. New or premium housing PH tends to have the lowest residential density and is preferred by the managerial-professional MP population group. Older houses tend to be inhabited by lower-income groups and have substantially higher living densities. The city-suburb model must therefore retain at least *two* housing categories to preserve the time-varying character of the urban housing system. The *Urban Dynamics* model also contains three categories of industrial buildings, which, like houses, are differentiated by age. The city-suburb model re-creates the basic characteristics of the *Urban*

Dynamics model's industrial sector by allowing newer buildings to correspond to the newer half of industry in the model, and older business structures to correspond to the older half in the original. Again, three system levels are aggregated into two. Finally, the population sector of the *Urban Dynamics* model had to be aggregated into two levels in each sector of the city-suburb model. The most appropriate aggregation of population seemed to be to lump labor L and managerial-professionals MP together as one level and to retain underemployed U as a separate level exactly equivalent to its definition in the *Urban Dynamics* model. The justification for aggregating managerial-professionals MP and labor L is that the most important urban problems, and therefore the solutions, directly concern lower-income or underemployed groups. Even though the *Urban Dynamics* model contains three population levels, most of the analysis in *Urban Dynamics* is based on dichotomies, such as "imbalance between upper- and lower-income city residents" or "excess of low-quality underemployed housing relative to demand." The two population levels in the city-suburb model are, respectively, labeled upper income UI and lower income LI, less ambiguous variable names than "labor" or "underemployed." Lower-income population LI corresponds exactly to underemployed U in the *Urban Dynamics* model. In other words, roughly 30 percent of the city's population occupies the lower-income category as the city nears the end of its growth phase. To remain consistent with the *Urban Dynamics* model, the lower-income population must reach 45 percent of the city's total population at equilibrium (year 250).[3] Managerial-professionals MP and labor L are subsumed into one level, upper income UI, in the city-suburb model. Upper income corresponds to middle- and upper-income groups in a real city. Upper- and lower-income families in the model are distinguished by their wage rates and skill levels. Skilled blue-collar workers would qualify as upper income; unskilled blue-collar workers would probably not. Housing in the city-suburb model appears in two categories: (1) upper-income housing structures and (2) lower-income housing structures. Upper-income housing, occupied by the upper-income population, is equivalent to the sum of worker housing WH and premium housing PH in the *Urban Dynamics* model. The rate of obsolescence of upper-income housing UIH into lower-income housing LIH depends on the demand for upper-income housing, which is normally occupied by one family. Lower-income structures typically have a higher living density of about one and one-half families per structure. Lower-income housing structures also have a lower assessed value ($5,000 versus $18,000) and therefore contribute fewer tax dollars per year than upper-income housing structures. Business structures in the city-suburb model are divided into new-business structures NBS and older-business structures OBS. Unlike the housing sector, there is no direct correspondence between the business structures and the population. Both categories of business structures employ both upper- and lower-income workers. The sum of NBS and OBS in the city-suburb model corresponds exactly to the sum of new enterprise NE, mature business MB, and declining industry DI in the *Urban Dynamics* model. New business structures have higher employment densities (36 workers per structure versus 20 workers per structure) and higher assessed values ($450,000 versus $150,000) than old business structures. The structure that creates dynamic behavior among the six system levels in the city-suburb model is fully consistent with the structure of the *Urban Dynamics* model. The same forces govern migration, construction, and demolition in each model. Consequently, the behavior of the aggregated model mirrors the behavior of the *Urban Dynamics* model in all respects.

A complete documentor listing of the city-suburb model and the definition file for the model are given in Appendixes A and B respectively. Equations for each of the city and suburb sectors are very similar to the corresponding equations in *Urban Dynamics*. Any interested reader familiar with the structure of the *Urban Dynamics* model should be able to understand them by going through the documentor listing equation by equation. Due to limited space only the equations pertaining to the interface sector, linking the city and suburb sectors, are described in detail in the following section.

12.4 Developing a City-Suburb Interface

A working city-suburb model explicitly accounts for flows into and between the two sectors. The interface sector is designed so that when one sector (either city or suburb) in the metropolitan system becomes more attractive than the other sector, the more attractive area receives more people and industry. For example, when the city is more attractive than its suburb for industrial location, the rate of city new-business-structures construction CNBSC should exceed the rate of suburb new-business-structures construction SNBSC.

Because the city-suburb model is designed to examine commuting, the interface sector should allow people who work in the city to live in the suburbs if the residential attractiveness of the suburbs exceeds that of the city. The interface sector contains four parts:

1. upper-income arrivals job location,
2. new arrivals and current population residential location,
3. access between city and suburb, and
4. industrial location.

Upper-Income-Arrivals Job Location. In the city-suburb model, in-migration is a staged process. First, people enter the system on the basis of average conditions, or overall attractiveness, of the metropolitan area. Once in the metropolitan area, new arrivals then choose their places of work and residency on the basis of local measures of employment and residential opportunity. As in the *Urban Dynamics* model, the city-suburb model assumes a normal rate of upper-income arrivals into the region. When the overall attractiveness of the metropolitan area equals the attractiveness of its environment (defined as the condition existing toward the end of the city's growth phase), the yearly rate of upper-income arrivals UIA is 3 percent. Figure 12-3 diagrams the pressures that modify normal in-migration to yield the actual rate of in-migration to the metropolitan system. Equation 101 computes upper-income arrivals UIA as total metropolitan upper-income population TMUIP multiplied by both upper-income arrivals normal UIAN (3 percent) and the metropolitan upper-income-arrivals multiplier perceived MUIAMP. MUIAMP is a delayed value of MUIAM, the metropolitan upper-income-arrivals multiplier, defined in equation 102. MUIAM is a measure of area

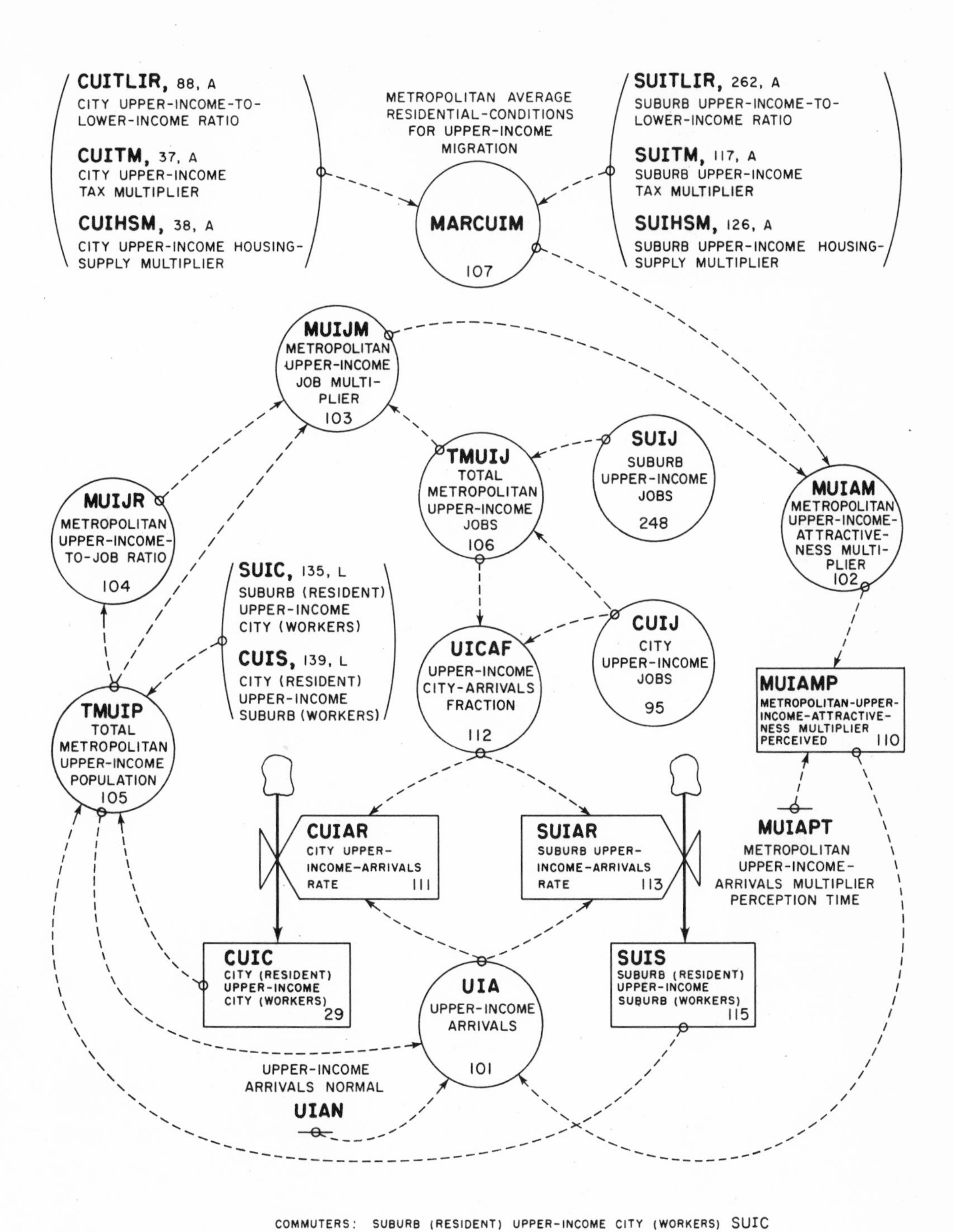

Figure 12-3 The in-migration of upper-income population to the metropolitan region depends on the upper-income-to-job ratio and the average residential conditions of the city and the suburb

conditions to which upper-income migration is assumed to be sensitive: the average job availability, as defined by the metropolitan upper-income job multiplier MUIJM, and the metropolitan average residential conditions for upper-income migration MARCUIM. The table function MUIJMT that relates the metropolitan-wide job ratio (MUIJR) to the metropolitan upper-income job multiplier (MUIJM) is identical to the curve in the *Urban Dynamics* model that relates job availability to the city's attractiveness for managerial-professionals and labor.

```
UIA.K=(TMUIP.K)(UIAN)(MUIAMP.K)                          101, A
UIAN=.03                                                 101.1, C
    UIA     - UPPER-INCOME ARRIVALS (MEN/YEAR)
    TMUIP   - TOTAL METROPOLITAN UPPER-INCOME POPULATION
                (MEN)
    UIAN    - UPPER-INCOME ARRIVALS NORMAL (FRACTION/
                YEAR)
    MUIAMP  - METROPOLITAN UPPER-INCOME-ATTRACTIVENESS
                MULTIPLIER PERCEIVED (DIMENSIONLESS)

MUIAM.K=(MUIJM.K)(MARCUIM.K)                             102, A
    MUIAM   - METROPOLITAN UPPER-INCOME-ATTRACTIVEMESS
                MULTIPLIER (DIMENSIONLESS)
    MUIJM   - METROPOLITAN UPPER-INCOME JOB MULTIPLIER
                (DIMENSIONLESS)
    MARCUIM- METROPOLITAN AVERAGE RESIDENTIAL-CONDITIONS
                FOR UPPER-INCOME MIGRATION
                (DIMENSIONLESS)

MUIJM.K=TABLE(MUIJMT,MUIJR.K,0,2,.25)                    103, A
MUIJMT=2.6/2.6/2.4/1.8/1/.4/.2/.1/.05                    103.1, T
    MUIJM   - METROPOLITAN UPPER-INCOME JOB MULTIPLIER
                (DIMENSIONLESS)
    MUIJMT  - METROPOLITAN UPPER-INCOME JOB MULTIPLIER
                TABLE (DIMENSIONLESS)
    MUIJR   - METROPOLITAN UPPER-INCOME-TO-JOB RATIO
                (DIMENSIONLESS)
```

The average residential condition of the metropolitan area takes into account the tax rate, population income distribution, and housing availability. Average metropolitan residential conditions, defined in equation 107, subsume both city and suburb conditions. Local city conditions are weighted in equation 107 according to the ratio of city upper-income population CUIP to total metropolitan upper-income population TMUIP. Suburb conditions are weighted according to the ratio of suburb upper-income population SUIP to total metropolitan upper-income population TMUIP. Therefore, metropolitan average residential-conditions for upper-income migration MARCUIM is weighted to reflect conditions in both sectors equitably (MARCUIM has a normal value of 1.0).

```
MARCUIM.K=((CUIRCM.K)(CUIS.K+CUIC.K)/(TMUIP.K))+      107, A
  ((SUIRCM.K)(SUIS.K+SUIC.K)/(TMUIP.K))
    MARCUIM- METROPOLITAN AVERAGE RESIDENTIAL-CONDITIONS
                FOR UPPER-INCOME MIGRATION
                (DIMENSIONLESS)
    CUIRCM  - CITY UPPER-INCOME RESIDENTIAL-CONDITIONS
                MULTIPLIER (DIMENSIONLESS)
    CUIS    - CITY(RESIDENT) UPPER-INCOME SUBURB(WORKERS)
                (MEN)
    CUIC    - CITY(RESIDENT) UPPER-INCOME CITY(WORKERS)
                (MEN)
    TMUIP   - TOTAL METROPOLITAN UPPER-INCOME POPULATION
                (MEN)
    SUIRCM  - SUBURB UPPER-INCOME RESIDENTIAL-CONDITIONS
                MULTIPLIER (DIMENSIONLESS)
    SUIS    - SUBURB(RESIDENT) UPPER-INCOME
                SUBURB(WORKERS) (MEN)
    SUIC    - SUBURB(RESIDENT) UPPER-INCOME CITY(WORKERS)
                (MEN)
```

```
CUIRCM.K=(CUIALIM.K)(CUITM.K)(CUIHSM.K)              108, A
    CUIRCM - CITY UPPER-INCOME RESIDENTIAL-CONDITIONS
               MULTIPLIER (DIMENSIONLESS)
    CUIALIM- CITY UPPER-INCOME-ARRIVALS LOWER-INCOME
               MULTIPLIER (DIMENSIONLESS)
    CUITM  - CITY UPPER-INCOME TAX MULTIPLIER
               (DIMENSIONLESS)
    CUIHSM - CITY UPPER-INCOME HOUSING-SUPPLY MULTIPLIER
               (DIMENSIONLESS)

SUIRCM.K=(SUIALIM.K)(SUITM.K)(SUIHSM.K)              109, A
    SUIRCM - SUBURB UPPER-INCOME RESIDENTIAL-CONDITIONS
               MULTIPLIER (DIMENSIONLESS)
    SUIALIM- SUBURB UPPER-INCOME-ARRIVALS LOWER-INCOME
               MULTIPLIER (DIMENSIONLESS)
    SUITM  - SUBURB UPPER-INCOME TAX MULTIPLIER
               (DIMENSIONLESS)
    SUIHSM - SUBURB UPPER-INCOME HOUSING-SUPPLY
               MULTIPLIER (DIMENSIONLESS)
```

Finally, Figure 12-3 shows how upper-income arrivals to the metropolitan area choose their place of work. The city upper-income-arrivals rate CUIAR represents the portion of metropolitan upper-income arrivals UIA that will tend to find work in the city. CUIAR is defined as UIA multiplied by the upper-income city-arrivals fraction UICAF in equation 111. UICAF varies between 0 and 1.0, as does the ratio of upper-income jobs found in the city CUIJ to the total of all metropolitan upper-income jobs TMUIJ. That is, the city-suburb model assumes that, if 75 percent of the metropolitan jobs are in the city, then about 75 percent of the total job openings will also tend to be there. As long as the unemployment rate for upper-income workers is fairly similar in the two sectors, the assumption is valid.

Upper-Income Residential Location. The city-suburb model also assumes that people prefer to both live and work in the same sector. But if the residential attractiveness of one sector becomes significantly greater than in the other, some families will prefer to live in the more attractive sector and commute to work. Commuting costs and constraints on access between city and suburb mitigate commuting in the city-suburb model. Commuters, as defined here, are upper-income breadwinners who live in the suburb and work in the city. Reverse commuting takes place when people live in the city and work in the suburb. Commuting and reverse commuting are limited in the model to upper-income workers. Lower-income people are assumed to be unable to afford commuting. The upper-income population of the city-suburb model consists of the four levels shown in Figure 12-4. One level is city (resident) upper-income city (workers) CUIC. The first C denotes the place of residence; the second C, the place of work. CUIC is therefore the upper-income population that lives and works in the city. Suburb (resident) upper-income city (workers) SUIC, conventionally called "commuters," live in the suburb and work in the city. The two other upper-income population levels, city (resident) upper-income suburb (workers) CUIS and suburb (resident) upper-income suburb (workers) SUIS, correspond to reverse commuters and suburban noncommuters. To simplify the model's migration formulation, new migrants to the metropolitan area enter only the CUIC or SUIS category. Therefore, newly arrived families who work in the city (as defined in equations 111 and 112) also live there and do not commute. But if the residential attractiveness of the suburb is greater than the

```
CUIAR.KL=(UICAF.K)(UIA.K)                                    111, R
    CUIAR   - CITY UPPER-INCOME-ARRIVALS RATE (MEN/YEAR)
    UICAF   - UPPER-INCOME CITY-ARRIVALS FRACTION
                (DIMENSIONLESS)
    UIA     - UPPER-INCOME ARRIVALS (MEN/YEAR)

UICAF.K=(CUIJ.K/TMUIJ.K)                                     112, A
    UICAF   - UPPER-INCOME CITY-ARRIVALS FRACTION
                (DIMENSIONLESS)
    CUIJ    - CITY UPPER-INCOME JOBS (MEN)
    TMUIJ   - TOTAL METROPOLITAN UPPER-INCOME JOBS (MEN)
```

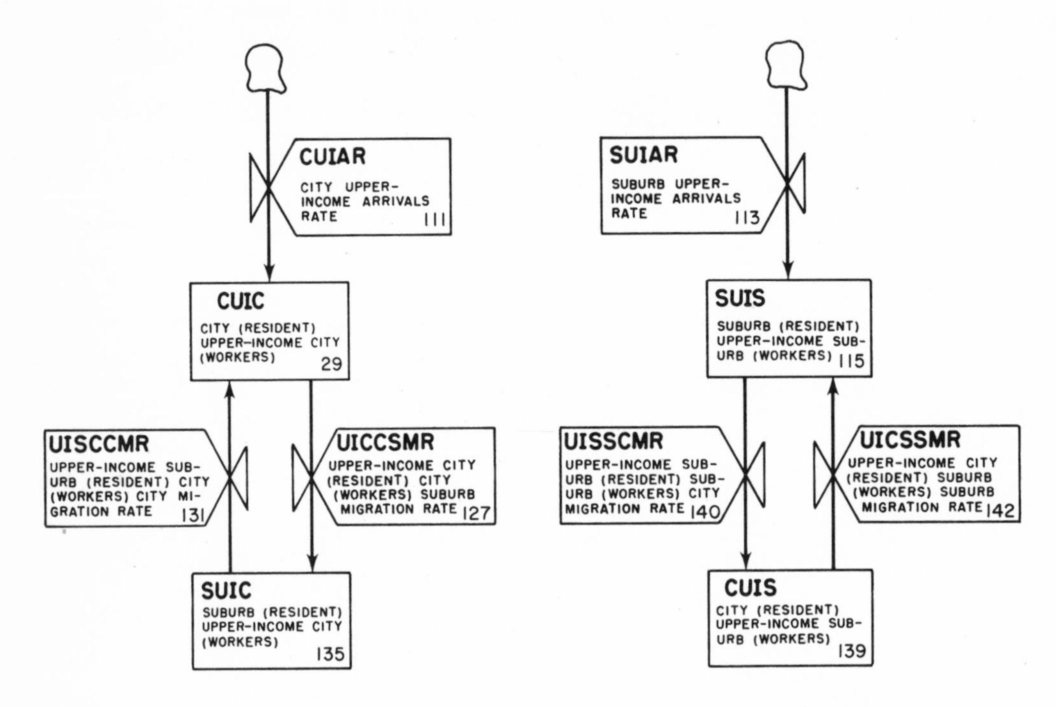

Figure 12-4 The four categories of upper-income population; internal rates correspond to changes in place of residence

residential attractiveness of the city, the residential allocation mechanism stimulates a positive rate of flow from the city (resident) upper-income city (workers) CUIC to the suburb (resident) upper-income city (workers) SUIC category. As shown in Figure 12-4, two rates of flow connect the level of the upper-income commuter population to the CUIC (noncommuter) level. The upper-income city (resident) city (worker) suburb-migration rate UICCSMR corresponds to the flow of people who move from the city to the suburb while keeping their city jobs. The flow in the opposite direction, upper-income suburb (resident) city (worker) city-migration rate UISCCMR, corresponds to commuters who choose to move back to the city and become noncommuters. The middle three letters of all four rates in Figure 12-4 are acronyms that conform to the abbreviation sequence of (1) place of residential origin, (2) place of work, and (3) place of residential destination. Therefore, UICCSMR is the migration rate of upper-income people who work in the city and are moving their place of residence to the suburb. All four internal migration rates in Figure 12-4 respond to differences between the residential attractiveness of the city and the residential attractiveness of the suburb. To illustrate the internal migration rates in more detail, Figure 12-5 diagrams the system structure underlying one of the four rates: the upper-income city (resident) city (worker) suburb-migration rate UICCSMR. Similar structures generate each of the other three rates.

The rate of entry into the commuter category (UICCSMR) is determined in equation 127 by the CUIC residents (noncommuters eligible to enter the SUIC category), upper-income city-city-suburb migration normal UICCSMN, access between the city and the suburb (ACCESM), and suburb/city relative residential-attractiveness multiplier SCRRAM. The normal rate of flow from the city noncommuter (CUIC) category to the commuter (SUIC) category is 1.0 percent annually of the city noncom-

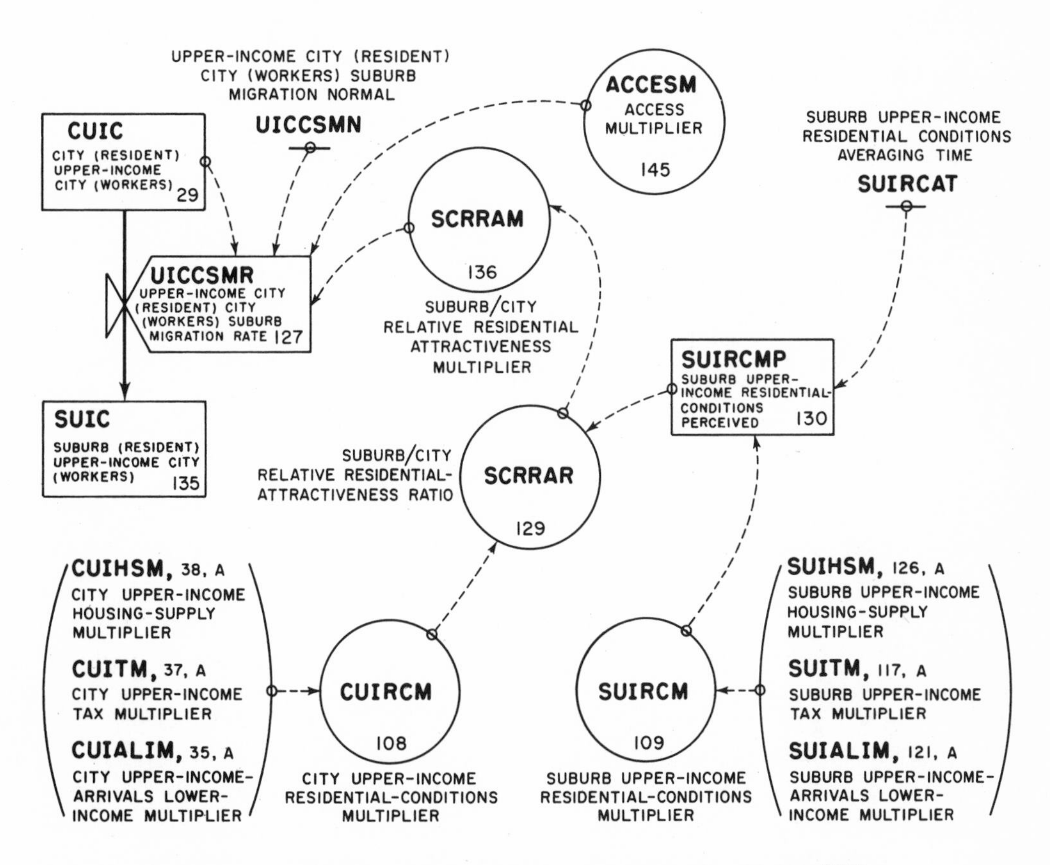

Figure 12-5 Flow diagram of the structure influencing the rate at which people enter the SUIC (commuter) category

muter population. One percent seems to be typical of a city toward the end of its growth phase. To keep the city-suburb model consistent with the *Urban Dynamics* model, the normal rate of departures (to the environment) of upper-income people from the city was reduced from 2.5 percent to 1.5 percent per year; the total outflow rate from the CUIC category remains equivalent to the total outflow of labor L and managerial-professionals MP in the *Urban Dynamics* model. Because the normal value for city upper-income city CUIC entering the commuter category is 1.5 percent, the model assumes that, as city growth begins to falter, 40 percent of the upper-income families leaving the city merely move into the commuter category and the other 60 percent move away from the metropolitan region entirely.

```
UICCSMR.KL=(CUIC.K)(UICCSMN)(ACCESM.K)(SCRRAM.K)     127, R
  (SCRRAF)
UICCSMN=.01                                          127.1, C
SCRRAF=1                                             127.2, C
    UICCSMR- UPPER-INCOME CITY(RESIDENT) CITY(WORKERS)
               SUBURB MIGRATION RATE (MEN/YEAR)
    CUIC   - CITY(RESIDENT) UPPER-INCOME CITY(WORKERS)
               (MEN)
    UICCSMN- UPPER-INCOME CITY(RESIDENT) CITY(WORKERS)
               SUBURB MIGRATION NORMAL (FRACTION/YEAR)
    ACCESM - ACCESS MULTIPLIER (DIMENSIONLESS)
    SCRRAM - SUBURB/CITY RELATIVE RESIDENTIAL-
               ATTRACTIVENESS MULTIPLIER (DIMENSIONLESS)
    SCRRAF - SUBURB/CITY RELATIVE-RESIDENTIAL
               ATTRACTIVENESS FACTOR (DIMENSIONLESS)

SCRRAM.K=TABLE(SCRRAMT,SCRRAR.K,0,4,.5)              128, A
SCRRAMT=.4/.5/1/1.8/2.5/3/3.2/3.3/3.3                128.1, T
    SCRRAM - SUBURB/CITY RELATIVE RESIDENTIAL-
               ATTRACTIVENESS MULTIPLIER (DIMENSIONLESS)
    SCRRAMT- SUBURB/CITY RELATIVE RESIDENTIAL-
               ATTRACTIVENESS MULTIPLIER TABLE
               (DIMENSIONLESS)
    SCRRAR - SUBURB/CITY RELATIVE RESIDENTIAL-
               ATTRACTIVENESS RATIO (DIMENSIONLESS)

SCRRAR.K=SUIRCMP.K/CUIRCM.K                          129, A
    SCRRAR - SUBURB/CITY RELATIVE RESIDENTIAL-
               ATTRACTIVENESS RATIO (DIMENSIONLESS)
    SUIRCMP- SUBURB UPPER-INCOME RESIDENTIAL-CONDITIONS
               MULTIPLIER PERCEIVED (DIMENSIONLESS)
    CUIRCM - CITY UPPER-INCOME RESIDENTIAL-CONDITIONS
               MULTIPLIER (DIMENSIONLESS)
```

The actual flow of city (resident) upper-income city (workers) CUIC into the commuter (SUIC) category depends upon the suburb/city relative residential-attractiveness multiplier SCRRAM. SCRRAM is defined in equations 128 and 129 by comparing the suburb upper-income residential conditions multiplier perceived SUIRCMP with the city upper-income residential-conditions multiplier CUIRCM. The relative weight of the two multipliers is manifested in the suburb/city relative residential-attractiveness ratio SCRRAR in equation 129. If SCRRAR, and therefore SCRRAM, is greater than 1.0, the suburb is perceived as a relatively better place than the city in which to reside, and the commuter category tends to grow more rapidly. Because a city resident does not have perfect information about the actual condition of the suburb, a five-year perception delay of suburb residential conditions is used to compute SCRRAR.

As shown in Figure 12-5, the city upper-income residential-conditions multipliers CUIRCM and its suburb counterpart SUIRCM are functions of three local factors: (1)

housing availability, (2) the tax rate, and (3) the income distribution of the local population. When these factors taken together are more favorable in the suburb than in the city, the suburb/city relative residential-attractiveness multiplier SCRRAM exceeds 1.0, and the flow of city noncommuters into the suburb commuter SUIC category tends to increase. The access multiplier ACCESM, an index of the cost and convenience of daily commuting between the two sectors, also influences UICCSMR. The normal value of ACCESM is 1.0. When the value of ACCESM is considerably less than 1.0, commuting is relatively difficult, and UICCSMR falls to a lower value. However, because the value of ACCESM is frequently less than 1.0, improved access is not really a cause of commuting. Commuting pressures arise only in the presence of a positive residential attractiveness differential. ACCESM can be viewed as a valve that controls the rate at which people enter the commuting class in response to perceived differences in residential conditions between the city and the suburb. On the other hand, people tend to leave the commuter category to become city noncommuters if access between the two sectors deteriorates. In the city-suburb model, therefore, the upper-income suburb (resident) city (worker) city-migration rate UISCCMR (the rate of flow from the commuter category to the noncommuter category defined in equation 131) is modulated by the reciprocal of ACCESM. When access is limited, 1/ACCESSM is greater than 1.0, so the pressure for noncommuting increases. Reversing the polarity of ACCESM through its reciprocal produces the observed real-world pressure for commuters to return to the city if access becomes severely inadequate.

Commuting between two areas tends to increase when the residential attractiveness of the sector in which a person lives and works falls relative to the residential attractiveness of the other sector. Access between the two sectors also determines willingness to commute. Each commuter category also increases according to an endogenous birth rate and is decreased by departures to the external environment.

```
UISCCMR.KL=(SUIC.K)(UISCMN)(CSRRAM.K)(CSRRAF)/        131, R
  (ACCESM.K)
UISCMN=.005                                           131.1, C
CSRRAF=1                                              131.2, C
    UISCCMR- UPPER-INCOME SUBURB(RESIDENT) CITY(WORKERS)
               CITY MIGRATION RATE (MEN/YEAR)
    SUIC   - SUBURB(RESIDENT) UPPER-INCOME CITY(WORKERS)
               (MEN)
    UISCMN - UPPER-INCOME SUBURB(RESIDENT) CITY(WORKERS)
               CITY MIGRATION NORMAL (FRACTION/YEAR)
    CSRRAM - CITY/SUBURB RELATIVE RESIDENTIAL-
               ATTRACTIVENESS MULTIPLIER (DIMENSIONLESS)
    CSRRAF - CITY/SUBURB RELATIVE RESIDENTIAL-
               ATTRACTIVENESS FACTOR (DIMENSIONLESS)
    ACCESM - ACCESS MULTIPLIER (DIMENSIONLESS)
```

Access between City and Suburb. The city-suburb model uses a simple representation of accessibility. ACCESM, as shown in Figure 12-6 and computed in equation 145, is a function of transportation capacity TRANCAP, transportation demand TRANSD, and transportation costs TRCOST. If demand rises faster than capacity, access routes become more crowded and less convenient, and the accessibility between city and suburb tends to decline. Similarly, as the suburban areas fill up, average commuting time and distance tend to increase, thereby discouraging further commuting.

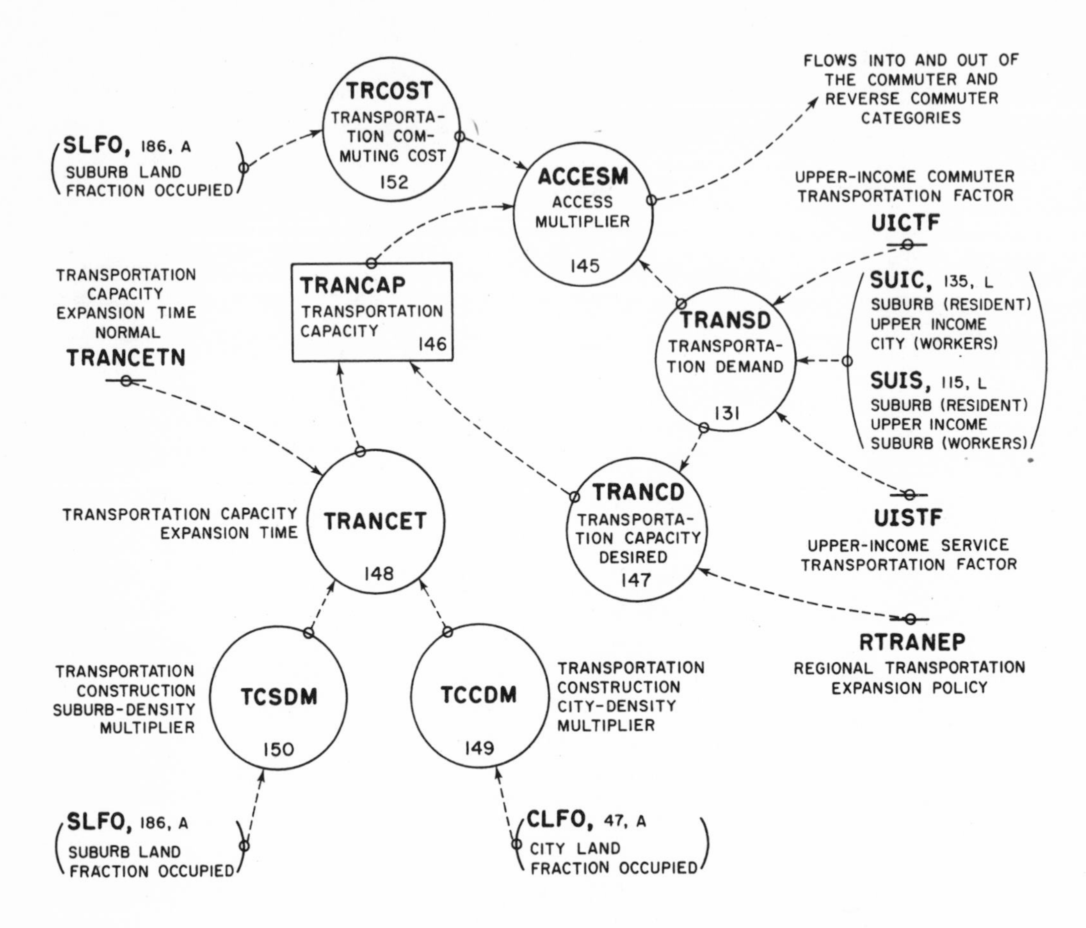

Figure 12-6 The access sector

```
ACCESM.K=(TRANCAP.K)/(TRANSD.K*TRCOST.K)              145, A
    ACCESM - ACCESS MULTIPLIER (DIMENSIONLESS)
    TRANCAP- TRANSPORTATION CAPACITY (DIMENSIONLESS)
    TRANSD - TRANSPORTATION DEMAND (DIMENSIONLESS)
    TRCOST - TRANSPORTATION COST (DIMENSIONLESS)

TRANCAP.K=TRANCAP.J+(DT/TRANCET.J)(TRANCD.J-          146, L
  TRANCAP.J)
TRANCAP=TRANSD                                         146.1, N
    TRANCAP- TRANSPORTATION CAPACITY (DIMENSIONLESS)
    TRANCET- TRANSPORTATION CAPACITY EXPANSION TIME
             (YEARS)
    TRANCD - TRANSPORTATION CAPACITY DESIRED
             (DIMENSIONLESS)
    TRANSD - TRANSPORTATION DEMAND (DIMENSIONLESS)
```

Transportation capacity TRANCAP, a system level, operates as a delayed value of transportation demand in equation 146. Transportation capacity desired TRANCD equals transportation demand, so actual transportation capacity is essentially a first-order delay of TRANSD. For policy testing, transportation capacity desired TRANCD can be changed to be proportional, rather than identical, to transportation demand TRANSD. Restraining TRANCD to accommodate only 70 percent of TRANSD would correspond to a regional transportation policy of substantial resistance to transportation expansion proposals. In equation 147, TRANCD is defined as TRANSD × RTRANEP, where RTRANEP is the regional transportation expansion policy. A neutral policy corresponds to a RTRANEP value of 1.0.

Land parceling and construction delays, among other factors, cause transportation capacity TRANCAP to lag behind transportation demand TRANSD. The lag has been modeled as a variable, TRANCET, with a normal value of 10 years. Transportation capacity expansion time TRANCET is computed in equation 148 as (TRANETN) × (TCCDM) × (TCSDM). TRANETN is the transportation expansion time normal of 10 years. TCCDM, the transportation construction city-density multiplier defined in equation 149, increases above a value of 1.0 as the city's land fraction occupied increases beyond 0.4. An increasing TCCDM, and its inhibiting impact on the response time of transportation capacity, represents the assumption that rights-of-way for construction become not only more difficult to acquire but also more costly as the city becomes fully occupied. TCSDM, the transportation construction suburb-density multiplier, operates similarly to TCCDM. When the city is 80 percent occupied and the suburb 60 percent occupied, transportation capacity responds to transportation demand with a delay of twenty-five years.

Transportation demand TRANSD, defined by the number and frequency of trips between city and suburb, is computed in equation 151 as (SUIC × UICTF) + (SUIS × UISTF). Transportation demand increases as SUIC (commuters) and SUIS (suburban noncommuters) increase. The upper-income commuter transportation factor UICTF and the upper-income service transportation factor UISTF are weighting factors to indicate the frequency of use. UICTF has been given a value of 1.0 (corresponding to one round trip per day for commuters). UISTF, set at 0.3, indicates that suburban noncommuters who rely on the city only for shopping, entertainment, and services use the transportation system 30 percent as often as commuters.

```
TRANCD.K=(TRANSD.K)(RTRANEP.K)                           147, A
    TRANCD - TRANSPORTATION CAPACITY DESIRED
               (DIMENSIONLESS)
    TRANSD - TRANSPORTATION DEMAND (DIMENSIONLESS)
    RTRANEP- REGIONAL TRANSPORTATION EXPANSION POLICY
               (DIMENSIONLESS)

TRANCET.K=(TRANETN)(TCCDM.K)(TCSDM.K)                    148, A
TRANETN=10                                               148.1, C
    TRANCET- TRANSPORTATION CAPACITY EXPANSION TIME
               (YEARS)
    TRANETN- TRANSPORTATION CAPACITY EXPANSION TIME
               NORMAL (YEARS)
    TCCDM  - TRANSPORTATION CONSTRUCTION CITY-DENSITY
               MULTIPLIER (DIMENSIONLESS)
    TCSDM  - TRANSPORTATION CONSTRUCTION SUBURB-DENSITY
               MULTIPLIER (DIMENSIONLESS)

TCCDM.K=TABLE(TCCDMT,CLFO.K,0,1,.2)                      149, A
TCCDMT=.6/.8/1/1.3/1.7/2.5                               149.1, T
    TCCDM  - TRANSPORTATION CONSTRUCTION CITY-DENSITY
               MULTIPLIER (DIMENSIONLESS)
    TCCDMT - TRANSPORTATION CONSTRUCTION CITY-DENSITY
               MULTIPLIER TABLE (DIMENSIONLESS)
    CLFO   - CITY LAND FRACTION OCCUPIED (DIMENSIONLESS)
```

Because the access multiplier is used to define only commuting propensities between city and suburb, other transportation users, such as industry, are not considered in the calculation for TRANSD. The access multiplier ACCESM is not a measure of the overall quality of the area's transportation system; instead, it is a measure of the typical commuter's ease in getting to and from the city each day.

The transportation cost TRCOST is a measure of the cost associated with traveling from one sector to the other. The term "cost" encompasses both time and financial expense. Commuting distances increase as the parts of the suburb closest to the city become full and outlying land is developed. In equation 152, TRCOST is determined by suburb land fraction occupied SLFO. As SLFO increases beyond 0.2, TRCOST rises; as TRCOST increases, ACCESM (and commuting propensities) decreases.

```
TCSDM.K=TABLE(TCSDMT,SLFO.K,0,1,.2)                     150, A
TCSDMT=.7/1/1.4/2.0/3.0/4.5                             150.1, T
    TCSDM  - TRANSPORTATION CONSTRUCTION SUBURB-DENSITY
               MULTIPLIER (DIMENSIONLESS)
    TCSDMT - TRANSPORTATION CONSTRUCTION SUBURB-DENSITY
               MULTIPLIER TABLE (DIMENSIONLESS)
    SLFO   - SUBURB LAND FRACTION OCCUPIED
               (DIMENSIONLESS)

TRANSD.K=(SUIC.K)(UICTF)+(SUIS.K)(UISTF)                151, A
UICTF=1                                                 151.1, C
UISTF=.3                                                151.2, C
    TRANSD - TRANSPORTATION DEMAND (DIMENSIONLESS)
    SUIC   - SUBURB(RESIDENT) UPPER-INCOME CITY(WORKERS)
               (MEN)
    UICTF  - UPPER-INCOME COMMUTER TRANSPORTATION FACTOR
               (DIMENSIONLESS)
    SUIS   - SUBURB(RESIDENT) UPPER-INCOME
               SUBURB(WORKERS) (MEN)
    UISTF  - UPPER-INCOME SERVICE TRANSPORTATION FACTOR
               (DIMENSIONLESS)

TRCOST.K=TABLE(TRCOSTT,SLFO.K,0,1,.2)                   152, A
TRCOSTT=1/1.05/1.2/1.4/1.45/1.5                         152.1, T
    TRCOST - TRANSPORTATION COST (DIMENSIONLESS)
    TRCOSTT- TRANSPORTATION-COST TABLE (DIMENSIONLESS)
    SLFO   - SUBURB LAND FRACTION OCCUPIED
               (DIMENSIONLESS)
```

Industrial Location within the Metropolitan Area. The structure that determines the amount and location of industrial development in the city-suburb model resembles the population interface described earlier. Metropolitan new-business-structures construction desired MNBSCD is computed in equation 153 from a normal rate of desired metropolitan new-business-structures construction MNBSDN multiplied by the metropolitan enterprise multiplier MEM, an index of the overall attractiveness of the metropolitan area as a site for new-business location. As shown in Figure 12-7, metropolitan new-business-structures construction desired MNBSCD is determined by (1) total current metropolitan business activity (the sum of city new-business structures CNBS, suburb new-business structures SNBS, and city and suburb older-business structures COBS and SOBS, respectively), (2) metropolitan new-business-structures desired normal MNBSDN (set at 4 percent), and (3) the metropolitan enterprise multiplier MEM, which has a normal value of 1.0.

The metropolitan enterprise multiplier MEM (equation 154) consists of two factors: (1) metropolitan enterprise labor-supply multiplier MELSM and (2) metropolitan enterprise average-local-conditions multiplier MEALCM. MELSM, defined in equation 155, increases as the supply of metropolitan workers exceeds the current number of jobs. MELSM takes into account the availability of both upper-income and lower-income labor, but it is derived from table functions in which industry is assumed to be about five times more sensitive to the supply of skilled (upper-income) labor than unskilled.

```
MNBSCD.K=(MNBSDN)(MEM.K)(CNBSWF*CNBS.K+SNBSWF*          153, A
  SNBS.K+COBSWF*COBS.K+SOBSWF*SOBS.K)
MNBSDN=.04                                             153.2, C
CNBSWF=1                                               153.3, C
SNBSWF=.6                                              153.4, C
COBSWF=.4                                              153.5, C
SOBSWF=.3                                              153.6, C
    MNBSCD - METROPOLITAN NEW-BUSINESS-STRUCTURES
               CONSTRUCTION DESIRED (STRUCTURES/YEAR)
    MNBSDN - METROPOLITAN NEW-BUSINESS-STRUCTURES
               DESIRED NORMAL (FRACTION/YEAR)
    MEM    - METROPOLITAN ENTERPRISE MULTIPLIER
               (DIMENSIONLESS)
    CNBSWF - CITY NEW-BUSINESS-STRUCTURES WEIGHTING
               FACTOR
    CNBS   - CITY NEW-BUSINESS STRUCTURES (STRUCTURES)
    SNBSWF - SUBURB NEW-BUSINESS-STRUCTURES WEIGHTING
               FACTOR (DIMENSIONLESS)
    SNBS   - SUBURB NEW-BUSINESS STRUCTURES (STRUCTURES)
    COBSWF - CITY OLDER-BUSINESS-STRUCTURES WEIGHTING
               FACTOR (DIMENSIONLESS)
    COBS   - CITY OLDER-BUSINESS STRUCTURES (STRUCTURES)
    SOBSWF - SUBURB OLDER-BUSINESS-STRUCTURES WEIGHTING
               FACTOR (DIMENSIONLESS)
    SOBS   - SUBURB OLDER-BUSINESS STRUCTURES
               (STRUCTURES)

MEM.K=(MELSM.K)(MEALCM.K)                              154, A
    MEM    - METROPOLITAN ENTERPRISE MULTIPLIER
               (DIMENSIONLESS)
    MELSM  - METROPOLITAN ENTERPRISE LABOR-SUPPLY
               MULTIPLIER (DIMENSIONLESS)
    MEALCM - METROPOLITAN ENTERPRISE AVERAGE-LOCAL-
               CONDITIONS MULTIPLER (DIMENSIONLESS)

MELSM.K=(MEUIWM.K)(MELIWM.K)                           155, A
    MELSM  - METROPOLITAN ENTERPRISE LABOR-SUPPLY
               MULTIPLIER (DIMENSIONLESS)
    MEUIWM - METROPOLITAN ENTERPRISE UPPER-INCOME-
               WORKFORCE MULTIPLIER (DIMENSIONLESS)
    MELIWM - METROPOLITAN ENTERPRISE LOWER-INCOME-
               WORKFORCE MULTIPLIER (DIMENSIONLESS)
```

MEALCM, a function of land availability, the tax rate, and recent enterprise growth in each of the two sectors, is computed in equation 163 as a weighted sum of the city enterprise local-conditions multiplier CELCM and the suburb equivalent, SELCM. The weighting factor is simply the percentage of total metropolitan business activity found in each sector. So, if the city contains 95 percent of the total metropolitan business structures, then the value of MEALCM is dominated by the city enterprise local-conditions multiplier CELCM.

```
MEALCM.K=(CELCM.K)(CBST.K/MBST.K)+(SELCM.K)(SBST.K/ 163, A
  MBST.K)
    MEALCM - METROPOLITAN ENTERPRISE AVERAGE-LOCAL-
               CONDITIONS MULTIPLER (DIMENSIONLESS)
    CELCM  - CITY ENTERPRISE LOCAL-CONDITIONS MULTIPLIER
               (DIMENSIONLESS)
    CBST   - CITY BUSINESS STRUCTURES TOTAL (STRUCTURES)
    MBST   - METROPOLITAN BUSINESS STRUCTURES TOTAL
               (STRUCTURES)
    SELCM  - SUBURB ENTERPRISE LOCAL-CONDITIONS
               MULTIPLIER (DIMENSIONLESS)
    SBST   - SUBURB BUSINESS-STRUCTURES TOTAL
               (STRUCTURES)
```

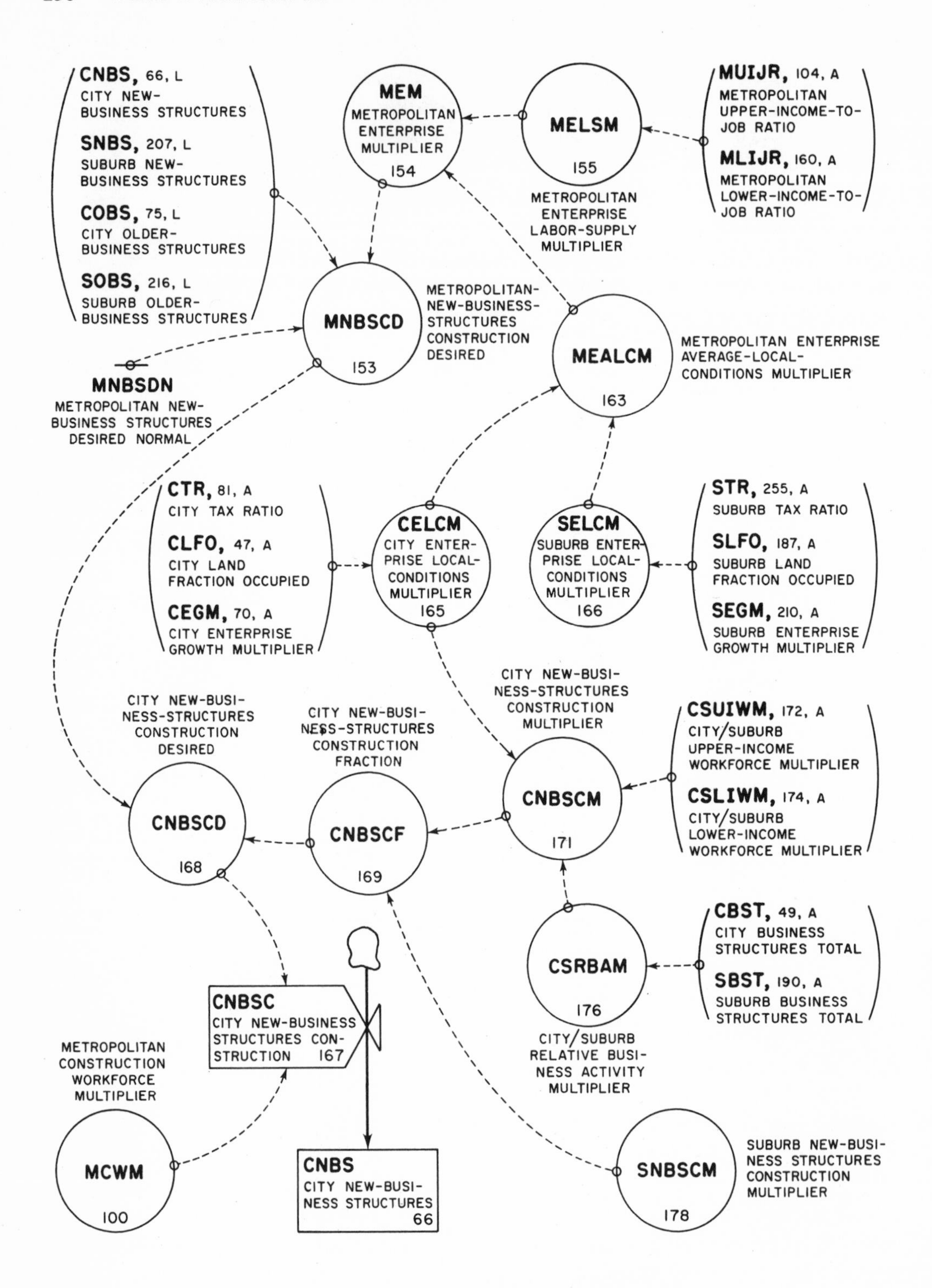

Figure 12-7 Structure of the industrial location sector

The allocation of actual business construction between city and suburb is derived from a set of multipliers that compute the city new-business-structures construction fraction CNBSCF. Its value varies between 0 and 1.0. Multiplying CNBSCF in equation 168 by the metropolitan new-business-structures construction desired MNBSCD, yields city new-business-structures construction desired CNBSCD. CNBSCF is determined in equation 169 by comparing the city new-business-structures construction multiplier CNBSCM with the corresponding suburb multiplier (SNBSCM). As the ratio CNBSCM/SNBSCM (equation 170) rises, the city is more attractive for industrial development, and a larger CNBSCF allocates a larger share of total metropolitan new-business-structures construction to the city.

```
CNBSCD.K=CNBSCF.K*MNBSCD.K                              168, A
    CNBSCD  - CITY NEW-BUSINESS-STRUCTURES CONSTRUCTION
                DESIRED (STRUCTURES/YEAR)
    CNBSCF  - CITY NEW-BUSINESS-STRUCTURES CONSTRUCTION
                FRACTION (DIMENSIONLESS)
    MNBSCD  - METROPOLITAN NEW-BUSINESS-STRUCTURES
                CONSTRUCTION DESIRED (STRUCTURES/YEAR)

CNBSCF.K=TABHL(CNBSCFT,CSRNBAM.K,0,3,.5)                169, A
CNBSCFT=.2/.4/.65/.75/.84/.90/.95                       169.1, T
    CNBSCF  - CITY NEW-BUSINESS-STRUCTURES CONSTRUCTION
                FRACTION (DIMENSIONLESS)
    CNBSCFT - CITY NEW-BUSINESS-STRUCTURES CONSTRUCTION
                FRACTION TABLE (DIMENSIONLESS)
    CSRNBAM - CITY/SUBURB RELATIVE NEW-BUSINESS-
                ATTRACTION MULTIPLIER

CSRNBAM.K=CNBSCM.K/SNBSCM.K                             170, A
    CSRNBAM - CITY/SUBURB RELATIVE NEW-BUSINESS-
                ATTRACTION MULTIPLIER
    CNBSCM  - CITY NEW-BUSINESS-STRUCTURES CONSTRUCTION
                MULTIPLIER (DIMENSIONLESS)
    SNBSCM  - SUBURB NEW-BUSINESS-STRUCTURES CONSTRUCTION
                MULTIPLIER (DIMENSIONLESS)

CNBSCM.K=(CELCM.K)(CSUIWM.K)(CSLIWM.K)(CSRBAM.K)        171, A
    CNBSCM  - CITY NEW-BUSINESS-STRUCTURES CONSTRUCTION
                MULTIPLIER (DIMENSIONLESS)
    CELCM   - CITY ENTERPRISE LOCAL-CONDITIONS MULTIPLIER
                (DIMENSIONLESS)
    CSUIWM  - CITY/SUBURB UPPER-INCOME WORKFORCE
                MULTIPLIER (DIMENSIONLESS)
    CSLIWM  - CITY/SUBURB LOWER-INCOME WORKFORCE
                MULTIPLIER (DIMENSIONLESS)
    CSRBAM  - CITY/SUBURB RELATIVE BUSINESS-ACTIVITY
                MULTIPLIER (DIMENSIONLESS)
```

The city new-business-structures construction multiplier CNBSCM in equation 171 (and equivalently SNBSCM) is a function of four variables:

1. the city enterprise local-conditions multiplier CELCM (based upon land availability, the tax rate, and recent enterprise growth just as in the *Urban Dynamics* model),
2. the city/suburb upper-income workforce multiplier CSUIWM,
3. the city/suburb lower-income workforce multiplier CSLIWM, and
4. the city/suburb relative business-activity multiplier CSRBAM.

The city/suburb upper-income workforce multiplier CSUIWM is defined in equation 172 as the ratio of city upper-income residents looking for employment to suburb upper-income residents looking for employment. Upper-income employment seekers in each sector are defined in equation 173 as the local upper-income population multiplied by the local upper-income-to-job ratio.

```
CSUIWM.K=TABHL(CSUIWT,CSUIWR.K,0,3,.5)                    172, A
CSUIWT=.6/.8/1/1.1/1.15/1.18/1.2                          172.1, T
    CSUIWM - CITY/SUBURB UPPER-INCOME WORKFORCE
               MULTIPLIER (DIMENSIONLESS)
    CSUIWT - CITY/SUBURB UPPER-INCOME WORKFORCE TABLE
               (DIMENSIONLESS)
    CSUIWR - CITY/SUBURB UPPER-INCOME WORKFORCE RATIO
               (DIMENSIONLESS)

CSUIWR.K=(CUIC.K+CUIS.K)(CUICJR.K)/((SUIS.K+SUIC.K) 173, A
  (SUISJR.K))
    CSUIWR - CITY/SUBURB UPPER-INCOME WORKFORCE RATIO
               (DIMENSIONLESS)
    CUIC   - CITY(RESIDENT) UPPER-INCOME CITY(WORKERS)
               (MEN)
    CUIS   - CITY(RESIDENT) UPPER-INCOME SUBURB(WORKERS)
               (MEN)
    CUICJR - CITY UPPER-INCOME-TO-CITY JOB RATIO
               (DIMENSIONLESS)
    SUIS   - SUBURB(RESIDENT) UPPER-INCOME
               SUBURB(WORKERS) (MEN)
    SUIC   - SUBURB(RESIDENT) UPPER-INCOME CITY(WORKERS)
               (MEN)
    SUISJR - SUBURB UPPER-INCOME-TO-SUBURB JOB RATIO
               (DIMENSIONLESS)
```

The multiplier for the lower-income workforce, CSLIWM, is defined in the same manner as the corresponding upper-income multiplier except that lower-income population and lower-income jobs in each sector are used in the equations. CSUIWM and CSLIWM are so defined that industry, once it has chosen to locate within the metropolitan region, has a slight preference to locate near available labor. The metropolitan area is assumed to be occupied by a physically mobile labor force, so a localized labor shortage poses no serious obstacles to industrial developers seeking to locate anywhere within the metropolitan area. Both curves would be steeper if industrial development within a metropolitan area was assumed to be more sensitive to the residential location of employees. The city/suburb relative business-activity multiplier CSRBAM assumes that location preferences for industry are influenced by existing concentrations of business activity. Equations 176 and 177 state that, if the city contains four times the total amount of business activity as the suburb (if the city/suburb relative business-activity ratio CSRBAR equals four), then the value of CSRBAM rises to 1.7. New industries will prefer to locate in the city by 1.7 to 1.0 (or 70 percent) over the suburb even if the city and suburb are alike in all other respects. The assumption behind this mechanism is that business tends to congregate in areas close to sources of supply and where economies of scale permit greater efficiency. A structure parallel to CSRBAM defines the suburb new-business-structures construction multiplier SNBSCM.

```
CSRBAM.K=TABHL(CSRBAMT,CSRBAR.K,0,4,.5)                   176, A
CSRBAMT=.6/.8/1/1.2/1.4/1.5/1.6/1.7/1.7                   176.1, T
    CSRBAM - CITY/SUBURB RELATIVE BUSINESS-ACTIVITY
               MULTIPLIER (DIMENSIONLESS)
    CSRBAMT- CITY/SUBURB RELATIVE BUSINESS-ACTIVITY
               MULTIPLIER TABLE (DIMENSIONLESS)
    CSRBAR - CITY/SUBURB RELATIVE BUSINESS-ACTIVITY
               RATIO (DIMENSIONLESS)

CSRBAR.K=CBST.K/SBST.K                                    177, A
    CSRBAR - CITY/SUBURB RELATIVE BUSINESS-ACTIVITY
               RATIO (DIMENSIONLESS)
    CBST   - CITY BUSINESS STRUCTURES TOTAL (STRUCTURES)
    SBST   - SUBURB BUSINESS-STRUCTURES TOTAL
               (STRUCTURES)
```

The ratio CNBSCM/SNBSCM determines the city new-business structures construction fraction CNBSCF, which is the fraction of total metropolitan new-business-structures construction allocated to the city. Suburb new-business-structures construction desired SNBSCD is the remainder of metropolitan industrial construction minus city industrial construction, or (MNBSCD) × (1 − CNBSCF). As in the *Urban Dynamics* model, the actual rate of business construction in each sector is computed as the desired construction rate multiplied by a metropolitan construction workforce multiplier MCWM. Equation 179 indicates that a shortage of construction labor operates to curtail suburb new-business-structures construction.

```
SNBSC.KL=(SNBSCD.K)(MCWM.K)                                  179, R
    SNBSC   - SUBURB NEW-BUSINESS-STRUCTURES CONSTRUCTION
                (STRUCTURES/YEAR)
    SNBSCD  - SUBURB NEW-BUSINESS-STRUCTURES CONSTRUCTION
                DESIRED (STRUCTURES/ YEAR)
    MCWM    - METROPOLITAN CONSTRUCTION WORKFORCE
                MULTIPLIER (DIMENSIONLESS)
```

The population and industrial location interfaces connect all the levels in the two-sector city-suburb model. A few minor structural and parametric adjustments are also necessary. With respect to structure, the equations that compute the ratio of upper-income workers to available jobs in each sector must be changed from the *Urban Dynamics* formulation. Because commuters (SUIC) compete with city residents for city jobs, the equation for the upper-income-to-job ratio in the city (UICJR) becomes:

```
UICJR.K=(CUIC.K+SUIC.K)/CUIJ.K                               30, A
    UICJR   - UPPER-INCOME CITY JOB RATIO (DIMENSIONLESS)
    CUIC    - CITY(RESIDENT) UPPER-INCOME CITY(WORKERS)
                (MEN)
    SUIC    - SUBURB(RESIDENT) UPPER-INCOME CITY(WORKERS)
                (MEN)
    CUIJ    - CITY UPPER-INCOME JOBS (MEN)
```

The original job ratio equations in *Urban Dynamics* did not deal with commuters. The revised equation compares total upper-income workers in the city (city residents plus commuters) to total upper-income jobs in the city. As UICJR rises, unemployment rises for both the noncommuting (CUIC) and the commuting (SUIC) categories. An equivalent change for the upper-income-to-job ratio in the suburb UISJR appears in equation 118.

```
UISJR.K=(SUIS.K+CUIS.K)/SUIJ.K                               118, A
    UISJR   - UPPER-INCOME SUBURB JOB RATIO
                (DIMENSIONLESS)
    SUIS    - SUBURB(RESIDENT) UPPER-INCOME
                SUBURB(WORKERS) (MEN)
    CUIS    - CITY(RESIDENT) UPPER-INCOME SUBURB(WORKERS)
                (MEN)
    SUIJ    - SUBURB UPPER-INCOME JOBS (MEN)
```

12.5 Model Behavior

With suburb land per housing structure SLPH set at 0.4 acres (four times the city land per housing structure CLPH), with the suburb land area SAREA set at 700,000 acres (seven times the area of the city),[4] and with the suburb initialized to contain less socioeconomic activity than the city, the city-suburb model behaves as shown in Figures 12-8a, 12-8b, and 12-8c.

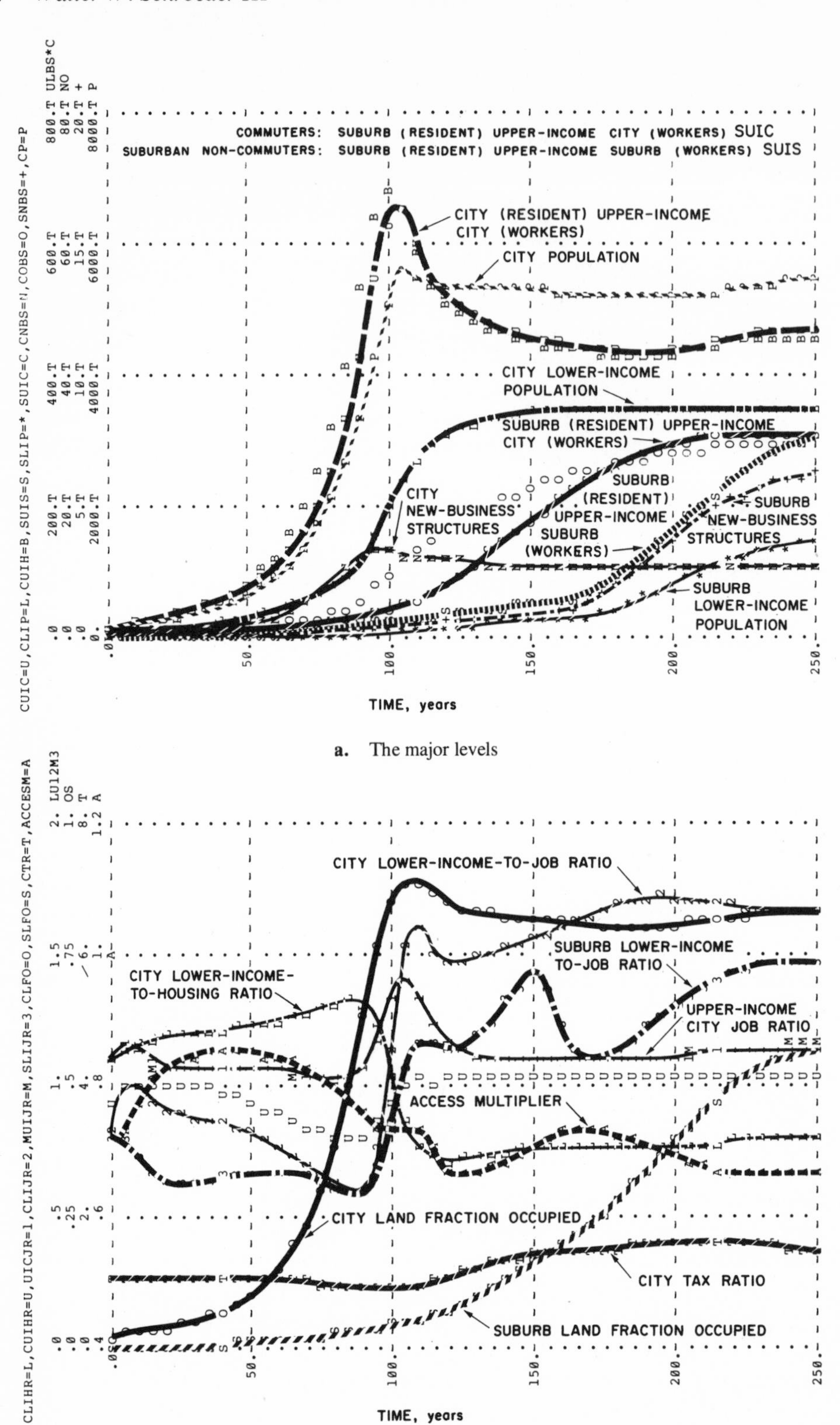

a. The major levels

b. The important ratios

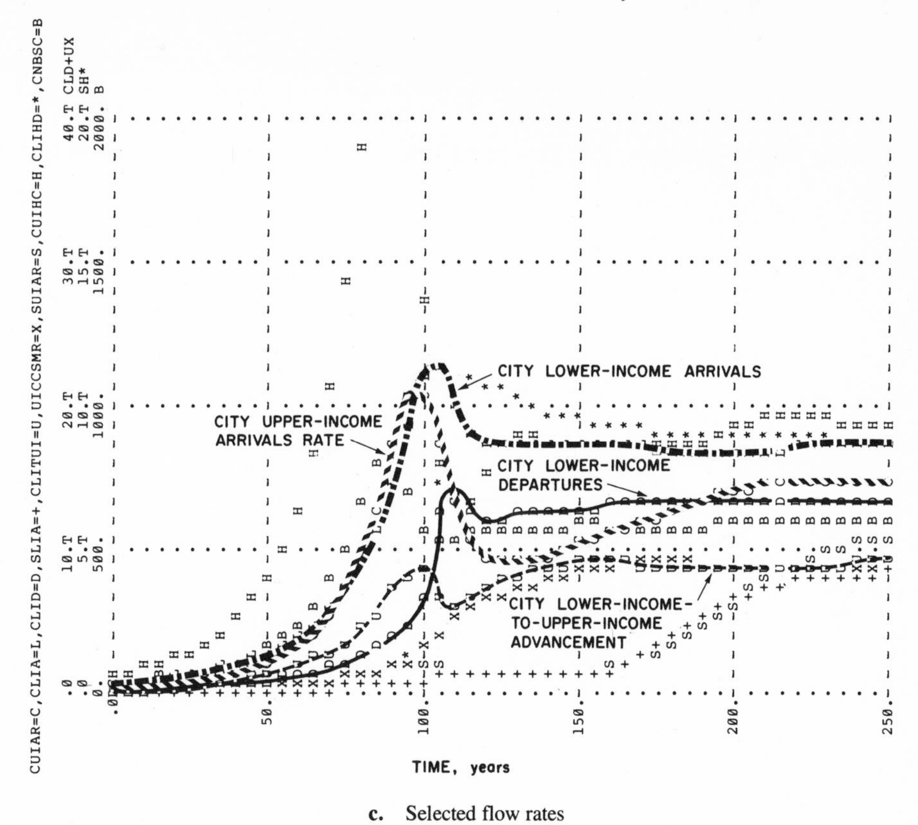

c. Selected flow rates

Figure 12-8 Behavior of the city-suburb model

Figure 12-8 portrays a metropolitan area in which commuting becomes substantial as the city begins to decline. The amount of city new-business structures peaks at year 100. As total new-business declines, so does the upper-income-to-city-job ratio UICJR. Since out-migration of city upper-income residents exceeds the inflow rate, the city (resident) upper-income city (workers) CUIC level begins to decline between years 100 and 110. The changing balance between upper- and lower-income groups in the city further exacerbates upper-income out-migration. A downward cycle takes hold. As residential conditions (city tax ratio, housing availability, and population balance) in the city deteriorate, the suburb becomes relatively more attractive. Beginning in year 100, suburb (resident) upper-income city (workers) SUIC (commuter category) begins to grow rapidly in response to declining residential conditions in the city compared with conditions in the suburb. The number of suburb (resident) upper-income city (workers) SUIC (commuters) reaches 180,000 at year 150 and 300,000 by year 200. At year 250, there are about two-thirds as many commuters as city (resident) upper-income city (workers) CUIC (noncommuters). Therefore, commuters at year 250 hold about 40 percent of all middle- and upper-income jobs in the city.

Measured commuting patterns in Lowell, Massachusetts, agree reasonably well with Figure 12-8a. In 1970, 72 percent of all jobs located within the city of Lowell were held by city residents, and commuters held the other 28 percent. Because Lowell's population peaked in 1920, today's conditions in Lowell should be compared with the model's conditions at year 150 (one hundred and fifty years after the city was incorporated and fifty years after its population peaked. In Figure 12-8a, the model contains 180,000 commuters (SUIC) at year 150, when the city (resident) upper-income city (workers) CUIC totals 450,000 and city lower-income population CLIP is 350,000. Figure 12-8b indicates that the city lower-income-to-job ratio is about 1.5 at year 150, so total city lower-income-jobs equal 350,000/1.5, or about 230,000. The total number of jobs for upper-income personnel is computed similarly: by dividing the city upper-income workforce (CUIC + SUIC) by the upper-income-to-city-job ratio UICJR (1.1 at year 150). Total upper-income jobs at year 150 are therefore:

$$(\text{CUIC} + \text{SUIC})/\text{UICJR}$$

or

$$(450{,}000 + 180{,}000)/1.1 = 560{,}000$$

If total city jobs is 230,000 + 560,000 and if the commuter population is 180,000, then the fraction of city jobs held by commuters at year 150 is:

$$180{,}000/(230{,}000 + 560{,}000)$$

or

$$0.23$$

The figure for Lowell in 1970 was 28 percent, so at year 150 the model has a slightly lower proportion of city jobs held by commuters than Lowell in 1970. A sampling of other cities suggests a normal range of about 20–30 percent of city jobs held by commuters in 1970.[5] The city-suburb model's behavior seems to come within a reasonable range of observed conditions. In Figure 12-8a, the growth of economic activity in the suburb occurs most rapidly after about year 150. The level of suburb (resident) upper-income suburb (workers) SUIS (suburban noncommuters) lags behind the commuting population (SUIC) by about fifty years. Suburb noncommuters (SUIS) reach 170,000 at year 200 but continue to grow to nearly 360,000 at year 250. Noncommuters (SUIS) exceed commuters at year 300, the suburb has become far more economically self-sufficient than at year 150; suburb upper-income jobs have attracted a large population that both lives and works in the suburbs.

Figure 12-8b plots the changing socioeconomic conditions in the metropolitan area. The city variables in Figure 12-8b closely resemble their values in the *Urban Dynamics* model (see *Urban Dynamics* standard runs in Reading 2 of this collection). Unemployment among lower-income residents, indicated by the city lower-income-to-job ratio CLIJR, remains low through year 100 but rises to a value of 1.5 or more thereafter. Conversely, the city lower-income-to-housing ratio CLIHR falls after year 100 as upper-income housing filters down to create an excess of lower-income housing. A rising city tax ratio after year 100 also contributes to the city's problems. Suburban development in Figure 12-8b lags behind city development by approximately one hundred years. The city land fraction occupied CLFO passes the 25 percent mark at year 70, while the suburb land fraction occupied SLFO reaches 25 percent at year 170. Upper-income-to-job ratios in both the city and the suburb remain within reasonably healthy limits. Both the metropolitan upper-income-to-job ratio MUIJR and the city upper-income-to-job ratio in the city UICJR exhibit nearly identical behavior in Figure

12-8b, so only one curve is visible. Upper-income-to-job ratios for the city and the metropolitan region show a slight worsening—to about 1.15 after year 160. The city upper-income-to-job ratio has a strong tendency to remain near 1.0 because upper-income families are assumed to be highly sensitive to employment conditions. When jobs are abundant, in-migration to the region is high. But when the growth of jobs slows, in-migration falls off. The migration mechanism keeps the system in balance. The suburb in Figures 12-8a and 12-8b shows signs of having its own life cycle. Suburb new-business structures SNBS appear to be at or near a peak by year 250. Suburb lower-income population SLIP is still increasing even though suburb new-business structures SNBS have stopped growing.

The behavior of the city-suburb model seems to be reasonable but deserves careful comparison with observed patterns of metropolitan development.

12.6 Policy Analysis

Three policy tests on the city-suburb model are presented here. The results of each policy test are then compared with the equivalent results from tests conducted on the *Urban Dynamics* model. Policy testing on the city-suburb model was performed in accordance with the normal procedure of allowing the model to reach its equilibrium, adding the policy change, and comparing the resultant conditions with the original (equilibrium) conditions. All observed differences are therefore produced solely by the policy change.

Lower-Income Housing Construction. Figure 12-9 summarizes the effects of a policy of constructing new lower-income housing for 5 percent of the city's lower-income population each year. The first two columns in Figure 12-9 give the name and symbol of each variable used to evaluate the policy; the third column provides the initial (equilibrium) value from the city-suburb model for each variable; the fourth column shows the value of each variable fifty years after the policy is implemented; the fifth column lists the percentage by which the variable has changed as a consequence of the policy; and the sixth column furnishes the percentage change that resulted from the same policy when tested on the *Urban Dynamics* model. Any differences between columns 5 and 6 reflect the effects of the expanded boundary of the city-suburb model. The seventh column gives the symbols of the corresponding variables from *Urban Dynamics* which were used in calculating the changes given in column 6.

As can be seen in Figure 12-9, the two models display relatively little difference in the fifty-year projection of the effects of a lower-income housing program. In the city-suburb model, the program reduces the city (resident) upper-income city (workers) CUIC by 24 percent and increases the city lower-income population CLIP by 7 percent. City upper-income housing CUIH falls by 25 percent because the lower-income housing program uses land, thereby depressing the rate of upper-income housing construction. As upper-income housing becomes scarcer and as the city population distribution shifts toward lower-income families, more upper-income families are inclined to leave the city for a suburban residence. Figure 12-9 also illustrates how the lower-income housing-construction program affects the socioeconomic condition of the

(1) Variable Name	(2) Symbol	(3) Initial Value	(4) Final Value	(5) Change after 50 Years (%)	(6) Change in *Urban Dynamics* (%) (p. 70)	(7) Corresponding *Urban Dynamics* Variables
1. City new-business structures	CNBS	10,900	8,900	−18	−49	NE
2. City older-business structures	COBS	30,600	28,100	−8	−6	DI
3. City upper-income housing	CUIH	458,100	345,600	−25	−32	PH + WH weighted average
4. City lower-income housing	CLIH	293,500	416,000	+42	+45	UH
5. City (resident) upper-income city (workers)	CUIC	465,400	354,300	−24	−31	MP + L weighted average
6. Suburb (resident) upper-income city (workers)	SUIC	308,100	303,000	−2	—	—
7. City lower-income population	CLIP	349,500	375,400	+7	−1	U
8. City upper-income-to-housing ratio	CUIHR	1.05	1.08	+3	+1	MHR + LHR weighted average
9. City lower-income-to-housing ratio	CLIHR	0.79	0.60	−24	−32	UHR
10. Metropolitan upper-income-to-job ratio	MUIJR	1.16	1.13	−3	−3	MR + LR weighted average
11. City lower-income-to-job ratio	CLIJR	1.68	2.14	+27	+30	UR
12. Suburb lower-income-to-job ratio	SLIJR	1.47	1.48	+1	—	—
13. City tax ratio needed	CTRN	1.59	1.90	+20	+36	TRN
14. City lower-income-to-upper-income advancement time	CLIP/CLITUI	38.4	56.3	+47	+50	U/UTL

Figure 12-9 Changes caused by the low-income-housing program
CLIHCPR = 0.05 (city-suburb model)
LCHPC = 0.05 (*Urban Dynamics* model)

city. Most significantly, the program produces a 27 percent increase in the already high city lower-income-to-job ratio CLIJR, indicating still higher unemployment. The falling lower-income-to-housing ratio signifies a larger excess of total lower-income housing units. The excess housing breeds low rents and attracts more lower-income families from other cities and towns to the city. The city tax ratio needed CTRN rises by 19 percent in Figure 12-9. The gap between city needs and city resources continues to widen. The policy apparently fails for the same reasons that the lower-income housing-construction policy fails in the *Urban Dynamics* model: housing is a symptom rather than a cause of the city's decay. Adding more housing only aggravates the problems of the city's lower-income residents, who now must compete even more aggressively for jobs and services in the city.

Lower-Income Job-Training Program. The second policy test focuses on job training for city lower-income residents. Assumed to be fully effective in its design, the pro-

(1) Variable Name	(2) Symbol	(3) Initial Value	(4) Final Value	(5) Change after 50 Years (%)	(6) Change in *Urban Dynamics* (%) (p. 60)	(7) Corresponding *Urban Dynamics* Variables
1. City new-business structures	CNBS	10,900	10,000	−8	+18	NE
2. City older-business structures	COBS	30,600	28,100	−8	+1	DI
3. City upper-income housing	CUIH	458,100	506,200	+11	+8	PH + WH weighted average
4. City lower-income housing	CLIH	293,500	279,600	−5	−1	UH
5. City (resident) upper-income city (workers)	CUIC	465,400	538,300	+16	+21	MP + L weighted average
6. Suburb (resident) upper-income city (workers)	SUIC	308,100	236,400	−23	—	—
7. City lower-income population	CLIP	349,500	325,700	−7	+1	U
8. City upper-income-to-housing ratio	CUIHR	1.05	1.10	+5	+7	MHR + LHR weighted average
9. City lower-income-to-housing ratio	CLIHR	0.79	0.78	−1	+2	UHR
10. Metropolitan upper-income-to-job ratio	MUIJR	1.16	1.21	+4	0	MR + LR weighted average
11. City lower-income-to-job ratio	CLIJR	1.67	1.68	+1	−2	UR
12. Suburb lower-income-to-job ratio	SLIJR	1.47	1.47	0	—	—
13. City tax ratio needed	CTRN	1.59	1.52	−4	−8	TRN
14. City lower-income-to-upper-income advancement time	CLIP/CLITUI	38.4	13.6	−65	−58	U/UTL

Figure 12-10 Changes caused by a lower-income job-training program
CLITR = 0.05 (city-suburb model)
UTR = 0.05 (*Urban Dynamics* model)

gram provides sufficient skills to boost an additional 5 percent of the city's lower-income population into the upper-income category each year. Again, the program mechanisms identically match the job-training program tested in *Urban Dynamics*. Figure 12-10 summarizes the reaction of the city-suburb model to the job-training program. After fifty years of the program, the city lower-income population CLIP falls because of the increased rate of upward economic mobility into the upper-income category. Not surprisingly, the city upper-income population increases as lower-income residents are upgraded.

Although the program successfully reduces the city lower-income population by 7 percent, the number of lower-income jobs in the city decreases by approximately the same amount with the result that there is no significant improvement in the city lower-income-to-job ratio CLIJR. A program that combines job training with job creation or with efforts to constrain the influx of lower-income arrivals could be expected to produce more significant gains for the city's lower-income residents.

(1) Variable Name	(2) Symbol	(3) Initial Value	(4) Final Value	(5) Change after 50 Years (%)	(6) Change in *Urban Dynamics* (%) (p. 101)	(7) Corresponding *Urban Dynamics* Variables
1. City new-business structures	CNBS	10,900	12,500	+15	+63	NE
2. City older-business structures	COBS	30,600	35,300	+15	+35	DI
3. City upper-income housing	CUIH	458,100	606,900	+32	+35	PH + WH weighted average
4. City lower-income housing	CLIH	293,500	170,800	−41	−43	UH
5. City (resident) upper-income city (workers)	CUIC	465,400	662,200	+42	+53	MP + L weighted average
6. Suburb (resident) upper-income city (workers)	SUIC	308,100	279,800	−9	—	—
7. City lower-income population	CLIP	349,500	300,200	−14	−11	U
8. City upper-income-to-housing ratio	CUIHR	1.05	1.14	+9	+13	MHR + LHR weighted average
9. City lower-income-to-housing ratio	CLIHR	0.79	1.17	+48	+58	UHR
10. Metropolitan upper-income-to-job ratio	MUIJR	1.16	1.20	+3	0	MR + LR weighted average
11. City lower-income-to-job ratio	CLIJR	1.67	1.16	−30	−41	UR
12. Suburb lower-income-to-job ratio	SLIJR	1.47	1.47	0	—	—
13. City tax ratio needed	CTRN	1.59	1.24	−22	−33	TRN
14. City lower-income-to-upper-income advancement time	CLIP/CLITUI	38.4	26.1	−32	−41	U/UTL

Figure 12-11 Changes caused by a combined policy of lower-income-housing demolition and the encouragement of city new-business construction
CNBSCR = 0.04, CLIHDR = 0.05 (city-suburb model)
NECN = 0.07, SHDR = 0.05 (*Urban Dynamics* model)

Columns 5 and 6 in Figure 12-10 show a substantial difference in the behavior of city new-business structures. In column 6, from *Urban Dynamics*, the level of new enterprise increases, but in column 5 the level of city new-business structures decreases. Why? Because upper-income workers in the city-suburb model have geographical mobility. They can work anywhere within the metropolitan area. Creating skilled city workers tends to attract more total new business to the metropolitan area, but the bulk of new business construction takes place in the suburb, where land is cheaper. The substantial decline in suburb (resident) upper-income city (workers) SUIC (commuters) in column 5 can be attributed to two factors. First, the decline in city employment conditions creates a net outward flow from the metropolitan area. Second, the improved employment condition in the suburb attracts commuters (SUIC) to the suburb noncommuting (SUIS) category. On the surface, this behavior seems reasonable and reinforces the position that a locally sponsored job-training program will probably not significantly reduce the problems of the central city unless other programs operate simultaneously to diminish the program's negative side effects.

Additional Encouragement of City New-Business-Structures Construction and Lower-Income-Housing Demolition. The third policy calls for the city to attract new-business construction by 40 percent over the normal rate. The policy also calls for demolishing 5 percent of the city lower-income-housing stock each year. The 40 percent increase in city new-business construction does not come directly at the expense of suburb industrial construction; instead, it is increased exogenously. Figure 12-11 shows that the number of city new-business structures rises 15 percent with the business encouragement policy. The city lower-income population decreases by 14 percent. In addition, the city (resident) upper-income city (workers) CUIC increase by 42 percent and the suburb (resident) upper-income city (workers) SUIC (commuters) lessen by 9 percent.

In Figure 12-11, major gains for the city are unmistakable. The city lower-income-to-job ratio CLIJR declines to 1.16, nearly a full-employment condition. The job-ratio improvement is sustained by a housing shortage that discourages the migration of more lower-income families into the city. The tax ratio also falls significantly. Figure 12-11 indicates that a policy to increase industrial construction and limit the lower-income-housing supply produces significant gains for both the city and its suburbs. Comparing columns 5 and 6, all city variables move in the same direction and with much the same magnitude. The revival program in *Urban Dynamics* seems to be no less effective when tested on a model in which the suburbs are represented explicitly.

12.7 Conclusions

This reading provides a conceptual framework for extending the *Urban Dynamics* model to permit a more comprehensive analysis of city-suburb interactions. The preliminary city-suburb model presented here is conducive to several observations. First, the city-suburb issue in *Urban Dynamics* can probably be best resolved through direct modeling. The interactions are observable, and a city-suburb model consisting of two parallel urban dynamics–type structures seems to be an appropriate starting point. Second, the behavior of the city-suburb model suggests that the suburb is more a symptom than a cause of central-city decline. City residents become commuters when residential conditions in the city decline sufficiently to justify the inconvenience and expense of traveling thirty or more minutes to work. If the causes of urban decline lie within cities, so do the solutions. The dominant feedback loops affecting urban behavior lie within cities themselves, as shown by the policy tests on the city-suburb model. For the most part, city-suburb feedback merely compounds urban difficulties. Efforts to revitalize our cities should focus more on local city policy alternatives than on regional, state, or federal programs. Programs that had a neutral to detrimental impact in *Urban Dynamics* are equally ineffective when tested on the city-suburb model. However, as demonstrated by both models, a program of industrial and commercial expansion, coupled with the removal of deteriorated housing, should bring major gains in city conditions.

Notes

1. The following reviews deal with the need for suburbs in the *Urban Dynamics* model: (a) Harvey A. Garn and Robert H. Wilson, "A Look at *Urban Dynamics*: The Forrester Model and Public Policy," *IEEE Transactions on Systems, Man, and Cybernetics*, vol. SMC-2, no. 2 (April 1972), p. 151; (b) Harold T. Moody, "*Urban Dynamics*: A Review of Forrester's Model of an Urban Area," *Economic Geography*, vol. 46, no. 4 (October 1970), pp. 8–9; (c) Jerome Rothenberg, "Problems in the Modeling of Urban Development: A Review Article on *Urban Dynamics*, by Jay W. Forrester," vol. 1 (1974), no. 1, p. 32; and (d) Herbert Weinblatt, *Policy Sciences*, vol. 1 (1970), p. 382.

2. See Louis Edward Alfeld and Walter W. Schroeder III, "*Urban Dynamics* and the Suburbs: A Preliminary Analysis and Model Extension," System Dynamics Group Memorandum D-1811-2 (Cambridge, Mass.: M.I.T., April 1974), and Alan K. Graham, "Understanding *Urban Dynamics*: An Analysis of Garn's Interpretation," in *Readings in Urban Dynamics*, vol. 1, ed. Nathaniel J. Mass (Cambridge, Mass.: Wright-Allen Press, 1974).

3. In *Urban Dynamics* the ratio of underemployed-to-total worker population is 377,000/840,000, or 45 percent.

4. The suburb area is actually a variable in the city-suburb model. The suburb area is computed as a base area (700,000 acres) multiplied by a normalized index of the extent to which the city is fully developed. When 20 percent of the city's land is occupied, the suburb land area index has a value of 0.6. If the city becomes completely developed, the value of the suburb land index reaches its theoretical maximum of 1.0, and the suburb land area reaches 700,000 acres. The initial values of the levels in the suburb are substantially less than those in the city and also, the initial growth rates of industrial and residential structures are much lower. This results in the model starting with less socioeconomic activity in the suburbs than in the city.

5. Based on 1970 census data, the figures are: New Bedford, 20 percent; New York, 10 percent; Chicago, 21 percent; Boston, 50 percent. These variances are attributable to many factors, including different city-suburb land area ratios, differences in the age of each metropolitan area, and geographical characteristics.

Appendix A: Documentor Listing of the City-Suburb Model

```
CLIA.KL=(CLIP.K+CUIS.K+CUIC.K)(CLIAN)(CLIAMP.K)        1, R
CLIAN=.04                                              1.1, C
    CLIA   - CITY LOWER-INCOME ARRIVALS (MEN/YEAR)
    CLIP   - CITY LOWER-INCOME POPULATION (MEN)
    CUIS   - CITY(RESIDENT) UPPER-INCOME SUBURB(WORKERS)
               (MEN)
    CUIC   - CITY(RESIDENT) UPPER-INCOME CITY(WORKERS)
               (MEN)
    CLIAN  - CITY LOWER-INCOME ARRIVALS NORMAL
               (FRACTION/YEAR)
    CLIAMP - CITY LOWER-INCOME ATTRACTIVENESS MULTIPLIER
               PERCEIVED (DIMENSIONLESS)

CLIAMP.K=CLIAMP.J+(DT/LIAPT)(CLIAM.J-CLIAMP.J)         2, L
CLIAMP=.65                                             2.1, N
LIAPT=20                                               2.2, C
    CLIAMP - CITY LOWER-INCOME ATTRACTIVENESS MULTIPLIER
               PERCEIVED (DIMENSIONLESS)
    LIAPT  - LOWER-INCOME-ARRIVALS PERCEPTION TIME
               (YEARS)
    CLIAM  - CITY LOWER-INCOME ATTRACTIVENESS MULTIPLIER
               (DIMENSIONLESS)

CLIAM.K=(CLIMM.K)(CLIHSM.K)(CPEM.K)(CLIJM.K)           3, A
  (CLIHCPM.K)(AMF)
AMF=1                                                  3.1, C
    CLIAM  - CITY LOWER-INCOME ATTRACTIVENESS MULTIPLIER
               (DIMENSIONLESS)
    CLIMM  - CITY LOWER-INCOME MOBILITY MULTIPLIER
               (DIMENSIONLESS)
    CLIHSM - CITY LOWER-INCOME-HOUSING-SUPPLY MULTIPLIER
               (DIMENSIONLESS)
    CPEM   - CITY PUBLIC EXPENDITURES MULTIPLIER
               (DIMENSIONLESS)
    CLIJM  - CITY LOWER-INCOME JOB MULTIPLIER
               (DIMENSIONLESS)
    CLIHCPM- CITY LOWER-INCOME-HOUSING-CONSTRUCTION-
               PROGRAM MULTIPLIER (DIMENSIONLESS)
    AMF    - ATTRACTIVENESS-FOR-MIGRATION FACTOR
               (DIMENSIONLESS)

CLIMM.K=TABLE(CLIMMT,CLIEM.K,0,.15,.025)               4, A
CLIMMT=.4/.9/1.3/1.5/1.7/1.9/2                         4.1, T
    CLIMM  - CITY LOWER-INCOME MOBILITY MULTIPLIER
               (DIMENSIONLESS)
    CLIMMT - CITY LOWER-INCOME MOBILITY MULTIPLIER TABLE
               (DIMENSIONLESS)
    CLIEM  - CITY LOWER-INCOME ECONOMIC MOBILITY
               (FRACTION/YEAR)

CLIHSM.K=TABLE(CLIHSMT,CLIHR.K,0,2,.25)                5, A
CLIHSMT=2.5/2.4/2.2/1.7/1/.4/.2/.1/.05                 5.1, T
    CLIHSM - CITY LOWER-INCOME-HOUSING-SUPPLY MULTIPLIER
               (DIMENSIONLESS)
    CLIHSMT- CITY LOWHR-INCOME-HOUSING-SUPPLY MULTIPLIER
               TABLE (DIMENSIONLESS)
    CLIHR  - CITY LOWER-INCOME-TO-HOUSING RATIO
               (DIMENSIONLESS)

CLIHR.K=(CLIP.K*CLIFS)/(CLIH.K*CLIHPD)                 6, A
CLIHPD=12                                              6.1, C
    CLIHR  - CITY LOWER-INCOME-TO-HOUSING RATIO
               (DIMENSIONLESS)
    CLIP   - CITY LOWER-INCOME POPULATION (MEN)
    CLIFS  - CITY LOWER-INCOME FAMILY SIZE (PEOPLE/MAN)
    CLIH   - CITY LOWER-INCOME HOUSING (STRUCTURES)
    CLIHPD - CITY LOWER-INCOME HOUSING POPULATION
               DENSITY (PEOPLE/HOUSING UNIT)
```

```
CPEM.K=TABLE(CPEMT,CTPCR.K,0,3,.5)                        7, A
CPEMT=.2/.6/1/1.6/2.4/3.2/4                               7.1, T
    CPEM    - CITY PUBLIC EXPENDITURES MULTIPLIER
                (DIMENSIONLESS)
    CPEMT   - CITY PUBLIC EXPENDITURES MULTIPLIER TABLE
                (DIMENSIONLESS)
    CTPCR   - CITY TAX PER CAPITA RATIO (DIMENSIONLESS)

CTPCR.K=((CTC.K/CP.K)+CTPCSP.K)/CTPCN                     8, A
CTPCN=250                                                 8.1, C
    CTPCR   - CITY TAX PER CAPITA RATIO (DIMENSIONLESS)
    CTC     - CITY TAX COLLECTIONS (DOLLARS/YEAR)
    CP      - CITY POPULATION (PEOPLE)
    CTPCSP  - CITY TAX PER CAPITA SUBSIDY PROGRAM
                (DOLLARS/PERSON/YEAR)
    CTPCN   - CITY TAX PER CAPITA NORMAL (DOLLARS/YEAR/
                PERSON)

CP.K=(CUIC.K+CUIS.K)(CUIFS)+(CLIP.K)(CLIFS)               9, A
CUIFS=5.5                                                 9.1, C
CLIFS=8                                                   9.2, C
    CP      - CITY POPULATION (PEOPLE)
    CUIC    - CITY(RESIDENT) UPPER-INCOME CITY(WORKERS)
                (MEN)
    CUIS    - CITY(RESIDENT) UPPER-INCOME SUBURB(WORKERS)
                (MEN)
    CUIFS   - CITY UPPER-INCOME FAMILY SIZE (PEOPLE/MAN)
    CLIP    - CITY LOWER-INCOME POPULATION (MEN)
    CLIFS   - CITY LOWER-INCOME FAMILY SIZE (PEOPLE/MAN)

CLIJM.K=TABLE(CLIJMT,CLIJR.K,0,3,.25)                     10, A
CLIJMT=2/2/1.9/1.6/1/.6/.4/.3/.2/.15/.1/.05/.02           10.1, T
    CLIJM   - CITY LOWER-INCOME JOB MULTIPLIER
                (DIMENSIONLESS)
    CLIJMT  - CITY LOWER-INCOME JOB MULTIPLIER TABLE
                (DIMENSIONLESS)
    CLIJR   - CITY LOWER-INCOME-TO-JOB RATIO
                (DIMENSIONLESS)

CLIHCPM.K=TABLE(CLIHCPT,CLIHPR.K,0,.05,.01)               11, A
CLIHCPT=1/1.2/1.5/1.9/2.4/3                               11.1, T
    CLIHCPM- CITY LOWER-INCOME-HOUSING-CONSTRUCTION-
                PROGRAM MULTIPLIER (DIMENSIONLESS)
    CLIHCPT- CITY LOWER-INCOME-HOUSING-CONSTRUCTION-
                PROGRAM TABLE (DIMENSIONLESS)
    CLIHPR  - CITY LOWER-INCOME-HOUSING-PROGRAM RATE
                (HOUSING UNITS/YEAR)

CLIHPR.K=CLIHCP.JK/CLIP.K                                 12, A
    CLIHPR  - CITY LOWER-INCOME-HOUSING-PROGRAM RATE
                (HOUSING UNITS/YEAR)
    CLIHCP  - CITY LOWER-INCOME-HOUSING-CONSTRUCTION
                PROGRAM (STRUCTURES/YEAR)
    CLIP    - CITY LOWER-INCOME POPULATION (MEN)

CLID.KL=(CLIDN)(CLIP.K)(CLIDM.K)                          13, R
CLIDN=.02                                                 13.1, C
    CLID    - CITY LOWER-INCOME DEPARTURES (MEN/YEAR)
    CLIDN   - CITY LOWER-INCOME DEPARTURES NORMAL
                (FRACTION/YEAR)
    CLIP    - CITY LOWER-INCOME POPULATION (MEN)
    CLIDM   - CITY LOWER-INCOME DEPARTURES MULTIPLIER
                (DIMENSIONLESS)

CLIDM.K=TABLE(CLIDMT,1.44*LOGN(CLIAM.K),-3,3,1)           14, A
CLIDMT=8/4/2/1/.5/.25/.125                                14.1, T
    CLIDM   - CITY LOWER-INCOME DEPARTURES MULTIPLIER
                (DIMENSIONLESS)
    CLIDMT  - CITY LOWER-INCOME DEPARTURES MULTIPLIER
                TABLE (DIMENSIONLESS)
    CLIAM   - CITY LOWER-INCOME ATTRACTIVENESS MULTIPLIER
                (DIMENSIONLESS)

CLIB.KL=(CLIP.K)(CLIBR)                                   15, R
CLIBR=.015                                                15.1, C
    CLIB    - CITY LOWER-INCOME BIRTHS (MEN/YEAR)
    CLIP    - CITY LOWER-INCOME POPULATION (MEN)
    CLIBR   - CITY LOWER-INCOME BIRTH RATE (FRACTION/
                YEAR)
```

```
CLIP.K=CLIP.J+(DT)(CLIA.JK+CLIB.JK-CLID.JK-          16, L
  CLITUI.JK)
CLIP=6000                                            16.1, N
    CLIP   - CITY LOWER-INCOME POPULATION (MEN)
    CLIA   - CITY LOWER-INCOME ARRIVALS (MEN/YEAR)
    CLIB   - CITY LOWER-INCOME BIRTHS (MEN/YEAR)
    CLID   - CITY LOWER-INCOME DEPARTURES (MEN/YEAR)
    CLITUI - CITY LOWER-INCOME-TO-UPPER-INCOME
               ADVANCEMENT (MEN/YEAR)

CLITUI.KL=(CUMN)(CLIW.K)(CLIEMMP.K)+CLITP.K          17, R
CUMN=.06                                             17.1, C
    CLITUI - CITY LOWER-INCOME-TO-UPPER-INCOME
               ADVANCEMENT (MEN/YEAR)
    CUMN   - CITY UPWARD MOBILITY NORMAL (FRACTION/YEAR)
    CLIW   - CITY LOWER-INCOME WORKERS (MEN)
    CLIEMMP- CITY LOWER-INCOME ECONOMIC MOBILITY
               MULTIPLIER PERCEIVED (DIMENSIONLESS)
    CLITP  - CITY LOWER-INCOME TRAINING PROGRAM (MEN/
               YEAR)

CLIW.K=(CLIP.K)(CLIFW.K)                             18, A
    CLIW   - CITY LOWER-INCOME WORKERS (MEN)
    CLIP   - CITY LOWER-INCOME POPULATION (MEN)
    CLIFW  - CITY LOWER-INCOME FRACTION WORKING
               (DIMENSIONLESS)

CLIFW.K=TABLE(CLIFWT,CLIJR.K,0,4,1)                  19, A
CLIFWT=.9/.8/.4/.3/.2                                19.1, T
    CLIFW  - CITY LOWER-INCOME FRACTION WORKING
               (DIMENSIONLESS)
    CLIFWT - CITY LOWER-INCOME FRACTION WORKING TABLE
               (DIMENSIONLESS)
    CLIJR  - CITY LOWER-INCOME-TO-JOB RATIO
               (DIMENSIONLESS)

CLITUIP.K=CLITUIP.J+(DT/CLIEAT)(CLITUI.JK-           20, L
  CLITUIP.J)
CLITUIP=400                                          20.1, N
CLIEAT=10                                            20.2, C
    CLITUIP- CITY LOWER-INCOME-TO-UPPER-INCOME
               ADVANCEMENT PERCEIVED (DIMENSIONLESS)
    CLIEAT - CITY LOWER-INCOME ECONOMIC ADVANCEMENT TIME
               (YEARS)
    CLITUI - CITY LOWER-INCOME-TO-UPPER-INCOME
               ADVANCEMENT (MEN/YEAR)

CLIEM.K=CLITUIP.K/CLIP.K                             21, A
    CLIEM  - CITY LOWER-INCOME ECONOMIC MOBILITY
               (FRACTION/YEAR)
    CLITUIP- CITY LOWER-INCOME-TO-UPPER-INCOME
               ADVANCEMENT PERCEIVED (DIMENSIONLESS)
    CLIP   - CITY LOWER-INCOME POPULATION (MEN)

CLIEMMP.K=CLIEMMP.J+(DT/CLIEMPT)(CLIEMM.J-           22, L
  CLIEMMP.J)
CLIEMMP=1.08                                         22.1, N
CLIEMPT=10                                           22.2, C
    CLIEMMP- CITY LOWER-INCOME ECONOMIC MOBILITY
               MULTIPLIER PERCEIVED (DIMENSIONLESS)
    CLIEMPT- CITY LOWER-INCOME ECONOMIC MOBILITY
               PERCEPTION TIME (YEARS)
    CLIEMM - CITY LOWER-INCOME ECONOMIC MOBILITY
               MULTIPLIER (DIMENSIONLESS)

CLIEMM.K=(CUIWSM.K)(UICLIM.K)(CLIQEM.K)(CLIEMF)      23, A
CLIEMF=1                                             23.1, C
    CLIEMM - CITY LOWER-INCOME ECONOMIC MOBILITY
               MULTIPLIER (DIMENSIONLESS)
    CUIWSM - CITY UPPER-INCOME WORKFORCE SUPPLY
               MULTIPLIER (DIMENSIONLESS)
    UICLIM - UPPER-INCOME-TO-CITY LOWER-INCOME
               MULTIPLIER (DIMENSIONLESS)
    CLIQEM - CITY LOWER-INCOME QUALITY-EDUCATION
               MULTIPLIER (DIMENSIONLESS)
    CLIEMF - CITY LOWER-INCOME ECONOMIC MOBILITY FACTOR
               (DIMENSIONLESS)
```

```
CUIWSM.K=TABLE(CUIWSMT,UICJR.K,0,2,.5)                  24, A
CUIWSMT=2/1.6/1/.4/.2                                   24.1, T
    CUIWSM - CITY UPPER-INCOME WORKFORCE SUPPLY
              MULTIPLIER (DIMENSIONLESS)
    CUIWSMT- CITY UPPER-INCOME WORKFORCE SUPPLY
              MULTIPLIER TABLE (DIMENSIONLESS)
    UICJR  - UPPER-INCOME CITY JOB RATIO (DIMENSIONLESS)

UICLIM.K=TABLE(UICLIMT,UICLIR.K,0,5,1)                  25, A
UICLIMT=.2/.8/1.1/1.2/1.3/1.4                           25.1, T
    UICLIM - UPPER-INCOME-TO-CITY LOWER-INCOME
              MULTIPLIER (DIMENSIONLESS)
    UICLIMT- UPPER-INCOME-TO-CITY LOWER-INCOME
              MULTIPLIER TABLE (DIMENSIONLESS)
    UICLIR - UPPER-INCOME-TO-CITY LOWER-INCOME RATIO
              (DIMENSIONLESS)

UICLIR.K=(CUIC.K+CUIS.K)/CLIP.K                         26, A
    UICLIR - UPPER-INCOME-TO-CITY LOWER-INCOME RATIO
              (DIMENSIONLESS)
    CUIC   - CITY(RESIDENT) UPPER-INCOME CITY(WORKERS)
              (MEN)
    CUIS   - CITY(RESIDENT) UPPER-INCOME SUBURB(WORKERS)
              (MEN)
    CLIP   - CITY LOWER-INCOME POPULATION (MEN)

CLIQEM.K=TABLE(CLIQEMT,CTPCR.K,0,3,.5)                  27, A
CLIQEMT=.2/.7/1/1.3/1.5/1.6/1.7                         27.1, T
    CLIQEM - CITY LOWER-INCOME QUALITY-EDUCATION
              MULTIPLIER (DIMENSIONLESS)
    CLIQEMT- CITY LOWER-INCOME QUALITY-EDUCATION
              MULTIPLIER TABLE (DIMENSIONLESS)
    CTPCR  - CITY TAX PER CAPITA RATIO (DIMENSIONLESS)


*****UPPER INCOME SECTOR*****
*****

CUICB.KL=(CUIC.K)(CUIBR)                                28, R
CUIBR=.0095                                             28.1, C
    CUICB  - CITY UPPER-INCOME CITY BIRTHS (MEN/YEAR)
    CUIC   - CITY(RESIDENT) UPPER-INCOME CITY(WORKERS)
              (MEN)
    CUIBR  - CITY UPPER-INCOME CITY BIRTH RATE
              (FRACTION/YEAR)

CUIC.K=CUIC.J+(DT)(CLITUI.JK+CUICB.JK+CUIAR.JK+         29, L
  UISCCMR.JK-UICCSMR.JK-CUICD.JK)
CUIC=17000                                              29.2, N
    CUIC   - CITY(RESIDENT) UPPER-INCOME CITY(WORKERS)
              (MEN)
    CLITUI - CITY LOWER-INCOME-TO-UPPER-INCOME
              ADVANCEMENT (MEN/YEAR)
    CUICB  - CITY UPPER-INCOME CITY BIRTHS (MEN/YEAR)
    CUIAR  - CITY UPPER-INCOME-ARRIVALS RATE (MEN/YEAR)
    UISCCMR- UPPER-INCOME SUBURB(RESIDENT) CITY(WORKERS)
              CITY MIGRATION RATE (MEN/YEAR)
    UICCSMR- UPPER-INCOME CITY(RESIDENT) CITY(WORKERS)
              SUBURB MIGRATION RATE (MEN/YEAR)
    CUICD  - CITY UPPER-INCOME CITY DEPARTURES (MEN/
              YEAR)

UICJR.K=(CUIC.K+SUIC.K)/CUIJ.K                          30, A
    UICJR  - UPPER-INCOME CITY JOB RATIO (DIMENSIONLESS)
    CUIC   - CITY(RESIDENT) UPPER-INCOME CITY(WORKERS)
              (MEN)
    SUIC   - SUBURB(RESIDENT) UPPER-INCOME CITY(WORKERS)
              (MEN)
    CUIJ   - CITY UPPER-INCOME JOBS (MEN)

CUIAMP.K=CUIAMP.J+(DT/CUIAMPT)(CUIAM.J-CUIAMP.J)        31, L
CUIAMP=.85                                              31.1, N
CUIAMPT=14                                              31.2, C
    CUIAMP - CITY UPPER-INCOME-ARRIVALS MULTIPLIER
              PERCEIVED (DIMENSIONLESS)
    CUIAMPT- CITY UPPER-INCOME-ARRIVALS MULTIPLIER
              PERCEPTION TIME (YEARS)
    CUIAM  - CITY UPPER-INCOME-ARRIVALS MULTIPLIER
              (DIMENSIONLESS)
```

```
CUIAM.K=(CUIJM.K)(CUIALIM.K)(CUITM.K)(CUIHSM.K)      32, A
  (CUIAF)
CUIAF=1                                               32.1, C
    CUIAM   - CITY UPPER-INCOME-ARRIVALS MULTIPLIER
                (DIMENSIONLESS)
    CUIJM   - CITY UPPER-INCOME JOB MULTIPLIER
                (DIMENSIONLESS)
    CUIALIM- CITY UPPER-INCOME-ARRIVALS LOWER-INCOME
                MULTIPLIER (DIMENSIONLESS)
    CUITM   - CITY UPPER-INCOME TAX MULTIPLIER
                (DIMENSIONLESS)
    CUIHSM  - CITY UPPER-INCOME HOUSING-SUPPLY MULTIPLIER
                (DIMENSIONLESS)
    CUIAF   - CITY UPPER-INCOME-ARRIVALS FACTOR
                (DIMENSIONLESS)

CUIJM.K=TABLE(CUIJMT,UICJR.K,0,2,.25)                 33, A
    CUIJM   - CITY UPPER-INCOME JOB MULTIPLIER
                (DIMENSIONLESS)
    CUIJMT  - CITY UPPER-INCOME JOB MULTIPLIER TABLE
                (DIMENSIONLESS)
    UICJR   - UPPER-INCOME CITY JOB RATIO (DIMENSIONLESS)

CUICJR.K=(CUIC.K+CUIS.K)/CUIJ.K                       34, A
CUIJMT=2.6/2.6/2.4/1.8/1/.4/.2/.1/.05                 34.1, T
    CUICJR  - CITY UPPER-INCOME-TO-CITY JOB RATIO
                (DIMENSIONLESS)
    CUIC    - CITY(RESIDENT) UPPER-INCOME CITY(WORKERS)
                (MEN)
    CUIS    - CITY(RESIDENT) UPPER-INCOME SUBURB(WORKERS)
                (MEN)
    CUIJ    - CITY UPPER-INCOME JOBS (MEN)
    CUIJMT  - CITY UPPER-INCOME JOB MULTIPLIER TABLE
                (DIMENSIONLESS)

CUIALIM.K=TABLE(CUIALIT,CUITLIR.K,0,4,1)              35, A
CUIALIT=.4/.5/.8/1.3/1.5                              35.1, T
    CUIALIM- CITY UPPER-INCOME-ARRIVALS LOWER-INCOME
                MULTIPLIER (DIMENSIONLESS)
    CUIALIT- CITY UPPER-INCOME-ARRIVALS LOWER-INCOME
                TABLE (DIMENSIONLESS)
    CUITLIR- CITY UPPER-INCOME-TO-LOWER-INCOME RATIO
                (DIMENSIONLESS)

CUITPR.K=(CUIC.K+CUIS.K)/(CUIC.K+CUIS.K+CLIP.K)       36, A
    CUITPR  - CITY UPPER-INCOME TO POPULATION RATIO
                (DIMENSIONLESS)
    CUIC    - CITY(RESIDENT) UPPER-INCOME CITY(WORKERS)
                (MEN)
    CUIS    - CITY(RESIDENT) UPPER-INCOME SUBURB(WORKERS)
                (MEN)
    CLIP    - CITY LOWER-INCOME POPULATION (MEN)

CUITM.K=TABLE(CUITMT,1.44*LOGN(CTR.K),-2,4,2)         37, A
CUITMT=1.3/1/.7/.3                                    37.1, T
    CUITM   - CITY UPPER-INCOME TAX MULTIPLIER
                (DIMENSIONLESS)
    CUITMT  - CITY UPPER-INCOME TAX MULTIPLIER TABLE
                (DIMENSIONLESS)
    CTR     - CITY TAX RATIO (DIMENSIONLESS)

CUIHSM.K=TABLE(CUIHSMT,CUIHR.K,0,3,.5)                38, A
CUIHSMT=1.3/1.2/1/.5/.2/.1/.05                        38.1, T
    CUIHSM  - CITY UPPER-INCOME HOUSING-SUPPLY MULTIPLIER
                (DIMENSIONLESS)
    CUIHSMT- CITY UPPER-INCOME HOUSING-SUPPLY MULTIPLIER
                TABLE (DIMENSIONLESS)
    CUIHR   - CITY UPPER-INCOME-TO-HOUSING RATIO
                (DIMENSIONLESS)

CUIHR.K=(CUIC.K+CUIS.K)(CUIFS)/(CUIH.K*CUIHPD)        39, A
CUIHPD=5.5                                            39.1, C
    CUIHR   - CITY UPPER-INCOME-TO-HOUSING RATIO
                (DIMENSIONLESS)
    CUIC    - CITY(RESIDENT) UPPER-INCOME CITY(WORKERS)
                (MEN)
    CUIS    - CITY(RESIDENT) UPPER-INCOME SUBURB(WORKERS)
                (MEN)
```

```
    CUIFS  - CITY UPPER-INCOME FAMILY SIZE (PEOPLE/MAN)
    CUIH   - CITY UPPER-INCOME HOUSING (STRUCTURES)
    CUIHPD - CITY UPPER-INCOME-HOUSING POPULATION
               DENSITY (PEOPLE/HOUSING UNIT)

CUICD.KL=(CUICDN)(CUIC.K)(CUICDM.K)                     40, R
CUICDN=.015                                             40.1, C
    CUICD  - CITY UPPER-INCOME CITY DEPARTURES (MEN/
               YEAR)
    CUICDN - CITY UPPER-INCOME CITY DEPARTURES NORMAL
               (FRACTION/YEAR)
    CUIC   - CITY(RESIDENT) UPPER-INCOME CITY(WORKERS)
               (MEN)
    CUICDM - CITY UPPER-INCOME CITY DEPARTURES
               MULTIPLIER (DIMENSIONLESS)

CUICDM.K=TABLE(CUICDMT,1.44*LOGN(CUIAM.K),-3,3,1)       41, A
CUICDMT=8/4/2/1/.5/.25/.125                             41.1, T
    CUICDM - CITY UPPER-INCOME CITY DEPARTURES
               MULTIPLIER (DIMENSIONLESS)
    CUICDMT- CITY UPPER-INCOME CITY DEPARTURES
               MULTIPLIER TABLE (DIMENSIONLESS)
    CUIAM  - CITY UPPER-INCOME-ARRIVALS MULTIPLIER
               (DIMENSIONLESS)


*****UPPER INCOME HOUSING SECTOR
*****

CUIHC.KL=(CUIHCD.K)(MCWM.K)                             42, R
    CUIHC  - CITY UPPER-INCOME-HOUSING CONSTRUCTION
               (STRUCTURES/YEAR)
    CUIHCD - CITY UPPER-INCOME-HOUSING CONSTRUCTION
               DESIRED (STRUCTURES/YEAR)
    MCWM   - METROPOLITAN CONSTRUCTION WORKFORCE
               MULTIPLIER (DIMENSIONLESS)


CUIHCD.K=(CUIHCN.K)(CUIH.K)(CUIHM.K)+CUIHCP.K           43, A
     CUIHCN IS DEFINED IN EQ. 2820

CUIHM.K=(CUIHAM.K)(CUIHLM.K)(CUIHPM.K)(CUIHTM.K)        44, A
  (CUIHEM.K)(CUIHGM.K)(CUIHF)
CUIHF=1                                                 44.2, C
    CUIHCD - CITY UPPER-INCOME-HOUSING CONSTRUCTION
               DESIRED (STRUCTURES/YEAR)
    CUIHCN - CITY UPPER-INCOME-HOUSING CONSTRUCTION
               NORMAL (FRACTION/YEAR)
    CUIH   - CITY UPPER-INCOME HOUSING (STRUCTURES)
    CUIHM  - CITY UPPER-INCOME-HOUSING MULTIPLIER
               (DIMENSIONLESS)
    CUIHCP - CITY UPPER-INCOME-HOUSING-CONSTRUCTION
               PROGRAM (STRUCTURES/YEAR)
    CUIHAM - CITY UPPER-INCOME-HOUSING AVAILABILITY
               MULTIPLIER (DIMENSIONLESS)
    CUIHLM - CITY UPPER-INCOME-HOUSING LAND MULTIPLIER
               (DIMENSIONLESS)
    CUIHPM - CITY UPPER-INCOME-HOUSING POPULATION
               MULTIPLIER (DIMENSIONLESS)
    CUIHTM - CITY UPPER-INCOME-HOUSING TAX MULTIPLIER
               (DIMENSIONLESS)
    CUIHEM - CITY UPPER-INCOME-HOUSING-ENTERPRISE
               MULTIPLIER (DIMENSIONLESS)
    CUIHGM - CITY UPPER-INCOME-HOUSING GROWTH MULTIPLIER
               (DIMENSIONLESS)
    CUIHF  - CITY UPPER-INCOME-HOUSING FACTOR
               (DIMENSIONLESS)

CUIHAM.K=TABLE(CUIHAMT,CUIHR.K,0,2,.25)                 45, A
CUIHAMT=0/.001/.01/.2/1/3/4.6/5.6/6                     45.1, T
    CUIHAM - CITY UPPER-INCOME-HOUSING AVAILABILITY
               MULTIPLIER (DIMENSIONLESS)
    CUIHAMT- CITY UPPER-INCOME-HOUSING AVAILABILITY
               MULTIPLIER TABLE (DIMENSIONLESS)
    CUIHR  - CITY UPPER-INCOME-TO-HOUSING RATIO
               (DIMENSIONLESS)
```

```
CUIHLM.K=TABLE(CUIHLMT,CLFO.K,0,1,.1)                    46, A
CUIHLMT=.4/.9/1.3/1.6/1.8/1.9/1.8/1.4/.7/.2/0           46.1, T
    CUIHLM - CITY UPPER-INCOME-HOUSING LAND MULTIPLIER
               (DIMENSIONLESS)
    CUIHLMT- CITY UPPER-INCOME-HOUSING LAND MULTIPLIER
               TABLE (DIMENSIONLESS)
    CLFO   - CITY LAND FRACTION OCCUPIED (DIMENSIONLESS)

CLFO.K=(CHT.K*CLPH+CBST.K*CLPBS)/CAREA                   47, A
CLPH=.1                                                  47.1, C
CLPBS=.2                                                 47.2, C
CAREA=100000                                             47.3, C
    CLFO   - CITY LAND FRACTION OCCUPIED (DIMENSIONLESS)
    CHT    - CITY HOUSING TOTAL (STRUCTURES)
    CLPH   - CITY LAND PER HOUSING STRUCTURE (ACRES/
               STRUCTURE)
    CBST   - CITY BUSINESS STRUCTURES TOTAL (STRUCTURES)
    CLPBS  - CITY LAND PER BUSINESS STRUCTURE (ACRES/
               STRUCTURE)
    CAREA  - CITY AREA (ACRES)

CHT.K=CUIH.K+CLIH.K                                      48, A
    CHT    - CITY HOUSING TOTAL (STRUCTURES)
    CUIH   - CITY UPPER-INCOME HOUSING (STRUCTURES)
    CLIH   - CITY LOWER-INCOME HOUSING (STRUCTURES)

CBST.K=CNBS.K+COBS.K                                     49, A
    CBST   - CITY BUSINESS STRUCTURES TOTAL (STRUCTURES)
    CNBS   - CITY NEW-BUSINESS STRUCTURES (STRUCTURES)
    COBS   - CITY OLDER-BUSINESS STRUCTURES (STRUCTURES)

CUIHPM.K=TABLE(CUIHPMT,CUITPR.K,0,.8,.2)                 50, A
CUIHPMT=.4/.6/.8/1/1.1                                   50.1, T
    CUIHPM - CITY UPPER-INCOME-HOUSING POPULATION
               MULTIPLIER (DIMENSIONLESS)
    CUIHPMT- CITY UPPER-INCOME-HOUSING POPULATION
               MULTIPLIER TABLE (DIMENSIONLESS)
    CUITPR - CITY UPPER-INCOME TO POPULATION RATIO
               (DIMENSIONLESS)

CUIHTM.K=TABLE(CUIHTMT,1.44*LOGN(CTR.K),-2,4,2)          51, A
CUIHTMT=1.2/1/.7/.3                                      51.1, T
    CUIHTM - CITY UPPER-INCOME-HOUSING TAX MULTIPLIER
               (DIMENSIONLESS)
    CUIHTMT- CITY UPPER-INCOME-HOUSING TAX MULTIPLIER
               TABLE (DIMENSIONLESS)
    CTR    - CITY TAX RATIO (DIMENSIONLESS)

CUIHEM.K=TABLE(CUIHEMT,CNBSGR.K,-.08,.12,.04)            52, A
CUIHEMT=.2/.6/1/1.8/2.6/3.2                              52.1, T
    CUIHEM - CITY UPPER-INCOME-HOUSING-ENTERPRISE
               MULTIPLIER (DIMENSIONLESS)
    CUIHEMT- CITY UPPER-INCOME-HOUSING-ENTERPRISE
               MULTIPLIER TABLE (DIMENSIONLESS)
    CNBSGR - CITY NEW-BUSINESS-STRUCTURES GROWTH RATE
               (PERCENT/YEAR)

CUIHGM.K=TABLE(CUIHGMT,CUIHGR.K,-.1,.15,.05)             53, A
CUIHGMT=.2/.6/1/1.8/2.6/3.2                              53.1, T
    CUIHGM - CITY UPPER-INCOME-HOUSING GROWTH MULTIPLIER
               (DIMENSIONLESS)
    CUIHGMT- CITY UPPER-INCOME-HOUSING GROWTH MULTIPLIER
               TABLE (DIMENSIONLESS)
    CUIHGR - CITY UPPER-INCOME-HOUSING GROWTH RATE
               (FRACTION/YEAR)

CUIHGR.K=(CUIH.K-CUIHA.K)/(CUIH.K*CUIHAT)                54, A
    CUIHGR - CITY UPPER-INCOME-HOUSING GROWTH RATE
               (FRACTION/YEAR)
    CUIH   - CITY UPPER-INCOME HOUSING (STRUCTURES)
    CUIHA  - CITY UPPER-INCOME-HOUSING AVERAGE (HOUSING
               STRUCTURES)
    CUIHAT - CITY UPPER-INCOME-HOUSING AVERAGING TIME
               (YEARS)
```

```
CUIHA.K=CUIHA.J+(DT/CUIHAT)(CUIH.J-CUIHA.J)              55, L
CUIHA=CUIH-(CUIHGRI)(CUIHAT)(CUIH)                       55.1, N
CUIHAT=10                                                55.2, C
CUIHGRI=.025                                             55.3, C
    CUIHA  - CITY UPPER-INCOME-HOUSING AVERAGE (HOUSING
               STRUCTURES)
    CUIHAT - CITY UPPER-INCOME-HOUSING AVERAGING TIME
               (YEARS)
    CUIH   - CITY UPPER-INCOME HOUSING (STRUCTURES)
    CUIHGRI- CITY UPPER-INCOME-HOUSING GROWTH RATE
               INITIAL (FRACTION/YEAR)

CUIH.K=CUIH.J+(DT)(CUIHC.JK-CUIHO.JK)                    56, L
CUIH=18000                                               56.1, N
    CUIH   - CITY UPPER-INCOME HOUSING (STRUCTURES)
    CUIHC  - CITY UPPER-INCOME-HOUSING CONSTRUCTION
               (STRUCTURES/YEAR)
    CUIHO  - CITY UPPER-INCOME HOUSING OBSOLESCENCE
               (STRUCTURES/YEAR)

CUIHO.KL=(CUIHON)(CUIH.K)(CUIHOM.K)                      57, R
CUIHON=.013                                              57.1, C
    CUIHO  - CITY UPPER-INCOME HOUSING OBSOLESCENCE
               (STRUCTURES/YEAR)
    CUIHON - CITY UPPER-INCOME HOUSING-OBSOLESCENCE
               NORMAL (FRACTION/YEAR)
    CUIH   - CITY UPPER-INCOME HOUSING (STRUCTURES)
    CUIHOM - CITY UPPER-INCOME HOUSING-OBSOLESCENCE
               MULTIPLIER (DIMENSIONLESS)

CUIHOM.K=TABLE(CUIHOMT,1.44*LOGN(CUIHM.K),-3,3,1)        58, A
CUIHOMT=2.8/2.6/2/1/.5/.3/.2                             58.1, T
    CUIHOM - CITY UPPER-INCOME HOUSING-OBSOLESCENCE
               MULTIPLIER (DIMENSIONLESS)
    CUIHOMT- CITY UPPER-INCOME HOUSING OBSOLESCENCE
               MULTIPLIER TABLE (DIMENSIONLESS)
    CUIHM  - CITY UPPER-INCOME-HOUSING MULTIPLIER
               (DIMENSIONLESS)


*****LOWER INCOME HOUSING SECTOR
*****

CLIH.K=CLIH.J+(DT)(CUIHO.JK-CLIHD.JK+CLIHCP.JK)          59, L
CLIH=3600                                                59.1, N
    CLIH   - CITY LOWER-INCOME HOUSING (STRUCTURES)
    CUIHO  - CITY UPPER-INCOME HOUSING OBSOLESCENCE
               (STRUCTURES/YEAR)
    CLIHD  - CITY LOWER-INCOME-HOUSING-DEMOLITION RATE
               (STRUCTURES/YEAR)
    CLIHCP - CITY LOWER-INCOME-HOUSING-CONSTRUCTION
               PROGRAM (STRUCTURES/YEAR)

CLIHD.KL=(CLIHDN)(CLIH.K)(CLIHDM.K)+CLIHDP.K             60, R
CLIHDN=.02                                               60.1, C
    CLIHD  - CITY LOWER-INCOME-HOUSING-DEMOLITION RATE
               (STRUCTURES/YEAR)
    CLIHDN - CITY LOWER-INCOME-HOUSING-DEMOLITION RATE
               NORMAL (FRACTION/YEAR)
    CLIH   - CITY LOWER-INCOME HOUSING (STRUCTURES)
    CLIHDM - CITY LOWER-INCOME-HOUSING-DEMOLITION
               MULTIPLIER (DIMENSIONLESS)
    CLIHDP - CITY LOWER-INCOME-HOUSING-DEMOLITION
               PROGRAM (STRUCTURES/YEAR)

CLIHDM.K=(CLIHDAM.K)(CLIHDLM.K)(CLIHDF)                  61, A
CLIHDF=1                                                 61.1, C
    CLIHDM - CITY LOWER-INCOME-HOUSING-DEMOLITION
               MULTIPLIER (DIMENSIONLESS)
    CLIHDAM- CITY LOWER-INCOME DEMOLITION ADEQUACY
               MULTIPLIER (DIMENSIONLESS)
    CLIHDLM- CITY LOWER-INCOME HOUSING DEMOLITION LAND
               MULTIPLIER (DIMENSIONLESS)
    CLIHDF - CITY LOWER-INCOME-HOUSING-DEMOLITION FACTOR
               (DIMENSIONLESS)
```

```
CLIHDAM.K=(CLIHDSM.K)(CLIHATM.K)                       62, A
    CLIHDAM- CITY LOWER-INCOME DEMOLITION ADEQUACY
               MULTIPLIER (DIMENSIONLESS)
    CLIHDSM- CITY LOWER-INCOME-HOUSING-DEMOLITION SUPPLY
               MULTIPLIER (DIMENSIONLESS)
    CLIHATM- CITY LOWER-INCOME HOUSING-ABANDONMENT TAX
               MULTIPLIER (DIMENSIONLESS)

CLIHDSM.K=TABLE(CLIHDST,CLIHR.K,0,2,.5)                63, A
CLIHDST=3.6/2/1/.6/.4                                  63.1, T
    CLIHDSM- CITY LOWER-INCOME-HOUSING-DEMOLITION SUPPLY
               MULTIPLIER (DIMENSIONLESS)
    CLIHDST- CITY LOWER-INCOME-HOUSING-DEMOLITION SUPPLY
               TABLE (DIMENSIONLESS)
    CLIHR  - CITY LOWER-INCOME-TO-HOUSING RATIO
               (DIMENSIONLESS)

CLIHATM.K=TABLE(CLIHATT,1.44*LOGN(CTR.K),-2,4,2)       64, A
CLIHATT=1/1/1/1                                        64.1, T
    CLIHATM- CITY LOWER-INCOME HOUSING-ABANDONMENT TAX
               MULTIPLIER (DIMENSIONLESS)
    CLIHATT- CITY LOWER-INCOME HOUSING-ABANDONMENT TAX
               MULTIPLIER TABLE (DIMENSIONLESS)
    CTR    - CITY TAX RATIO (DIMENSIONLESS)

CLIHDLM.K=TABHL(CLIHDLT,CLFO.K,.8,1,.05)               65, A
CLIHDLT=1/1.2/1.6/2.2/6                                65.1, T
    CLIHDLM- CITY LOWER-INCOME HOUSING DEMOLITION LAND
               MULTIPLIER (DIMENSIONLESS)
    CLIHDLT- CITY LOWER-INCOME HOUSING DEMOLITION LAND
               TABLE (DIMENSIONLESS)
    CLFO   - CITY LAND FRACTION OCCUPIED (DIMENSIONLESS)

*****NEW BUSINESS STRUCTURES SECTOR
*****

CNBS.K=CNBS.J+(DT)(CNBSC.JK-CNBSO.JK)                  66, L
CNBS=424                                               66.1, N
    CNBS   - CITY NEW-BUSINESS STRUCTURES (STRUCTURES)
    CNBSC  - CITY NEW-BUSINESS-STRUCTURES CONSTRUCTION
               (STRUCTURES/YEAR)
    CNBSO  - CITY NEW-BUSINESS-STRUCTURES OBSOLESCENCE
               (STRUCTURES/YEAR)

CEM.K=(MEUIWM.K)(CELM.K)(MELIWM.K)(CETM.K)(CEGM.K)     67, A
  (CEF)
CEF=1                                                  67.1, C
    CEM    - CITY ENTERPRISE MULTIPLIER (DIMENSIONLESS)
    MEUIWM - METROPOLITAN ENTERPRISE UPPER-INCOME-
               WORKFORCE MULTIPLIER (DIMENSIONLESS)
    CELM   - CITY ENTERPRISE LAND MULTIPLIER
               (DIMENSIONLESS)
    MELIWM - METROPOLITAN ENTERPRISE LOWER-INCOME-
               WORKFORCE MULTIPLIER (DIMENSIONLESS)
    CETM   - CITY ENTERPRISE TAX MULTIPLIER
               (DIMENSIONLESS)
    CEGM   - CITY ENTERPRISE GROWTH MULTIPLIER
               (DIMENSIONLESS)
    CEF    - CITY ENTERPRISE FACTOR (DIMENSIONLESS)

CELM.K=TABLE(CELMT,CLFO.K,0,1,.1)                      68, A
CELMT=1/1.15/1.3/1.4/1.45/1.4/1.3/1/.7/.4/0            68.1, T
    CELM   - CITY ENTERPRISE LAND MULTIPLIER
               (DIMENSIONLESS)
    CELMT  - CITY ENTERPRISE LAND MULTIPLIER TABLE
               (DIMENSIONLESS)
    CLFO   - CITY LAND FRACTION OCCUPIED (DIMENSIONLESS)

CETM.K=TABLE(CETMT,1.44*LOGN(CTR.K),-2,4,1)            69, A
CETMT=1.3/1.2/1/.8/.5/.25/.1                           69.1, T
    CETM   - CITY ENTERPRISE TAX MULTIPLIER
               (DIMENSIONLESS)
    CETMT  - CITY ENTERPRISE TAX MULTIPLIER TABLE
               (DIMENSIONLESS)
    CTR    - CITY TAX RATIO (DIMENSIONLESS)
```

```
CEGM.K=TABLE(CEGMT,CNBSGR.K,-.08,.12,.04)             70, A
CEGMT=.8/.9/1/1.4/1.8/2.2                             70.1, T
    CEGM    - CITY ENTERPRISE GROWTH MULTIPLIER
               (DIMENSIONLESS)
    CEGMT   - CITY ENTERPRISE GROWTH MULTIPLIER TABLE
               (DIMENSIONLESS)
    CNBSGR  - CITY NEW-BUSINESS-STRUCTURES GROWTH RATE
               (PERCENT/YEAR)

CNBSGR.K=(CNBS.K-CNBSA.K)/(CNBS.K*CNBSAT)             71, A
    CNBSGR  - CITY NEW-BUSINESS-STRUCTURES GROWTH RATE
               (PERCENT/YEAR)
    CNBS    - CITY NEW-BUSINESS STRUCTURES (STRUCTURES)
    CNBSA   - CITY NEW-BUSINESS-STRUCTURES AVERAGE
               (STRUCTURES)
    CNBSAT  - CITY NEW-BUSINESS-STRUCTURES AVERAGING TIME
               (YEARS)

CNBSA.K=CNBSA.J+(DT/CNBSAT)(CNBS.J-CNBSA.J)           72, L
CNBSA=CNBS-(CNBSGRI)(CNBSAT)(CNBS)                    72.1, N
CNBSAT=10                                             72.2, C
CNBSGRI=.025                                          72.3, C
    CNBSA   - CITY NEW-BUSINESS-STRUCTURES AVERAGE
               (STRUCTURES)
    CNBSAT  - CITY NEW-BUSINESS-STRUCTURES AVERAGING TIME
               (YEARS)
    CNBS    - CITY NEW-BUSINESS STRUCTURES (STRUCTURES)
    CNBSGRI- CITY NEW-BUSINESS-STRUCTURES GROWTH RATE
               INITIAL (PERCENT/YEAR)

*****OLDER BUSINESS STRUCTURES SECTOR
*****

CNBSO.KL=(CNBSON)(CNBS.K)(CNBSOM.K)                   73, R
CNBSON=.045                                           73.1, C
    CNBSO   - CITY NEW-BUSINESS-STRUCTURES OBSOLESCENCE
               (STRUCTURES/YEAR)
    CNBSON  - CITY NEW-BUSINESS-STRUCTURES OBSOLESCENCE
               NORMAL (PERCENT/YEAR)
    CNBS    - CITY NEW-BUSINESS STRUCTURES (STRUCTURES)
    CNBSOM  - CITY NEW-BUSINESS-STRUCTURES OBSOLESCENCE
               MULTIPLIER (DIMENSIONLESS)

CNBSOM.K=TABLE(CNBSOMT,1.44*LOGN(CEM.K),-3,3,1)       74, A
CNBSOMT=2/1.8/1.5/1/.7/.5/.5                          74.1, T
    CNBSOM  - CITY NEW-BUSINESS-STRUCTURES OBSOLESCENCE
               MULTIPLIER (DIMENSIONLESS)
    CNBSOMT- CITY NEW-BUSINESS-STRUCTURES OBSOLESCENCE
               MULTIPLIER TABLE (DIMENSIONLESS)
    CEM     - CITY ENTERPRISE MULTIPLIER (DIMENSIONLESS)

COBS.K=COBS.J+(DT)(CNBSO.JK-COBSD.JK)                 75, L
COBS=290                                              75.1, N
    COBS    - CITY OLDER-BUSINESS STRUCTURES (STRUCTURES)
    CNBSO   - CITY NEW-BUSINESS-STRUCTURES OBSOLESCENCE
               (STRUCTURES/YEAR)
    COBSD   - CITY OLDER-BUSINESS-STRUCTURES DEMOLITION
               (STRUCTURES/YEAR)

COBSD.KL=(COBSDN)(COBS.K)(COBSDM.K)+COBSDP.K          76, R
COBSDN=.02                                            76.1, C
    COBSD   - CITY OLDER-BUSINESS-STRUCTURES DEMOLITION
               (STRUCTURES/YEAR)
    COBSDN  - CITY OLDER-BUSINESS-STRUCTURES DEMOLITION
               NORMAL (PERCENT/YEAR)
    COBS    - CITY OLDER-BUSINESS STRUCTURES (STRUCTURES)
    COBSDM  - CITY OLDER-BUSINESS-STRUCTURES DEMOLITION
               MULTIPLIER (DIMENSIONLESS)
    COBSDP  - CITY OLDER-BUSINESS-STRUCTURES DEMOLITION
               PROGRAM (STRUCTURES/YEAR)

COBSDM.K=(COBSEM.K)(COBSLM.K)(COBSDF)                 77, A
COBSDF=1                                              77.1, C
    COBSDM  - CITY OLDER-BUSINESS-STRUCTURES DEMOLITION
               MULTIPLIER (DIMENSIONLESS)
    COBSEM  - CITY OLDER-BUSINESS-STRUCTURES ENTERPRISE
               MULTIPLIER (DIMENSIONLESS)
```

```
    COBSLM - CITY OLDER-BUSINESS-STRUCTURES LAND
               MULTIPLIER (DIMENSIONLESS)
    COBSDF - CITY OLDER-BUSINESS-STRUCTURES DEMOLITION
               FACTOR (DIMENSIONLESS)

COBSEM.K=TABLE(COBSEMT,1.44*LOGN(CEM.K),-3,3,1)      78, A
COBSEMT=.4/.5/.7/1/1.6/2.4/4                         78.1, T
    COBSEM - CITY OLDER-BUSINESS-STRUCTURES ENTERPRISE
               MULTIPLIER (DIMENSIONLESS)
    COBSEMT- CITY OLDER-BUSINESS-STRUCTURES ENTERPRISE
               MULTIPLIER TABLE (DIMENSIONLESS)
    CEM    - CITY ENTERPRISE MULTIPLIER (DIMENSIONLESS)

COBSLM.K=TABHL(COBSLMT,CLFO.K,.8,1,.05)              79, A
COBSLMT=1/1.2/1.6/2.2/6                              79.1, T
    COBSLM - CITY OLDER-BUSINESS-STRUCTURES LAND
               MULTIPLIER (DIMENSIONLESS)
    COBSLMT- CITY OLDER-BUSINESS-STRUCTURES LAND
               MULTIPLIER TABLE (DIMENSIONLESS)
    CLFO   - CITY LAND FRACTION OCCUPIED (DIMENSIONLESS)

*****TAX SECTOR
*****

CTC.K=(CAV.K)(CTAN)(CTR.K)                           80, A
CTAN=50                                              80.1, C
    CTC    - CITY TAX COLLECTIONS (DOLLARS/YEAR)
    CAV    - CITY ASSESSED VALUE (THOUSAND DOLLARS)
    CTAN   - CITY TAX ASSESSMENT NORMAL (DOLLARS/YEAR/
               THOUSAND DOLLARS)
    CTR    - CITY TAX RATIO (DIMENSIONLESS)

CTR.K=TABLE(CTRT,1.44*LOGN(CTRNP.K),-2,4,1)          81, A
CTRT=.3/.5/1/1.8/2.8/3.6/4                           81.1, T
    CTR    - CITY TAX RATIO (DIMENSIONLESS)
    CTRT   - CITY TAX-RATIO TABLE (DIMENSIONLESS)
    CTRNP  - CITY TAX RATIO NEEDED PERCEIVED
               (DIMENSIONLESS)

CTRNP.K=CTRNP.J+(DT/CTRNPT)(CTRN.J-CTRNP.J)          82, L
CTRNP=CTRN                                           82.1, N
CTRNPT=30                                            82.2, C
    CTRNP  - CITY TAX RATIO NEEDED PERCEIVED
               (DIMENSIONLESS)
    CTRNPT - CITY TAX RATIO NEEDED PERCEPTION TIME
               (YEARS)
    CTRN   - CITY TAX RATIO NEEDED (DIMENSIONLESS)

CTRN.K=CTAI.K/CTAN                                   83, A
    CTRN   - CITY TAX RATIO NEEDED (DIMENSIONLESS)
    CTAI   - CITY TAX ASSESSMENT INDICATED (DOLLARS/
               YEAR/THOUSAND DOLLARS)
    CTAN   - CITY TAX ASSESSMENT NORMAL (DOLLARS/YEAR/
               THOUSAND DOLLARS)

CTAI.K=CTN.K/CAV.K                                   84, A
    CTAI   - CITY TAX ASSESSMENT INDICATED (DOLLARS/
               YEAR/THOUSAND DOLLARS)
    CTN    - CITY TAXES NEEDED (DOLLARS/YEAR)
    CAV    - CITY ASSESSED VALUE (THOUSAND DOLLARS)

CTN.K=(CTCUIP*CUIFS*CUIP.K+CTCLIP*CLIFS*CLIP.K+      85, A
  CTPCOMM*SUIC.K)(CTCM.K)
    CTN    - CITY TAXES NEEDED (DOLLARS/YEAR)
    CTCUIP - CITY TAX PER UPPER-INCOME PERSON (DOLLARS/
               PERSON/YEAR)
    CUIFS  - CITY UPPER-INCOME FAMILY SIZE (PEOPLE/MAN)
    CUIP   - CITY UPPER-INCOME POPULATION (MEN)
    CTCLIP - CITY TAX PER LOWER-INCOME PERSON (DOLLARS/
               PERSON/YEAR)

    CLIFS  - CITY LOWER-INCOME FAMILY SIZE (PEOPLE/MAN)
    CLIP   - CITY LOWER-INCOME POPULATION (MEN)
    CTPCOMM- CITY TAX PER COMMUTER (DOLLARS/PERSON/YEAR)
    SUIC   - SUBURB(RESIDENT) UPPER-INCOME CITY(WORKERS)
               (MEN)
    CTCM   - CITY TAX COLLECTION MULTIPLIER
               (DIMENSIONLESS)
```

```
CUIP.K=CUIC.K+CUIS.K                                    86, A
CTCUIP=190                                              86.1, C
CTCLIP=300                                              86.2, C
CTPCOMM=50                                              86.3, C
    CUIP    - CITY UPPER-INCOME POPULATION (MEN)
    CUIC    - CITY(RESIDENT) UPPER-INCOME CITY(WORKERS)
                (MEN)
    CUIS    - CITY(RESIDENT) UPPER-INCOME SUBURB(WORKERS)
                (MEN)
    CTCUIP - CITY TAX PER UPPER-INCOME PERSON (DOLLARS/
                PERSON/YEAR)
    CTCLIP - CITY TAX PER LOWER-INCOME PERSON (DOLLARS/
                PERSON/YEAR)
    CTPCOMM- CITY TAX PER COMMUTER (DOLLARS/PERSON/YEAR)

CTCM.K=TABLE(CTCMT,CUITLIR.K,0,5,1)                     87, A
CTCMT=1.4/1.2/1/.9/.8/.8                                87.1, T
    CTCM    - CITY TAX COLLECTION MULTIPLIER
                (DIMENSIONLESS)
    CTCMT   - CITY TAX COLLECTION MULTIPLIER TABLE
                (DIMENSIONLESS)
    CUITLIR- CITY UPPER-INCOME-TO-LOWER-INCOME RATIO
                (DIMENSIONLESS)

CUITLIR.K=(CUIC.K+CUIS.K)/CLIP.K                        88, A
    CUITLIR- CITY UPPER-INCOME-TO-LOWER-INCOME RATIO
                (DIMENSIONLESS)
    CUIC    - CITY(RESIDENT) UPPER-INCOME CITY(WORKERS)
                (MEN)
    CUIS    - CITY(RESIDENT) UPPER-INCOME SUBURB(WORKERS)
                (MEN)
    CLIP    - CITY LOWER-INCOME POPULATION (MEN)

CAV.K=(CHSAV.K+CBSAV.K)                                 89, A
    CAV     - CITY ASSESSED VALUE (THOUSAND DOLLARS)
    CHSAV   - CITY HOUSING STRUCTURES ASSESSED VALUE
                (THOUSAND DOLLARS)
    CBSAV   - CITY BUSINESS STRUCTURES ASSESSED VALUE
                (THOUSAND DOLLARS)

CHSAV.K=CUIH.K*CUIHAV+CLIH.K*CLIHAV                     90, A
CUIHAV=18                                               90.1, C
CLIHAV=5                                                90.2, C
    CHSAV   - CITY HOUSING STRUCTURES ASSESSED VALUE
                (THOUSAND DOLLARS)
    CUIH    - CITY UPPER-INCOME HOUSING (STRUCTURES)
    CUIHAV - CITY UPPER-INCOME-HOUSING ASSESSED VALUE
                (THOUSAND DOLLARS)
    CLIH    - CITY LOWER-INCOME HOUSING (STRUCTURES)
    CLIHAV - CITY LOWER-INCOME-HOUSING ASSESSED VALUE
                (THOUSAND DOLLARS)

CBSAV.K=CNBS.K*CNBSAV+COBS.K*COBSAV                     91, A
CNBSAV=450                                              91.1, C
COBSAV=150                                              91.2, C
    CBSAV   - CITY BUSINESS STRUCTURES ASSESSED VALUE
                (THOUSAND DOLLARS)
    CNBS    - CITY NEW-BUSINESS STRUCTURES (STRUCTURES)
    CNBSAV - CITY NEW-BUSINESS-STRUCTURES ASSESSED VALUE
                (THOUSAND DOLLARS)
    COBS    - CITY OLDER-BUSINESS STRUCTURES (STRUCTURES)
    COBSAV - CITY OLDER-BUSINESS-STRUCTURES ASSESSED
                VALUE (THOUSAND DOLLARS)


*****JOB SECTOR
*****

CWDC.K=CUIHCD.K*UIHCWN+CLIHCP.JK*LIHCWN+CNBSCD.K*       92, A
  NBSCWN
UIHCWN=2                                                92.1, C
LIHCWN=1                                                92.2, C
    CWDC    - CITY WORKFORCE DESIRED FOR CONSTRUCTION
                (MEN)
    CUIHCD - CITY UPPER-INCOME-HOUSING CONSTRUCTION
                DESIRED (STRUCTURES/YEAR)
    UIHCWN - UPPER-INCOME HOUSING-CONSTRUCTION-WORKERS
                NEEDED (MAN-YEARS/HOUSING STRUCTURE)
```

```
    CLIHCP - CITY LOWER-INCOME-HOUSING-CONSTRUCTION
               PROGRAM (STRUCTURES/YEAR)
    LIHCWN - LOWER-INCOME-HOUSING CONSTRUCTION WORKERS
               NEEDED (MAN-YEARS/HOUSING STRUCTURE)
    CNBSCD - CITY NEW-BUSINESS-STRUCTURES CONSTRUCTION
               DESIRED (STRUCTURES/YEAR)
    NBSCWN - NEW-BUSINESS-STRUCTURES CONSTRUCTION-
               WORKERS NEEDED (MAN-YEARS/STRUCTURE)

CUICJ.K=CUICJ.J+(DT/CCWAT)(CWDC.J-CUICJ.J)            93, L
CUICJ=1800                                            93.1, N
CCWAT=5                                               93.2, C
NBSCWN=20                                             93.3, C
    CUICJ  - CITY UPPER-INCOME CONSTRUCTION JOBS (MEN)
    CCWAT  - CITY CONSTRUCTION WORKFORCE ADJUSTMENT TIME
               (YEARS)
    CWDC   - CITY WORKFORCE DESIRED FOR CONSTRUCTION
               (MEN)
    NBSCWN - NEW-BUSINESS-STRUCTURES CONSTRUCTION-
               WORKERS NEEDED (MAN-YEARS/STRUCTURE)

CUIBJ.K=(CNBS.K)(UIPCNBS)+(COBS.K)(UIPCOBS)           94, A
UIPCNBS=24                                            94.1, C
UIPCOBS=13                                            94.2, C
    CUIBJ  - CITY UPPER-INCOME BUSINESS JOBS (MEN)
    CNBS   - CITY NEW-BUSINESS STRUCTURES (STRUCTURES)
    UIPCNBS- UPPER-INCOME JOBS PER CITY NEW-BUSINESS
               STRUCTURE (MEN/STRUCTURE)
    COBS   - CITY OLDER-BUSINESS STRUCTURES (STRUCTURES)
    UIPCOBS- UPPER-INCOME JOBS PER CITY OLDER BUSINESS
               STRUCTURE (MEN/STRUCTURE)

CUIJ.K=CUICJ.K+CUIBJ.K                                95, A
    CUIJ   - CITY UPPER-INCOME JOBS (MEN)
    CUICJ  - CITY UPPER-INCOME CONSTRUCTION JOBS (MEN)
    CUIBJ  - CITY UPPER-INCOME BUSINESS JOBS (MEN)

CLIJOM.K=TABLE(CLIJOMT,AUICJR.K,0,2,.25)              96, A
CLIJOMT=1.2/1.1/.8/.7/.5/.4/.3/.2/.15                 96.1, T
    CLIJOM - CITY LOWER-INCOME JOB-OPPORTUNITY
               MULTIPLIER (DIMENSIONLESS)
    CLIJOMT- CITY LOWER-INCOME JOB-OPPORTUNITY
               MULTIPLIER TABLE (DIMENSIONLESS)
    AUICJR - ACCESIBLE UPPER-INCOME-TO-CITY JOB RATIO
               (DIMENSIONLESS)

AUICJR.K=(UICJR.K)((CCJSLI*SUIC.K)+CUIC.K)/(CUIC.K)  97, A
CCJSLI=.5                                             97.1, C
    AUICJR - ACCESIBLE UPPER-INCOME-TO-CITY JOB RATIO
               (DIMENSIONLESS)
    UICJR  - UPPER-INCOME CITY JOB RATIO (DIMENSIONLESS)
    CCJSLI - CONSTANTS FOR COMMUTER JOB-SKILL-LEVEL
               INDEX (DIMENSIONLESS)
    SUIC   - SUBURB(RESIDENT) UPPER-INCOME CITY(WORKERS)
               (MEN)
    CUIC   - CITY(RESIDENT) UPPER-INCOME CITY(WORKERS)
               (MEN)

CLIJ.K=(CUIJ.K)(CLIJOM.K+CLIJP.K)                     98, A
    CLIJ   - CITY LOWER-INCOME JOBS (MEN)
    CUIJ   - CITY UPPER-INCOME JOBS (MEN)
    CLIJOM - CITY LOWER-INCOME JOB-OPPORTUNITY
               MULTIPLIER (DIMENSIONLESS)
    CLIJP  - CITY LOWER-INCOME JOB PROGRAM (MEN)

CLIJR.K=CLIP.K/CLIJ.K                                 99, A
    CLIJR  - CITY LOWER-INCOME-TO-JOB RATIO
               (DIMENSIONLESS)
    CLIP   - CITY LOWER-INCOME POPULATION (MEN)
    CLIJ   - CITY LOWER-INCOME JOBS (MEN)

MCWM.K=TABLE(MCWMT,MUIJR.K,0,2,.5)                    100, A
MCWMT=0/.55/1/1.1/1.2                                 100.1, T
    MCWM   - METROPOLITAN CONSTRUCTION WORKFORCE
               MULTIPLIER (DIMENSIONLESS)
    MCWMT  - METROPOLITAN CONSTRUCTION WORKFORCE
               MULTIPLIER TABLE (DIMENSION LESS)
    MUIJR  - METROPOLITAN UPPER-INCOME-TO-JOB RATIO
               (DIMENSIONLESS)
```

```
*****INTERFACE SECTOR
*****
*****UPPER INCOME ARRIVALS
*****

UIA.K=(TMUIP.K)(UIAN)(MUIAMP.K)                             101, A
UIAN=.03                                                    101.1, C
    UIA    - UPPER-INCOME ARRIVALS (MEN/YEAR)
    TMUIP  - TOTAL METROPOLITAN UPPER-INCOME POPULATION
               (MEN)
    UIAN   - UPPER-INCOME ARRIVALS NORMAL (FRACTION/
               YEAR)
    MUIAMP - METROPOLITAN UPPER-INCOME-ATTRACTIVENESS
               MULTIPLIER PERCEIVED (DIMENSIONLESS)

MUIAM.K=(MUIJM.K)(MARCUIM.K)                                102, A
    MUIAM  - METROPOLITAN UPPER-INCOME-ATTRACTIVEMESS
               MULTIPLIER (DIMENSIONLESS)
    MUIJM  - METROPOLITAN UPPER-INCOME JOB MULTIPLIER
               (DIMENSIONLESS)
    MARCUIM- METROPOLITAN AVERAGE RESIDENTIAL-CONDITIONS
               FOR UPPER-INCOME MIGRATION
               (DIMENSIONLESS)

MUIJM.K=TABLE(MUIJMT,MUIJR.K,0,2,.25)                       103, A
MUIJMT=2.6/2.6/2.4/1.8/1/.4/.2/.1/.05                       103.1, T
    MUIJM  - METROPOLITAN UPPER-INCOME JOB MULTIPLIER
               (DIMENSIONLESS)
    MUIJMT - METROPOLITAN UPPER-INCOME JOB MULTIPLIER
               TABLE (DIMENSIONLESS)
    MUIJR  - METROPOLITAN UPPER-INCOME-TO-JOB RATIO
               (DIMENSIONLESS)

MUIJR.K=TMUIP.K/TMUIJ.K                                     104, A
    MUIJR  - METROPOLITAN UPPER-INCOME-TO-JOB RATIO
               (DIMENSIONLESS)
    TMUIP  - TOTAL METROPOLITAN UPPER-INCOME POPULATION
               (MEN)
    TMUIJ  - TOTAL METROPOLITAN UPPER-INCOME JOBS (MEN)

TMUIP.K=CUIC.K+CUIS.K+SUIC.K+SUIS.K                         105, A
    TMUIP  - TOTAL METROPOLITAN UPPER-INCOME POPULATION
               (MEN)
    CUIC   - CITY(RESIDENT) UPPER-INCOME CITY(WORKERS)
               (MEN)
    CUIS   - CITY(RESIDENT) UPPER-INCOME SUBURB(WORKERS)
               (MEN)
    SUIC   - SUBURB(RESIDENT) UPPER-INCOME CITY(WORKERS)
               (MEN)
    SUIS   - SUBURB(RESIDENT) UPPER-INCOME
               SUBURB(WORKERS) (MEN)

TMUIJ.K=CUIJ.K+SUIJ.K                                       106, A
    TMUIJ  - TOTAL METROPOLITAN UPPER-INCOME JOBS (MEN)
    CUIJ   - CITY UPPER-INCOME JOBS (MEN)
    SUIJ   - SUBURB UPPER-INCOME JOBS (MEN)

MARCUIM.K=((CUIRCM.K)(CUIS.K+CUIC.K)/(TMUIP.K))+            107, A
  ((SUIRCM.K)(SUIS.K+SUIC.K)/(TMUIP.K))
    MARCUIM- METROPOLITAN AVERAGE RESIDENTIAL-CONDITIONS
               FOR UPPER-INCOME MIGRATION
               (DIMENSIONLESS)
    CUIRCM - CITY UPPER-INCOME RESIDENTIAL-CONDITIONS
               MULTIPLIER (DIMENSIONLESS)
    CUIS   - CITY(RESIDENT) UPPER-INCOME SUBURB(WORKERS)
               (MEN)
    CUIC   - CITY(RESIDENT) UPPER-INCOME CITY(WORKERS)
               (MEN)
    TMUIP  - TOTAL METROPOLITAN UPPER-INCOME POPULATION
               (MEN)
    SUIRCM - SUBURB UPPER-INCOME RESIDENTIAL-CONDITIONS
               MULTIPLIER (DIMENSIONLESS)
    SUIS   - SUBURB(RESIDENT) UPPER-INCOME
               SUBURB(WORKERS) (MEN)
    SUIC   - SUBURB(RESIDENT) UPPER-INCOME CITY(WORKERS)
               (MEN)
```

```
CUIRCM.K=(CUIALIM.K)(CUITM.K)(CUIHSM.K)              108, A
    CUIRCM - CITY UPPER-INCOME RESIDENTIAL-CONDITIONS
               MULTIPLIER (DIMENSIONLESS)
    CUIALIM- CITY UPPER-INCOME-ARRIVALS LOWER-INCOME
               MULTIPLIER (DIMENSIONLESS)
    CUITM  - CITY UPPER-INCOME TAX MULTIPLIER
               (DIMENSIONLESS)
    CUIHSM - CITY UPPER-INCOME HOUSING-SUPPLY MULTIPLIER
               (DIMENSIONLESS)

SUIRCM.K=(SUIALIM.K)(SUITM.K)(SUIHSM.K)              109, A
    SUIRCM - SUBURB UPPER-INCOME RESIDENTIAL-CONDITIONS
               MULTIPLIER (DIMENSIONLESS)
    SUIALIM- SUBURB UPPER-INCOME-ARRIVALS LOWER-INCOME
               MULTIPLIER (DIMENSIONLESS)
    SUITM  - SUBURB UPPER-INCOME TAX MULTIPLIER
               (DIMENSIONLESS)
    SUIHSM - SUBURB UPPER-INCOME HOUSING-SUPPLY
               MULTIPLIER (DIMENSIONLESS)

MUIAMP.K=MUIAMP.J+(DT/MUIAPT)(MUIAM.J-MUIAMP.J)      110, L
MUIAPT=14                                            110.1, C
MUIAMP=1                                             110.2, N
    MUIAMP - METROPOLITAN UPPER-INCOME-ATTRACTIVENESS
               MULTIPLIER PERCEIVED (DIMENSIONLESS)
    MUIAPT - METROPOLITAN UPPER-INCOME-ARRIVALS
               MULTIPLIER PERCEPTION TIME
               (DIMENSIONLESS)
    MUIAM  - METROPOLITAN UPPER-INCOME-ATTRACTIVEMESS
               MULTIPLIER (DIMENSIONLESS)

CUIAR.KL=(UICAF.K)(UIA.K)                            111, R
    CUIAR  - CITY UPPER-INCOME-ARRIVALS RATE (MEN/YEAR)
    UICAF  - UPPER-INCOME CITY-ARRIVALS FRACTION
               (DIMENSIONLESS)
    UIA    - UPPER-INCOME ARRIVALS (MEN/YEAR)

UICAF.K=(CUIJ.K/TMUIJ.K)                             112, A
    UICAF  - UPPER-INCOME CITY-ARRIVALS FRACTION
               (DIMENSIONLESS)
    CUIJ   - CITY UPPER-INCOME JOBS (MEN)
    TMUIJ  - TOTAL METROPOLITAN UPPER-INCOME JOBS (MEN)

SUIAR.KL=(1-UICAF.K)(UIA.K)                          113, R
    SUIAR  - SUBURB UPPER-INCOME-ARRIVALS RATE (MEN/
               YEAR)
    UICAF  - UPPER-INCOME CITY-ARRIVALS FRACTION
               (DIMENSIONLESS)
    UIA    - UPPER-INCOME ARRIVALS (MEN/YEAR)

*****SUBURB UPPER INCOME SECTOR
*****
SUISB.KL=(SUIS.K)(SUIBR)                             114, R
SUIBR=.0095                                          114.1, C
    SUISB  - SUBURB UPPER-INCOME SUBURB BIRTHS (MEN/
               YEAR)
    SUIS   - SUBURB(RESIDENT) UPPER-INCOME
               SUBURB(WORKERS) (MEN)
    SUIBR  - SUBURB UPPER-INCOME BIRTH RATE (FRACTION/
               YEAR)

SUIS.K=(SUIS.J)+(DT)(SLITUI.JK+SUISB.JK+SUIAR.JK+    115, L
  UICSSMR.JK-UISSCMR.JK-SUISD.JK)
SUIS=800                                             115.2, N
    SUIS   - SUBURB(RESIDENT) UPPER-INCOME
               SUBURB(WORKERS) (MEN)
    SLITUI - SUBURB LOWER-INCOME-TO-UPPER-INCOME
               ADVANCEMENT (MEN/YEAR)
    SUISB  - SUBURB UPPER-INCOME SUBURB BIRTHS (MEN/
               YEAR)
    SUIAR  - SUBURB UPPER-INCOME-ARRIVALS RATE (MEN/
               YEAR)
    UICSSMR- UPPER-INCOME CITY(RESIDENT) SUBURB(WORKERS)
               SUBURB MIGRATION RATE (MEN/YEAR)
    UISSCMR- UPPER-INCOME SUBURB(RESIDENT)
               SUBURB(WORKERS) CITY MIGRATION RATE (MEN/
               YEAR)
    SUISD  - SUBURB UPPER-INCOME SUBURB DEPARTURES (MEN/
               YEAR)
```

```
SUIAM.K=(SUIJM.K)(SUIALIM.K)(SUITM.K)(SUIHSM.K)       116, A
    SUIAM   - SUBURB UPPER-INCOME-ARRIVALS MULTIPLIER
                (DIMENSIONLESS)
    SUIJM   - SUBURB UPPER-INCOME JOB MULTIPLIER
                (DIMENSIONLESS)
    SUIALIM- SUBURB UPPER-INCOME-ARRIVALS LOWER-INCOME
                MULTIPLIER (DIMENSIONLESS)
    SUITM   - SUBURB UPPER-INCOME TAX MULTIPLIER
                (DIMENSIONLESS)
    SUIHSM  - SUBURB UPPER-INCOME HOUSING-SUPPLY
                MULTIPLIER (DIMENSIONLESS)

SUITM.K=TABLE(SUITMT,1.44*LOGN(STR.K),-2,4,2)         117, A
SUITMT=1.3/1/.7/.3                                    117.1, T
    SUITM   - SUBURB UPPER-INCOME TAX MULTIPLIER
                (DIMENSIONLESS)
    SUITMT  - SUBURB UPPER-INCOME TAX MULTIPLIER TABLE
                (DIMENSIONLESS)
    STR     - SUBURB TAX RATIO (DIMENSIONLESS)

UISJR.K=(SUIS.K+CUIS.K)/SUIJ.K                        118, A
    UISJR   - UPPER-INCOME SUBURB JOB RATIO
                (DIMENSIONLESS)
    SUIS    - SUBURB(RESIDENT) UPPER-INCOME
                SUBURB(WORKERS) (MEN)
    CUIS    - CITY(RESIDENT) UPPER-INCOME SUBURB(WORKERS)
                (MEN)
    SUIJ    - SUBURB UPPER-INCOME JOBS (MEN)

SUIJM.K=TABLE(SUIJMT,SUISJR.K,0,2,.25)                119, A
SUIJMT=2.6/2.6/2.4/1.8/1/.4/.2/.1/.05                 119.1, T
    SUIJM   - SUBURB UPPER-INCOME JOB MULTIPLIER
                (DIMENSIONLESS)
    SUIJMT  - SUBURB UPPER-INCOME JOB MULTIPLIER TABLE
                (DIMENSIONLESS)
    SUISJR  - SUBURB UPPER-INCOME-TO-SUBURB JOB RATIO
                (DIMENSIONLESS)

SUISJR.K=(SUIS.K+CUIS.K)/SUIJ.K                       120, A
    SUISJR  - SUBURB UPPER-INCOME-TO-SUBURB JOB RATIO
                (DIMENSIONLESS)
    SUIS    - SUBURB(RESIDENT) UPPER-INCOME
                SUBURB(WORKERS) (MEN)
    CUIS    - CITY(RESIDENT) UPPER-INCOME SUBURB(WORKERS)
                (MEN)
    SUIJ    - SUBURB UPPER-INCOME JOBS (MEN)

SUIALIM.K=TABHL(SUIALIT,SUITLIR.K,0,4,1)              121, A
SUIALIT=.4/.6/.8/1/1.2                                121.1, T
    SUIALIM- SUBURB UPPER-INCOME-ARRIVALS LOWER-INCOME
                MULTIPLIER (DIMENSIONLESS)
    SUIALIT- SUBURB UPPER-INCOME-ARRIVALS LOWER-INCOME
                MULTIPLIER TABLE (DIMENSIONLESS)
    SUITLIR- SUBURB UPPER-INCOME-TO-LOWER-INCOME RATIO
                (DIMENSIONLESS)

SUITPR.K=(SUIS.K+SUIC.K)/(SUIS.K+SUIC.K+SLIP.K)       122, A
    SUITPR  - SUBURB UPPER-INCOME TO POPULATION RATIO
                (DIMENSIONLESS)
    SUIS    - SUBURB(RESIDENT) UPPER-INCOME
                SUBURB(WORKERS) (MEN)
    SUIC    - SUBURB(RESIDENT) UPPER-INCOME CITY(WORKERS)
                (MEN)
    SLIP    - SUBURB LOWER-INCOME POPULATION (MEN)

SUISD.KL=(SUISDN)(SUIS.K)(SUISDM.K)                   123, R
SUISDN=.02                                            123.1, C
    SUISD   - SUBURB UPPER-INCOME SUBURB DEPARTURES (MEN/
                YEAR)
    SUISDN  - SUBURB UPPER-INCOME SUBURB DEPARTURES
                NORMAL (FRACTION/YEAR)
    SUIS    - SUBURB(RESIDENT) UPPER-INCOME
                SUBURB(WORKERS) (MEN)
    SUISDM  - SUBURB UPPER-INCOME SUBURB DEPARTURES
                MULTIPLIER (DIMENSIONLESS)
```

```
SUISDM.K=TABLE(SUISDMT,1.44*LOGN(SUIAM.K),-3,3,1)      124, A
SUISDMT=8/4/2/1/.5/.25/.125                            124.1, T
    SUISDM - SUBURB UPPER-INCOME SUBURB DEPARTURES
               MULTIPLIER (DIMENSIONLESS)
    SUISDMT- SUBURB UPPER-INCOME SUBURB DEPARTURES
               MULTIPLIER TABLE (DIMENSIONLESS)
    SUIAM  - SUBURB UPPER-INCOME-ARRIVALS MULTIPLIER
               (DIMENSIONLESS)

SUIHR.K=(SUIC.K+SUIS.K)(CUIFS)/(SUIH.K*CUIHPD)         125, A
    SUIHR  - SUBURB UPPER-INCOME-TO-HOUSING RATIO
               (DIMENSIONLESS)
    SUIC   - SUBURB(RESIDENT) UPPER-INCOME CITY(WORKERS)
               (MEN)
    SUIS   - SUBURB(RESIDENT) UPPER-INCOME
               SUBURB(WORKERS) (MEN)
    CUIFS  - CITY UPPER-INCOME FAMILY SIZE (PEOPLE/MAN)
    SUIH   - SUBURB UPPER-INCOME HOUSING (STRUCTURES)
    CUIHPD - CITY UPPER-INCOME-HOUSING POPULATION
               DENSITY (PEOPLE/HOUSING UNIT)

SUIHSM.K=TABLE(SUIHSMT,SUIHR.K,0,3,.5)                 126, A
SUIHSMT=1.3/1.2/1/.5/.2/.1/.05                         126.1, T
    SUIHSM - SUBURB UPPER-INCOME HOUSING-SUPPLY
               MULTIPLIER (DIMENSIONLESS)
    SUIHSMT- SUBURB UPPER-INCOME HOUSING-SUPPLY
               MULTIPLIER TABLE (DIMENSIONLESS)
    SUIHR  - SUBURB UPPER-INCOME-TO-HOUSING RATIO
               (DIMENSIONLESS)

*****UPPER INCOME COMMUTER SECTOR
*****
UICCSMR.KL=(CUIC.K)(UICCSMN)(ACCESM.K)(SCRRAM.K)       127, R
  (SCRRAF)
UICCSMN=.01                                            127.1, C
SCRRAF=1                                               127.2, C
    UICCSMR- UPPER-INCOME CITY(RESIDENT) CITY(WORKERS)
               SUBURB MIGRATION RATE (MEN/YEAR)
    CUIC   - CITY(RESIDENT) UPPER-INCOME CITY(WORKERS)
               (MEN)
    UICCSMN- UPPER-INCOME CITY(RESIDENT) CITY(WORKERS)
               SUBURB MIGRATION NORMAL (FRACTION/YEAR)
    ACCESM - ACCESS MULTIPLIER (DIMENSIONLESS)
    SCRRAM - SUBURB/CITY RELATIVE RESIDENTIAL-
               ATTRACTIVENESS MULTIPLIER (DIMENSIONLESS)
    SCRRAF - SUBURB/CITY RELATIVE-RESIDENTIAL
               ATTRACTIVENESS FACTOR (DIMENSIONLESS)

SCRRAM.K=TABLE(SCRRAMT,SCRRAR.K,0,4,.5)                128, A
SCRRAMT=.4/.5/1/1.8/2.5/3/3.2/3.3/3.3                  128.1, T
    SCRRAM - SUBURB/CITY RELATIVE RESIDENTIAL-
               ATTRACTIVENESS MULTIPLIER (DIMENSIONLESS)
    SCRRAMT- SUBURB/CITY RELATIVE RESIDENTIAL-
               ATTRACTIVENESS MULTIPLIER TABLE
               (DIMENSIONLESS)
    SCRRAR - SUBURB/CITY RELATIVE RESIDENTIAL-
               ATTRACTIVENESS RATIO (DIMENSIONLESS)

SCRRAR.K=SUIRCMP.K/CUIRCM.K                            129, A
    SCRRAR - SUBURB/CITY RELATIVE RESIDENTIAL-
               ATTRACTIVENESS RATIO (DIMENSIONLESS)
    SUIRCMP- SUBURB UPPER-INCOME RESIDENTIAL-CONDITIONS
               MULTIPLIER PERCEIVED (DIMENSIONLESS)
    CUIRCM - CITY UPPER-INCOME RESIDENTIAL-CONDITIONS
               MULTIPLIER (DIMENSIONLESS)

SUIRCMP.K=SUIRCMP.J+(DT/SUIRCAT)(SUIRCM.J-             130, L
  SUIRCMP.J)
SUIRCAT=5                                              130.1, C
SUIRCMP=1                                              130.2, N
    SUIRCMP- SUBURB UPPER-INCOME RESIDENTIAL-CONDITIONS
               MULTIPLIER PERCEIVED (DIMENSIONLESS)
    SUIRCAT- SUBURB UPPER-INCOME RESIDENTIAL-CONDITIONS
               AVERAGING TIME (YEARS)
    SUIRCM - SUBURB UPPER-INCOME RESIDENTIAL-CONDITIONS
               MULTIPLIER (DIMENSIONLESS)
```

```
UISCCMR.KL=(SUIC.K)(UISCMN)(CSRRAM.K)(CSRRAF)/        131, R
  (ACCESM.K)
UISCMN=.005                                          131.1, C
CSRRAF=1                                             131.2, C
    UISCCMR- UPPER-INCOME SUBURB(RESIDENT) CITY(WORKERS)
               CITY MIGRATION RATE (MEN/YEAR)
    SUIC    - SUBURB(RESIDENT) UPPER-INCOME CITY(WORKERS)
               (MEN)
    UISCMN  - UPPER-INCOME SUBURB(RESIDENT) CITY(WORKERS)
               CITY MIGRATION NORMAL (FRACTION/YEAR)
    CSRRAM  - CITY/SUBURB RELATIVE RESIDENTIAL-
               ATTRACTIVENESS MULTIPLIER (DIMENSIONLESS)
    CSRRAF  - CITY/SUBURB RELATIVE RESIDENTIAL-
               ATTRACTIVENESS FACTOR (DIMENSIONLESS)
    ACCESM  - ACCESS MULTIPLIER (DIMENSIONLESS)

CSRRAM.K=TABLE(CSRRAMT,CSRRAR.K,0,4,.5)               132, A
CSRRAMT=.4/.5/1/1.6/2/2.3/2.4/2.4/2.5                132.1, T
    CSRRAM  - CITY/SUBURB RELATIVE RESIDENTIAL-
               ATTRACTIVENESS MULTIPLIER (DIMENSIONLESS)
    CSRRAMT- CITY/SUBURB RELATIVE RESIDENTIAL-
               ATTRACTIVENESS MULTIPLIER TABLE
               (DIMENSIONLESS)
    CSRRAR  - CITY/SUBURB RELATIVE RESIDENTIAL-
               ATTRACTIVENESS RATIO (DIMENSIONLESS)

CSRRAR.K=CUIRCMP.K/SUIRCM.K                          133, A
    CSRRAR  - CITY/SUBURB RELATIVE RESIDENTIAL-
               ATTRACTIVENESS RATIO (DIMENSIONLESS)
    CUIRCMP- CITY UPPER-INCOME RESIDENTIAL-CONDITIONS
               MULTIPLIER PERCEIVED (DIMENSIONLESS)
    SUIRCM  - SUBURB UPPER-INCOME RESIDENTIAL-CONDITIONS
               MULTIPLIER (DIMENSIONLESS)

CUIRCMP.K=CUIRCMP.J+(DT/CUIRCAT)(CUIRCM.J-           134, L
  CUIRCMP.J)
CUIRCMP=1                                            134.1, N
CUIRCAT=5                                            134.2, C
    CUIRCMP- CITY UPPER-INCOME RESIDENTIAL-CONDITIONS
               MULTIPLIER PERCEIVED (DIMENSIONLESS)
    CUIRCAT- CITY UPPER-INCOME RESIDENTIAL-CONDITIONS
               AVERAGING TIME (YEARS)
    CUIRCM  - CITY UPPER-INCOME RESIDENTIAL-CONDITIONS
               MULTIPLIER (DIMENSIONLESS)

SUIC.K=SUIC.J+(DT)(UICCSMR.JK+SUICNB.JK-UISCCMR.JK-  135, L
  SUICD.JK)
SUIC=500                                             135.1, N
    SUIC    - SUBURB(RESIDENT) UPPER-INCOME CITY(WORKERS)
               (MEN)
    UICCSMR- UPPER-INCOME CITY(RESIDENT) CITY(WORKERS)
               SUBURB MIGRATION RATE (MEN/YEAR)
    SUICNB  - SUBURB UPPER-INCOME CITY NET BIRTHS (MEN/
               YEAR)
    UISCCMR- UPPER-INCOME SUBURB(RESIDENT) CITY(WORKERS)
               CITY MIGRATION RATE (MEN/YEAR)
    SUICD   - SUBURB UPPER-INCOME CITY DEPARTURES (MEN/
               YEAR)

SUICNB.KL=(SUIC.K)(SUICNBN)                          136, R
SUICNBN=.0095                                        136.1, C
    SUICNB  - SUBURB UPPER-INCOME CITY NET BIRTHS (MEN/
               YEAR)
    SUIC    - SUBURB(RESIDENT) UPPER-INCOME CITY(WORKERS)
               (MEN)
    SUICNBN- SUBURB UPPER-INCOME CITY NET BIRTHS NORMAL
               (FRACTION/YEAR)

SUICD.KL=(SUIC.K)(SUICDN)(SUICDM.K)                  137, R
SUICDN=.02                                           137.1, C
    SUICD   - SUBURB UPPER-INCOME CITY DEPARTURES (MEN/
               YEAR)
    SUIC    - SUBURB(RESIDENT) UPPER-INCOME CITY(WORKERS)
               (MEN)
    SUICDN  - SUBURB UPPER-INCOME CITY DEPARTURES NORMAL
               (FRACTION/YEAR)
    SUICDM  - SUBURB UPPER-INCOME CITY DEPARTURES
               MULTIPLIER (DIMENSIONLESS)
```

```
SUICDM.K=TABLE(SUICDMT,1.44*LOGN(MUIAM.K),-3,3,1)      138, A
SUICDMT=8/4/2/1/.5/.25/.125                            138.1, T
    SUICDM - SUBURB UPPER-INCOME CITY DEPARTURES
               MULTIPLIER (DIMENSIONLESS)
    SUICDMT- SUBURB UPPER-INCOME CITY DEPARTURES
               MULTIPLIER TABLE (DIMENSIONLESS)
    MUIAM  - METROPOLITAN UPPER-INCOME-ATTRACTIVEMESS
               MULTIPLIER (DIMENSIONLESS)


*****UPPER INCOME REVERSE COMMUTERS
*****

CUIS.K=CUIS.J+(DT)(UISSCMR.JK+CUISNB.JK-UICSSMR.JK-  139, L
  CUISD.JK)
CUIS=0                                                 139.1, N
    CUIS   - CITY(RESIDENT) UPPER-INCOME SUBURB(WORKERS)
               (MEN)
    UISSCMR- UPPER-INCOME SUBURB(RESIDENT)
               SUBURB(WORKERS) CITY MIGRATION RATE (MEN/
               YEAR)
    CUISNB - CITY UPPER-INCOME SUBURB NET BIRTHS (MEN/
               YEAR)
    UICSSMR- UPPER-INCOME CITY(RESIDENT) SUBURB(WORKERS)
               SUBURB MIGRATION RATE (MEN/YEAR)
    CUISD  - CITY UPPER-INCOME SUBURB DEPARTURES (MEN/
               YEAR)

UISSCMR.KL=(SUIS.K)(UISSCMN)(ACCESM.K)(CSRRAM.K)      140, R
UISSCMN=.01                                            140.1, C
    UISSCMR- UPPER-INCOME SUBURB(RESIDENT)
               SUBURB(WORKERS) CITY MIGRATION RATE (MEN/
               YEAR)
    SUIS   - SUBURB(RESIDENT) UPPER-INCOME
               SUBURB(WORKERS) (MEN)
    UISSCMN- UPPER-INCOME SUBURB(RESIDENT)
               SUBURB(WORKERS) CITY MIGRATION NORMAL
               (FRACTION/YEAR)
    ACCESM - ACCESS MULTIPLIER (DIMENSIONLESS)
    CSRRAM - CITY/SUBURB RELATIVE RESIDENTIAL-
               ATTRACTIVENESS MULTIPLIER (DIMENSIONLESS)

CUISNB.KL=(CUIS.K)(CUISBN)                             141, R
CUISBN=.0095                                           141.1, C
    CUISNB - CITY UPPER-INCOME SUBURB NET BIRTHS (MEN/
               YEAR)
    CUIS   - CITY(RESIDENT) UPPER-INCOME SUBURB(WORKERS)
               (MEN)
    CUISBN - CITY UPPER-INCOME SUBURB NET BIRTHS NORMAL
               (FRACTION/YEAR)


UICSSMR.KL=(CUIS.K)(UICSMN)(SCRRAM.K)/(ACCESM.K)      142, R
UICSMN=.01                                             142.1, C
    UICSSMR- UPPER-INCOME CITY(RESIDENT) SUBURB(WORKERS)
               SUBURB MIGRATION RATE (MEN/YEAR)
    CUIS   - CITY(RESIDENT) UPPER-INCOME SUBURB(WORKERS)
               (MEN)
    UICSMN - UPPER-INCOME CITY(RESIDENT) SUBURB(WORKERS)
               SUBURB MIGRATION NORMAL (FRACTION/YEAR)
               YEAR)
    SCRRAM - SUBURB/CITY RELATIVE RESIDENTIAL-
               ATTRACTIVENESS MULTIPLIER (DIMENSIONLESS)
    ACCESM - ACCESS MULTIPLIER (DIMENSIONLESS)


CUISD.KL=(CUIS.K)(CUISDN)(CUISDM.K)                    143, R
CUISDN=.02                                             143.1, C
    CUISD  - CITY UPPER-INCOME SUBURB DEPARTURES (MEN/
               YEAR)
    CUIS   - CITY(RESIDENT) UPPER-INCOME SUBURB(WORKERS)
               (MEN)
    CUISDN - CITY UPPER-INCOME SUBURB DEPARTURES NORMAL
               (FRACTION/YEAR)
    CUISDM - CITY UPPER-INCOME SUBURB DEPARTURES
               MULTIPLIER (DIMENSIONLESS)
```

```
CUISDM.K=TABLE(CUISDMT,1.44*LOGN(MUIAM.K),-3,3,1)    144, A
CUISDMT=8/4/2/1/.5/.25/.125                          144.1, T
    CUISDM - CITY UPPER-INCOME SUBURB DEPARTURES
               MULTIPLIER (DIMENSIONLESS)
    CUISDMT- CITY UPPER-INCOME SUBURB DEPARTURES
               MULTIPLIER TABLE (DIMENSIONLESS)
    MUIAM  - METROPOLITAN UPPER-INCOME-ATTRACTIVEMESS
               MULTIPLIER (DIMENSIONLESS)

*****ACCESS SECTOR
*****

ACCESM.K=(TRANCAP.K)/(TRANSD.K*TRCOST.K)             145, A
    ACCESM - ACCESS MULTIPLIER (DIMENSIONLESS)
    TRANCAP- TRANSPORTATION CAPACITY (DIMENSIONLESS)
    TRANSD - TRANSPORTATION DEMAND (DIMENSIONLESS)
    TRCOST - TRANSPORTATION COST (DIMENSIONLESS)

TRANCAP.K=TRANCAP.J+(DT/TRANCET.J)(TRANCD.J-         146, L
  TRANCAP.J)
TRANCAP=TRANSD                                       146.1, N
    TRANCAP- TRANSPORTATION CAPACITY (DIMENSIONLESS)
    TRANCET- TRANSPORTATION CAPACITY EXPANSION TIME
               (YEARS)
    TRANCD - TRANSPORTATION CAPACITY DESIRED
               (DIMENSIONLESS)
    TRANSD - TRANSPORTATION DEMAND (DIMENSIONLESS)

TRANCD.K=(TRANSD.K)(RTRANEP.K)                       147, A
    TRANCD - TRANSPORTATION CAPACITY DESIRED
               (DIMENSIONLESS)
    TRANSD - TRANSPORTATION DEMAND (DIMENSIONLESS)
    RTRANEP- REGIONAL TRANSPORTATION EXPANSION POLICY
               (DIMENSIONLESS)

TRANCET.K=(TRANETN)(TCCDM.K)(TCSDM.K)                148, A
TRANETN=10                                           148.1, C
    TRANCET- TRANSPORTATION CAPACITY EXPANSION TIME
               (YEARS)
    TRANETN- TRANSPORTATION CAPACITY EXPANSION TIME
               NORMAL (YEARS)
    TCCDM  - TRANSPORTATION CONSTRUCTION CITY-DENSITY
               MULTIPLIER (DIMENSIONLESS)
    TCSDM  - TRANSPORTATION CONSTRUCTION SUBURB-DENSITY
               MULTIPLIER (DIMENSIONLESS)


TCCDM.K=TABLE(TCCDMT,CLFO.K,0,1,.2)                  149, A
TCCDMT=.6/.8/1/1.3/1.7/2.5                           149.1, T
    TCCDM  - TRANSPORTATION CONSTRUCTION CITY-DENSITY
               MULTIPLIER (DIMENSIONLESS)
    TCCDMT - TRANSPORTATION CONSTRUCTION CITY-DENSITY
               MULTIPLIER TABLE (DIMENSIONLESS)
    CLFO   - CITY LAND FRACTION OCCUPIED (DIMENSIONLESS)

TCSDM.K=TABLE(TCSDMT,SLFO.K,0,1,.2)                  150, A
TCSDMT=.7/1/1.4/2.0/3.0/4.5                          150.1, T
    TCSDM  - TRANSPORTATION CONSTRUCTION SUBURB-DENSITY
               MULTIPLIER (DIMENSIONLESS)
    TCSDMT - TRANSPORTATION CONSTRUCTION SUBURB-DENSITY
               MULTIPLIER TABLE (DIMENSIONLESS)
    SLFO   - SUBURB LAND FRACTION OCCUPIED
               (DIMENSIONLESS)

TRANSD.K=(SUIC.K)(UICTF)+(SUIS.K)(UISTF)             151, A
UICTF=1                                              151.1, C
UISTF=.3                                             151.2, C
    TRANSD - TRANSPORTATION DEMAND (DIMENSIONLESS)
    SUIC   - SUBURB(RESIDENT) UPPER-INCOME CITY(WORKERS)
               (MEN)
    UICTF  - UPPER-INCOME COMMUTER TRANSPORTATION FACTOR
               (DIMENSIONLESS)
    SUIS   - SUBURB(RESIDENT) UPPER-INCOME
               SUBURB(WORKERS) (MEN)
    UISTF  - UPPER-INCOME SERVICE TRANSPORTATION FACTOR
               (DIMENSIONLESS)
```

```
TRCOST.K=TABLE(TRCOSTT,SLFO.K,0,1,.2)                    152, A
TRCOSTT=1/1.05/1.2/1.4/1.45/1.5                          152.1, T
    TRCOST - TRANSPORTATION COST (DIMENSIONLESS)
    TRCOSTT- TRANSPORTATION-COST TABLE (DIMENSIONLESS)
    SLFO   - SUBURB LAND FRACTION OCCUPIED
               (DIMENSIONLESS)

*****INDUSTRIAL LOCATION SECTOR
*****

MNBSCD.K=(MNBSDN)(MEM.K)(CNBSWF*CNBS.K+SNBSWF*          153, A
  SNBS.K+COBSWF*COBS.K+SOBSWF*SOBS.K)
MNBSDN=.04                                               153.2, C
CNBSWF=1                                                 153.3, C
SNBSWF=.6                                                153.4, C
COBSWF=.4                                                153.5, C
SOBSWF=.3                                                153.6, C
    MNBSCD - METROPOLITAN NEW-BUSINESS-STRUCTURES
               CONSTRUCTION DESIRED (STRUCTURES/YEAR)
    MNBSDN - METROPOLITAN NEW-BUSINESS-STRUCTURES
               DESIRED NORMAL (FRACTION/YEAR)
    MEM    - METROPOLITAN ENTERPRISE MULTIPLIER
               (DIMENSIONLESS)
    CNBSWF - CITY NEW-BUSINESS-STRUCTURES WEIGHTING
               FACTOR
    CNBS   - CITY NEW-BUSINESS STRUCTURES (STRUCTURES)
    SNBSWF - SUBURB NEW-BUSINESS-STRUCTURES WEIGHTING
               FACTOR (DIMENSIONLESS)
    SNBS   - SUBURB NEW-BUSINESS STRUCTURES (STRUCTURES)
    COBSWF - CITY OLDER-BUSINESS-STRUCTURES WEIGHTING
               FACTOR (DIMENSIONLESS)
    COBS   - CITY OLDER-BUSINESS STRUCTURES (STRUCTURES)
    SOBSWF - SUBURB OLDER-BUSINESS-STRUCTURES WEIGHTING
               FACTOR (DIMENSIONLESS)
    SOBS   - SUBURB OLDER-BUSINESS STRUCTURES
               (STRUCTURES)

MEM.K=(MELSM.K)(MEALCM.K)                                154, A
    MEM    - METROPOLITAN ENTERPRISE MULTIPLIER
               (DIMENSIONLESS)
    MELSM  - METROPOLITAN ENTERPRISE LABOR-SUPPLY
               MULTIPLIER (DIMENSIONLESS)
    MEALCM - METROPOLITAN ENTERPRISE AVERAGE-LOCAL-
               CONDITIONS MULTIPLER (DIMENSIONLESS)

MELSM.K=(MEUIWM.K)(MELIWM.K)                             155, A
    MELSM  - METROPOLITAN ENTERPRISE LABOR-SUPPLY
               MULTIPLIER (DIMENSIONLESS)
    MEUIWM - METROPOLITAN ENTERPRISE UPPER-INCOME-
               WORKFORCE MULTIPLIER (DIMENSIONLESS)
    MELIWM - METROPOLITAN ENTERPRISE LOWER-INCOME-
               WORKFORCE MULTIPLIER (DIMENSIONLESS)

MEUIWM.K=TABLE(MEUIWMT,MUIJRP.K,0,2,.25)                 156, A
MEUIWMT=.1/.15/.3/.5/1/1.4/1.7/1.9/2                     156.1, T
    MEUIWM - METROPOLITAN ENTERPRISE UPPER-INCOME-
               WORKFORCE MULTIPLIER (DIMENSIONLESS)
    MEUIWMT- METROPOLITAN ENTERPRISE UPPER-INCOME-
               WORKFORCE MULTIPLIER TABLE
               (DIMENSIONLESS)
    MUIJRP - METROPOLITAN ENTERPRISE UPPER-INCOME-TO-JOB
               RATIO PERCEIVED (DIMENSIONLESS)

MUIJRP.K=MUIJRP.J+(DT/MUIJRPT)(MUIJR.J-MUIJRP.J)         157, L
MUIJRPT=5                                                157.1, C
MUIJRP=1                                                 157.2, N
    MUIJRP - METROPOLITAN ENTERPRISE UPPER-INCOME-TO-JOB
               RATIO PERCEIVED (DIMENSIONLESS)
    MUIJRPT- METROPOLITAN ENTERPRISE UPPER-INCOME-TO-JOB
               RATIO PERCEPTION TIME (YEARS)
    MUIJR  - METROPOLITAN UPPER-INCOME-TO-JOB RATIO
               (DIMENSIONLESS)
```

```
MELIWM.K=TABLE(MELIWMT,MLIJRP.K,0,2,.25)                  158, A
MELIWMT=.8/.85/.9/.95/1/1.05/1.1/1.15/1.2                  158.1, T
    MELIWM  - METROPOLITAN ENTERPRISE LOWER-INCOME-
                WORKFORCE MULTIPLIER (DIMENSIONLESS)
    MELIWMT- METROPOLITAN ENTERPRISE LOWER-INCOME-
                WORKFORCE MULTIPLIER TABLE
                (DIMENSIONLESS)
    MLIJRP  - METROPOLITAN LOWER-INCOME-TO-JOB RATIO
                PERCEIVED (DIMENSIONLESS)

MLIJRP.K=MLIJRP.J+(DT/MLIJRPT)(MLIJR.J-MLIJRP.J)          159, L
MLIJRPT=5                                                  159.1, C
MLIJRP=1                                                   159.2, N
    MLIJRP  - METROPOLITAN LOWER-INCOME-TO-JOB RATIO
                PERCEIVED (DIMENSIONLESS)
    MLIJRPT- METROPOLITAN LOWER-INCOME-TO-JOB RATIO
                PERCEPTION TIME (YEARS)
    MLIJR   - METROPOLITAN LOWER-INCOME-TO-JOB RATIO
                (DIMENSIONLESS)

MLIJR.K=TMLIP.K/TMLIJ.K                                    160, A
    MLIJR   - METROPOLITAN LOWER-INCOME-TO-JOB RATIO
                (DIMENSIONLESS)
    TMLIP   - TOTAL METROPOLITAN LOWER-INCOME POPULATION
                (MEN)
    TMLIJ   - TOTAL METROPOLITAN LOWER-INCOME JOBS (MEN)

TMLIP.K=CLIP.K+SLIP.K                                      161, A
    TMLIP   - TOTAL METROPOLITAN LOWER-INCOME POPULATION
                (MEN)
    CLIP    - CITY LOWER-INCOME POPULATION (MEN)
    SLIP    - SUBURB LOWER-INCOME POPULATION (MEN)

TMLIJ.K=CLIJ.K+SLIJ.K                                      162, A
    TMLIJ   - TOTAL METROPOLITAN LOWER-INCOME JOBS (MEN)
    CLIJ    - CITY LOWER-INCOME JOBS (MEN)
    SLIJ    - SUBURB LOWER-INCOME JOBS (MEN)

MEALCM.K=(CELCM.K)(CBST.K/MBST.K)+(SELCM.K)(SBST.K/ 163, A
  MBST.K)
    MEALCM - METROPOLITAN ENTERPRISE AVERAGE-LOCAL-
                CONDITIONS MULTIPLER (DIMENSIONLESS)
    CELCM   - CITY ENTERPRISE LOCAL-CONDITIONS MULTIPLIER
                (DIMENSIONLESS)
    CBST    - CITY BUSINESS STRUCTURES TOTAL (STRUCTURES)
    MBST    - METROPOLITAN BUSINESS STRUCTURES TOTAL
                (STRUCTURES)
    SELCM   - SUBURB ENTERPRISE LOCAL-CONDITIONS
                MULTIPLIER (DIMENSIONLESS)
    SBST    - SUBURB BUSINESS-STRUCTURES TOTAL
                (STRUCTURES)

MBST.K=CBST.K+SBST.K                                       164, A
    MBST    - METROPOLITAN BUSINESS STRUCTURES TOTAL
                (STRUCTURES)
    CBST    - CITY BUSINESS STRUCTURES TOTAL (STRUCTURES)
    SBST    - SUBURB BUSINESS-STRUCTURES TOTAL
                (STRUCTURES)

CELCM.K=(CELM.K)(CETM.K)(CEGM.K)(CRTNBS)                   165, A
CRTNBS=1                                                   165.1, C
    CELCM   - CITY ENTERPRISE LOCAL-CONDITIONS MULTIPLIER
                (DIMENSIONLESS)
    CELM    - CITY ENTERPRISE LAND MULTIPLIER
                (DIMENSIONLESS)
    CETM    - CITY ENTERPRISE TAX MULTIPLIER
                (DIMENSIONLESS)
    CEGM    - CITY ENTERPRISE GROWTH MULTIPLIER
                (DIMENSIONLESS)
    CRTNBS  - CITY RECEPTIVENESS TO NEW-BUSINESS
                STRUCTURES (DIMENSIONLESS)

SELCM.K=(SELM.K)(SETM.K)(SEGM.K)(SRTNBS)                   166, A
SRTNBS=.5                                                  166.1, C
    SELCM   - SUBURB ENTERPRISE LOCAL-CONDITIONS
                MULTIPLIER (DIMENSIONLESS)
    SELM    - SUBURB ENTERPRISE LAND MULTIPLIER
                (DIMENSIONLESS)
```

```
    SETM   - SUBURB ENTERPRISE TAX MULTIPLIER
               (DIMENSIONLESS)
    SEGM   - SUBURB ENTERPRISE GROWTH MULTIPLIER
               (DIMENSIONLESS)
    SRTNBS - SUBURB RECEPTIVENESS TO NEW-BUSINESS
               STRUCTURES (DIMENSIONLESS)

CNBSC.KL=(CNBSCD.K)(MCWM.K)+CNBSCP.K                   167, R
    CNBSC  - CITY NEW-BUSINESS-STRUCTURES CONSTRUCTION
               (STRUCTURES/YEAR)
    CNBSCD - CITY NEW-BUSINESS-STRUCTURES CONSTRUCTION
               DESIRED (STRUCTURES/YEAR)
    MCWM   - METROPOLITAN CONSTRUCTION WORKFORCE
               MULTIPLIER (DIMENSIONLESS)
    CNBSCP - CITY NEW-BUSINESS-STRUCTURES CONSTRUCTION
               PROGRAM (STRUCTURES/YEAR)

CNBSCD.K=CNBSCF.K*MNBSCD.K                             168, A
    CNBSCD - CITY NEW-BUSINESS-STRUCTURES CONSTRUCTION
               DESIRED (STRUCTURES/YEAR)
    CNBSCF - CITY NEW-BUSINESS-STRUCTURES CONSTRUCTION
               FRACTION (DIMENSIONLESS)
    MNBSCD - METROPOLITAN NEW-BUSINESS-STRUCTURES
               CONSTRUCTION DESIRED (STRUCTURES/YEAR)

CNBSCF.K=TABHL(CNBSCFT,CSRNBAM.K,0,3,.5)               169, A
CNBSCFT=.2/.4/.65/.75/.84/.90/.95                      169.1, T
    CNBSCF - CITY NEW-BUSINESS-STRUCTURES CONSTRUCTION
               FRACTION (DIMENSIONLESS)
    CNBSCFT- CITY NEW-BUSINESS-STRUCTURES CONSTRUCTION
               FRACTION TABLE (DIMENSIONLESS)
    CSRNBAM- CITY/SUBURB RELATIVE NEW-BUSINESS-
               ATTRACTION MULTIPLIER

CSRNBAM.K=CNBSCM.K/SNBSCM.K                            170, A
    CSRNBAM- CITY/SUBURB RELATIVE NEW-BUSINESS-
               ATTRACTION MULTIPLIER
    CNBSCM - CITY NEW-BUSINESS-STRUCTURES CONSTRUCTION
               MULTIPLIER (DIMENSIONLESS)
    SNBSCM - SUBURB NEW-BUSINESS-STRUCTURES CONSTRUCTION
               MULTIPLIER (DIMENSIONLESS)

CNBSCM.K=(CELCM.K)(CSUIWM.K)(CSLIWM.K)(CSRBAM.K)       171, A
    CNBSCM - CITY NEW-BUSINESS-STRUCTURES CONSTRUCTION
               MULTIPLIER (DIMENSIONLESS)
    CELCM  - CITY ENTERPRISE LOCAL-CONDITIONS MULTIPLIER
               (DIMENSIONLESS)
    CSUIWM - CITY/SUBURB UPPER-INCOME WORKFORCE
               MULTIPLIER (DIMENSIONLESS)
    CSLIWM - CITY/SUBURB LOWER-INCOME WORKFORCE
               MULTIPLIER (DIMENSIONLESS)
    CSRBAM - CITY/SUBURB RELATIVE BUSINESS-ACTIVITY
               MULTIPLIER (DIMENSIONLESS)

CSUIWM.K=TABHL(CSUIWT,CSUIWR.K,0,3,.5)                 172, A
CSUIWT=.6/.8/1/1.1/1.15/1.18/1.2                       172.1, T
    CSUIWM - CITY/SUBURB UPPER-INCOME WORKFORCE
               MULTIPLIER (DIMENSIONLESS)
    CSUIWT - CITY/SUBURB UPPER-INCOME WORKFORCE TABLE
               (DIMENSIONLESS)
    CSUIWR - CITY/SUBURB UPPER-INCOME WORKFORCE RATIO
               (DIMENSIONLESS)

CSUIWR.K=(CUIC.K+CUIS.K)(CUICJR.K)/((SUIS.K+SUIC.K)  173, A
  (SUISJR.K))
    CSUIWR - CITY/SUBURB UPPER-INCOME WORKFORCE RATIO
               (DIMENSIONLESS)
    CUIC   - CITY(RESIDENT) UPPER-INCOME CITY(WORKERS)
               (MEN)
    CUIS   - CITY(RESIDENT) UPPER-INCOME SUBURB(WORKERS)
               (MEN)
    CUICJR - CITY UPPER-INCOME-TO-CITY JOB RATIO
               (DIMENSIONLESS)
    SUIS   - SUBURB(RESIDENT) UPPER-INCOME
               SUBURB(WORKERS) (MEN)
    SUIC   - SUBURB(RESIDENT) UPPER-INCOME CITY(WORKERS)
               (MEN)
    SUISJR - SUBURB UPPER-INCOME-TO-SUBURB JOB RATIO
               (DIMENSIONLESS)
```

```
CSLIWM.K=TABHL(CSLIWT,CSLIWR.K,0,3,.5)                   174, A
CSLIWT=.9/.94/1/1.04/1.06/1.09/1.1                       174.1, T
    CSLIWM - CITY/SUBURB LOWER-INCOME WORKFORCE
               MULTIPLIER (DIMENSIONLESS)
    CSLIWT - CITY/SUBURB LOWER-INCOME WORKFORCE TABLE
               (DIMENSIONLESS)
    CSLIWR - CITY/SUBURB LOWER-INCOME WORKFORCE RATIO
               (DIMENSIONLESS)

CSLIWR.K=(CLIP.K)(CLIJR.K)/((SLIP.K)(SLIJR.K))           175, A
    CSLIWR - CITY/SUBURB LOWER-INCOME WORKFORCE RATIO
               (DIMENSIONLESS)
    CLIP   - CITY LOWER-INCOME POPULATION (MEN)
    CLIJR  - CITY LOWER-INCOME-TO-JOB RATIO
               (DIMENSIONLESS)
    SLIP   - SUBURB LOWER-INCOME POPULATION (MEN)
    SLIJR  - SUBURB LOWER-INCOME-TO-JOB RATIO
               (DIMENSIONLESS)

CSRBAM.K=TABHL(CSRBAMT,CSRBAR.K,0,4,.5)                  176, A
CSRBAMT=.6/.8/1/1.2/1.4/1.5/1.6/1.7/1.7                  176.1, T
    CSRBAM - CITY/SUBURB RELATIVE BUSINESS-ACTIVITY
               MULTIPLIER (DIMENSIONLESS)
    CSRBAMT- CITY/SUBURB RELATIVE BUSINESS-ACTIVITY
               MULTIPLIER TABLE (DIMENSIONLESS)
    CSRBAR - CITY/SUBURB RELATIVE BUSINESS-ACTIVITY
               RATIO (DIMENSIONLESS)

CSRBAR.K=CBST.K/SBST.K                                   177, A
    CSRBAR - CITY/SUBURB RELATIVE BUSINESS-ACTIVITY
               RATIO (DIMENSIONLESS)
    CBST   - CITY BUSINESS STRUCTURES TOTAL (STRUCTURES)
    SBST   - SUBURB BUSINESS-STRUCTURES TOTAL
               (STRUCTURES)

SNBSCM.K=(SELCM.K)/((CSUIWM.K)(CSLIWM.K))                178, A
    SNBSCM - SUBURB NEW-BUSINESS-STRUCTURES CONSTRUCTION
               MULTIPLIER (DIMENSIONLESS)
    SELCM  - SUBURB ENTERPRISE LOCAL-CONDITIONS
               MULTIPLIER (DIMENSIONLESS)
    CSUIWM - CITY/SUBURB UPPER-INCOME WORKFORCE
               MULTIPLIER (DIMENSIONLESS)
    CSLIWM - CITY/SUBURB LOWER-INCOME WORKFORCE
               MULTIPLIER (DIMENSIONLESS)

SNBSC.KL=(SNBSCD.K)(MCWM.K)                              179, R
    SNBSC  - SUBURB NEW-BUSINESS-STRUCTURES CONSTRUCTION
               (STRUCTURES/YEAR)
    SNBSCD - SUBURB NEW-BUSINESS-STRUCTURES CONSTRUCTION
               DESIRED (STRUCTURES/ YEAR)
    MCWM   - METROPOLITAN CONSTRUCTION WORKFORCE
               MULTIPLIER (DIMENSIONLESS)

SNBSCD.K=(1-CNBSCF.K)(MNBSCD.K)                          180, A
    SNBSCD - SUBURB NEW-BUSINESS-STRUCTURES CONSTRUCTION
               DESIRED (STRUCTURES/ YEAR)
    CNBSCF - CITY NEW-BUSINESS-STRUCTURES CONSTRUCTION
               FRACTION (DIMENSIONLESS)
    MNBSCD - METROPOLITAN NEW-BUSINESS-STRUCTURES
               CONSTRUCTION DESIRED (STRUCTURES/YEAR)

*****SUBURB UPPER INCOME HOUSING SECTOR
*****

SUIHC.KL=(SUIHCD.K)(MCWM.K)                              181, R
    SUIHC  - SUBURB UPPER-INCOME-HOUSING CONSTRUCTION
               (STRUCTURES/YEAR)
    SUIHCD - SUBURB UPPER-INCOME-HOUSING CONSTRUCTION
               DESIRED (STRUCTURES/YEAR)
    MCWM   - METROPOLITAN CONSTRUCTION WORKFORCE
               MULTIPLIER (DIMENSIONLESS)

SUIHCD.K=(SUIHCN)(SUIH.K)(SUIHM.K)+SUIHCP.K              182, A
SUIHCN=.02                                               182.1, C
    SUIHCD - SUBURB UPPER-INCOME-HOUSING CONSTRUCTION
               DESIRED (STRUCTURES/YEAR)
    SUIHCN - SUBURB UPPER-INCOME-HOUSING CONSTRUCTION
               NORMAL (FRACTION/YEAR)
```

```
    SUIH   - SUBURB UPPER-INCOME HOUSING (STRUCTURES)
    SUIHM  - SUBURB UPPER-INCOME-HOUSING MULTIPLIER
               (DIMENSIONLESS)
    SUIHCP - SUBURB UPPER-INCOME HOUSING CONSTRUCTION
               PROGRAM (STRUCTURES/YEAR)

SUIHM.K=(SUIHAM.K)(SUIHLM.K)(SUIHPM.K)(SUIHTM.K)     183, A
  (SUIHEM.K)(SUIHGM.K)(SUIHF)
SUIHF=1                                              183.2, C
    SUIHM  - SUBURB UPPER-INCOME-HOUSING MULTIPLIER
               (DIMENSIONLESS)
    SUIHAM - SUBURB UPPER-INCOME-HOUSING AVAILABILITY
               MULTIPLIER (DIMENSIONLESS)
    SUIHLM - SUBURB UPPER-INCOME-HOUSING LAND MULTIPLIER
               (DIMENSIONLESS)
    SUIHPM - SUBURB UPPER-INCOME-HOUSING POPULATION
               MULTIPLIER (DIMENSIONLESS)
    SUIHTM - SUBURB UPPER-INCOME-HOUSING TAX MULTIPLIER
               (DIMENSIONLESS)
    SUIHEM - SUBURB UPPER-INCOME-HOUSING-ENTERPRISE
               MULTIPLIER (DIMENSIONLESS)
    SUIHGM - SUBURB UPPER-INCOME-HOUSING GROWTH
               MULTIPLIER (DIMENSIONLESS)
    SUIHF  - SUBURB UPPER-INCOME-HOUSING FACTOR
               (DIMENSIONLESS)

SUIHAM.K=TABLE(SUIHAMT,SUIHR.K,0,2,.25)              184, A
SUIHAMT=0/.001/.01/.2/1/3/4.6/5.6/6                  184.1, T
    SUIHAM - SUBURB UPPER-INCOME-HOUSING AVAILABILITY
               MULTIPLIER (DIMENSIONLESS)
    SUIHAMT- SUBURB UPPER-INCOME-HOUSING AVAILABILITY
               MULTIPLIER TABLE (DIMENSIONLESS)
    SUIHR  - SUBURB UPPER-INCOME-TO-HOUSING RATIO
               (DIMENSIONLESS)

SUIHLM.K=TABLE(SUIHLMT,SLFO.K,0,1,.1)                185, A
SUIHLMT=.4/.8/1.1/1.4/1.5/1.3/1/.8/.4/.2/0           185.1, T
    SUIHLM - SUBURB UPPER-INCOME-HOUSING LAND MULTIPLIER
               (DIMENSIONLESS)
    SUIHLMT- SUBURB UPPER-INCOME-HOUSING LAND MULTIPLIER
               TABLE (DIMENSIONLESS)NLESS)
    SLFO   - SUBURB LAND FRACTION OCCUPIED
               (DIMENSIONLESS)

SLFO.K=(SHT.K*SLPH+SBST.K*SLPBS)/(SAREA.K)           186, A
SLPH=.4                                              186.1, C
SLPBS=.8                                             186.2, C
    SLFO   - SUBURB LAND FRACTION OCCUPIED
               (DIMENSIONLESS)
    SHT    - SUBURB HOUSING STRUCTURES TOTAL
               (STRUCTURES)
    SLPH   - SUBURB LAND PER HOUSING STRUCTURE (ACRES/
               STRUCTURE)
    SBST   - SUBURB BUSINESS-STRUCTURES TOTAL
               (STRUCTURES)
    SLPBS  - SUBURB LAND PER BUSINESS STRUCTURE (ACRES/
               STRUCTURE)
    SAREA  - SUBURB AREA (ACRES)

SAREA.K=(SAREAB)(CDENSM.K)                           187, A
SAREAB=700000                                        187.1, C
    SAREA  - SUBURB AREA (ACRES)
    SAREAB - SUBURB AREA BASE (ACRES)
    CDENSM - CITY DENSITY MULTIPLIER (DIMENSIONLESS)

CDENSM.K=TABLE(CDENSMT,CLFO.K,0,1,.2)                188, A
CDENSMT=.5/.6/.7/.8/.9/1                             188.1, T
    CDENSM - CITY DENSITY MULTIPLIER (DIMENSIONLESS)
    CDENSMT- CITY DENSITY MULTIPLIER TABLE
               (DIMENSIONLESS)
    CLFO   - CITY LAND FRACTION OCCUPIED (DIMENSIONLESS)

SHT.K=SUIH.K+SLIH.K                                  189, A
    SHT    - SUBURB HOUSING STRUCTURES TOTAL
               (STRUCTURES)
    SUIH   - SUBURB UPPER-INCOME HOUSING (STRUCTURES)
    SLIH   - SUBURB LOWER-INCOME HOUSING (STRUCTURES)
```

```
SBST.K=SNBS.K+SOBS.K                                    190, A
    SBST    - SUBURB BUSINESS-STRUCTURES TOTAL
                (STRUCTURES)
    SNBS    - SUBURB NEW-BUSINESS STRUCTURES (STRUCTURES)
    SOBS    - SUBURB OLDER-BUSINESS STRUCTURES
                (STRUCTURES)

SUIHPM.K=TABHL(SUIHPMT,SUITPR.K,0,.8,.2)                191, A
SUIHPMT=.4/.6/.8/1/1.1                                  191.1, T
    SUIHPM  - SUBURB UPPER-INCOME-HOUSING POPULATION
                MULTIPLIER (DIMENSIONLESS)
    SUIHPMT- SUBURB UPPER-INCOME-HOUSING POPULATION
                MULTIPLIER TABLE (DIMENSIONLESS)
    SUITPR  - SUBURB UPPER-INCOME TO POPULATION RATIO
                (DIMENSIONLESS)

SUIHTM.K=1                                              192, A
    SUIHTM  - SUBURB UPPER-INCOME-HOUSING TAX MULTIPLIER
                (DIMENSIONLESS)

SUIHEM.K=TABLE(SUIHEMT,SNBSGR.K,-.08,.12,.04)           193, A
SUIHEMT=.8/.9/1/1.1/1.2/1.2                             193.1, T
    SUIHEM  - SUBURB UPPER-INCOME-HOUSING-ENTERPRISE
                MULTIPLIER (DIMENSIONLESS)
    SUIHEMT- SUBURB UPPER-INCOME-HOUSING-ENTERPRISE
                MULTIPLIER TABLE (DIMENSIONLESS)
    SNBSGR  - SUBURB NEW-BUSINESS-STRUCTURES GROWTH RATE
                (PERCENT/YEAR)

SUIHGM.K=TABLE(SUIHGMT,SUIHGR.K,-.1,.15,.05)            194, A
SUIHGMT=.2/.6/1/1.4/1.8/2.2                             194.1, T
    SUIHGM  - SUBURB UPPER-INCOME-HOUSING GROWTH
                MULTIPLIER (DIMENSIONLESS)
    SUIHGMT- SUBURB UPPER-INCOME-HOUSING GROWTH
                MULTIPLIER TABLE (DIMENSIONLESS)
    SUIHGR  - SUBURB UPPER-INCOME-HOUSING GROWTH RATE
                (FRACTION/YEAR)

SUIHGR.K=(SUIH.K-SUIHA.K)/(SUIH.K*SUIHAT)               195, A
    SUIHGR  - SUBURB UPPER-INCOME-HOUSING GROWTH RATE
                (FRACTION/YEAR)
    SUIH    - SUBURB UPPER-INCOME HOUSING (STRUCTURES)
    SUIHA   - SUBURB UPPER-INCOME-HOUSING STRUCTURES
                AVERAGE (HOUSING STRUCTURES)
    SUIHAT  - SUBURB UPPER-INCOME-HOUSING AVERAGING TIME
                (YEARS)

SUIHA.K=SUIHA.J+(DT/SUIHAT)(SUIH.J-SUIHA.J)             196, L
SUIHA=SUIH-(SUIHGRI)(SUIHAT)(SUIH)                      196.1, N
SUIHAT=10                                               196.2, C
SUIHGRI=.015                                            196.3, C
    SUIHA   - SUBURB UPPER-INCOME-HOUSING STRUCTURES
                AVERAGE (HOUSING STRUCTURES)
    SUIHAT  - SUBURB UPPER-INCOME-HOUSING AVERAGING TIME
                (YEARS)
    SUIH    - SUBURB UPPER-INCOME HOUSING (STRUCTURES)
    SUIHGRI- SUBURB UPPER-INCOME- HOUSING GROWTH RATE
                INITIAL (FRACTION/YEAR)

SUIH.K=SUIH.J+(DT)(SUIHC.JK-SUIHO.JK)                   197, L
SUIH=1500                                               197.1, N
    SUIH    - SUBURB UPPER-INCOME HOUSING (STRUCTURES)
    SUIHC   - SUBURB UPPER-INCOME-HOUSING CONSTRUCTION
                (STRUCTURES/YEAR)
    SUIHO   - SUBURB UPPER-INCOME-HOUSING-OBSOLESCENCE
                (STRUCTURES/YEAR)

SUIHO.KL=(SUIHON)(SUIH.K)(SUIHOM.K)                     198, R
SUIHON=.012                                             198.1, C
    SUIHO   - SUBURB UPPER-INCOME-HOUSING-OBSOLESCENCE
                (STRUCTURES/YEAR)
    SUIHON  - SUBURB UPPER-INCOME-HOUSING-OBSOLESCENCE
                NORMAL (FRACTION/YEAR)
    SUIH    - SUBURB UPPER-INCOME HOUSING (STRUCTURES)
    SUIHOM  - SUBURB UPPER-INCOME HOUSING-OBSOLESCENCE
                MULTIPLIER (DIMENSIONLESS)
```

```
SUIHOM.K=TABLE(SUIHOMT,1.44*LOGN(SUIHM.K),-3,3,1)    199, A
SUIHOMT=2.8/2.6/2/1/.5/.3/.2                         199.1, T
    SUIHOM  - SUBURB UPPER-INCOME HOUSING-OBSOLESCENCE
                MULTIPLIER (DIMENSIONLESS)
    SUIHOMT- SUBURB UPPER-INCOME HOUSING-OBSOLESCENCE
                MULTIPLIER TABLE (DIMENSIONLESS)
    SUIHM   - SUBURB UPPER-INCOME-HOUSING MULTIPLIER
                (DIMENSIONLESS)


*****SUBURB LOWER INCOME HOUSING SECTOR
*****

SLIH.K=SLIH.J+(DT)(SUIHO.JK-SLIHD.JK)                200, L
SLIH=200                                             200.1, N
    SLIH    - SUBURB LOWER-INCOME HOUSING (STRUCTURES)
    SUIHO   - SUBURB UPPER-INCOME-HOUSING-OBSOLESCENCE
                (STRUCTURES/YEAR)
    SLIHD   - SUBURB LOWER-INCOME-HOUSING-DEMOLITION RATE
                (STRUCTURES/YEAR)

SLIHD.KL=(SLIHDN)(SLIH.K)(SLIHDM.K)                  201, R
SLIHDN=.02                                           201.1, C
    SLIHD   - SUBURB LOWER-INCOME-HOUSING-DEMOLITION RATE
                (STRUCTURES/YEAR)
    SLIHDN  - SUBURB LOWER-INCOME-HOUSING-DEMOLITION RATE
                NORMAL (STRUCTURES/YEAR)
    SLIH    - SUBURB LOWER-INCOME HOUSING (STRUCTURES)
    SLIHDM  - SUBURB LOWER-INCOME-HOUSING-DEMOLITION
                MULTIPLIER (DIMENSIONLESS)

SLIHDM.K=(SLIHDAM.K)(SLIHDLM.K)(SLIHDF)              202, A
SLIHDF=1                                             202.1, C
    SLIHDM  - SUBURB LOWER-INCOME-HOUSING-DEMOLITION
                MULTIPLIER (DIMENSIONLESS)
    SLIHDAM- SUBURB LOWER-INCOME-HOUSING-DEMOLITION
                ADEQUACY MULTIPLIER (DIMENSIONLESS)
    SLIHDLM- SUBURB LOWER-INCOME-HOUSING-DEMOLITION LAND
                MULTIPLIER (DIMENSIONLESS)
    SLIHDF  - SUBURB LOWER-INCOME-HOUSING-DEMOLITION
                FACTOR (DIMENSIONLESS)

SLIHDAM.K=(SLIHDSM.K)(SLIHATM.K)                     203, A
    SLIHDAM- SUBURB LOWER-INCOME-HOUSING-DEMOLITION
                ADEQUACY MULTIPLIER (DIMENSIONLESS)
    SLIHDSM- SUBURB LOWER-INCOME-HOUSING-DEMOLITION
                SUPPLY MULTIPLIER (DIMEN SIONLESS)
    SLIHATM- SUBURB LOWER-INCOME HOUSING-ABANDONMENT TAX
                MULTIPLIER (DIMENSIONLESS)

SLIHDSM.K=TABLE(SLIHDST,SLIHR.K,0,2,.5)              204, A
SLIHDST=3.6/2/1/.6/.4                                204.1, T
    SLIHDSM- SUBURB LOWER-INCOME-HOUSING-DEMOLITION
                SUPPLY MULTIPLIER (DIMEN SIONLESS)
    SLIHDST- SUBURB LOWER-INCOME-HOUSING-DEMOLITION
                SUPPLY TABLE (DIMENSIONLESS)
    SLIHR   - SUBURB LOWER-INCOME-TO-HOUSING RATIO
                (DIMENSIONLESS)

SLIHATM.K=TABLE(SLIHATT,1.44*LOGN(CTR.K),-2,4,2)     205, A
SLIHATT=1/1/1/1                                      205.1, T
    SLIHATM- SUBURB LOWER-INCOME HOUSING-ABANDONMENT TAX
                MULTIPLIER (DIMENSIONLESS)
    SLIHATT- SUBURB LOWER-INCOME HOUSING-ABANDONMENT TAX
                TABLE (DIMENSIONLESS)
    CTR     - CITY TAX RATIO (DIMENSIONLESS)


SLIHDLM.K=TABHL(SLIHDLT,SLFO.K,.8,1,.05)             206, A
SLIHDLT=1/1.2/1.6/2.2/6                              206.1, T
    SLIHDLM- SUBURB LOWER-INCOME-HOUSING-DEMOLITION LAND
                MULTIPLIER (DIMENSIONLESS)
    SLIHDLT- SUBURB LOWER-INCOME-HOUSING-DEMOLITION LAND
                TABLE (DIMENSIONLESS)
    SLFO    - SUBURB LAND FRACTION OCCUPIED
                (DIMENSIONLESS)
```

```
*****SUBURB NEW BUSINESS STRUCTURES SECTOR
*****

SNBS.K=SNBS.J+(DT)(SNBSC.JK-SNBSO.JK)                    207, L
SNBS=20                                                  207.1, N
    SNBS   - SUBURB NEW-BUSINESS STRUCTURES (STRUCTURES)
    SNBSC  - SUBURB NEW-BUSINESS-STRUCTURES CONSTRUCTION
               (STRUCTURES/YEAR)
    SNBSO  - SUBURB NEW-BUSINESS-STRUCTURES OBSOLESCENCE
               (STRUCTURES/YEAR)

SEM.K=(MEUIWM.K)(SELM.K)(MELIWM.K)(SETM.K)(SEGM.K)       208, A
  (SEF)
SEF=1                                                    208.1, C
    SEM    - SUBURB ENTERPRISE MULTIPLIER
               (DIMENSIONLESS)
    MEUIWM - METROPOLITAN ENTERPRISE UPPER-INCOME-
               WORKFORCE MULTIPLIER (DIMENSIONLESS)
    SELM   - SUBURB ENTERPRISE LAND MULTIPLIER
               (DIMENSIONLESS)
    MELIWM - METROPOLITAN ENTERPRISE LOWER-INCOME-
               WORKFORCE MULTIPLIER (DIMENSIONLESS)
    SETM   - SUBURB ENTERPRISE TAX MULTIPLIER
               (DIMENSIONLESS)
    SEGM   - SUBURB ENTERPRISE GROWTH MULTIPLIER
               (DIMENSIONLESS)
    SEF    - SUBURB ENTERPRISE FACTOR (DIMENSIONLESS)

SELM.K=TABLE(SELMT,SLFO.K,0,1,.1)                        209, A
SELMT=.7/.9/.95/1/1.05/1/.95/.7/.5/.3/0                  209.1, T
    SELM   - SUBURB ENTERPRISE LAND MULTIPLIER
               (DIMENSIONLESS)
    SELMT  - SUBURB ENTERPRISE LAND MULTIPLIER TABLE
               (DIMENSIONLESS)
    SLFO   - SUBURB LAND FRACTION OCCUPIED
               (DIMENSIONLESS)

SEGM.K=TABLE(SEGMT,SNBSGR.K,-.08,.12,.04)                210, A
SEGMT=.8/.9/1/1.3/1.6/2                                  210.1, T
    SEGM   - SUBURB ENTERPRISE GROWTH MULTIPLIER
               (DIMENSIONLESS)
    SEGMT  - SUBURB ENTERPRISE GROWTH MULTIPLIER TABLE
               (DIMENSIONLESS)
    SNBSGR - SUBURB NEW-BUSINESS-STRUCTURES GROWTH RATE
               (PERCENT/YEAR)


SNBSGR.K=(SNBS.K-SNBSA.K)/(SNBS.K*SNBSAT)                211, A
    SNBSGR - SUBURB NEW-BUSINESS-STRUCTURES GROWTH RATE
               (PERCENT/YEAR)
    SNBS   - SUBURB NEW-BUSINESS STRUCTURES (STRUCTURES)
    SNBSA  - SUBURB NEW-BUSINESS-STRUCTURES AVERAGE
               (STRUCTURES)
    SNBSAT - SUBURB NEW-BUSINESS-STRUCTURES AVERAGING
               TIME (YEARS)

SNBSA.K=SNBSA.J+(DT/SNBSAT)(SNBS.J-SNBSA.J)              212, L
SNBSA=SNBS-(SNBSGRI)(SNBSAT)(SNBS)                       212.1, N
SNBSAT=10                                                212.2, C
SNBSGRI=.01                                              212.3, C
    SNBSA  - SUBURB NEW-BUSINESS-STRUCTURES AVERAGE
               (STRUCTURES)
    SNBSAT - SUBURB NEW-BUSINESS-STRUCTURES AVERAGING
               TIME (YEARS)
    SNBS   - SUBURB NEW-BUSINESS STRUCTURES (STRUCTURES)
    SNBSGRI- SUBURB NEW-BUSINESS STRUCTURES GROWTH RATE
               INITIAL (PERCENT/YEAR)

SETM.K=TABLE(SETMT,1.44*LOGN(STR.K),-2,4,1)              213, A
SETMT=1.3/1.2/1/.8/.5/.25/.1                             213.1, T
    SETM   - SUBURB ENTERPRISE TAX MULTIPLIER
               (DIMENSIONLESS)
    SETMT  - SUBURB ENTERPRISE TAX MULTIPLIER TABLE
               (DIMENSIONLESS)
    STR    - SUBURB TAX RATIO (DIMENSIONLESS)
```

```
*****SUBURB OLDER BUSINESS STRUCTURES SECTOR
*****

SNBSO.KL=(SNBSON)(SNBS.K)(SNBSOM.K)                     214, R
SNBSON=.045                                             214.1, C
     SNBSO  - SUBURB NEW-BUSINESS-STRUCTURES OBSOLESCENCE
                (STRUCTURES/YEAR)
     SNBSON - SUBURB NEW-BUSINESS-STRUCTURES OBSOLESCENCE
                NORMAL (PERCENT/YEAR)
     SNBS   - SUBURB NEW-BUSINESS STRUCTURES (STRUCTURES)
     SNBSOM - SUBURB NEW-BUSINESS-STRUCTURES OBSOLESCENCE
                MULTIPLIER (DIMENSIONLESS)

SNBSOM.K=TABLE(SNBSOMT,1.44*LOGN(SEM.K),-3,3,1)         215, A
SNBSOMT=2/1.8/1.5/1/.7/.5/.5                            215.1, T
     SNBSOM - SUBURB NEW-BUSINESS-STRUCTURES OBSOLESCENCE
                MULTIPLIER (DIMENSIONLESS)
     SNBSOMT- SUBURB NEW-BUSINESS-STRUCTURES OBSOLESCENCE
                MULTIPLIER TABLE (DIMENSIONLESS)
     SEM    - SUBURB ENTERPRISE MULTIPLIER
                (DIMENSIONLESS)

SOBS.K=SOBS.J+(DT)(SNBSO.JK-SOBSD.JK)                   216, L
SOBS=15                                                 216.1, N
     SOBS   - SUBURB OLDER-BUSINESS STRUCTURES
                (STRUCTURES)
     SNBSO  - SUBURB NEW-BUSINESS-STRUCTURES OBSOLESCENCE
                (STRUCTURES/YEAR)
     SOBSD  - SUBURB OLDER-BUSINESS-STRUCTURES DEMOLITION
                (STRUCTURES/YEAR)

SOBSD.KL=(SOBSDN)(SOBS.K)(SOBSDM.K)                     217, R
SOBSDN=.02                                              217.1, C
     SOBSD  - SUBURB OLDER-BUSINESS-STRUCTURES DEMOLITION
                (STRUCTURES/YEAR)
     SOBSDN - SUBURB OLDER-BUSINESS-STRUCTURES DEMOLITION
                NORMAL (PERCENT/YEAR)
     SOBS   - SUBURB OLDER-BUSINESS STRUCTURES
                (STRUCTURES)
     SOBSDM - SUBURB OLDER-BUSINESS-STRUCTURES DEMOLITION
                MULTIPLIER (DIMENSIONLESS)

SOBSDM.K=(SOBSEM.K)(SOBSLM.K)(SOBSDF)                   218, A
SOBSDF=1                                                218.1, C
     SOBSDM - SUBURB OLDER-BUSINESS-STRUCTURES DEMOLITION
                MULTIPLIER (DIMENSIONLESS)
     SOBSEM - SUBURB OLDER-BUSINESS-STRUCTURES ENTERPRISE
                MULTIPLIER (DIMENSIONLESS)
     SOBSLM - SUBURB OLDER-BUSINESS-STRUCTURES LAND
                MULTIPLIER (DIMENSIONLESS)
     SOBSDF - SUBURB OLDER-BUSINESS-STRUCTURES DEMOLITION
                FACTOR (DIMENSIONLESS)

SOBSEM.K=TABLE(SOBSEMT,1.44*LOGN(SEM.K),-3,3,1)         219, A
SOBSEMT=.4/.5/.7/1/1.6/2.4/4                            219.1, T
     SOBSEM - SUBURB OLDER-BUSINESS-STRUCTURES ENTERPRISE
                MULTIPLIER (DIMENSIONLESS)
     SOBSEMT- SUBURB OLDER-BUSINESS-STRUCTURES ENTERPRISE
                MULTIPLIER TABLE (DIMENSIONLESS)
     SEM    - SUBURB ENTERPRISE MULTIPLIER
                (DIMENSIONLESS)

SOBSLM.K=TABHL(SOBSLMT,SLFO.K,.8,1,.05)                 220, A
SOBSLMT=1/1.2/1.6/2.2/6                                 220.1, T
     SOBSLM - SUBURB OLDER-BUSINESS-STRUCTURES LAND
                MULTIPLIER (DIMENSIONLESS)
     SOBSLMT- SUBURB OLDER-BUSINESS-STRUCTURES LAND
                MULTIPLIER TABLE (DIMENSIONLESS)
     SLFO   - SUBURB LAND FRACTION OCCUPIED
                (DIMENSIONLESS)
```

```
*****SUBURB LOWER INCOME POPULATION
*****
SLIA.KL=(SLIP.K+SUIS.K)(SLIAN)(SLIAMP.K)                221, R
SLIAN=.03                                               221.1, C
     SLIA    - SUBURB LOWER-INCOME ARRIVALS (MEN/YEAR)
     SLIP    - SUBURB LOWER-INCOME POPULATION (MEN)
     SUIS    - SUBURB(RESIDENT) UPPER-INCOME
                 SUBURB(WORKERS) (MEN)
     SLIAN   - SUBURB LOWER-INCOME ARRIVALS NORMAL
                 (FRACTION/YEAR)
     SLIAMP  - SUBURB LOWER-INCOME-ATTRACTIVENESS
                 MULTIPLIER PERCEIVED (DIMENSIONLESS)

SLIAMP.K=SLIAMP.J+(DT/LIAPT)(SLIAM.J-SLIAMP.J)          222, L
SLIAMP=.6                                               222.1, N
     SLIAMP  - SUBURB LOWER-INCOME-ATTRACTIVENESS
                 MULTIPLIER PERCEIVED (DIMENSIONLESS)
     LIAPT   - LOWER-INCOME-ARRIVALS PERCEPTION TIME
                 (YEARS)
     SLIAM   - SUBURB LOWER-INCOME-ATTRACTIVENESS
                 MULTIPLIER (DIMENSIONLESS)

SLIAM.K=(SLIMM.K)(SLIHSM.K)(SPEM.K)(SLIJM.K)            223, A
     SLIAM   - SUBURB LOWER-INCOME-ATTRACTIVENESS
                 MULTIPLIER (DIMENSIONLESS)
     SLIMM   - SUBURB LOWER-INCOME MOBILITY MULTIPLIER
                 (DIMENSIONLESS)
     SLIHSM  - SUBURB LOWER-INCOME-HOUSING-SUPPLY
                 MULTIPLIER (DIMENSIONLESS)
     SPEM    - SUBURB PUBLIC EXPENDITURES MULTIPLIER
                 (DIMENSIONLESS)
     SLIJM   - SUBURB LOWER-INCOME JOB MULTIPLIER
                 (DIMENSIONLESS)

SLIMM.K=TABLE(SLIMMT,SLIEM.K,0,.15,.025)                224, A
SLIMMT=.3/.7/1/1.2/1.3/1.4/1.5                          224.1, T
     SLIMM   - SUBURB LOWER-INCOME MOBILITY MULTIPLIER
                 (DIMENSIONLESS)
     SLIMMT  - SUBURB LOWER-INCOME MOBILITY MULTIPLIER
                 TABLE (DIMENSIONLESS)
     SLIEM   - SUBURB LOWER-INCOME ECONOMIC MOBILITY
                 (DIMENSIONLESS)

SLIHSM.K=TABLE(SLIHSMT,SLIHR.K,0,2,.25)                 225, A
SLIHSMT=2.5/2.4/2.2/1.7/1/.4/.2/.1/.05                  225.1, T
     SLIHSM  - SUBURB LOWER-INCOME-HOUSING-SUPPLY
                 MULTIPLIER (DIMENSIONLESS)
     SLIHSMT- SUBURB LOWER-INCOME-HOUSING-SUPPLY
                 MULTIPLIER TABLE (DIMENSIONLESS)
     SLIHR   - SUBURB LOWER-INCOME-TO-HOUSING RATIO
                 (DIMENSIONLESS)

SLIHR.K=(SLIP.K*SLIFS)/(SLIH.K*SLIHPD)                  226, A
SLIFS=8                                                 226.1, C
SLIHPD=12                                               226.2, C
     SLIHR   - SUBURB LOWER-INCOME-TO-HOUSING RATIO
                 (DIMENSIONLESS)
     SLIP    - SUBURB LOWER-INCOME POPULATION (MEN)
     SLIFS   - SUBURB LOWER-INCOME FAMILY SIZE (PEOPLE/
                 MAN)
     SLIH    - SUBURB LOWER-INCOME HOUSING (STRUCTURES)
     SLIHPD  - SUBURB LOWER-INCOME-HOUSING POPULATION
                 DENSITY (PEOPLE/STRUCTURE)

SPEM.K=TABLE(SPEMT,STPCR.K,0,3,.5)                      227, A
SPEMT=.2/.6/1/1.6/2.4/3.2/4                             227.1, T
     SPEM    - SUBURB PUBLIC EXPENDITURES MULTIPLIER
                 (DIMENSIONLESS)
     SPEMT   - SUBURB PUBLIC EXPENDITURES MULTIPLIER TABLE
                 (DIMENSIONLESS)
     STPCR   - SUBURB TAX PER CAPITA RATIO (DIMENSIONLESS)

STPCR.K=(STC.K/SP.K)/STPCN                              228, A
STPCN=250                                               228.1, C
     STPCR   - SUBURB TAX PER CAPITA RATIO (DIMENSIONLESS)
     STC     - SUBURB TAX COLLECTION (DOLLARS/YEAR)
     SP      - SUBURB POPULATION (PEOPLE)
     STPCN   - SUBURB TAX PER CAPITA NORMAL (DOLLARS/YEAR/
                 PERSON)
```

```
SP.K=(SUIS.K+SUIC.K)(SUIFS)+(SLIP.K)(SLIFS)              229, A
SUIFS=5.5                                                229.1, C
    SP     - SUBURB POPULATION (PEOPLE)
    SUIS   - SUBURB(RESIDENT) UPPER-INCOME
               SUBURB(WORKERS) (MEN)
    SUIC   - SUBURB(RESIDENT) UPPER-INCOME CITY(WORKERS)
               (MEN)
    SUIFS  - SUBURB UPPER-INCOME FAMILY SIZE (PEOPLE/
               MAN)
    SLIP   - SUBURB LOWER-INCOME POPULATION (MEN)
    SLIFS  - SUBURB LOWER-INCOME FAMILY SIZE (PEOPLE/
               MAN)

SLIJM.K=TABLE(SLIJMT,SLIJR.K,0,3,.25)                    230, A
SLIJMT=2/2/1.9/1.6/1/.6/.4/.3/.2/.15/.1/.05/.02          230.1, T
    SLIJM  - SUBURB LOWER-INCOME JOB MULTIPLIER
               (DIMENSIONLESS)
    SLIJMT - SUBURB LOWER-INCOME JOB MULTIPLIER TABLE
               (DIMENSIONLESS)
    SLIJR  - SUBURB LOWER-INCOME-TO-JOB RATIO
               (DIMENSIONLESS)
SLID.KL=(SLIDN)(SLIP.K)(SLIDM.K)                         231, R
SLIDN=.02                                                231.1, C
    SLID   - SUBURB LOWER-INCOME DEPARTURES (MEN/YEAR)
    SLIDN  - SUBURB LOWER-INCOME DEPARTURES NORMAL
               (FRACTION/YEAR)
    SLIP   - SUBURB LOWER-INCOME POPULATION (MEN)
    SLIDM  - SUBURB LOWER-INCOME DEPARTURES MULTIPLIER
               (DIMENSIONLESS)

SLIDM.K=TABLE(SLIDMT,1.44*LOGN(SLIAM.K),-3,3,1)          232, A
SLIDMT=8/4/2/1/.5/.25/.125                               232.1, T
    SLIDM  - SUBURB LOWER-INCOME DEPARTURES MULTIPLIER
               (DIMENSIONLESS)
    SLIDMT - SUBURB LOWER-INCOME DEPARTURES MULTIPLIER
               TABLE (DIMENSIONLESS)
    SLIAM  - SUBURB LOWER-INCOME-ATTRACTIVENESS
               MULTIPLIER (DIMENSIONLESS)

SLIB.KL=(SLIP.K)(SLIBR)                                  233, R
SLIBR=.015                                               233.1, C
    SLIB   - SUBURB LOWER-INCOME BIRTHS (MEN/YEAR)
    SLIP   - SUBURB LOWER-INCOME POPULATION (MEN)
    SLIBR  - SUBURB LOWER-INCOME BIRTH RATE (FRACTION/
               YEAR)
SLIP.K=SLIP.J+(DT)(SLIA.JK+SLIB.JK-SLID.JK-              234, L
  SLITUI.JK)
SLIP=300                                                 234.1, N
    SLIP   - SUBURB LOWER-INCOME POPULATION (MEN)
    SLIA   - SUBURB LOWER-INCOME ARRIVALS (MEN/YEAR)
    SLIB   - SUBURB LOWER-INCOME BIRTHS (MEN/YEAR)
    SLID   - SUBURB LOWER-INCOME DEPARTURES (MEN/YEAR)
    SLITUI - SUBURB LOWER-INCOME-TO-UPPER-INCOME
               ADVANCEMENT (MEN/YEAR)

SLITUI.KL=(SUMN)(SLIW.K)(SLIEMMP.K)                      235, R
SUMN=.07                                                 235.1, C
    SLITUI - SUBURB LOWER-INCOME-TO-UPPER-INCOME
               ADVANCEMENT (MEN/YEAR)
    SUMN   - SUBURB UPWARD MOBILITY NORMAL (FRACTION/
               YEAR)
    SLIW   - SUBURB LOWER-INCOME WORKERS (MEN)
    SLIEMMP- SUBURB LOWER-INCOME ECONOMIC MOBILITY
               MULTIPLIER PERCEIVED (DIMENSIONLESS)
SLIW.K=(SLIP.K)(SLIFW.K)                                 236, A
    SLIW   - SUBURB LOWER-INCOME WORKERS (MEN)
    SLIP   - SUBURB LOWER-INCOME POPULATION (MEN)
    SLIFW  - SUBURB LOWER-INCOME FRACTION WORKING
               (DIMENSIONLESS)

SLIFW.K=TABLE(SLIFWT,SLIJR.K,0,4,1)                      237, A
SLIFWT=.9/.8/.5/.33/.25                                  237.1, T
    SLIFW  - SUBURB LOWER-INCOME FRACTION WORKING
               (DIMENSIONLESS)
    SLIFWT - SUBURB LOWER-INCOME FRACTION WORKING TABLE
               (DIMENSIONLESS)
    SLIJR  - SUBURB LOWER-INCOME-TO-JOB RATIO
               (DIMENSIONLESS)
```

```
SLITUIP.K=SLITUIP.J+(DT/SLIEAT)(SLITUI.JK-          238, L
  SLITUIP.J)
SLITUIP=10                                          238.1, N
SLIEAT=10                                           238.2, C
    SLITUIP- SUBURB LOWER-INCOME-TO-UPPER-INCOME
               ADVANCEMENT PERCEIVED (DIMENSIONLESS)
    SLIEAT - SUBURB LOWER INCOME ECONOMIC ADVANCEMENT
               TIME (YEARS)
    SLITUI - SUBURB LOWER-INCOME-TO-UPPER-INCOME
               ADVANCEMENT (MEN/YEAR)

SLIEM.K=SLITUIP.K/SLIP.K                            239, A
    SLIEM  - SUBURB LOWER-INCOME ECONOMIC MOBILITY
               (DIMENSIONLESS)
    SLITUIP- SUBURB LOWER-INCOME-TO-UPPER-INCOME
               ADVANCEMENT PERCEIVED (DIMENSIONLESS)
    SLIP   - SUBURB LOWER-INCOME POPULATION (MEN)

SLIEMMP.K=SLIEMMP.J+(DT/SLIEMMT)(SLIEMM.J-          240, L
  SLIEMMP.J)
SLIEMMP=1                                           240.1, N
SLIEMMT=10                                          240.2, C
    SLIEMMP- SUBURB LOWER-INCOME ECONOMIC MOBILITY
               MULTIPLIER PERCEIVED (DIMENSIONLESS)
    SLIEMMT- SUBURB LOWER INCOME ECONOMIC MOBILITY
               MULTIPLIER PERCEPTION TIME (YEARS)
    SLIEMM - SUBURB LOWER-INCOME ECONOMIC MOBILITY
               MULTIPLIER (DIMENSIONLES S)

SLIEMM.K=(SUIWSM.K)(UISLIM.K)(SLIQEM.K)(SLIEMF)     241, A
SLIEMF=1                                            241.1, C
    SLIEMM - SUBURB LOWER-INCOME ECONOMIC MOBILITY
               MULTIPLIER (DIMENSIONLES S)
    SUIWSM - SUBURB UPPER-INCOME-WORKFORCE SUPPLY
               MULTIPLIER (DIMENSIONLESS)
    UISLIM - UPPER-INCOME-TO-SUBURB LOWER-INCOME
               MULTIPLIER (DIMENSIONLESS)
    SLIQEM - SUBURB LOWER-INCOME QUALITY-EDUCATION
               MULTIPLIER (DIMENSIONLESS)
    SLIEMF - SUBURB LOWER-INCOME ECONOMIC MOBILITY
               FACTOR (DIMENSIONLESS)

SUIWSM.K=TABLE(SUIWSMT,UISJR.K,0,2,.5)              242, A
SUIWSMT=2/1.6/1/.4/.2                               242.1, T
    SUIWSM - SUBURB UPPER-INCOME-WORKFORCE SUPPLY
               MULTIPLIER (DIMENSIONLESS)
    SUIWSMT- SUBURB UPPER-INCOME-WORKFORCE SUPPLY
               MULTIPLIER TABLE (DIMENSIONLESS)
    UISJR  - UPPER-INCOME SUBURB JOB RATIO
               (DIMENSIONLESS)

UISLIM.K=TABHL(UISLIMT,UISLIR.K,0,5,1)              243, A
UISLIMT=.2/.7/.9/1/1.1/1.2                          243.1, T
    UISLIM - UPPER-INCOME-TO-SUBURB LOWER-INCOME
               MULTIPLIER (DIMENSIONLESS)
    UISLIMT- UPPER-INCOME-TO-SUBURB LOWER-INCOME
               MULTIPLIER TABLE (DIMENSIONLESS)
    UISLIR - UPPER-INCOME-TO-SUBURB LOWER-INCOME RATIO
               (DIMENSIONLESS)

UISLIR.K=(SUIS.K+SUIC.K)/SLIP.K                     244, A
    UISLIR - UPPER-INCOME-TO-SUBURB LOWER-INCOME RATIO
               (DIMENSIONLESS)
    SUIS   - SUBURB(RESIDENT) UPPER-INCOME
               SUBURB(WORKERS) (MEN)
    SUIC   - SUBURB(RESIDENT) UPPER-INCOME CITY(WORKERS)
               (MEN)
    SLIP   - SUBURB LOWER-INCOME POPULATION (MEN)

SLIQEM.K=TABLE(SLIQEMT,STPCR.K,0,3,.5)              245, A
SLIQEMT=.2/.7/1/1.3/1.5/1.6/1.7                     245.1, T
    SLIQEM - SUBURB LOWER-INCOME QUALITY-EDUCATION
               MULTIPLIER (DIMENSIONLESS)
    SLIQEMT- SUBURB LOWER-INCOME QUALITY-EDUCATION
               MULTIPLIER TABLE (DIMENSIONLESS)
    STPCR  - SUBURB TAX PER CAPITA RATIO (DIMENSIONLESS)
```

```
*****SUBURB JOB SECTOR
*****

SWDC.K=SUIHCD.K*UIHCWN+SNBSCD.K*NBSCWN              246, A
    SWDC   - SUBURB WORKFORCE DESIRED FOR CONSTRUCTION
               (MEN)
    SUIHCD - SUBURB UPPER-INCOME-HOUSING CONSTRUCTION
               DESIRED (STRUCTURES/YEAR)
    UIHCWN - UPPER-INCOME HOUSING-CONSTRUCTION-WORKERS
               NEEDED (MAN-YEARS/HOUSING STRUCTURE)
    SNBSCD - SUBURB NEW-BUSINESS-STRUCTURES CONSTRUCTION
               DESIRED (STRUCTURES/ YEAR)
    NBSCWN - NEW-BUSINESS-STRUCTURES CONSTRUCTION-
               WORKERS NEEDED (MAN-YEARS/STRUCTURE)


SUICJ.K=SUICJ.J+(DT/SCWFAT)(SWDC.J-SUICJ.J)          247, L
SUICJ=100                                            247.1, N
SCWFAT=5                                             247.2, C
    SUICJ  - SUBURB UPPER-INCOME CONSTRUCTION JOBS (MEN)
    SCWFAT - SUBURB CONSTRUCTION WORK FORCE ADJUSTMENT
               TIME (YEARS)
    SWDC   - SUBURB WORKFORCE DESIRED FOR CONSTRUCTION
               (MEN)

SUIJ.K=SUICJ.K+SUIBJ.K                               248, A
    SUIJ   - SUBURB UPPER-INCOME JOBS (MEN)
    SUICJ  - SUBURB UPPER-INCOME CONSTRUCTION JOBS (MEN)
    SUIBJ  - SUBURB UPPER-INCOME BUSINESS JOBS (MEN)


SLIJOM.K=TABLE(SLIJOMT,AUISJR.K,0,2,.5)              249, A
SLIJOMT=1.15/.8/.5/.25/.1                            249.1, T
    SLIJOM - SUBURB LOWER-INCOME JOB-OPPORTUNITY
               MULTIPLIER (DIMENSIONLESS)
    SLIJOMT- SUBURB LOWER-INCOME JOB-OPPORTUNITY
               MULTIPLIER TABLE (DIMENSIONLESS)
    AUISJR - ACCESSIBLE UPPER-INCOME-TO-SUBURB JOB RATIO
               (DIMENSIONLESS)

AUISJR.K=(UISJR.K)((RCJSLI*CUIS.K)+SUIS.K)/(SUIS.K) 250, A
RCJSLI=.3                                            250.1, C
    AUISJR - ACCESSIBLE UPPER-INCOME-TO-SUBURB JOB RATIO
               (DIMENSIONLESS)
    UISJR  - UPPER-INCOME SUBURB JOB RATIO
               (DIMENSIONLESS)
    RCJSLI - REVERSE-COMMUTER JOB-SKILL-LEVEL INDEX
               (DIMENSIONLESS)
    CUIS   - CITY(RESIDENT) UPPER-INCOME SUBURB(WORKERS)
               (MEN)
    SUIS   - SUBURB(RESIDENT) UPPER-INCOME
               SUBURB(WORKERS) (MEN)


SLIJ.K=(SUIJ.K)(SLIJOM.K)                            251, A
    SLIJ   - SUBURB LOWER-INCOME JOBS (MEN)
    SUIJ   - SUBURB UPPER-INCOME JOBS (MEN)
    SLIJOM - SUBURB LOWER-INCOME JOB-OPPORTUNITY
               MULTIPLIER (DIMENSIONLESS)

SLIJR.K=(SLIP.K/SLIJ.K)                              252, A
    SLIJR  - SUBURB LOWER-INCOME-TO-JOB RATIO
               (DIMENSIONLESS)
    SLIP   - SUBURB LOWER-INCOME POPULATION (MEN)
    SLIJ   - SUBURB LOWER-INCOME JOBS (MEN)


SUIBJ.K=(SNBS.K)(UIPCNBS)+(SOBS.K)(UIPCOBS)          253, A
    SUIBJ  - SUBURB UPPER-INCOME BUSINESS JOBS (MEN)
    SNBS   - SUBURB NEW-BUSINESS STRUCTURES (STRUCTURES)
    UIPCNBS- UPPER-INCOME JOBS PER CITY NEW-BUSINESS
               STRUCTURE (MEN/STRUCTURE)
    SOBS   - SUBURB OLDER-BUSINESS STRUCTURES
               (STRUCTURES)
    UIPCOBS- UPPER-INCOME JOBS PER CITY OLDER BUSINESS
               STRUCTURE (MEN/STRUCTURE)
```

```
*****SUBURB TAX SECTOR
*****

STC.K=(SAV.K)(STAN)(STR.K)                                  254, A
STAN=50                                                     254.1, C
     STC     - SUBURB TAX COLLECTION (DOLLARS/YEAR)
     SAV     - SUBURB ASSESSED VALUE (THOUSAND DOLLARS)
     STAN    - SUBURB TAX ASSESSMENT NORMAL (DOLLARS/YEAR/
                 THOUSAND DOLLARS)
     STR     - SUBURB TAX RATIO (DIMENSIONLESS)

STR.K=TABLE(STRT,1.44*LOGN(STRNP.K),-2,4,1)                 255, A
STRT=.3/.5/1/1.8/2.8/3.6/4                                  255.1, T
     STR     - SUBURB TAX RATIO (DIMENSIONLESS)
     STRT    - SUBURB TAX-RATIO TABLE (DIMENSIONLESS)
     STRNP   - SUBURB TAX RATIO NEEDED PERCEIVED
                 (DIMENSIONLESS)

STRNP.K=STRNP.J+(DT/STRNPT)(STRN.J-STRNP.J)                 256, L
STRNP=STRN                                                  256.1, N
STRNPT=30                                                   256.2, C
     STRNP   - SUBURB TAX RATIO NEEDED PERCEIVED
                 (DIMENSIONLESS)
     STRNPT  - SUBURB TAX RATIO NEEDED PERCEPTION TIME
                 (YEARS)
     STRN    - SUBURB TAX RATIO NEEDED (DIMENSIONLESS)

STRN.K=STAI.K/STAN                                          257, A
     STRN    - SUBURB TAX RATIO NEEDED (DIMENSIONLESS)
     STAI    - SUBURB TAX ASSESSMENT INDICATED (DOLLARS/
                 YEAR/THOUSAND DOLLARS)
     STAN    - SUBURB TAX ASSESSMENT NORMAL (DOLLARS/YEAR/
                 THOUSAND DOLLARS)

STAI.K=STN.K/SAV.K                                          258, A
     STAI    - SUBURB TAX ASSESSMENT INDICATED (DOLLARS/
                 YEAR/THOUSAND DOLLARS)
     STN     - SUBURB TAXES NEEDED (DOLLARS/YEAR)
     SAV     - SUBURB ASSESSED VALUE (THOUSAND DOLLARS)


STN.K=(STSUIP*SUIFS*SUIP.K+STSLIP*SLIFS*SLIP.K+             259, A
  STPRCOM*CUIS.K)(STCM.K)
     STN     - SUBURB TAXES NEEDED (DOLLARS/YEAR)
     STSUIP  - SUBURB TAX PER UPPER-INCOME PERSON
                 (DOLLARS/PERSON/YEAR)
     SUIFS   - SUBURB UPPER-INCOME FAMILY SIZE (PEOPLE/
                 MAN)
     SUIP    - SUBURB UPPER-INCOME POPULATION (MEN)
     STSLIP  - SUBURB TAX PER LOWER-INCOME PERSON
                 (DOLLARS/PERSON/YEAR)
     SLIFS   - SUBURB LOWER-INCOME FAMILY SIZE (PEOPLE/
                 MAN)
     SLIP    - SUBURB LOWER-INCOME POPULATION (MEN)
     STPRCOM- SUBURB TAX PER REVERSE COMMUTER (DOLLARS/
                 PERSON/YEAR)
     CUIS    - CITY(RESIDENT) UPPER-INCOME SUBURB(WORKERS)
                 (MEN)
     STCM    - SUBURB TAX COLLECTION MULTIPLIER
                 (DIMENSIONLESS)

SUIP.K=SUIS.K+SUIC.K                                        260, A
STSUIP=190                                                  260.1, C
STSLIP=300                                                  260.2, C
STPRCOM=50                                                  260.3, C
     SUIP    - SUBURB UPPER-INCOME POPULATION (MEN)
     SUIS    - SUBURB(RESIDENT) UPPER-INCOME
                 SUBURB(WORKERS) (MEN)
     SUIC    - SUBURB(RESIDENT) UPPER-INCOME CITY(WORKERS)
                 (MEN)
     STSUIP  - SUBURB TAX PER UPPER-INCOME PERSON
                 (DOLLARS/PERSON/YEAR)
     STSLIP  - SUBURB TAX PER LOWER-INCOME PERSON
                 (DOLLARS/PERSON/YEAR)
     STPRCOM- SUBURB TAX PER REVERSE COMMUTER (DOLLARS/
                 PERSON/YEAR)
```

```
STCM.K=TABHL(STCMT,SUITLIR.K,0,5,1)                       261, A
STCMT=1.4/1.2/1/.9/.8/.8                                  261.1, T
    STCM    - SUBURB TAX COLLECTION MULTIPLIER
                (DIMENSIONLESS)
    STCMT   - SUBURB TAX COLLECTION MULTIPLIER TABLE
                (DIMENSIONLESS)
    SUITLIR- SUBURB UPPER-INCOME-TO-LOWER-INCOME RATIO
                (DIMENSIONLESS)

SUITLIR.K=(SUIS.K+SUIC.K)/SLIP.K                          262, A
    SUITLIR- SUBURB UPPER-INCOME-TO-LOWER-INCOME RATIO
                (DIMENSIONLESS)
    SUIS    - SUBURB(RESIDENT) UPPER-INCOME
                SUBURB(WORKERS) (MEN)
    SUIC    - SUBURB(RESIDENT) UPPER-INCOME CITY(WORKERS)
                (MEN)
    SLIP    - SUBURB LOWER-INCOME POPULATION (MEN)


SAV.K=(SHSAV.K+SBSAV.K)                                   263, A
    SAV     - SUBURB ASSESSED VALUE (THOUSAND DOLLARS)
    SHSAV   - SUBURB HOUSING STRUCTURES ASSESSED VALUE
                (THOUSAND DOLLARS)
    SBSAV   - SUBURB BUSINESS-STRUCTURES ASSESSED VALUE
                (THOUSAND DOLLARS)

SHSAV.K=SUIH.K*SUIHAV+SLIH.K*SLIHAV                       264, A
SUIHAV=18                                                 264.1, C
SLIHAV=5                                                  264.2, C
    SHSAV   - SUBURB HOUSING STRUCTURES ASSESSED VALUE
                (THOUSAND DOLLARS)
    SUIH    - SUBURB UPPER-INCOME HOUSING (STRUCTURES)
    SUIHAV  - SUBURB UPPER-INCOME-HOUSING ASSESSED VALUE
                (THOUSAND DOLLARS)
    SLIH    - SUBURB LOWER-INCOME HOUSING (STRUCTURES)
    SLIHAV  - SUBURB LOWER-INCOME-HOUSING ASSESSED VALUE
                (THOUSIND DOLLARS)

SBSAV.K=SNBS.K*SNBSAV+SOBS.K*SOBSAV                       265, A
SNBSAV=450                                                265.1, C
SOBSAV=150                                                265.2, C
    SBSAV   - SUBURB BUSINESS-STRUCTURES ASSESSED VALUE
                (THOUSAND DOLLARS)
    SNBS    - SUBURB NEW-BUSINESS STRUCTURES (STRUCTURES)
    SNBSAV  - SUBURB NEW-BUSINESS-STRUCTURES ASSESSED
                VALUE (THOUSAND DOLLARS)
    SOBS    - SUBURB OLDER-BUSINESS STRUCTURES
                (STRUCTURES)
    SOBSAV  - SUBURB OLDER-BUSINESS-STRUCTURES ASSESSED
                VALUE (THOUSAND DOLLAR S)

*****URBAN DEVELOPMENT PROGRAMS
*****

CLITP.K=CLITR*CLIP.K*CLIP(0,1,SWT1,TIME.K)                266, A
CLITR=0                                                   266.1, C
SWT1=0                                                    266.2, C
    CLITP   - CITY LOWER-INCOME TRAINING PROGRAM (MEN/
                YEAR)
    CLITR   - CITY LOWER-INCOME TRAINING RATE (FRACTION/
                YEAR)
    SWT1    - SWITCH TIME 1 (YEAR)


CUIHCP.K=CUIHCR*CUIH.K*CUIHLM.K*CLIP(0,1,SWT2,            267, A
  TIME.K)
CUIHCR=0                                                  267.1, C
SWT2=0                                                    267.2, C
    CUIHCP  - CITY UPPER-INCOME-HOUSING-CONSTRUCTION
                PROGRAM (STRUCTURES/YEAR)
    CUIHCR  - CITY UPPER-INCOME-HOUSING-CONSTRUCTION RATE
                (FRACTION/YEAR)
    CUIH    - CITY UPPER-INCOME HOUSING (STRUCTURES)
    CUIHLM  - CITY UPPER-INCOME-HOUSING LAND MULTIPLIER
                (DIMENSIONLESS)
    SWT2    - SWITCH TIME 2 (YEAR)
```

```
CLIHCP.KL=CLIHCPR*CLIP.K*CLIHLM.K*MCWM.K*CLIP(Ø,1,  268, R
  SWT3,TIME.K)
CLIHCPR=Ø                                           268.1, C
SWT3=Ø                                              268.2, C
    CLIHCP  - CITY LOWER-INCOME-HOUSING-CONSTRUCTION
                PROGRAM (STRUCTURES/YEAR)
    CLIHCPR- CITY LOWER-INCOME-HOUSING-CONSTRUCTION RATE
                (FRACTION/YEAR)
    CLIHLM  - CITY LOWER-INCOME-HOUSING LAND MULTIPLIER
                (DIMENSIONLESS)
    MCWM    - METROPOLITAN CONSTRUCTION WORKFORCE
                MULTIPLIER (DIMENSIONLESS)
    SWT3    - SWITCH TIME 3 (YEAR)

CLIHLM.K=TABLE(CLIHLMT,CLFO.K,Ø,1,.1)               269, A
CLIHLMT=.4/.9/1.3/1.6/1.8/1.9/1.8/1.4/.7/.2/Ø       269.1, T
    CLIHLM  - CITY LOWER-INCOME-HOUSING LAND MULTIPLIER
                (DIMENSIONLESS)
    CLIHLMT- CITY LOWER-INCOME-HOUSING LAND MULTIPLIER
                TABLE (DIMENSIONLESS)
    CLFO    - CITY LAND FRACTION OCCUPIED (DIMENSIONLESS)

CLIHDP.K=CLIHDR*CLIH.K*CLIP(Ø,1,SWT4,TIME.K)        270, A
CLIHDR=Ø                                            270.1, C
SWT4=Ø                                              270.2, C
    CLIHDP  - CITY LOWER-INCOME-HOUSING-DEMOLITION
                PROGRAM (STRUCTURES/YEAR)
    CLIHDR  - CITY LOWER-INCOME-HOUSING-DEMOLITION RATE
                (FRACTION/YEAR)
    CLIH    - CITY LOWER-INCOME HOUSING (STRUCTURES)
    SWT4    - SWITCH TIME 4 (YEAR)


CNBSCP.K=(CNBSCR)(CANBSC.K)*CELM.K*CLIP(Ø,1,SWT5,   271, A
  TIME.K)
CNBSCR=Ø                                            271.1, C
SWT5=Ø                                              271.2, C
    CNBSCP  - CITY NEW-BUSINESS-STRUCTURES CONSTRUCTION
                PROGRAM (STRUCTURES/YEAR)
    CNBSCR  - CITY NEW-BUSINESS-STRUCTURES CONSTRUCTION
                RATE (FRACTION/YEAR)
    CANBSC  - CITY AVERAGE-NEW-BUSINESS-STRUCTURES-
                CONSTRUCTION (STRUCTURES/YEAR)
    CELM    - CITY ENTERPRISE LAND MULTIPLIER
                (DIMENSIONLESS)
    SWT5    - SWITCH TIME 5 (YEAR)

CANBSC.K=CANBSC.J+(DT/CANBSCT)(CNBSC.JK-CANBSC.J)   272, L
CANBSC=Ø                                            272.1, N
CANBSCT=2                                           272.2, C
    CANBSC  - CITY AVERAGE-NEW-BUSINESS-STRUCTURES-
                CONSTRUCTION (STRUCTURES/YEAR)
    CANBSCT- CITY AVERAGE-NEW-BUSINESS-STRUCTURES-
                CONSTRUCTION TIME (YEARS)
    CNBSC   - CITY NEW-BUSINESS-STRUCTURES CONSTRUCTION
                (STRUCTURES/YEAR)

COBSDP.K=COBSDR*COBS.K*CLIP(Ø,1,SWT6,TIME.K)        273, A
COBSDR=Ø                                            273.1, C
SWT6=Ø                                              273.2, C
    COBSDP  - CITY OLDER-BUSINESS-STRUCTURES DEMOLITION
                PROGRAM (STRUCTURES/YEAR)
    COBSDR  - CITY OLDER-BUSINESS-STRUCTURES DEMOLITION
                RATE (FRACTION/YEAR)
    COBS    - CITY OLDER-BUSINESS STRUCTURES (STRUCTURES)
    SWT6    - SWITCH TIME 6 (YEAR)

CTPCSP.K=CTPCS*CLIP(Ø,1,SWT7,TIME.K)                274, A
CTPCS=Ø                                             274.1, C
SWT7=Ø                                              274.2, C
    CTPCSP  - CITY TAX PER CAPITA SUBSIDY PROGRAM
                (DOLLARS/PERSON/YEAR)
    CTPCS   - CITY TAX PER CAPITA SUBSIDY (DOLLARS/
                PERSON/YEAR)
    SWT7    - SWITCH TIME 7 (YEAR)
```

```
CLIJP.K=CLIJPC*CLIP.K*CLIP(0,1,SWT8,TIME.K)            275, A
CLIJPC=0                                               275.1, C
SWT8=0                                                 275.2, C
    CLIJP  - CITY LOWER-INCOME JOB PROGRAM (MEN)
    CLIJPC - CITY LOWER-INCOME JOB-PROGRAM COEFFICIENT
               (DIMENSIONLESS)
    SWT8   - SWITCH TIME 8 (YEAR)

SUIHCP.K=SUIHCR*SUIH.K*SUIHLM.K*CLIP(0,1,SWT9,         276, A
  TIME.K)
SUIHCR=0                                               276.1, C
SWT9=0                                                 276.2, C
    SUIHCP - SUBURB UPPER-INCOME HOUSING CONSTRUCTION
               PROGRAM (STRUCTURES/YEAR)
    SUIHCR - SUBURB UPPER-INCOME HOUSING CONSTRUCTION
               RATE (FRACTION/YEAR)
    SUIH   - SUBURB UPPER-INCOME HOUSING (STRUCTURES)
    SUIHLM - SUBURB UPPER-INCOME-HOUSING LAND MULTIPLIER
               (DIMENSIONLESS)
    SWT9   - SWITCH TIME 9 (YEARS)

RTRANEP.K=1*CLIP(1,RTRANPS,SWT10,TIME.K)               277, A
RTRANPS=1                                              277.1, C
SWT10=0                                                277.2, C
    RTRANEP- REGIONAL TRANSPORTATION EXPANSION POLICY
               (DIMENSIONLESS)
    RTRANPS- REGIONAL TRANSPORTATION POLICY SWITCH
               (DIMENSIONLESS)
    SWT10  - SWITCH TIME 10 (YEARS)

TCJ.K=CUIJ.K+CLIJ.K                                    278, S
    TCJ    - TOTAL CITY JOBS (MEN)
    CUIJ   - CITY UPPER-INCOME JOBS (MEN)
    CLIJ   - CITY LOWER-INCOME JOBS (MEN)

TCH.K=CUIH.K+CLIH.K                                    279, S
    TCH    - TOTAL CITY HOUSING (STRUCTURES)
    CUIH   - CITY UPPER-INCOME HOUSING (STRUCTURES)
    CLIH   - CITY LOWER-INCOME HOUSING (STRUCTURES)

TMAV.K=CAV.K+SAV.K                                     280, S
    TMAV   - TOTAL METROPOLITAN ACCESSED VALUE (THOUSAND
               DOLLARS)
    CAV    - CITY ASSESSED VALUE (THOUSAND DOLLARS)
    SAV    - SUBURB ASSESSED VALUE (THOUSAND DOLLARS)

CLITUIF.K=CLITUI.JK/CLIP.K                             281, S
    CLITUIF- CITY LOWER-INCOME TO UPPER-INCOME FRACTION
               (FRACTION/YEAR)
    CLITUI - CITY LOWER-INCOME-TO-UPPER-INCOME
               ADVANCEMENT (MEN/YEAR)

*****CITY UPPER-INCOME HOUSING CONSTRUCTION NORMAL
*****SWITCH--SEE EQ.430
*****

CUIHCN.K=.03*CLIP(1,.66,SWT11,TIME.K)                  282, A
SWT11=2000                                             282.1, C
    CUIHCN - CITY UPPER-INCOME-HOUSING CONSTRUCTION
               NORMAL (FRACTION/YEAR)
    SWT11  - SWITCH TIME 11 (YEARS)

*****CONTROL CARDS
*****

DT=.5                                                  282.5, C
LENGTH=250                                             282.6, C
TIME=TIMEI                                             282.7, N
TIMEI=0                                                282.8, C

PLTPER.K=CLIP(PLTMIN,PLTMAX,PLTCT,TIME.K)              283, A
PLTMIN=5                                               283.1, C
PLTMAX=5                                               283.2, C
PLTCT=500                                              283.3, C
```

```
PRTPER.K=CLIP(PRTMIN,PRTMAX,PRTCT,TIME.K)                 284, A
PRTMIN=Ø                                                  284.1, C
PRTMAX=Ø                                                  284.2, C
PRTCT=5ØØ                                                 284.3, C

PLOT  CUIC=U,CLIP=L,CUIH=B,SUIS=S,SLIP=*,SUIC=C(Ø,        284.4
  8ØØE3)/CNBS=N,COBS=O(Ø,8ØE3)/SNBS=+(Ø,2ØE3)/CP=
  P(Ø,8E6)
    CUIC    - CITY(RESIDENT) UPPER-INCOME CITY(WORKERS)
                (MEN)
    CUIH    - CITY UPPER-INCOME HOUSING (STRUCTURES)
    SUIS    - SUBURB(RESIDENT) UPPER-INCOME
                SUBURB(WORKERS) (MEN)
    SLIP    - SUBURB LOWER-INCOME POPULATION (MEN)
    CNBS    - CITY NEW-BUSINESS STRUCTURES (STRUCTURES)
    COBS    - CITY OLDER-BUSINESS STRUCTURES (STRUCTURES)
    SNBS    - SUBURB NEW-BUSINESS STRUCTURES (STRUCTURES)

PLOT  CLIHR=L,CUIHR=U,UICJR=1,CLIJR=2,MUIJR=M,            284.6
  SLIJR=3(Ø,2)/CLFO=O,SLFO=S(Ø,1)/CTR=T(Ø,8)/
  ACCESM=A(.4,1.2)
    CLIHR   - CITY LOWER-INCOME-TO-HOUSING RATIO
                (DIMENSIONLESS)
    CUIHR   - CITY UPPER-INCOME-TO-HOUSING RATIO
                (DIMENSIONLESS)
    UICJR   - UPPER-INCOME CITY JOB RATIO (DIMENSIONLESS)
    SLIJR   - SUBURB LOWER-INCOME-TO-JOB RATIO
                (DIMENSIONLESS)
    CLFO    - CITY LAND FRACTION OCCUPIED (DIMENSIONLESS)
    SLFO    - SUBURB LAND FRACTION OCCUPIED
                (DIMENSIONLESS)
    CTR     - CITY TAX RATIO (DIMENSIONLESS)
    ACCESM  - ACCESS MULTIPLIER (DIMENSIONLESS)


PLOT  CUIAR=C,CLIA=L,CLID=D,SLIA=+,CLITUI=U,              284.8
  UICCSMR=X(Ø,4ØE3)/SUIAR=S,CUIHC=H,CLIHD=*(Ø,2ØE3)
  /CNBSC=B(Ø,2E3)
    CUIAR   - CITY UPPER-INCOME-ARRIVALS RATE (MEN/YEAR)
    CLIA    - CITY LOWER-INCOME ARRIVALS (MEN/YEAR)
    CLID    - CITY LOWER-INCOME DEPARTURES (MEN/YEAR)
    SLIA    - SUBURB LOWER-INCOME ARRIVALS (MEN/YEAR)
    UICCSMR- UPPER-INCOME CITY(RESIDENT) CITY(WORKERS)
                SUBURB MIGRATION RATE (MEN/YEAR)
    SUIAR   - SUBURB UPPER-INCOME-ARRIVALS RATE (MEN/
                YEAR)
    CUIHC   - CITY UPPER-INCOME-HOUSING CONSTRUCTION
                (STRUCTURES/YEAR)
    CLIHD   - CITY LOWER-INCOME-HOUSING-DEMOLITION RATE
                (STRUCTURES/YEAR)


NOTE
NOTE*****CONTROL CARDS
NOTE*****
C        DT=.5
C        LENGTH=25Ø
N        TIME=TIMEI
C        TIMEI=Ø
A        PLTPER.K=CLIP(PLTMIN,PLTMAX,PLTCT,TIME.K)
C        PLTMIN=5
C        PLTMAX=5
C        PLTCT=5ØØ
A        PRTPER.K=CLIP(PRTMIN,PRTMAX,PRTCT,TIME.K)
C        PRTMIN=Ø
C        PRTMAX=Ø
C        PRTCT=5ØØ
PLOT     CUIC=U,CLIP=L,CUIH=B,SUIS=S,SLIP=*,SUIC=C(Ø,8ØØE3)/
X        CNBS=N,COBS=O(Ø,8ØE3)/SNBS=+(Ø,2ØE3)/CP=P(Ø,8E6)
PLOT     CLIHR=L,CUIHR=U,UICJR=1,CLIJR=2,MUIJR=M,SLIJR=3(Ø,2)/CLFO=O,
X        SLFO=S(Ø,1)/CTR=T(Ø,8)/ACCESM=A(.4,1.2)
PLOT     CUIAR=C,CLIA=L,CLID=D,SLIA=+,CLITUI=U,UICCSMR=X(Ø,4ØE3)/
X        SUIAR=S,CUIHC=H,CLIHD=*(Ø,2ØE3)/CNBSC=B(Ø,2E3)
RUN      FIGURE 12-8A  12-8B  12-8C
PRINT    1)ACCESM,CAV,CDENSM,CEGM,CEM,CETM,CLFO,CLIA,CLIAM,CLIAMP,CLID,
X        CLIDM,CLIEM,2),CLIEMM,CLIEMMP,CLIFW,CLIH,CLIHCP,CLIHD,CLIHDM,
X        CLIHDP,CLIHLM,CLIHR,CLIHSM,CLIJ,CLIJM,3)CLIJP,CLIJR,CLIMM,CLIP,
```

```
X        CLIQEM,CLITUI,CLIW,CNBS,CNBSC,CNBSCF,CNBSCF,CNBSCP,CNBSGR,
X        4)CNBSOM,COBS,COBSD,COBSDM,COBSDP,COBSEM,COBSLM,CP,CPEM,
X        CSLIWM,CSUIWM,CTCM,CTPCR,5)CTR,CTRN,CUIALIM,CUIAM,CUIAMP,CUIAR,
X        CUIBJ,CUIC,CUICD,CUICDM,CUICJ,CUICJR,CUIH,6)CUIHAM,CUIHC,
X        CUIHCP,CUIHEM,CUIHGM,CUIHGR,CUIHLM,CUIHM,CUIHO,CUIHOM,CUIHPM,
X        CUIHR,CUIHSM,7)CUIHTM,CUIJ,CUIJM,CUIRCM,CUIS,CUITM,CWDC,
X        MARCUIM,MELIWM,MELSM,MEUIWM,MUIJR,SELM,8)SEM,SLFO,SLIA,
X        SLIJR,SLIP,SNBS,SNBSC,SNBSOM,SOBS,SOBSEM,SUIAR,SUIBJ,SUIC,
X        9)SUIH,SUIHAM,SUIHC,SUIHLM,SUIHOM,SUIHR,SUIHSM,SUIJM,SUIP,
X        SUIRCM,SUIS,UICCSMR,UICJR
CP       LENGTH=350
CP       PLTMIN=0
CP       PRTCT=289.5
CP       PRTMIN=0
CP       PRTMAX=10
C        CLIHCPR=0.05
C        SWT3=299.5
RUN      FIGURE  12-9
C        CLITR=0.05
C        SWT1=299.5
RUN      FIGURE  12-10
C        CNBSCR=0.4
C        SWT5=299.5
C        CLIHDR=0.05
C        SWT4=299.5
RUN      FIGURE  12-11
```

Appendix B: Definition File for the City-Suburb Model

```
NAME     NO     T  DEFINITION

ACCESM   145    A    12-8B  12-8C
                     ACCESM - ACCESS MULTIPLIER
                     (DIMENSIONLESS)
AMF        3.1  C  ATTRACTIVENESS-FOR-MIGRATION FACTOR
                     (DIMENSIONLESS)
AUICJR    97    A  ACCESIBLE UPPER-INCOME-TO-CITY JOB RATIO
                     (DIMENSIONLESS)
AUISJR   250    A  ACCESSIBLE UPPER-INCOME-TO-SUBURB JOB RATIO
                     (DIMENSIONLESS)
CANBSC   272    L  CITY AVERAGE-NEW-BUSINESS-STRUCTURES-
         272.1  N    CONSTRUCTION (STRUCTURES/YEAR)
CANBSCT  272.2  C  CITY AVERAGE-NEW-BUSINESS-STRUCTURES-
                     CONSTRUCTION TIME (YEARS)
CAREA     47.3  C  CITY AREA (ACRES)
CAV       89    A  CITY ASSESSED VALUE (THOUSAND DOLLARS)
CBSAV     91    A  CITY BUSINESS STRUCTURES ASSESSED VALUE
                     (THOUSAND DOLLARS)
CBST      49    A  CITY BUSINESS STRUCTURES TOTAL (STRUCTURES)
CCJSLI    97.1  C  CONSTANTS FOR COMMUTER JOB-SKILL-LEVELINDEX
                     (DIMENSIONLESS)
CCWAT     93.2  C  CITY CONSTRUCTION WORKFORCE ADJUSTMENT TIME
                     (YEARS)
CDENSM   188    A  CITY DENSITY MULTIPLIER (DIMENSIONLESS)
CDENSMT  188.1  T  CITY DENSITY MULTIPLIER TABLE
                     (DIMENSIONLESS)
CEF       67.1  C  CITY ENTERPRISE FACTOR (DIMENSIONLESS)
CEGM      70    A  CITY ENTERPRISE GROWTH MULTIPLIER
                     (DIMENSIONLESS)
CEGMT     70.1  T  CITY ENTERPRISE GROWTH MULTIPLIER TABLE
                     (DIMENSIONLESS)
CELCM    165    A  CITY ENTERPRISE LOCAL-CONDITIONS MULTIPLIER
                     (DIMENSIONLESS)
CELM      68    A  CITY ENTERPRISE LAND MULTIPLIER
                     (DIMENSIONLESS)
CELMT     68.1  T  CITY ENTERPRISE LAND MULTIPLIER TABLE
                     (DIMENSIONLESS)
CEM       67    A  CITY ENTERPRISE MULTIPLIER (DIMENSIONLESS)
CETM      69    A  CITY ENTERPRISE TAX MULTIPLIER
                     (DIMENSIONLESS)
CETMT     69.1  T  CITY ENTERPRISE TAX MULTIPLIER TABLE
                     (DIMENSIONLESS)
CHSAV     90    A  CITY HOUSING STRUCTURES ASSESSED VALUE
                     (THOUSAND DOLLARS)
```

CHT	48	A	CITY HOUSING TOTAL (STRUCTURES)
CLFO	47	A	CITY LAND FRACTION OCCUPIED (DIMENSIONLESS)
CLIA	1	R	CITY LOWER-INCOME ARRIVALS (MEN/YEAR)
CLIAM	3	A	CITY LOWER-INCOME ATTRACTIVENESS MULTIPLIER (DIMENSIONLESS)
CLIAMP	2	L	CITY LOWER-INCOME ATTRACTIVENESS MULTIPLIER PERCEIVED (DIMENSIONLESS)
	2.1	N	
CLIAN	1.1	C	CITY LOWER-INCOME ARRIVALS NORMAL(FRACTION/ YEAR)
CLIB	15	R	CITY LOWER-INCOME BIRTHS (MEN/YEAR)
CLIBR	15.1	C	CITY LOWER-INCOME BIRTH RATE (FRACTION/ YEAR)
CLID	13	R	CITY LOWER-INCOME DEPARTURES (MEN/YEAR)
CLIDM	14	A	CITY LOWER-INCOME DEPARTURES MULTIPLIER (DIMENSIONLESS)
CLIDMT	14.1	T	CITY LOWER-INCOME DEPARTURES MULTIPLIER TABLE (DIMENSIONLESS)
CLIDN	13.1	C	CITY LOWER-INCOME DEPARTURES NORMAL (FRACTION/YEAR)
CLIEAT	20.2	C	CITY LOWER-INCOME ECONOMIC ADVANCEMENT TIME (YEARS)
CLIEM	21	A	CITY LOWER-INCOME ECONOMIC MOBILITY (FRACTION/YEAR)
CLIEMF	23.1	C	CITY LOWER-INCOME ECONOMIC MOBILITY FACTOR (DIMENSIONLESS)
CLIEMM	23	A	CITY LOWER-INCOME ECONOMIC MOBILITY MULTIPLIER (DIMENSIONLESS)
CLIEMMP	22	L	CITY LOWER-INCOME ECONOMIC MOBILITY MULTIPLIER PERCEIVED (DIMENSIONLESS)
	22.1	N	
CLIEMPT	22.2	C	CITY LOWER-INCOME ECONOMIC MOBILITY PERCEPTION TIME (YEARS)
CLIFS	9.2	C	CITY LOWER-INCOME FAMILY SIZE (PEOPLE/MAN)
CLIFW	19	A	CITY LOWER-INCOME FRACTION WORKING (DIMENSIONLESS)
CLIFWT	19.1	T	CITY LOWER-INCOME FRACTION WORKING TABLE (DIMENSIONLESS)
CLIH	59	L	CITY LOWER-INCOME HOUSING (STRUCTURES)
	59.1	N	
CLIHATM	64	A	CITY LOWER-INCOME HOUSING-ABANDONMENT TAX MULTIPLIER (DIMENSIONLESS)
CLIHATT	64.1	T	CITY LOWER-INCOME HOUSING-ABANDONMENT TAX MULTIPLIER TABLE (DIMENSIONLESS)
CLIHAV	90.2	C	CITY LOWER-INCOME-HOUSING ASSESSED VALUE (THOUSAND DOLLARS)
CLIHCP	268	R	CITY LOWER-INCOME-HOUSING-CONSTRUCTION PROGRAM (STRUCTURES/YEAR)
CLIHCPM	11	A	CITY LOWER-INCOME-HOUSING-CONSTRUCTION-PROGRAM MULTIPLIER (DIMENSIONLESS)
CLIHCPR	268.1	C	CITY LOWER-INCOME-HOUSING-CONSTRUCTION RATE (FRACTION/YEAR)
CLIHCPT	11.1	T	CITY LOWER-INCOME-HOUSING-CONSTRUCTION-PROGRAM TABLE (DIMENSIONLESS)
CLIHD	60	R	CITY LOWER-INCOME-HOUSING-DEMOLITION RATE (STRUCTURES/YEAR)
CLIHDAM	62	A	CITY LOWER-INCOME DEMOLITION ADEQUACY MULTIPLIER (DIMENSIONLESS)
CLIHDF	61.1	C	CITY LOWER-INCOME-HOUSING-DEMOLITION FACTOR (DIMENSIONLESS)
CLIHDLM	65	A	CITY LOWER-INCOME HOUSING DEMOLITION LAND MULTIPLIER (DIMENSIONLESS)
CLIHDLT	65.1	T	CITY LOWER-INCOME HOUSING DEMOLITION LAND TABLE (DIMENSIONLESS)
CLIHDM	61	A	CITY LOWER-INCOME-HOUSING-DEMOLITION MULTIPLIER (DIMENSIONLESS)
CLIHDN	60.1	C	CITY LOWER-INCOME-HOUSING-DEMOLITION RATE NORMAL (FRACTION/YEAR)
CLIHDP	270	A	CITY LOWER-INCOME-HOUSING-DEMOLITIONPROGRAM (STRUCTURES/YEAR)
CLIHDR	270.1	C	CITY LOWER-INCOME-HOUSING-DEMOLITION RATE (FRACTION/YEAR)
CLIHDSM	63	A	CITY LOWER-INCOME-HOUSING-DEMOLITION SUPPLY MULTIPLIER (DIMENSIONLESS)
CLIHDST	63.1	T	CITY LOWER-INCOME-HOUSING-DEMOLITION SUPPLY TABLE (DIMENSIONLESS)
CLIHLM	269	A	CITY LOWER-INCOME-HOUSING LAND MULTIPLIER (DIMENSIONLESS)

```
CLIHLMT 269.1 T  CITY LOWER-INCOME-HOUSING LAND MULTIPLIER
                   TABLE (DIMENSIONLESS)
CLIHPD    6.1 C  CITY LOWER-INCOME HOUSING POPULATIONDENSITY
                   (PEOPLE/HOUSING UNIT)
CLIHPR   12   A  CITY LOWER-INCOME-HOUSING-PROGRAM RATE
                   (HOUSING UNITS/YEAR)
CLIHR     6   A  CITY LOWER-INCOME-TO-HOUSING RATIO
                   (DIMENSIONLESS)
CLIHSM    5   A  CITY LOWER-INCOME-HOUSING-SUPPLY MULTIPLIER
                   (DIMENSIONLESS)
CLIHSMT   5.1 T  CITY LOWHR-INCOME-HOUSING-SUPPLY MULTIPLIER
                   TABLE (DIMENSIONLESS)
CLIJ     98   A  CITY LOWER-INCOME JOBS (MEN)
CLIJM    10   A  CITY LOWER-INCOME JOB MULTIPLIER
                   (DIMENSIONLESS)
CLIJMT   10.1 T  CITY LOWER-INCOME JOB MULTIPLIER TABLE
                   (DIMENSIONLESS)
CLIJOM   96   A  CITY LOWER-INCOME JOB-OPPORTUNITYMULTIPLIER
                   (DIMENSIONLESS)
CLIJOMT  96.1 T  CITY LOWER-INCOME JOB-OPPORTUNITY
                   MULTIPLIER TABLE (DIMENSIONLESS)
CLIJP   275   A  CITY LOWER-INCOME JOB PROGRAM (MEN)
CLIJPC  275.1 C  CITY LOWER-INCOME JOB-PROGRAM COEFFICIENT
                   (DIMENSIONLESS)
CLIJR    99   A  CITY LOWER-INCOME-TO-JOB RATIO
                   (DIMENSIONLESS)
CLIMM     4   A  CITY LOWER-INCOME MOBILITY MULTIPLIER
                   (DIMENSIONLESS)
CLIMMT    4.1 T  CITY LOWER-INCOME MOBILITY MULTIPLIER TABLE
                   (DIMENSIONLESS)
CLIP     16   L  CITY LOWER-INCOME POPULATION (MEN)
         16.1 N

CLIQEM   27   A  CITY LOWER-INCOME QUALITY-EDUCATION
                   MULTIPLIER (DIMENSIONLESS)
CLIQEMT  27.1 T  CITY LOWER-INCOME QUALITY-EDUCATION
                   MULTIPLIER TABLE (DIMENSIONLESS)
CLITP   266   A  CITY LOWER-INCOME TRAINING PROGRAM (MEN/
                   YEAR)
CLITR   266.1 C  CITY LOWER-INCOME TRAINING RATE (FRACTION/
                   YEAR)
CLITUI   17   R  CITY LOWER-INCOME-TO-UPPER-INCOME
                   ADVANCEMENT (MEN/YEAR)
CLITUIF 281   S  CITY LOWER-INCOME TO UPPER-INCOME FRACTION
                   (FRACTION/YEAR)
CLITUIP  20   L  CITY LOWER-INCOME-TO-UPPER-INCOME
         20.1 N    ADVANCEMENT PERCEIVED (DIMENSIONLESS)
CLIW     18   A  CITY LOWER-INCOME WORKERS (MEN)
CLPBS    47.2 C  CITY LAND PER BUSINESS STRUCTURE (ACRES/
                   STRUCTURE)
CLPH     47.1 C  CITY LAND PER HOUSING STRUCTURE (ACRES/
                   STRUCTURE)
CNBS     66   L  CITY NEW-BUSINESS STRUCTURES (STRUCTURES)
         66.1 N
CNBSA    72   L  CITY NEW-BUSINESS-STRUCTURES AVERAGE
         72.1 N    (STRUCTURES)
CNBSAT   72.2 C  CITY NEW-BUSINESS-STRUCTURES AVERAGING TIME
                   (YEARS)
CNBSAV   91.1 C  CITY NEW-BUSINESS-STRUCTURES ASSESSED VALUE
                   (THOUSAND DOLLARS)
CNBSC   167   R  CITY NEW-BUSINESS-STRUCTURES CONSTRUCTION
                   (STRUCTURES/YEAR)
CNBSCD  168   A  CITY NEW-BUSINESS-STRUCTURES CONSTRUCTION
                   DESIRED (STRUCTURES/YEAR)
CNBSCF  169   A  CITY NEW-BUSINESS-STRUCTURES CONSTRUCTION
                   FRACTION (DIMENSIONLESS)
CNBSCFT 169.1 T  CITY NEW-BUSINESS-STRUCTURES CONSTRUCTION
                   FRACTION TABLE (DIMENSIONLESS)
CNBSCM  171   A  CITY NEW-BUSINESS-STRUCTURES CONSTRUCTION
                   MULTIPLIER (DIMENSIONLESS)
CNBSCP  271   A  CITY NEW-BUSINESS-STRUCTURES CONSTRUCTION
                   PROGRAM (STRUCTURES/YEAR)
CNBSCR  271.1 C  CITY NEW-BUSINESS-STRUCTURES CONSTRUCTION
                   RATE (FRACTION/YEAR)
```

CNBSGR	71	A	CITY NEW-BUSINESS-STRUCTURES GROWTH RATE (PERCENT/YEAR)
CNBSGRI	72.3	C	CITY NEW-BUSINESS-STRUCTURES GROWTH RATE INITIAL (PERCENT/YEAR)
CNBSO	73	R	CITY NEW-BUSINESS-STRUCTURES OBSOLESCENCE (STRUCTURES/YEAR)
CNBSOM	74	A	CITY NEW-BUSINESS-STRUCTURES OBSOLESCENCE MULTIPLIER (DIMENSIONLESS)
CNBSOMT	74.1	T	CITY NEW-BUSINESS-STRUCTURES OBSOLESCENCE MULTIPLIER TABLE (DIMENSIONLESS)
CNBSON	73.1	C	CITY NEW-BUSINESS-STRUCTURES OBSOLESCENCE NORMAL (PERCENT/YEAR)
CNBSWF	153.3	C	CITY NEW-BUSINESS-STRUCTURES WEIGHTING FACTOR
COBS	75	L	CITY OLDER-BUSINESS STRUCTURES (STRUCTURES)
	75.1	N	
COBSAV	91.2	C	CITY OLDER-BUSINESS-STRUCTURES ASSESSED VALUE (THOUSAND DOLLARS)
COBSD	76	R	CITY OLDER-BUSINESS-STRUCTURES DEMOLITION (STRUCTURES/YEAR)
COBSDF	77.1	C	CITY OLDER-BUSINESS-STRUCTURES DEMOLITION FACTOR (DIMENSIONLESS)
COBSDM	77	A	CITY OLDER-BUSINESS-STRUCTURES DEMOLITION MULTIPLIER (DIMENSIONLESS)
COBSDN	76.1	C	CITY OLDER-BUSINESS-STRUCTURES DEMOLITION NORMAL (PERCENT/YEAR)
COBSDP	273	A	CITY OLDER-BUSINESS-STRUCTURES DEMOLITION PROGRAM (STRUCTURES/YEAR)
COBSDR	273.1	C	CITY OLDER-BUSINESS-STRUCTURES DEMOLITION RATE (FRACTION/YEAR)
COBSEM	78	A	CITY OLDER-BUSINESS-STRUCTURES ENTERPRISE MULTIPLIER (DIMENSIONLESS)
COBSEMT	78.1	T	CITY OLDER-BUSINESS-STRUCTURES ENTERPRISE MULTIPLIER TABLE (DIMENSIONLESS)
COBSLM	79	A	CITY OLDER-BUSINESS-STRUCTURES LAND MULTIPLIER (DIMENSIONLESS)
COBSLMT	79.1	T	CITY OLDER-BUSINESS-STRUCTURES LAND MULTIPLIER TABLE (DIMENSIONLESS)
COBSWF	153.5	C	CITY OLDER-BUSINESS-STRUCTURES WEIGHTING FACTOR (DIMENSIONLESS)
CP	9	A	CITY POPULATION (PEOPLE)
CPEM	7	A	CITY PUBLIC EXPENDITURES MULTIPLIER (DIMENSIONLESS)
CPEMT	7.1	T	CITY PUBLIC EXPENDITURES MULTIPLIER TABLE (DIMENSIONLESS)
CRTNBS	165.1	C	CITY RECEPTIVENESS TO NEW-BUSINESS STRUCTURES (DIMENSIONLESS)
CSLIWM	174	A	CITY/SUBURB LOWER-INCOME WORKFORCE MULTIPLIER (DIMENSIONLESS)
CSLIWR	175	A	CITY/SUBURB LOWER-INCOME WORKFORCE RATIO (DIMENSIONLESS)
CSLIWT	174.1	T	CITY/SUBURB LOWER-INCOME WORKFORCE TABLE (DIMENSIONLESS)
CSRBAM	176	A	CITY/SUBURB RELATIVE BUSINESS-ACTIVITY MULTIPLIER (DIMENSIONLESS)
CSRBAMT	176.1	T	CITY/SUBURB RELATIVE BUSINESS-ACTIVITY MULTIPLIER TABLE (DIMENSIONLESS)
CSRBAR	177	A	CITY/SUBURB RELATIVE BUSINESS-ACTIVITYRATIO (DIMENSIONLESS)
CSRNBAM	170	A	CITY/SUBURB RELATIVE NEW-BUSINESS-ATTRACTION MULTIPLIER
CSRRAF	131.2	C	CITY/SUBURB RELATIVE RESIDENTIAL-ATTRACTIVENESS FACTOR (DIMENSIONLESS)
CSRRAM	132	A	CITY/SUBURB RELATIVE RESIDENTIAL-ATTRACTIVENESS MULTIPLIER (DIMENSIONLESS)
CSRRAMT	132.1	T	CITY/SUBURB RELATIVE RESIDENTIAL-ATTRACTIVENESS MULTIPLIER TABLE (DIMENSIONLESS)
CSRRAR	133	A	CITY/SUBURB RELATIVE RESIDENTIAL-ATTRACTIVENESS RATIO (DIMENSIONLESS)
CSUIWM	172	A	CITY/SUBURB UPPER-INCOME WORKFORCE MULTIPLIER (DIMENSIONLESS)
CSUIWR	173	A	CITY/SUBURB UPPER-INCOME WORKFORCE RATIO (DIMENSIONLESS)
CSUIWT	172.1	T	CITY/SUBURB UPPER-INCOME WORKFORCE TABLE (DIMENSIONLESS)
CTAI	84	A	CITY TAX ASSESSMENT INDICATED (DOLLARS/YEAR/THOUSAND DOLLARS)

Name	Equation	Type	Definition
CTAN	80.1	C	CITY TAX ASSESSMENT NORMAL (DOLLARS/YEAR/ THOUSAND DOLLARS)
CTC	80	A	CITY TAX COLLECTIONS (DOLLARS/YEAR)
CTCLIP	86.2	C	CITY TAX PER LOWER-INCOME PERSON (DOLLARS/ PERSON/YEAR)
CTCM	87	A	CITY TAX COLLECTION MULTIPLIER (DIMENSIONLESS)
CTCMT	87.1	T	CITY TAX COLLECTION MULTIPLIER TABLE (DIMENSIONLESS)
CTCUIP	86.1	C	CITY TAX PER UPPER-INCOME PERSON (DOLLARS/ PERSON/YEAR)
CTN	85	A	CITY TAXES NEEDED (DOLLARS/YEAR)
CTPCN	8.1	C	CITY TAX PER CAPITA NORMAL (DOLLARS/YEAR/ PERSON)
CTPCOMM	86.3	C	CITY TAX PER COMMUTER (DOLLARS/PERSON/YEAR)
CTPCR	8	A	CITY TAX PER CAPITA RATIO (DIMENSIONLESS)
CTPCS	274.1	C	CITY TAX PER CAPITA SUBSIDY (DOLLARS/ PERSON/YEAR)
CTPCSP	274	A	CITY TAX PER CAPITA SUBSIDY PROGRAM (DOLLARS/PERSON/YEAR)
CTR	81	A	CITY TAX RATIO (DIMENSIONLESS)
CTRN	83	A	CITY TAX RATIO NEEDED (DIMENSIONLESS)
CTRNP	82 82.1	L N	CITY TAX RATIO NEEDED PERCEIVED (DIMENSIONLESS)
CTRNPT	82.2	C	CITY TAX RATIO NEEDED PERCEPTION TIME (YEARS)
CTRT	81.1	T	CITY TAX-RATIO TABLE (DIMENSIONLESS)
CUIAF	32.1	C	CITY UPPER-INCOME-ARRIVALS FACTOR (DIMENSIONLESS)
CUIALIM	35	A	CITY UPPER-INCOME-ARRIVALS LOWER-INCOME MULTIPLIER (DIMENSIONLESS)
CUIALIT	35.1	T	CITY UPPER-INCOME-ARRIVALS LOWER-INCOME TABLE (DIMENSIONLESS)
CUIAM	32	A	CITY UPPER-INCOME-ARRIVALS MULTIPLIER (DIMENSIONLESS)
CUIAMP	31 31.1	L N	CITY UPPER-INCOME-ARRIVALS MULTIPLIER PERCEIVED (DIMENSIONLESS)
CUIAMPT	31.2	C	CITY UPPER-INCOME-ARRIVALS MULTIPLIER PERCEPTION TIME (YEARS)
CUIAR	111	R	CITY UPPER-INCOME-ARRIVALS RATE (MEN/YEAR)
CUIBJ	94	A	CITY UPPER-INCOME BUSINESS JOBS (MEN)
CUIBR	28.1	C	CITY UPPER-INCOME CITY BIRTH RATE(FRACTION/ YEAR)
CUIC	29 29.2	L N	CITY(RESIDENT) UPPER-INCOME CITY(WORKERS) (MEN)
CUICB	28	R	CITY UPPER-INCOME CITY BIRTHS (MEN/YEAR)
CUICD	40	R	CITY UPPER-INCOME CITY DEPARTURES (MEN/ YEAR)
CUICDM	41	A	CITY UPPER-INCOME CITY DEPARTURESMULTIPLIER (DIMENSIONLESS)
CUICDMT	41.1	T	CITY UPPER-INCOME CITY DEPARTURES MULTIPLIER TABLE (DIMENSIONLESS)
CUICDN	40.1	C	CITY UPPER-INCOME CITY DEPARTURES NORMAL (FRACTION/YEAR)
CUICJ	93 93.1	L N	CITY UPPER-INCOME CONSTRUCTION JOBS (MEN)
CUICJR	34	A	CITY UPPER-INCOME-TO-CITY JOB RATIO (DIMENSIONLESS)
CUIFS	9.1	C	CITY UPPER-INCOME FAMILY SIZE (PEOPLE/MAN)
CUIH	56 56.1	L N	CITY UPPER-INCOME HOUSING (STRUCTURES)
CUIHA	55 55.1	L N	CITY UPPER-INCOME-HOUSING AVERAGE (HOUSING STRUCTURES)
CUIHAM	45	A	CITY UPPER-INCOME-HOUSING AVAILABILITY MULTIPLIER (DIMENSIONLESS)
CUIHAMT	45.1	T	CITY UPPER-INCOME-HOUSING AVAILABILITY MULTIPLIER TABLE (DIMENSIONLESS)
CUIHAT	55.2	C	CITY UPPER-INCOME-HOUSING AVERAGING TIME (YEARS)
CUIHAV	90.1	C	CITY UPPER-INCOME-HOUSING ASSESSED VALUE (THOUSAND DOLLARS)
CUIHC	42	R	CITY UPPER-INCOME-HOUSING CONSTRUCTION (STRUCTURES/YEAR)
CUIHCD	43	A	CITY UPPER-INCOME-HOUSING CONSTRUCTION DESIRED (STRUCTURES/YEAR)

CUIHCN	282	A	CITY UPPER-INCOME-HOUSING CONSTRUCTION NORMAL (FRACTION/YEAR)
CUIHCP	267	A	CITY UPPER-INCOME-HOUSING-CONSTRUCTION PROGRAM (STRUCTURES/YEAR)
CUIHCR	267.1	C	CITY UPPER-INCOME-HOUSING-CONSTRUCTION RATE (FRACTION/YEAR)
CUIHEM	52	A	CITY UPPER-INCOME-HOUSING-ENTERPRISE MULTIPLIER (DIMENSIONLESS)
CUIHEMT	52.1	T	CITY UPPER-INCOME-HOUSING-ENTERPRISE MULTIPLIER TABLE (DIMENSIONLESS)
CUIHF	44.2	C	CITY UPPER-INCOME-HOUSING FACTOR (DIMENSIONLESS)
CUIHGM	53	A	CITY UPPER-INCOME-HOUSING GROWTH MULTIPLIER (DIMENSIONLESS)
CUIHGMT	53.1	T	CITY UPPER-INCOME-HOUSING GROWTH MULTIPLIER TABLE (DIMENSIONLESS)
CUIHGR	54	A	CITY UPPER-INCOME-HOUSING GROWTH RATE (FRACTION/YEAR)
CUIHGRI	55.3	C	CITY UPPER-INCOME-HOUSING GROWTH RATE INITIAL (FRACTION/YEAR)
CUIHLM	46	A	CITY UPPER-INCOME-HOUSING LAND MULTIPLIER (DIMENSIONLESS)
CUIHLMT	46.1	T	CITY UPPER-INCOME-HOUSING LAND MULTIPLIER TABLE (DIMENSIONLESS)
CUIHM	44	A	CITY UPPER-INCOME-HOUSING MULTIPLIER (DIMENSIONLESS)
CUIHO	57	R	CITY UPPER-INCOME HOUSING OBSOLESCENCE (STRUCTURES/YEAR)
CUIHOM	58	A	CITY UPPER-INCOME HOUSING-OBSOLESCENCE MULTIPLIER (DIMENSIONLESS)
CUIHOMT	58.1	T	CITY UPPER-INCOME HOUSING OBSOLESCENCE MULTIPLIER TABLE (DIMENSIONLESS)
CUIHON	57.1	C	CITY UPPER-INCOME HOUSING-OBSOLESCENCE NORMAL (FRACTION/YEAR)
CUIHPD	39.1	C	CITY UPPER-INCOME-HOUSING POPULATIONDENSITY (PEOPLE/HOUSING UNIT)
CUIHPM	50	A	CITY UPPER-INCOME-HOUSING POPULATION MULTIPLIER (DIMENSIONLESS)
CUIHPMT	50.1	T	CITY UPPER-INCOME-HOUSING POPULATION MULTIPLIER TABLE (DIMENSIONLESS)
CUIHR	39	A	CITY UPPER-INCOME-TO-HOUSING RATIO (DIMENSIONLESS)
CUIHSM	38	A	CITY UPPER-INCOME HOUSING-SUPPLY MULTIPLIER (DIMENSIONLESS)
CUIHSMT	38.1	T	CITY UPPER-INCOME HOUSING-SUPPLY MULTIPLIER TABLE (DIMENSIONLESS)
CUIHTM	51	A	CITY UPPER-INCOME-HOUSING TAX MULTIPLIER (DIMENSIONLESS)
CUIHTMT	51.1	T	CITY UPPER-INCOME-HOUSING TAX MULTIPLIER TABLE (DIMENSIONLESS)
CUIJ	95	A	CITY UPPER-INCOME JOBS (MEN)
CUIJM	33	A	CITY UPPER-INCOME JOB MULTIPLIER (DIMENSIONLESS)
CUIJMT	34.1	T	CITY UPPER-INCOME JOB MULTIPLIER TABLE (DIMENSIONLESS)
CUIP	86	A	CITY UPPER-INCOME POPULATION (MEN)
CUIRCAT	134.2	C	CITY UPPER-INCOME RESIDENTIAL-CONDITIONS AVERAGING TIME (YEARS)
CUIRCM	108	A	CITY UPPER-INCOME RESIDENTIAL-CONDITIONS MULTIPLIER (DIMENSIONLESS)
CUIRCMP	134 134.1	L N	CITY UPPER-INCOME RESIDENTIAL-CONDITIONS MULTIPLIER PERCEIVED (DIMENSIONLESS)
CUIS	139 139.1	L N	CITY(RESIDENT) UPPER-INCOME SUBURB(WORKERS) (MEN)
CUISBN	141.1	C	CITY UPPER-INCOME SUBURB NET BIRTHS NORMAL (FRACTION/YEAR)
CUISD	143	R	CITY UPPER-INCOME SUBURB DEPARTURES (MEN/YEAR)
CUISDM	144	A	CITY UPPER-INCOME SUBURB DEPARTURES MULTIPLIER (DIMENSIONLESS)
CUISDMT	144.1	T	CITY UPPER-INCOME SUBURB DEPARTURES MULTIPLIER TABLE (DIMENSIONLESS)
CUISDN	143.1	C	CITY UPPER-INCOME SUBURB DEPARTURES NORMAL (FRACTION/YEAR)
CUISNB	141	R	CITY UPPER-INCOME SUBURB NET BIRTHS (MEN/YEAR)

```
CUITLIR  88    A  CITY UPPER-INCOME-TO-LOWER-INCOME RATIO
                     (DIMENSIONLESS)
CUITM     37   A  CITY UPPER-INCOME TAX MULTIPLIER
                     (DIMENSIONLESS)
CUITMT    37.1 T  CITY UPPER-INCOME TAX MULTIPLIER TABLE
                     (DIMENSIONLESS)
CUITPR    36   A  CITY UPPER-INCOME TO POPULATION RATIO
                     (DIMENSIONLESS)
CUIWSM    24   A  CITY UPPER-INCOME WORKFORCE SUPPLY
                     MULTIPLIER (DIMENSIONLESS)
CUIWSMT   24.1 T  CITY UPPER-INCOME WORKFORCE SUPPLY
                     MULTIPLIER TABLE (DIMENSIONLESS)
CUMN      17.1 C  CITY UPWARD MOBILITY NORMAL (FRACTION/YEAR)
CWDC      92   A  CITY WORKFORCE DESIRED FOR CONSTRUCTION
                     (MEN)
DT       282.5 C
LENGTH   282.6 C
LIAPT      2.2 C  LOWER-INCOME-ARRIVALS PERCEPTION TIME
                     (YEARS)
LIHCWN    92.2 C  LOWER-INCOME-HOUSING CONSTRUCTION WORKERS
                     NEEDED (MAN-YEARS/HOUSING STRUCTURE)
MARCUIM 107    A  METROPOLITAN AVERAGE RESIDENTIAL-CONDITIONS
                     FOR UPPER-INCOME MIGRATION(DIMENSIONLESS)
MBST     164   A  METROPOLITAN BUSINESS STRUCTURES TOTAL
                     (STRUCTURES)
MCWM     100   A  METROPOLITAN CONSTRUCTION WORKFORCE
                     MULTIPLIER (DIMENSIONLESS)
MCWMT    100.1 T  METROPOLITAN CONSTRUCTION WORKFORCE
                     MULTIPLIER TABLE (DIMENSION LESS)
MEALCM   163   A  METROPOLITAN ENTERPRISE AVERAGE-LOCAL-
                     CONDITIONS MULTIPLER (DIMENSIONLESS)
MELIWM   158   A  METROPOLITAN ENTERPRISE LOWER-INCOME-
                     WORKFORCE MULTIPLIER (DIMENSIONLESS)
MELIWMT 158.1 T  METROPOLITAN ENTERPRISE LOWER-INCOME-
                     WORKFORCE MULTIPLIER TABLE(DIMENSIONLESS)
MELSM    155   A  METROPOLITAN ENTERPRISE LABOR-SUPPLY
                     MULTIPLIER (DIMENSIONLESS)
MEM      154   A  METROPOLITAN ENTERPRISE MULTIPLIER
                     (DIMENSIONLESS)
MEUIWM   156   A  METROPOLITAN ENTERPRISE UPPER-INCOME-
                     WORKFORCE MULTIPLIER (DIMENSIONLESS)
MEUIWMT 156.1 T  METROPOLITAN ENTERPRISE UPPER-INCOME-
                     WORKFORCE MULTIPLIER TABLE(DIMENSIONLESS)
MLIJR    160   A  METROPOLITAN LOWER-INCOME-TO-JOB RATIO
                     (DIMENSIONLESS)
MLIJRP   159   L  METROPOLITAN LOWER-INCOME-TO-JOB RATIO
         159.2 N     PERCEIVED (DIMENSIONLESS)
MLIJRPT 159.1 C  METROPOLITAN LOWER-INCOME-TO-JOB RATIO
                     PERCEPTION TIME (YEARS)
MNBSCD   153   A  METROPOLITAN NEW-BUSINESS-STRUCTURES
                     CONSTRUCTION DESIRED (STRUCTURES/YEAR)
MNBSDN   153.2 C  METROPOLITAN NEW-BUSINESS-STRUCTURESDESIRED
                     NORMAL (FRACTION/YEAR)
MUIAM    102   A  METROPOLITAN UPPER-INCOME-ATTRACTIVEMESS
                     MULTIPLIER (DIMENSIONLESS)
MUIAMP   110   L  METROPOLITAN UPPER-INCOME-ATTRACTIVENESS
         110.2 N     MULTIPLIER PERCEIVED (DIMENSIONLESS)
MUIAPT   110.1 C  METROPOLITAN UPPER-INCOME-ARRIVALS
                     MULTIPLIER PERCEPTION TIME(DIMENSIONLESS)
MUIJM    103   A  METROPOLITAN UPPER-INCOME JOB MULTIPLIER
                     (DIMENSIONLESS)
MUIJMT   103.1 T  METROPOLITAN UPPER-INCOME JOB MULTIPLIER
                     TABLE (DIMENSIONLESS)
MUIJR    104   A  METROPOLITAN UPPER-INCOME-TO-JOB RATIO
                     (DIMENSIONLESS)
MUIJRP   157   L  METROPOLITAN ENTERPRISE UPPER-INCOME-TO-JOB
         157.2 N     RATIO PERCEIVED (DIMENSIONLESS)
MUIJRPT 157.1 C  METROPOLITAN ENTERPRISE UPPER-INCOME-TO-JOB
                     RATIO PERCEPTION TIME (YEARS)
NBSCWN    93.3 C  NEW-BUSINESS-STRUCTURES CONSTRUCTION-
                     WORKERS NEEDED (MAN-YEARS/STRUCTURE)
PLTCT    283.3 C
PLTMAX   283.2 C
PLTMIN   283.1 C
PLTPER   283   A
PRTCT    284.3 C
PRTMAX   284.2 C
```

PRTMIN	284.1	C	
PRTPER	284	A.	
RCJSLI	250.1	C	REVERSE-COMMUTER JOB-SKILL-LEVEL INDEX (DIMENSIONLESS)
RTRANEP	277	A	REGIONAL TRANSPORTATION EXPANSION POLICY (DIMENSIONLESS)
RTRANPS	277.1	C	REGIONAL TRANSPORTATION POLICY SWITCH (DIMENSIONLESS)
SAREA	187	A	SUBURB AREA (ACRES)
SAREAB	187.1	C	SUBURB AREA BASE (ACRES)
SAV	263	A	SUBURB ASSESSED VALUE (THOUSAND DOLLARS)
SBSAV	265	A	SUBURB BUSINESS-STRUCTURES ASSESSED VALUE (THOUSAND DOLLARS)
SBST	190	A	SUBURB BUSINESS-STRUCTURES TOTAL (STRUCTURES)
SCRRAF	127.2	C	SUBURB/CITY RELATIVE-RESIDENTIAL ATTRACTIVENESS FACTOR (DIMENSIONLESS)
SCRRAM	128	A	SUBURB/CITY RELATIVE RESIDENTIAL-ATTRACTIVENESS MULTIPLIER (DIMENSIONLESS)
SCRRAMT	128.1	T	SUBURB/CITY RELATIVE RESIDENTIAL-ATTRACTIVENESS MULTIPLIER TABLE (DIMENSIONLESS)
SCRRAR	129	A	SUBURB/CITY RELATIVE RESIDENTIAL-ATTRACTIVENESS RATIO (DIMENSIONLESS)
SCWFAT	247.2	C	SUBURB CONSTRUCTION WORK FORCE ADJUSTMENT TIME (YEARS)
SEF	208.1	C	SUBURB ENTERPRISE FACTOR (DIMENSIONLESS)
SEGM	210	A	SUBURB ENTERPRISE GROWTH MULTIPLIER (DIMENSIONLESS)
SEGMT	210.1	T	SUBURB ENTERPRISE GROWTH MULTIPLIER TABLE (DIMENSIONLESS)
SELCM	166	A	SUBURB ENTERPRISE LOCAL-CONDITIONS MULTIPLIER (DIMENSIONLESS)
SELM	209	A	SUBURB ENTERPRISE LAND MULTIPLIER (DIMENSIONLESS)
SELMT	209.1	T	SUBURB ENTERPRISE LAND MULTIPLIER TABLE (DIMENSIONLESS)
SEM	208	A	SUBURB ENTERPRISE MULTIPLIER(DIMENSIONLESS)
SETM	213	A	SUBURB ENTERPRISE TAX MULTIPLIER (DIMENSIONLESS)
SETMT	213.1	T	SUBURB ENTERPRISE TAX MULTIPLIER TABLE (DIMENSIONLESS)
SHSAV	264	A	SUBURB HOUSING STRUCTURES ASSESSED VALUE (THOUSAND DOLLARS)
SHT	189	A	SUBURB HOUSING STRUCTURES TOTAL(STRUCTURES)
SLFO	186	A	SUBURB LAND FRACTION OCCUPIED (DIMENSIONLESS)
SLIA	221	R	SUBURB LOWER-INCOME ARRIVALS (MEN/YEAR)
SLIAM	223	A	SUBURB LOWER-INCOME-ATTRACTIVENESS MULTIPLIER (DIMENSIONLESS)
SLIAMP	222	L	SUBURB LOWER-INCOME-ATTRACTIVENESS
	222.1	N	MULTIPLIER PERCEIVED (DIMENSIONLESS)
SLIAN	221.1	C	SUBURB LOWER-INCOME ARRIVALS NORMAL (FRACTION/YEAR)
SLIB	233	R	SUBURB LOWER-INCOME BIRTHS (MEN/YEAR)
SLIBR	233.1	C	SUBURB LOWER-INCOME BIRTH RATE (FRACTION/YEAR)
SLID	231	R	SUBURB LOWER-INCOME DEPARTURES (MEN/YEAR)
SLIDM	232	A	SUBURB LOWER-INCOME DEPARTURES MULTIPLIER (DIMENSIONLESS)
SLIDMT	232.1	T	SUBURB LOWER-INCOME DEPARTURES MULTIPLIER TABLE (DIMENSIONLESS)
SLIDN	231.1	C	SUBURB LOWER-INCOME DEPARTURES NORMAL (FRACTION/YEAR)
SLIEAT	238.2	C	SUBURB LOWER INCOME ECONOMIC ADVANCEMENT TIME (YEARS)
SLIEM	239	A	SUBURB LOWER-INCOME ECONOMIC MOBILITY (DIMENSIONLESS)
SLIEMF	241.1	C	SUBURB LOWER-INCOME ECONOMIC MOBILITYFACTOR (DIMENSIONLESS)
SLIEMM	241	A	SUBURB LOWER-INCOME ECONOMIC MOBILITY MULTIPLIER (DIMENSIONLES S)
SLIEMMP	240	L	SUBURB LOWER-INCOME ECONOMIC MOBILITY
	240.1	N	MULTIPLIER PERCEIVED (DIMENSIONLESS)
SLIEMMT	240.2	C	SUBURB LOWER INCOME ECONOMIC MOBILITY MULTIPLIER PERCEPTION TIME (YEARS)
SLIFS	226.1	C	SUBURB LOWER-INCOME FAMILY SIZE (PEOPLE/MAN)

```
SLIFW    237    A  SUBURB LOWER-INCOME FRACTION WORKING
                      (DIMENSIONLESS)
SLIFWT   237.1  T  SUBURB LOWER-INCOME FRACTION WORKING TABLE
                      (DIMENSIONLESS)
SLIH     200    L  SUBURB LOWER-INCOME HOUSING (STRUCTURES)
         200.1  N
SLIHATM  205    A  SUBURB LOWER-INCOME HOUSING-ABANDONMENT TAX
                      MULTIPLIER (DIMENSIONLESS)
SLIHATT  205.1  T  SUBURB LOWER-INCOME HOUSING-ABANDONMENT TAX
                      TABLE (DIMENSIONLESS)
SLIHAV   264.2  C  SUBURB LOWER-INCOME-HOUSING ASSESSED VALUE
                      (THOUSIND DOLLARS)
SLIHD    201    R  SUBURB LOWER-INCOME-HOUSING-DEMOLITION RATE
                      (STRUCTURES/YEAR)
SLIHDAM  203    A  SUBURB LOWER-INCOME-HOUSING-DEMOLITION
                      ADEQUACY MULTIPLIER (DIMENSIONLESS)
SLIHDF   202.1  C  SUBURB LOWER-INCOME-HOUSING-DEMOLITION
                      FACTOR (DIMENSIONLESS)
SLIHDLM  206    A  SUBURB LOWER-INCOME-HOUSING-DEMOLITION LAND
                      MULTIPLIER (DIMENSIONLESS)
SLIHDLT  206.1  T  SUBURB LOWER-INCOME-HOUSING-DEMOLITION LAND
                      TABLE (DIMENSIONLESS)
SLIHDM   202    A  SUBURB LOWER-INCOME-HOUSING-DEMOLITION
                      MULTIPLIER (DIMENSIONLESS)
SLIHDN   201.1  C  SUBURB LOWER-INCOME-HOUSING-DEMOLITION RATE
                      NORMAL (STRUCTURES/YEAR)
SLIHDSM  204    A  SUBURB LOWER-INCOME-HOUSING-DEMOLITION
                      SUPPLY MULTIPLIER (DIMEN SIONLESS)
SLIHDST  204.1  T  SUBURB LOWER-INCOME-HOUSING-DEMOLITION
                      SUPPLY TABLE (DIMENSIONLESS)
SLIHPD   226.2  C  SUBURB LOWER-INCOME-HOUSING POPULATION
                      DENSITY (PEOPLE/STRUCTURE)
SLIHR    226    A  SUBURB LOWER-INCOME-TO-HOUSING RATIO
                      (DIMENSIONLESS)
SLIHSM   225    A  SUBURB LOWER-INCOME-HOUSING-SUPPLY
                      MULTIPLIER (DIMENSIONLESS)
SLIHSMT  225.1  T  SUBURB LOWER-INCOME-HOUSING-SUPPLY
                      MULTIPLIER TABLE (DIMENSIONLESS)
SLIJ     251    A  SUBURB LOWER-INCOME JOBS (MEN)
SLIJM    230    A  SUBURB LOWER-INCOME JOB MULTIPLIER
                      (DIMENSIONLESS)
SLIJMT   230.1  T  SUBURB LOWER-INCOME JOB MULTIPLIER TABLE
                      (DIMENSIONLESS)
SLIJOM   249    A  SUBURB LOWER-INCOME JOB-OPPORTUNITY
                      MULTIPLIER (DIMENSIONLESS)
SLIJOMT  249.1  T  SUBURB LOWER-INCOME JOB-OPPORTUNITY
                      MULTIPLIER TABLE (DIMENSIONLESS)
SLIJR    252    A  SUBURB LOWER-INCOME-TO-JOB RATIO
                      (DIMENSIONLESS)
SLIMM    224    A  SUBURB LOWER-INCOME MOBILITY MULTIPLIER
                      (DIMENSIONLESS)
SLIMMT   224.1  T  SUBURB LOWER-INCOME MOBILITY MULTIPLIER
                      TABLE (DIMENSIONLESS)
SLIP     234    L  SUBURB LOWER-INCOME POPULATION (MEN)
         234.1  N
SLIQEM   245    A  SUBURB LOWER-INCOME QUALITY-EDUCATION
                      MULTIPLIER (DIMENSIONLESS)
SLIQEMT  245.1  T  SUBURB LOWER-INCOME QUALITY-EDUCATION
                      MULTIPLIER TABLE (DIMENSIONLESS)
SLITUI   235    R  SUBURB LOWER-INCOME-TO-UPPER-INCOME
                      ADVANCEMENT (MEN/YEAR)
SLITUIP  238    L  SUBURB LOWER-INCOME-TO-UPPER-INCOME
         238.1  N     ADVANCEMENT PERCEIVED (DIMENSIONLESS)
SLIW     236    A  SUBURB LOWER-INCOME WORKERS (MEN)
SLPBS    186.2  C  SUBURB LAND PER BUSINESS STRUCTURE (ACRES/
                      STRUCTURE)
SLPH     186.1  C  SUBURB LAND PER HOUSING STRUCTURE (ACRES/
                      STRUCTURE)
SNBS     207    L  SUBURB NEW-BUSINESS STRUCTURES (STRUCTURES)
         207.1  N
SNBSA    212    L  SUBURB NEW-BUSINESS-STRUCTURES AVERAGE
         212.1  N     (STRUCTURES)
SNBSAT   212.2  C  SUBURB NEW-BUSINESS-STRUCTURES AVERAGING
                      TIME (YEARS)
SNBSAV   265.1  C  SUBURB NEW-BUSINESS-STRUCTURES ASSESSED
                      VALUE (THOUSAND DOLLARS)
SNBSC    179    R  SUBURB NEW-BUSINESS-STRUCTURES CONSTRUCTION
                      (STRUCTURES/YEAR)
```

SNBSCD	180	A	SUBURB NEW-BUSINESS-STRUCTURES CONSTRUCTION DESIRED (STRUCTURES/ YEAR)
SNBSCM	178	A	SUBURB NEW-BUSINESS-STRUCTURES CONSTRUCTION MULTIPLIER (DIMENSIONLESS)
SNBSGR	211	A	SUBURB NEW-BUSINESS-STRUCTURES GROWTH RATE (PERCENT/YEAR)
SNBSGRI	212.3	C	SUBURB NEW-BUSINESS STRUCTURES GROWTH RATE INITIAL (PERCENT/YEAR)
SNBSO	214	R	SUBURB NEW-BUSINESS-STRUCTURES OBSOLESCENCE (STRUCTURES/YEAR)
SNBSOM	215	A	SUBURB NEW-BUSINESS-STRUCTURES OBSOLESCENCE MULTIPLIER (DIMENSIONLESS)
SNBSOMT	215.1	T	SUBURB NEW-BUSINESS-STRUCTURES OBSOLESCENCE MULTIPLIER TABLE (DIMENSIONLESS)
SNBSON	214.1	C	SUBURB NEW-BUSINESS-STRUCTURES OBSOLESCENCE NORMAL (PERCENT/YEAR)
SNBSWF	153.4	C	SUBURB NEW-BUSINESS-STRUCTURES WEIGHTING FACTOR (DIMENSIONLESS)
SOBS	216 216.1	L N	SUBURB OLDER-BUSINESS STRUCTURES (STRUCTURES)
SOBSAV	265.2	C	SUBURB OLDER-BUSINESS-STRUCTURES ASSESSED VALUE (THOUSAND DOLLAR S)
SOBSD	217	R	SUBURB OLDER-BUSINESS-STRUCTURES DEMOLITION (STRUCTURES/YEAR)
SOBSDF	218.1	C	SUBURB OLDER-BUSINESS-STRUCTURES DEMOLITION FACTOR (DIMENSIONLESS)
SOBSDM	218	A	SUBURB OLDER-BUSINESS-STRUCTURES DEMOLITION MULTIPLIER (DIMENSIONLESS)
SOBSDN	217.1	C	SUBURB OLDER-BUSINESS-STRUCTURES DEMOLITION NORMAL (PERCENT/YEAR)
SOBSEM	219	A	SUBURB OLDER-BUSINESS-STRUCTURES ENTERPRISE MULTIPLIER (DIMENSIONLESS)
SOBSEMT	219.1	T	SUBURB OLDER-BUSINESS-STRUCTURES ENTERPRISE MULTIPLIER TABLE (DIMENSIONLESS)
SOBSLM	220	A	SUBURB OLDER-BUSINESS-STRUCTURES LAND MULTIPLIER (DIMENSIONLESS)
SOBSLMT	220.1	T	SUBURB OLDER-BUSINESS-STRUCTURES LAND MULTIPLIER TABLE (DIMENSIONLESS)
SOBSWF	153.6	C	SUBURB OLDER-BUSINESS-STRUCTURES WEIGHTING FACTOR (DIMENSIONLESS)
SP	229	A	SUBURB POPULATION (PEOPLE)
SPEM	227	A	SUBURB PUBLIC EXPENDITURES MULTIPLIER (DIMENSIONLESS)
SPEMT	227.1	T	SUBURB PUBLIC EXPENDITURES MULTIPLIER TABLE (DIMENSIONLESS)
SRTNBS	166.1	C	SUBURB RECEPTIVENESS TO NEW-BUSINESS STRUCTURES (DIMENSIONLESS)
STAI	258	A	SUBURB TAX ASSESSMENT INDICATED (DOLLARS/ YEAR/THOUSAND DOLLARS)
STAN	254.1	C	SUBURB TAX ASSESSMENT NORMAL (DOLLARS/YEAR/ THOUSAND DOLLARS)
STC	254	A	SUBURB TAX COLLECTION (DOLLARS/YEAR)
STCM	261	A	SUBURB TAX COLLECTION MULTIPLIER (DIMENSIONLESS)
STCMT	261.1	T	SUBURB TAX COLLECTION MULTIPLIER TABLE (DIMENSIONLESS)
STN	259	A	SUBURB TAXES NEEDED (DOLLARS/YEAR)
STPCN	228.1	C	SUBURB TAX PER CAPITA NORMAL (DOLLARS/YEAR/ PERSON)
STPCR	228	A	SUBURB TAX PER CAPITA RATIO (DIMENSIONLESS)
STPRCOM	260.3	C	SUBURB TAX PER REVERSE COMMUTER (DOLLARS/ PERSON/YEAR)
STR	255	A	SUBURB TAX RATIO (DIMENSIONLESS)
STRN	257	A	SUBURB TAX RATIO NEEDED (DIMENSIONLESS)
STRNP	256 256.1	L N	SUBURB TAX RATIO NEEDED PERCEIVED (DIMENSIONLESS)
STRNPT	256.2	C	SUBURB TAX RATIO NEEDED PERCEPTION TIME (YEARS)
STRT	255.1	T	SUBURB TAX-RATIO TABLE (DIMENSIONLESS)
STSLIP	260.2	C	SUBURB TAX PER LOWER-INCOME PERSON(DOLLARS/ PERSON/YEAR)
STSUIP	260.1	C	SUBURB TAX PER UPPER-INCOME PERSON(DOLLARS/ PERSON/YEAR)
SUIALIM	121	A	SUBURB UPPER-INCOME-ARRIVALS LOWER-INCOME MULTIPLIER (DIMENSIONLESS)
SUIALIT	121.1	T	SUBURB UPPER-INCOME-ARRIVALS LOWER-INCOME MULTIPLIER TABLE (DIMENSIONLESS)

SUIAM	116	A	SUBURB UPPER-INCOME-ARRIVALS MULTIPLIER (DIMENSIONLESS)
SUIAR	113	R	SUBURB UPPER-INCOME-ARRIVALS RATE (MEN/YEAR)
SUIBJ	253	A	SUBURB UPPER-INCOME BUSINESS JOBS (MEN)
SUIBR	114.1	C	SUBURB UPPER-INCOME BIRTH RATE (FRACTION/YEAR)
SUIC	135	L	SUBURB(RESIDENT) UPPER-INCOME CITY(WORKERS) (MEN)
	135.1	N	
SUICD	137	R	SUBURB UPPER-INCOME CITY DEPARTURES (MEN/YEAR)
SUICDM	138	A	SUBURB UPPER-INCOME CITY DEPARTURES MULTIPLIER (DIMENSIONLESS)
SUICDMT	138.1	T	SUBURB UPPER-INCOME CITY DEPARTURES MULTIPLIER TABLE (DIMENSIONLESS)
SUICDN	137.1	C	SUBURB UPPER-INCOME CITY DEPARTURES NORMAL (FRACTION/YEAR)
SUICJ	247	L	SUBURB UPPER-INCOME CONSTRUCTION JOBS (MEN)
	247.1	N	
SUICNB	136	R	SUBURB UPPER-INCOME CITY NET BIRTHS (MEN/YEAR)
SUICNBN	136.1	C	SUBURB UPPER-INCOME CITY NET BIRTHS NORMAL (FRACTION/YEAR)
SUIFS	229.1	C	SUBURB UPPER-INCOME FAMILY SIZE (PEOPLE/MAN)
SUIH	197	L	SUBURB UPPER-INCOME HOUSING (STRUCTURES)
	197.1	N	
SUIHA	196	L	SUBURB UPPER-INCOME-HOUSING STRUCTURES AVERAGE (HOUSING STRUCTURES)
	196.1	N	
SUIHAM	184	A	SUBURB UPPER-INCOME-HOUSING AVAILABILITY MULTIPLIER (DIMENSIONLESS)
SUIHAMT	184.1	T	SUBURB UPPER-INCOME-HOUSING AVAILABILITY MULTIPLIER TABLE (DIMENSIONLESS)
SUIHAT	196.2	C	SUBURB UPPER-INCOME-HOUSING AVERAGING TIME (YEARS)
SUIHAV	264.1	C	SUBURB UPPER-INCOME-HOUSING ASSESSED VALUE (THOUSAND DOLLARS)
SUIHC	181	R	SUBURB UPPER-INCOME-HOUSING CONSTRUCTION (STRUCTURES/YEAR)
SUIHCD	182	A	SUBURB UPPER-INCOME-HOUSING CONSTRUCTION DESIRED (STRUCTURES/YEAR)
SUIHCN	182.1	C	SUBURB UPPER-INCOME-HOUSING CONSTRUCTION NORMAL (FRACTION/YEAR)
SUIHCP	276	A	SUBURB UPPER-INCOME HOUSING CONSTRUCTION PROGRAM (STRUCTURES/YEAR)
SUIHCR	276.1	C	SUBURB UPPER-INCOME HOUSING CONSTRUCTION RATE (FRACTION/YEAR)
SUIHEM	193	A	SUBURB UPPER-INCOME-HOUSING-ENTERPRISE MULTIPLIER (DIMENSIONLESS)
SUIHEMT	193.1	T	SUBURB UPPER-INCOME-HOUSING-ENTERPRISE MULTIPLIER TABLE (DIMENSIONLESS)
SUIHF	183.2	C	SUBURB UPPER-INCOME-HOUSING FACTOR (DIMENSIONLESS)
SUIHGM	194	A	SUBURB UPPER-INCOME-HOUSING GROWTH MULTIPLIER (DIMENSIONLESS)
SUIHGMT	194.1	T	SUBURB UPPER-INCOME-HOUSING GROWTH MULTIPLIER TABLE (DIMENSIONLESS)
SUIHGR	195	A	SUBURB UPPER-INCOME-HOUSING GROWTH RATE (FRACTION/YEAR)
SUIHGRI	196.3	C	SUBURB UPPER-INCOME- HOUSING GROWTH RATE INITIAL (FRACTION/YEAR)
SUIHLM	185	A	SUBURB UPPER-INCOME-HOUSING LAND MULTIPLIER (DIMENSIONLESS)
SUIHLMT	185.1	T	SUBURB UPPER-INCOME-HOUSING LAND MULTIPLIER TABLE (DIMENSIONLESS)NLESS)
SUIHM	183	A	SUBURB UPPER-INCOME-HOUSING MULTIPLIER (DIMENSIONLESS)
SUIHO	198	R	SUBURB UPPER-INCOME-HOUSING-OBSOLESCENCE (STRUCTURES/YEAR)
SUIHOM	199	A	SUBURB UPPER-INCOME HOUSING-OBSOLESCENCE MULTIPLIER (DIMENSIONLESS)
SUIHOMT	199.1	T	SUBURB UPPER-INCOME HOUSING-OBSOLESCENCE MULTIPLIER TABLE (DIMENSIONLESS)
SUIHON	198.1	C	SUBURB UPPER-INCOME-HOUSING-OBSOLESCENCE NORMAL (FRACTION/YEAR)

SUIHPM	191	A	SUBURB UPPER-INCOME-HOUSING POPULATION MULTIPLIER (DIMENSIONLESS)
SUIHPMT	191.1	T	SUBURB UPPER-INCOME-HOUSING POPULATION MULTIPLIER TABLE (DIMENSIONLESS)
SUIHR	125	A	SUBURB UPPER-INCOME-TO-HOUSING RATIO (DIMENSIONLESS)
SUIHSM	126	A	SUBURB UPPER-INCOME HOUSING-SUPPLY MULTIPLIER (DIMENSIONLESS)
SUIHSMT	126.1	T	SUBURB UPPER-INCOME HOUSING-SUPPLY MULTIPLIER TABLE (DIMENSIONLESS)
SUIHTM	192	A	SUBURB UPPER-INCOME-HOUSING TAX MULTIPLIER (DIMENSIONLESS)
SUIJ	248	A	SUBURB UPPER-INCOME JOBS (MEN)
SUIJM	119	A	SUBURB UPPER-INCOME JOB MULTIPLIER (DIMENSIONLESS)
SUIJMT	119.1	T	SUBURB UPPER-INCOME JOB MULTIPLIER TABLE (DIMENSIONLESS)
SUIP	260	A	SUBURB UPPER-INCOME POPULATION (MEN)
SUIRCAT	130.1	C	SUBURB UPPER-INCOME RESIDENTIAL-CONDITIONS AVERAGING TIME (YEARS)
SUIRCM	109	A	SUBURB UPPER-INCOME RESIDENTIAL-CONDITIONS MULTIPLIER (DIMENSIONLESS)
SUIRCMP	130	L	SUBURB UPPER-INCOME RESIDENTIAL-CONDITIONS
	130.2	N	MULTIPLIER PERCEIVED (DIMENSIONLESS)
SUIS	115	L	SUBURB(RESIDENT) UPPER-INCOME
	115.2	N	SUBURB(WORKERS) (MEN)
SUISB	114	R	SUBURB UPPER-INCOME SUBURB BIRTHS (MEN/ YEAR)
SUISD	123	R	SUBURB UPPER-INCOME SUBURB DEPARTURES (MEN/ YEAR)
SUISDM	124	A	SUBURB UPPER-INCOME SUBURB DEPARTURES MULTIPLIER (DIMENSIONLESS)
SUISDMT	124.1	T	SUBURB UPPER-INCOME SUBURB DEPARTURES MULTIPLIER TABLE (DIMENSIONLESS)
SUISDN	123.1	C	SUBURB UPPER-INCOME SUBURB DEPARTURESNORMAL (FRACTION/YEAR)
SUISJR	120	A	SUBURB UPPER-INCOME-TO-SUBURB JOB RATIO (DIMENSIONLESS)
SUITLIR	262	A	SUBURB UPPER-INCOME-TO-LOWER-INCOME RATIO (DIMENSIONLESS)
SUITM	117	A	SUBURB UPPER-INCOME TAX MULTIPLIER (DIMENSIONLESS)
SUITMT	117.1	T	SUBURB UPPER-INCOME TAX MULTIPLIER TABLE (DIMENSIONLESS)
SUITPR	122	A	SUBURB UPPER-INCOME TO POPULATION RATIO (DIMENSIONLESS)
SUIWSM	242	A	SUBURB UPPER-INCOME-WORKFORCE SUPPLY MULTIPLIER (DIMENSIONLESS)
SUIWSMT	242.1	T	SUBURB UPPER-INCOME-WORKFORCE SUPPLY MULTIPLIER TABLE (DIMENSIONLESS)
SUMN	235.1	C	SUBURB UPWARD MOBILITY NORMAL (FRACTION/ YEAR)
SWDC	246	A	SUBURB WORKFORCE DESIRED FOR CONSTRUCTION (MEN)
SWT1	266.2	C	SWITCH TIME 1 (YEAR)
SWT10	277.2	C	SWITCH TIME 10 (YEARS)
SWT11	282.1	C	SWITCH TIME 11 (YEARS)
SWT2	267.2	C	SWITCH TIME 2 (YEAR)
SWT3	268.2	C	SWITCH TIME 3 (YEAR)
SWT4	270.2	C	SWITCH TIME 4 (YEAR)
SWT5	271.2	C	SWITCH TIME 5 (YEAR)
SWT6	273.2	C	SWITCH TIME 6 (YEAR)
SWT7	274.2	C	SWITCH TIME 7 (YEAR)
SWT8	275.2	C	SWITCH TIME 8 (YEAR)
SWT9	276.2	C	SWITCH TIME 9 (YEARS)
TCCDM	149	A	TRANSPORTATION CONSTRUCTION CITY-DENSITY MULTIPLIER (DIMENSIONLESS)
TCCDMT	149.1	T	TRANSPORTATION CONSTRUCTION CITY-DENSITY MULTIPLIER TABLE (DIMENSIONLESS)
TCH	279	S	TOTAL CITY HOUSING (STRUCTURES)
TCJ	278	S	TOTAL CITY JOBS (MEN)
TCSDM	150	A	TRANSPORTATION CONSTRUCTION SUBURB-DENSITY MULTIPLIER (DIMENSIONLESS)
TCSDMT	150.1	T	TRANSPORTATION CONSTRUCTION SUBURB-DENSITY MULTIPLIER TABLE (DIMENSIONLESS)
TIME	282.7	N	

```
TIMEI    282.8 C
TMAV     280    S  TOTAL METROPOLITAN ACCESSED VALUE (THOUSAND
                      DOLLARS)
TMLIJ    162    A  TOTAL METROPOLITAN LOWER-INCOME JOBS (MEN)
TMLIP    161    A  TOTAL METROPOLITAN LOWER-INCOME POPULATION
                      (MEN)
TMUIJ    106    A  TOTAL METROPOLITAN UPPER-INCOME JOBS (MEN)
TMUIP    105    A  TOTAL METROPOLITAN UPPER-INCOME POPULATION
                      (MEN)
TRANCAP  146    L  TRANSPORTATION CAPACITY (DIMENSIONLESS)
         146.1 N
TRANCD   147    A  TRANSPORTATION CAPACITY DESIRED
                      (DIMENSIONLESS)
TRANCET  148    A  TRANSPORTATION CAPACITY EXPANSION TIME
                      (YEARS)
TRANETN  148.1 C   TRANSPORTATION CAPACITY EXPANSION TIME
                      NORMAL (YEARS)
TRANSD   151    A  TRANSPORTATION DEMAND (DIMENSIONLESS)
TRCOST   152    A  TRANSPORTATION COST (DIMENSIONLESS)
TRCOSTT  152.1 T   TRANSPORTATION-COST TABLE (DIMENSIONLESS)
UIA      101    A  UPPER-INCOME ARRIVALS (MEN/YEAR)
UIAN     101.1 C   UPPER-INCOME ARRIVALS NORMAL (FRACTION/
                      YEAR)
UICAF    112    A  UPPER-INCOME CITY-ARRIVALS FRACTION
                      (DIMENSIONLESS)
UICCSMN  127.1 C   UPPER-INCOME CITY(RESIDENT) CITY(WORKERS)
                      SUBURB MIGRATION NORMAL (FRACTION/YEAR)
UICCSMR  127    R  UPPER-INCOME CITY(RESIDENT) CITY(WORKERS)
                      SUBURB MIGRATION RATE (MEN/YEAR)
UICJR     30    A  UPPER-INCOME CITY JOB RATIO (DIMENSIONLESS)
UICLIM    25    A  UPPER-INCOME-TO-CITY LOWER-INCOME          C
                      MULTIPLIER (DIMENSIONLESS)
UICLIMT   25.1 T   UPPER-INCOME-TO-CITY LOWER-INCOME
                      MULTIPLIER TABLE (DIMENSIONLESS)
UICLIR    26    A  UPPER-INCOME-TO-CITY LOWER-INCOME RATIO
                      (DIMENSIONLESS)
UICSMN   142.1 C   UPPER-INCOME CITY(RESIDENT) SUBURB(WORKERS)
                      SUBURB MIGRATION NORMAL (FRACTION/YEAR)
                      YEAR)
UICSSMR  142    R  UPPER-INCOME CITY(RESIDENT) SUBURB(WORKERS)
                      SUBURB MIGRATION RATE (MEN/YEAR)
UICTF    151.1 C   UPPER-INCOME COMMUTER TRANSPORTATION FACTOR
                      (DIMENSIONLESS)
UIHCWN    92.1 C   UPPER-INCOME HOUSING-CONSTRUCTION-WORKERS
                      NEEDED (MAN-YEARS/HOUSING STRUCTURE)
UIPCNBS   94.1 C   UPPER-INCOME JOBS PER CITY NEW-BUSINESS
                      STRUCTURE (MEN/STRUCTURE)
UIPCOBS   94.2 C   UPPER-INCOME JOBS PER CITY OLDER BUSINESS
                      STRUCTURE (MEN/STRUCTURE)
UISCCMR  131    R  UPPER-INCOME SUBURB(RESIDENT) CITY(WORKERS)
                      CITY MIGRATION RATE (MEN/YEAR)
UISCMN   131.1 C   UPPER-INCOME SUBURB(RESIDENT) CITY(WORKERS)
                      CITY MIGRATION NORMAL (FRACTION/YEAR)
UISJR    118    A  UPPER-INCOME SUBURB JOB RATIO
                      (DIMENSIONLESS)
UISLIM   243    A  UPPER-INCOME-TO-SUBURB LOWER-INCOME
                      MULTIPLIER (DIMENSIONLESS)
UISLIMT  243.1 T   UPPER-INCOME-TO-SUBURB LOWER-INCOME
                      MULTIPLIER TABLE (DIMENSIONLESS)
UISLIR   244    A  UPPER-INCOME-TO-SUBURB LOWER-INCOME RATIO
                      (DIMENSIONLESS)
UISSCMN  140.1 C   UPPER-INCOME SUBURB(RESIDENT)
                      SUBURB(WORKERS) CITY MIGRATION NORMAL
                      (FRACTION/YEAR)
UISSCMR  140    R  UPPER-INCOME SUBURB(RESIDENT)
                      SUBURB(WORKERS) CITY MIGRATION RATE (MEN/
                      YEAR)
UISTF    151.2 C   UPPER-INCOME SERVICE TRANSPORTATION FACTOR
                      (DIMENSIONLESS)
READY
```

Index

Notes

Notes

Notes

THE LIFE CYCLE OF ECONOMIC DEVELOPMENT

by Nathan B. Forrester

Describes a system dynamics model of national economic development for an industrial economy. It interrelates the five production sectors of a national economy to examine the shifting allocation of labor and capital between these sectors as development progresses. The model deals with a 250-year period of economic development and focuses on changes during the 100 year transition phase between growth and equilibrium.

1973, second edition, 194 pages, illustrated

STUDY NOTES IN SYSTEM DYNAMICS

by Michael R. Goodman

Collects supplementary material for teaching or self-study in system dynamics. It focuses on simple structures and describes elements of positive, negative, and combined positive and negative feedback loops. A large number of practice exercises with accompanying solutions are included.

1974, paperback, 388 pages, illustrated

ECONOMIC CYCLES: AN ANALYSIS OF UNDERLYING CAUSES

by Nathaniel J. Mass

Develops a sequence of system dynamics models to analyze the causes underlying business cycles and long-term economic cycles. Provides a general framework for assessing the validity of alternative theories of economic cycles.

Forthcoming Fall 1975, approximately 120 pages, illustrated

READINGS IN URBAN DYNAMICS: VOLUME 1

edited by Nathaniel J. Mass

Explores and extends concepts introduced by Jay W. Forrester's *Urban Dynamics*. This collection of papers addresses many of the basic issues raised by reviewers of *Urban Dynamics* and discusses applications of system dynamics to urban policy design.

1974, 303 pages, illustrated

DYNAMICS OF COMMODITY PRODUCTION CYCLES

by Dennis L. Meadows

Develops a general model of the economic, biological, technological, and psychological factors which lead to instability in commodity systems. With appropriate parameter values, the model explains the hog, cattle and chicken cycles observed in the real world.

1970, 104 pages, illustrated

DYNAMICS OF GROWTH IN A FINITE WORLD

by Dennis L. Meadows, William W. Behrens III, Donella H. Meadows, Roger F. Naill, Jørgen Randers, and Erich K. O. Zahn

Details the research on which the Club of Rome's first report *The Limits To Growth* is based. This technical report describes the purpose and methodology of the global modeling effort and presents the World 3 model equation by equation.

1974, 637 pages, illustrated

TOWARD GLOBAL EQUILIBRIUM: COLLECTED PAPERS

edited by Dennis L. Meadows and Donella H. Meadows

Contains 13 papers which describe individual research on dynamic issues evolving from the Club of Rome project. It presents detailed analyses of several important global problems, e.g. DDT and mercury pollution, natural resource depletion, solid waste disposal, etc., and provides policy suggestions which may alleviate these problems. It also examines the economic, political, and ethical implications of growth and the transition to equilibrium.

1973, 358 pages, illustrated

All Wright-Allen Press titles are distributed outside of the United States and Canada exclusively by John Wiley & Sons:

John Wiley & Sons, Inc.
605 Third Avenue
New York, New York 10016
U.S.A.

Orders should be placed with John Wiley & Sons through a local bookseller.